Test Bank

for

McMurry's

Organic Chemistry

Sixth Edition

Tammy Tiner
Texas A & M University

Australia • Canada • Mexico • Singapore • Spain • United Kingdom • United States

Printed in the United States of America
1 2 3 4 5 6 7 06 05 04 03

Printer: Phoenix Color Corp

ISBN: 0-534-40943-1

For more information about our products, contact us at:
Thomson Learning Academic Resource Center
1-800-423-0563

For permission to use material from this text, contact us by:
Phone: 1-800-730-2214
Fax: 1-800-731-2215
Web: http://www.thomsonrights.com

Wadsworth/Thomson Learning
10 Davis Drive
Belmont, CA 94002-3098
USA

Asia
Thomson Learning
5 Shenton Way #01-01
UIC Building
Singapore 068808

Australia
Nelson Thomson Learning
102 Dodds Street
South Street
South Melbourne, Victoria 3205
Australia

Canada
Nelson Thomson Learning
1120 Birchmount Road
Toronto, Ontario M1K 5G4
Canada

Europe/Middle East/South Africa
Thomson Learning
High Holborn House
50/51 Bedford Row
London WC1R 4LR
United Kingdom

Latin America
Thomson Learning
Seneca, 53
Colonia Polanco
11560 Mexico D.F.
Mexico

Spain
Paraninfo Thomson Learning
Calle/Magallanes, 25
28015 Madrid, Spain

Table of Contents

Table of Contents

Chapter 1 – Structure and Bonding

1. Give the ground-state electron configuration for carbon (atomic number 6).

Answer: $1s^22s^22p_x{}^12p_y{}^1$ or $1s^22s^22p^2$

2. Give the ground-state electron configuration for fluorine (atomic number 9).

Answer: $1s^22s^22p_x{}^2\ 2p_y{}^2\ 2p_z{}^1$ or $1s^22s^22p^5$

3. Give the ground-state electron configuration for magnesium (atomic number 12).

Answer: $1s^22s^22p^63s^2$

4. How many electrons does silicon have in its valence shell?

Answer: four

Write valid Lewis (electron-dot) structures for each formula below. Show all electrons as dots and show all non-bonding electrons.

5. C_2Cl_4 tetrachloroethylene ***Answer:*** :C̈l:
:C̈l:C::C:C̈l:
:C̈l:

6. CO_2 carbon dioxide ***Answer:*** :Ö::C::Ö:

7. CH_4O methanol

Answer: H
H:C̈:Ö:H
H

8. The structure of urea is shown below. Fill in any non-bonding valence electrons that are missing from the line-bond structure.

O
||
H_2N—C—NH_2

Answer: :O:
||
$H_2\ddot{N}$—C—$\ddot{N}H_2$

9. The structure of urea is shown below. The carbon atom in urea is:

O
||
H_2N—C—NH_2

a. sp^3 hybridized
b. sp^2 hybridized
c. sp hybridized
d. not hybridized

Answer: b. sp^2 hybridized

10. The structure of urea is shown below. The predicted N-C=O bond angle in urea is:

$$H_2N-\overset{\overset{\Large O}{||}}{C}-NH_2$$

a. 109.5°
b. 120°
c. 180°
d. not predictable

Answer: b. 120°

Determine the hybridization for the indicated atoms in each structure below.

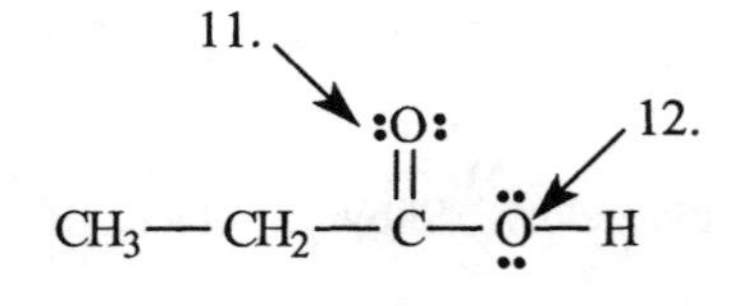

13. 14.

$CH_3-C\equiv N$:

11. The hybridization of this oxygen atom is ______ .

Answer: sp^2

12. The hybridization of this oxygen atom is ______ .

Answer: sp^3

13. The hybridization of this carbon atom is ______ .

Answer: sp^3

14. The hybridization of this carbon atom is ______ .

Answer: sp

15. The molecular formula C_2H_4O can be converted into three-line bond (Kekulé) structures that are consistent with valence rules. Which one of the following Kekulé structures is ***not*** consistent with valence rules?

a. H—C(H)(H)—C(=O)—H   b. (H)(H)C=C(H)(O—H)   c. H—C(H)—C(H)—H with bridging O   d. (H)(H)C—C(H)(H)=O

Answer: d

16. Explain why the structure you chose in question **15.** is not consistent with valence rules.

Answer: The carbon bonded to the oxygen atom in structure d is pentavalent; it has 10 valence electrons. Carbon can only have eight valence electrons. In addition, the other carbon has only six valence electrons when it would prefer to have eight.

17. Predict the H – C – H bond angle in singlet (spin-paired electrons in a single orbital) methylene, $:CH_2$.

Answer: Approximately 120° since singlet methylene is sp^2 hybridized.

18. Draw an orbital picture for acetylene, C_2H_2. Clearly label each bond type and indicate the type of orbitals involved in each bond.

Answer:

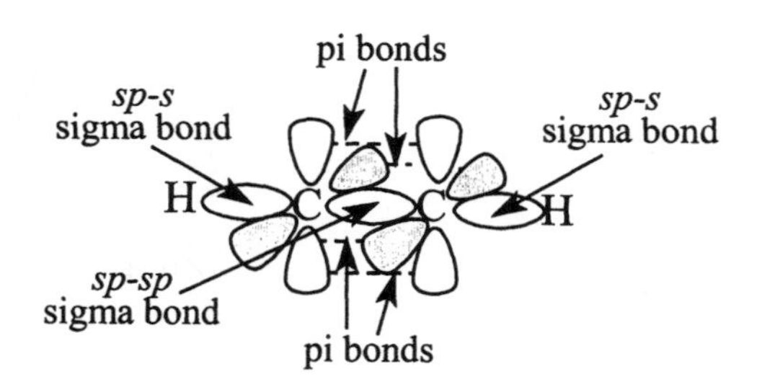

Propose a structure for a molecule that meets the following description.

19. Contains two sp^3 hybridized carbons and two *sp* hybridized carbons.

Answer:

$H_3C—C≡C—CH_3$

20. Contains one sp^3 hybridized carbon and two sp^2 hybridized carbons.

Answer:

$H_3C—C(H)=CH_2$

Chapter 2 - Polar Covalent Bonds; Acids and Bases

Convert the following structures into skeletal drawings.

1.

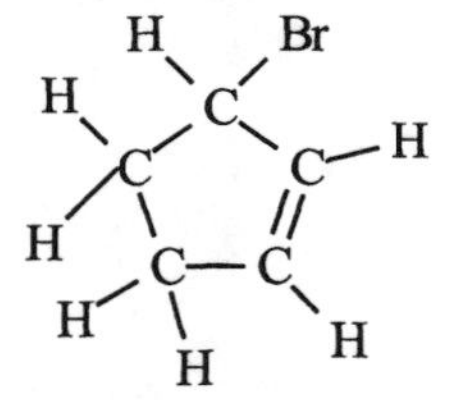

H Br
H C
C C—H
H C—C
H H
H

3-bromo-1-cyclopentene

Answer:

Br

2.

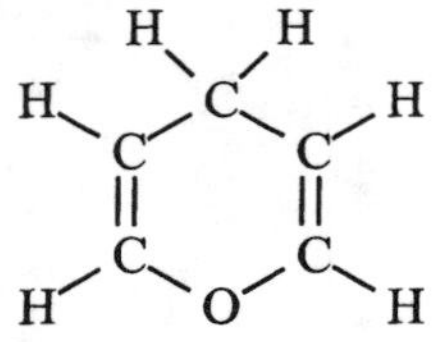

H H
H C H
C C
C C
H O H

pyran

Answer:

O

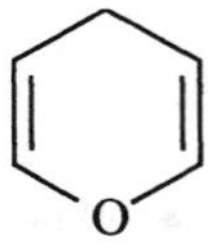

Consider the structural representation below to answer the following questions.

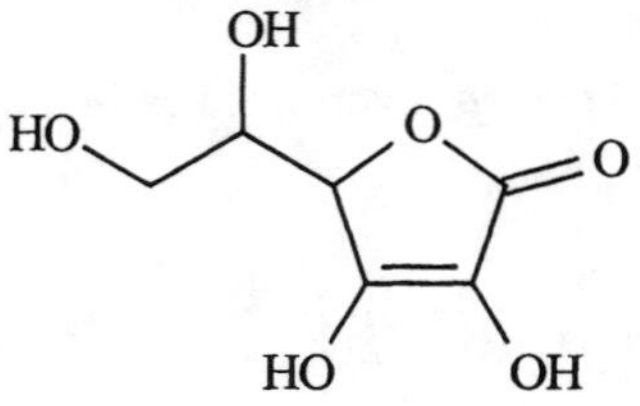

OH
HO O
O
HO OH

Vitamin C

3. This skeletal structure corresponds to the molecular formula:

a. $C_5H_6O_6$
b. $C_7H_{10}O_6$
c. $C_6H_6O_6$
d. $C_6H_8O_6$

Answer: d

4. Show how many hydrogen atoms are bonded to each carbon in Vitamin C.

Answer:

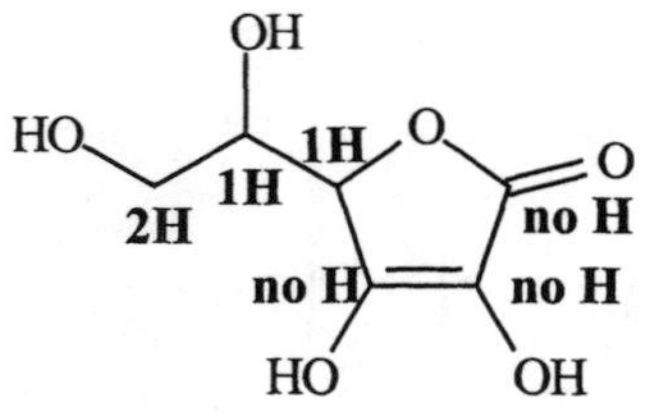

OH
HO 1H O
1H O
2H no H
no H no H
HO OH

Calculate the formal charges on the indicated atoms in each compound below.

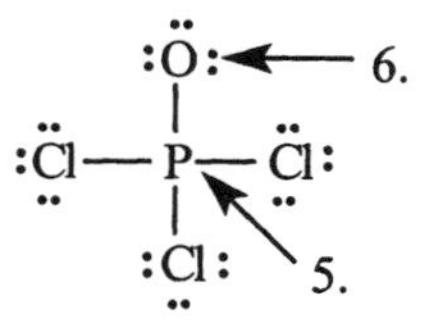

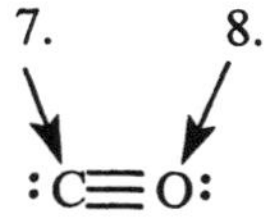

5. The formal charge on phosphorous is ______ .

Answer: +1

6. The formal charge on oxygen is ______ .

Answer: –1

7. The formal charge on carbon is ______ .

Answer: –1

8. The formal charge on oxygen is ______ .

Answer: +1

Phenylalanine is an amino acid that is essential to human nutrition. The representation below shows the structure of phenylalanine at physiological pH. Consider this structure to answer the following questions.

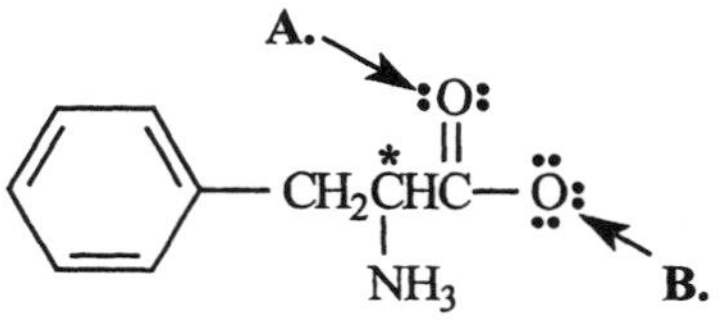

phenylalanine

9. Assign any formal charges to atoms in this representation of phenylalanine.

Answer:

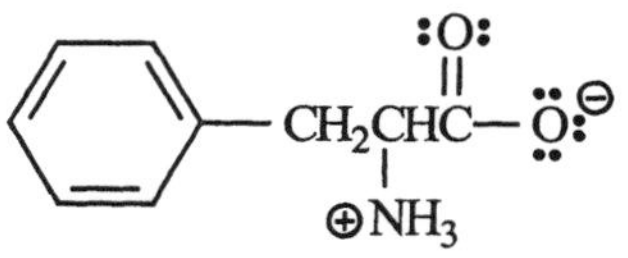

10. The oxygen atom labeled **A.** has ______ non-bonding electrons.

Answer: four

11. The oxygen atom labeled **B.** has _____ bonding electrons.

Answer: two

12. Draw a tetrahedral representation of phenylalanine showing the geometry at the carbon atom with the asterisk (*). Use the standard wedge-dash convention.

Answer:

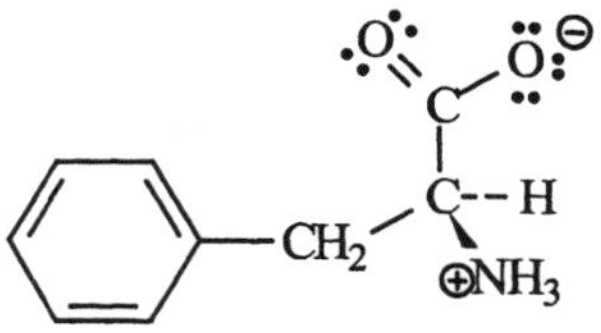

Use the $\delta-/\delta+$ convention and the crossed arrow (⟴) to show the direction of the expected polarity of the indicated bonds in the following compounds.

13. The C – F bond in fluorobenzene, 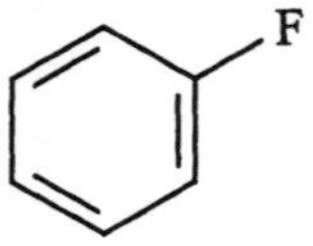

Answer: 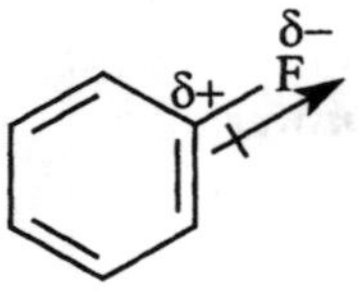

14. The C-Si bond in tetramethylsilane, $(CH_3)_4Si$

Answer: 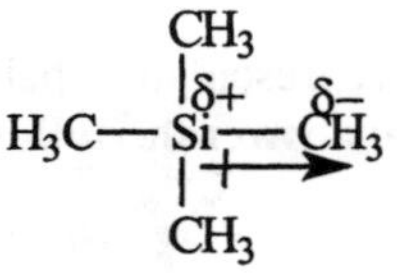

15. The C – O bond in furan, 

Answer: 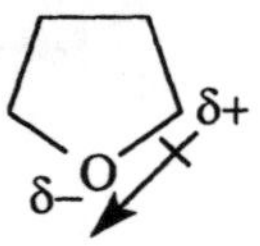

Label the acid and base in each reaction below.

16. $CH_3OH + NaH \longrightarrow CH_3O^- Na^+ + H_2$

Answer:

CH_3OH	+	NaH	$\longrightarrow$	$CH_3O^- Na^+$	+	H_2
acid		*base*		*conjugate base*		*conjugate acid*

17. $CH_3OCH_3 + BH_3 \longrightarrow$ 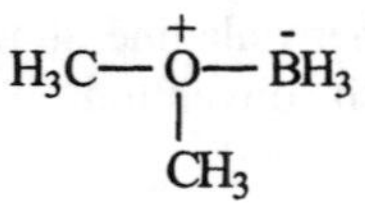

Answer:

CH_3OCH_3	+	BH_3	$\longrightarrow$	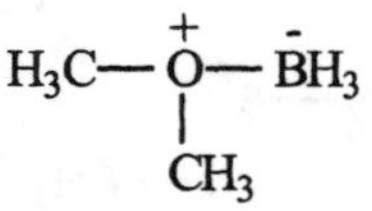
base		*acid*		

Refer to the following equation to answer the questions below. Place the letter corresponding to the correct answer in the blank.

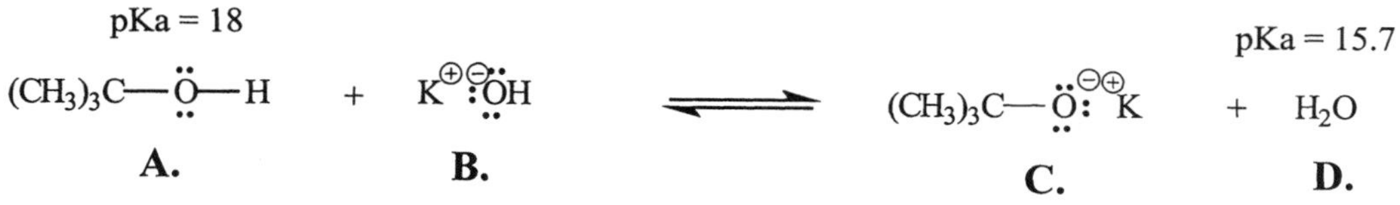

pKa = 18 | | | pKa = 15.7
$(CH_3)_3C—\ddot{\underset{..}{O}}—H$ + $K^{\oplus}\,{}^{\ominus}\!:\!\ddot{\underset{..}{O}}H$ ⇌ $(CH_3)_3C—\ddot{\underset{..}{O}}\!:^{\ominus}\,{}^{\oplus}K$ + H_2O

A. **B.** **C.** **D.**

18. The strongest Brønsted-Lowry acid in the equation is ______ .

Answer: **D**

19. The strongest Brønsted-Lowry base in the equation is ______ .

Answer: **C**

20. Will this reaction take place as written? Explain.

Answer: No, the reaction will not take place as written because the strongest acid reacts with the strongest base to give the weakest conjugate acid and the weakest conjugate base. **D** (pK_a = 15.7) is a stronger acid than **A** (pK_a = 18).

21. An acid with a low pK_a:

a. is a weak acid
b. is a strong acid
c. has a weak conjugate base
d. both b and c

Answer: d

The following questions refer to cocaine, whose skeletal structure is shown below.

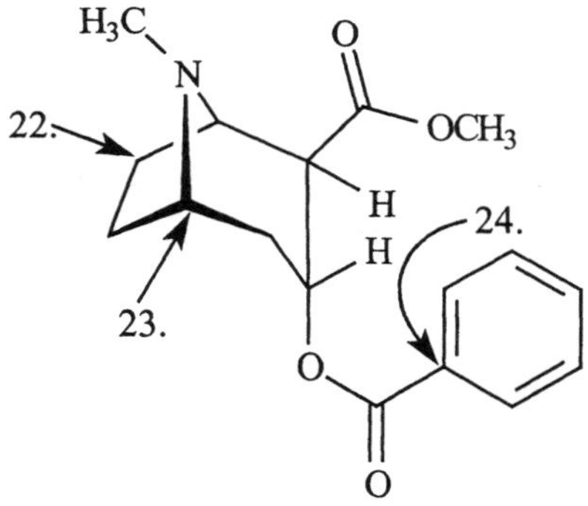

H_3C N O OCH_3 22. H H 24. 23. O O

22. The number of hydrogens bonded to this carbon is ______ .

Answer: two

23. The number of hydrogens bonded to this carbon is ______ .

Answer: one

24. The number of hydrogens bonded to this carbon is ______ .

Answer: zero

25. The molecular formula for cocaine is ______ .

Answer: $C_{17}H_{21}NO_4$

26. Circle all the Lewis bases in the group of compounds below.

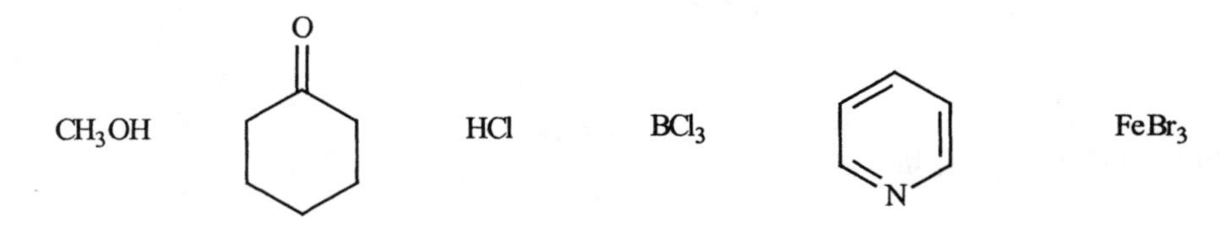

Answer:

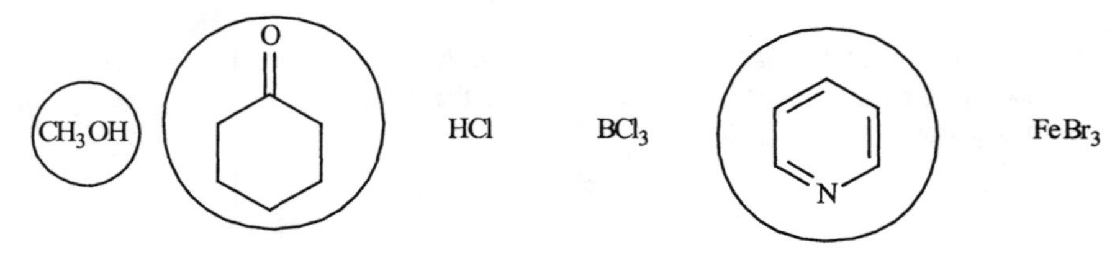

27. Put a box around all the Lewis acids in the group of compounds below.

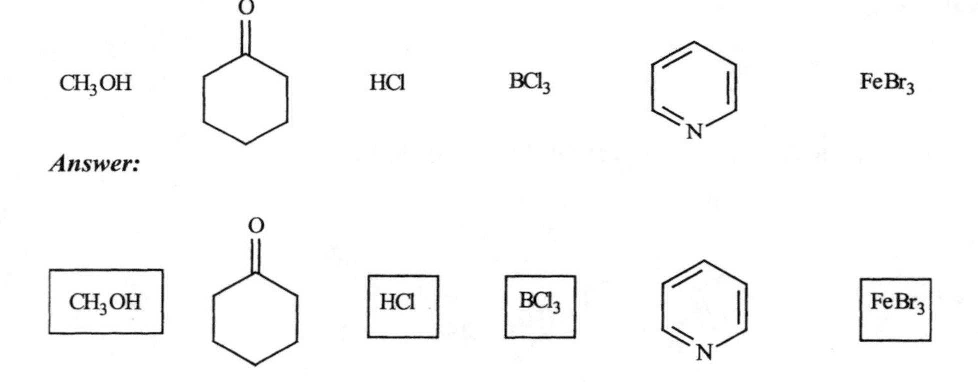

28. Draw *two* resonance structures for the species below.

CH_3

Answer:

CH_3 ⟷ CH_3 ⟷ CH_3

29. Draw *two* resonance structures for the species below.

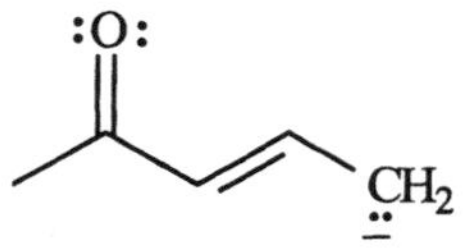

Answer:

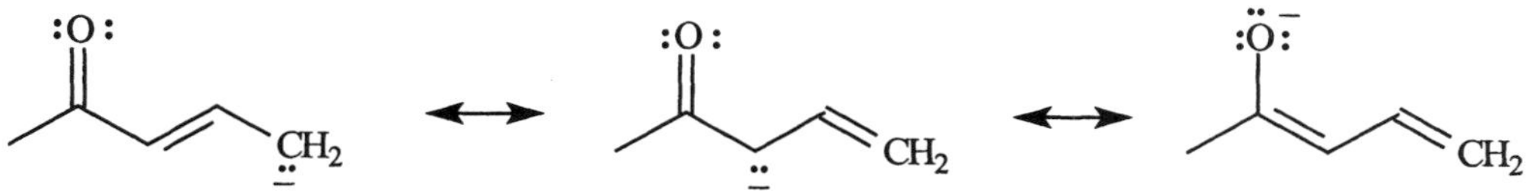

30. Draw two resonance structures for the species below.

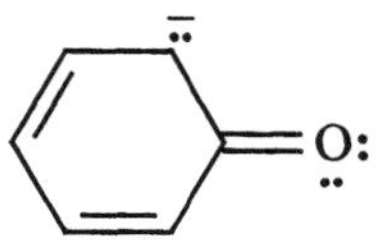

Answer:

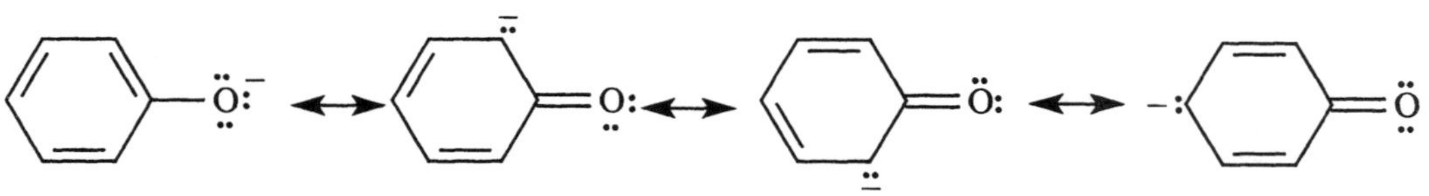

Consider the acidity constants below to answer the following questions.

ACID	STRUCTURE	pK_a
phenol	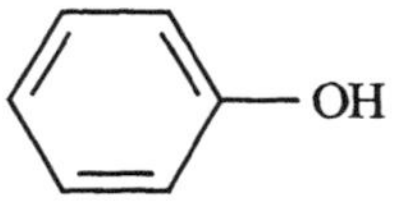 C_6H_5–OH	10.00
ethanol	CH_3CH_2OH	16.00
water	HOH	15.74

31. Which acid above will be almost completely deprotonated by NaOH?

Answer: phenol

32. Which acid has the *strongest* conjugate base?

Answer: Ethanol is the weakest acid (largest pK_a) so its conjugate base, ethoxide, $CH_3CH_2O^-$, will be the strongest base.

33. Explain why phenol has a much lower pK_a than ethanol.

Answer: Phenol is more acidic (has a lower pK_a) than ethanol because the phenoxide anion is resonance stabilized by the pi electrons in the ring. Sharing (delocalizing) the negative charge on oxygen with the three ring carbons stabilizes the phenoxide anion relative to undissociated phenol.

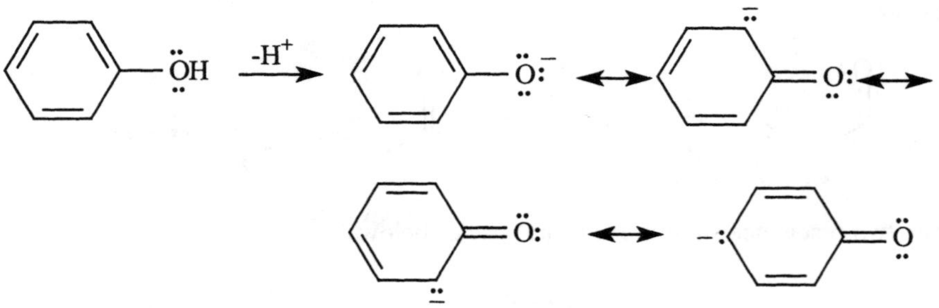

Ethoxide anion has no resonance stabilization. The negative charge is borne fully by oxygen.

$$CH_3CH_2OH \xrightarrow{-H^+} CH_3CH_2\ddot{O}:^-$$

Consider the reaction below to answer the following questions.

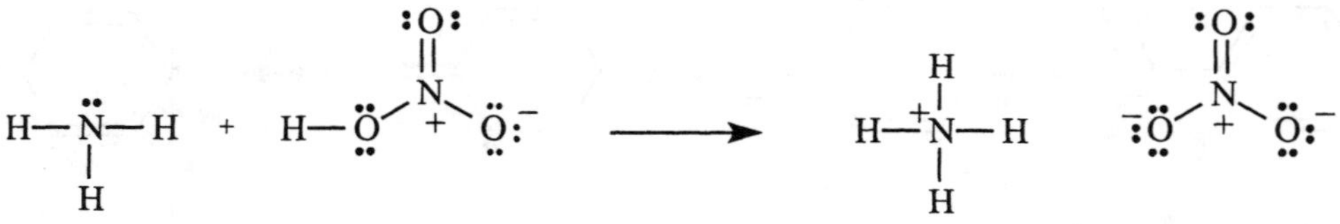

34. Using the curved arrow formalism, show the flow of electrons for this reaction.

Answer:

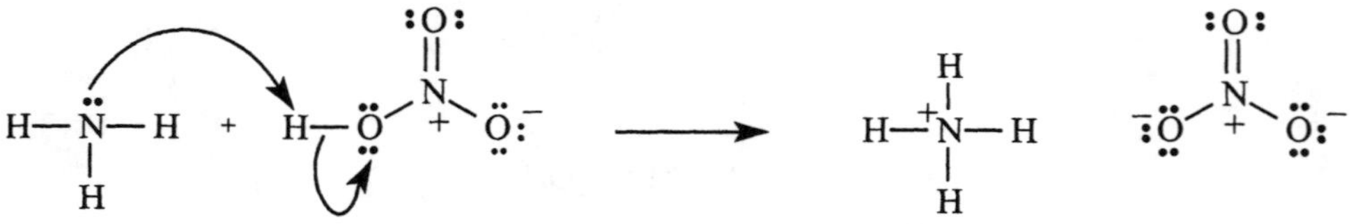

35. Label the acid and the base in the reaction.

Answer:

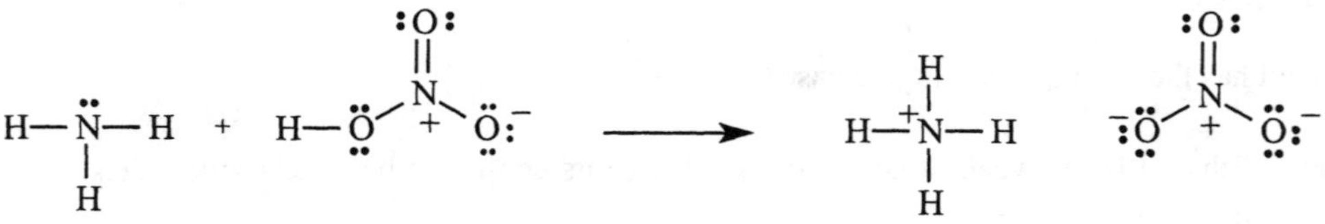

base **acid**

Indole is pleasant smelling in highly dilute solutions and had been used in perfumery. Use the structure of indole, below, to answer the following questions.

indole

34. Indole can function as a Bronsted-Lowry acid in the presence of strong bases. Formulate a reaction, showing electron flow with arrows, that demonstrates this reactivity of indole.

Answer:

35. Indole can function as a Lewis base in the presence of strong acid. Formulate a reaction, showing electron flow with arrows, that demonstrates this reactivity of indole.

Answer:

36. The condensed structure for dimethyl ether looks symmetrical. However, dimethyl ether has a dipole moment. Draw a structure that explains this and indicate the expected direction of the molecular dipole moment.

$CH_3\ddot{\underset{\bullet\bullet}{O}}CH_3$

dimethyl ether

Answer:

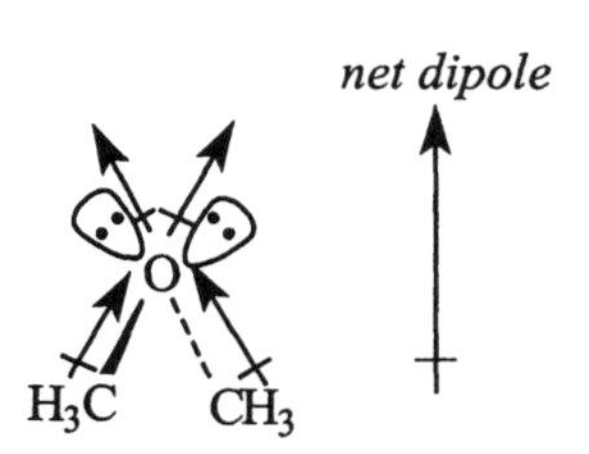

Consider the acid-base reaction below to answer the following questions.

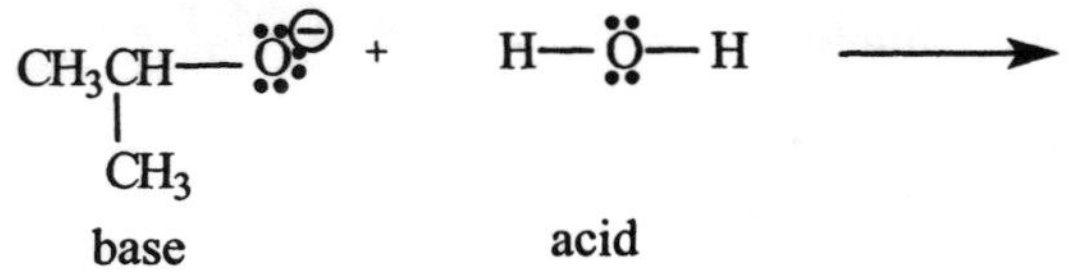

$$\underset{\text{base}}{CH_3\underset{\substack{|\\ CH_3}}{CH}-\ddot{\underset{\cdot\cdot}{O}}{:}^{\ominus}} \; + \; \underset{\text{acid}}{H-\ddot{\underset{\cdot\cdot}{O}}-H} \longrightarrow$$

37. Using the curved arrow formalism, show the flow of electrons for this reaction.

Answer:

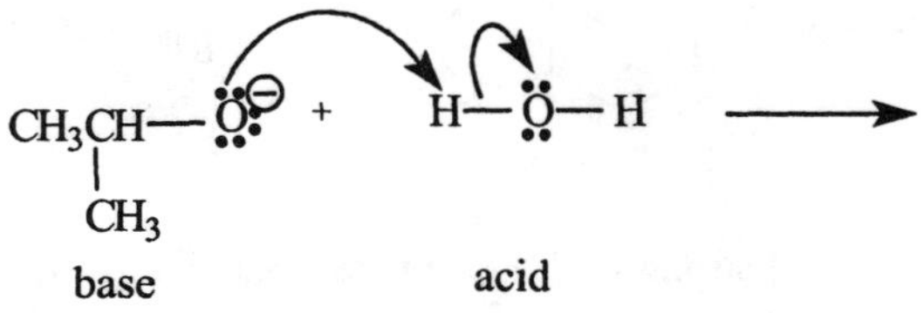

$$\underset{\text{base}}{CH_3\underset{\substack{|\\ CH_3}}{CH}-\ddot{\underset{\cdot\cdot}{O}}{:}^{\ominus}} \; + \; \underset{\text{acid}}{H-\ddot{\underset{\cdot\cdot}{O}}-H} \longrightarrow$$

38. Write the products of this Lewis acid - base reaction.

Answer:

$$\underset{\text{base}}{CH_3\underset{\substack{|\\ CH_3}}{CH}-\ddot{\underset{\cdot\cdot}{O}}{:}^{\ominus}} \; + \; \underset{\text{acid}}{H-\ddot{\underset{\cdot\cdot}{O}}-H} \longrightarrow CH_3\underset{\substack{|\\ CH_3}}{CH}-\ddot{\underset{\cdot\cdot}{O}}-H \; + \; {}^{\ominus}{:}\ddot{\underset{\cdot\cdot}{O}}-H$$

Chapter 3 - Organic Compounds: Alkanes and Cycloalkanes

MATCH a structure below to each of the following descriptions and place the letter corresponding to the structure in the blank.

A.

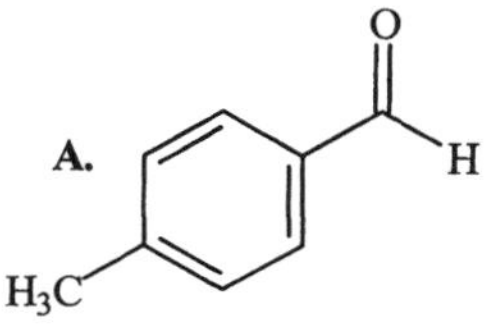

B. $CH_3CH(NH_2)CHO$

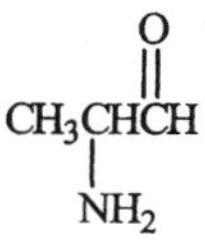

C.

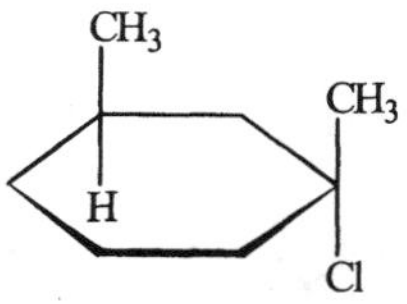

D.

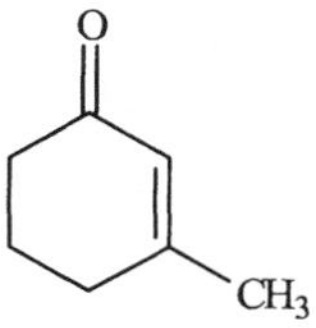

E.

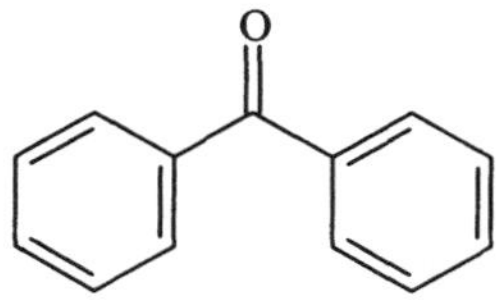

F. $CH_3CHClCH_3$

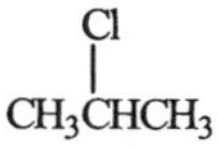

G.

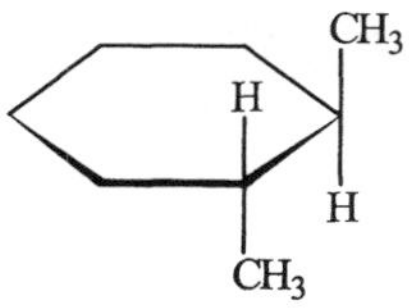

1. _____ is an amino aldehyde. *Answer:* B.

2. _____ is an aromatic ketone. *Answer:* E.

3. _____ is a tertiary chloride. *Answer:* C.

4. _____ is a cyclic alkane with two cis methyl groups. *Answer:* C.

5. Circle and name each functional group in the following structure.

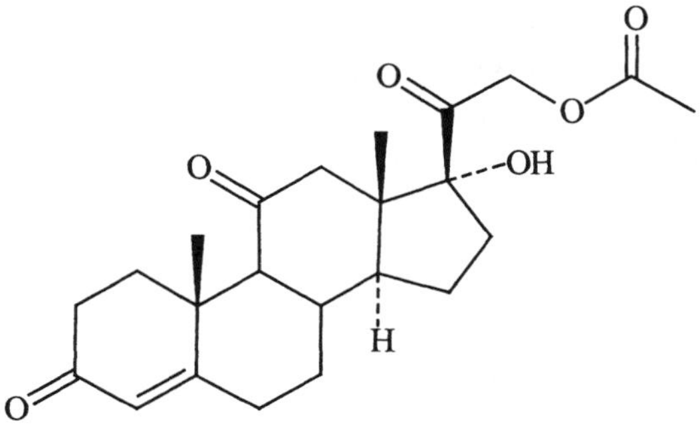

cortisone acetate *(active ingredient in steriod skin cream)*

Answer:

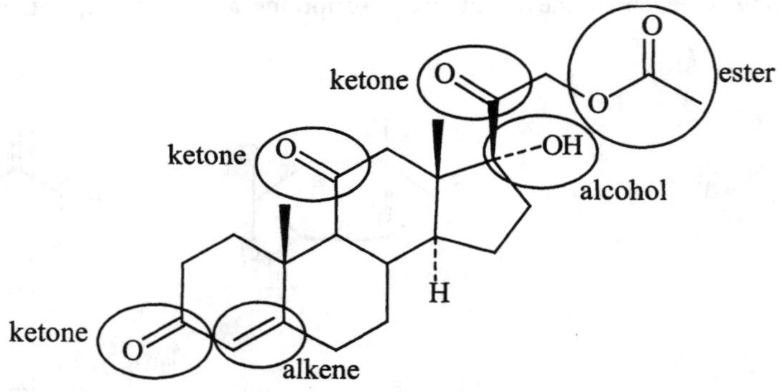

Label the indicated atoms in the structure below as 1°, 2°, 3°, or 4°.

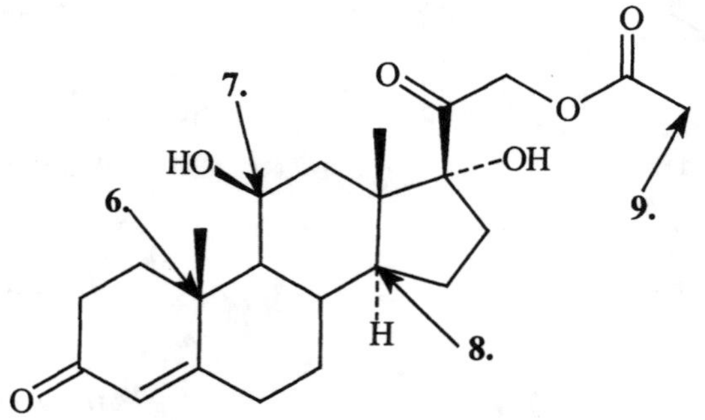

6. This atom is _____ . ***Answer:*** 4°

7. This atom is _____ . ***Answer:*** 2°

8. This atom is _____ . ***Answer:*** 3°

9. This atom is _____ . ***Answer:*** 1°

Label the following pairs of compounds as:

a. identical
b. constitutional isomers
c. stereoisomers

Place the letter of the correct answer in the blank to the left of the structures.

10. ____ 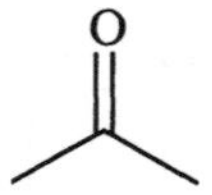 and

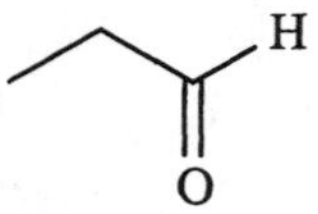

Answer: b

11. ______ 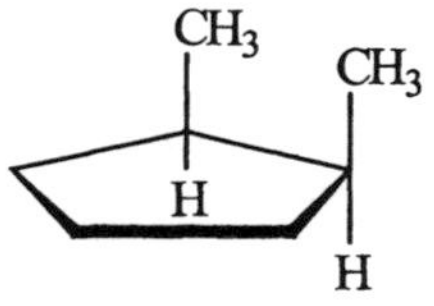 and

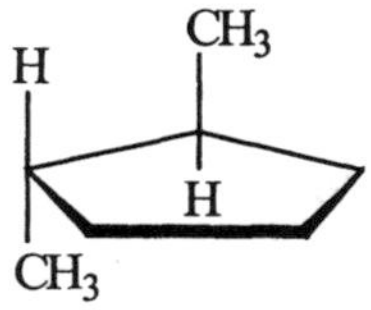

Answer: c

12. ______ 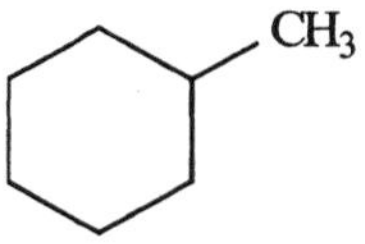 and

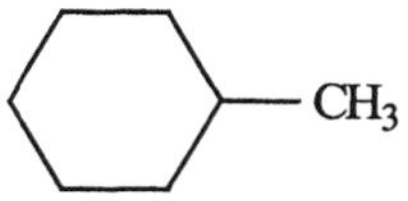

Answer: a

Provide proper IUPAC names for each compound below.

13. $(CH_3)_2CHCH_2CH_2CH(CH_2CH_3)CH_2C(CH_3)_3$

Answer: 4-ethyl-2,2,7-trimethyloctane

14.

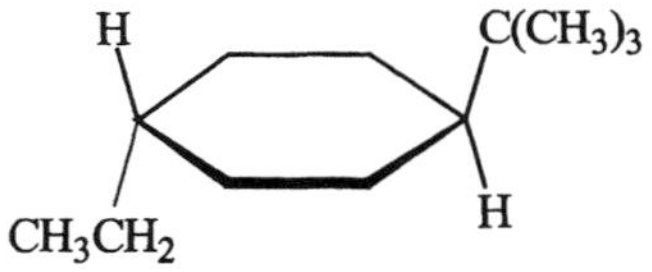

Answer: *trans*-1-*tert*-butyl-4-ethylcyclohexane *or trans*-1-(1,1-dimethylethyl)-4-ethylcyclohexane

15.

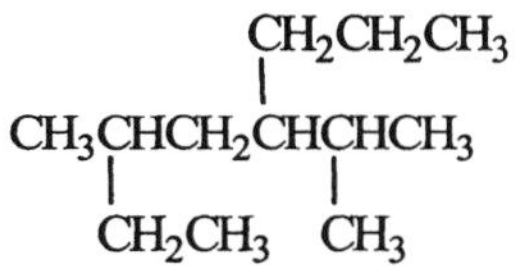

$CH_2CH_2CH_3$

$CH_3CHCH_2CHCHCH_3$

$CH_2CH_3 \quad CH_3$

Answer: 3-methyl-5-isopropyloctane *or* 3-methyl-5-(1-methylethyl)octane

Consider the representation below to answer the following questions.

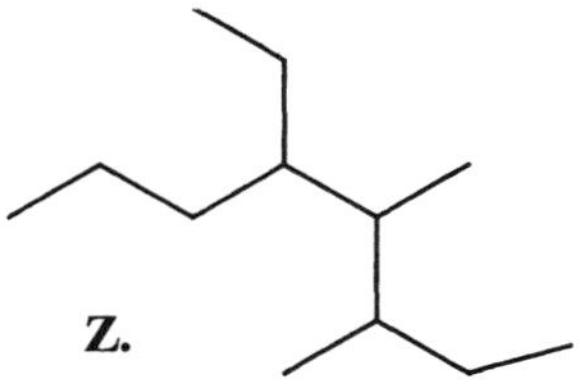

Z.

16. Provide the IUPAC name for compound **Z.**

Answer: 5-ethyl-3,4-dimethyloctane

17. Draw a constitutional isomer of compound **Z.** that contains an isopropyl group.

Answer:

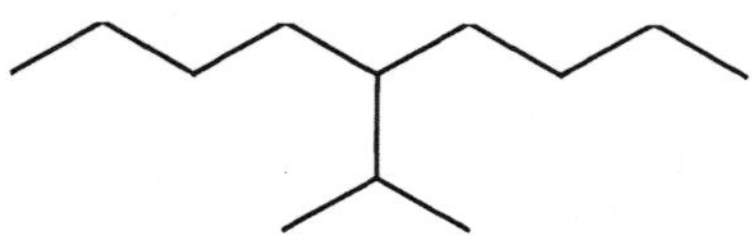

(other structures are possible)

Draw structures corresponding to each of the following names.

18. *cis*-1-*sec*-butyl-2-ethylcyclopentane

Answer:

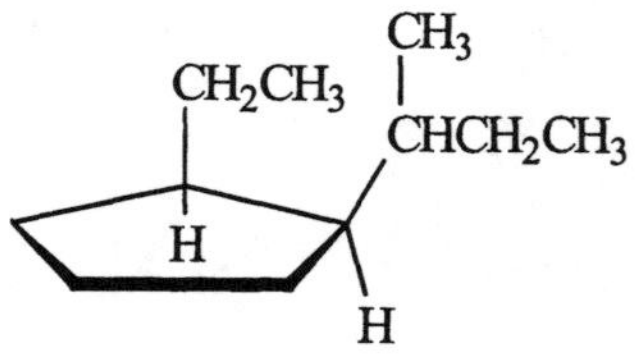

CH_3

CH_2CH_3

$CHCH_2CH_3$

H

H

19. 3-cyclobutylpentane

Answer:

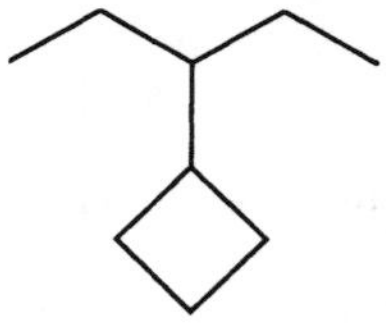

20. 4-(2,2-dibromoethyl)-3,5-dichloroheptane

Answer:

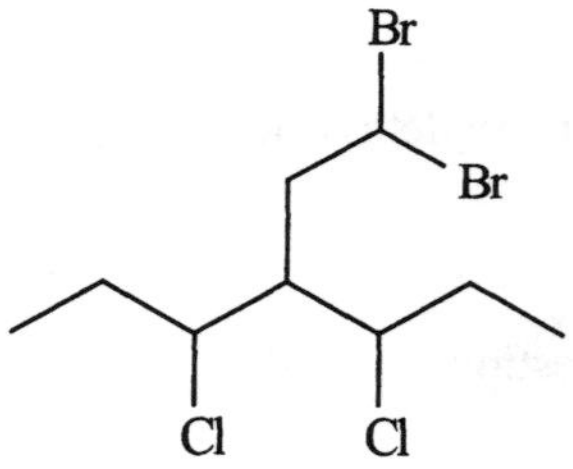

Br

Br

Cl Cl

21. There are seven (7) constitutional isomers for cycloalkane formula C_6H_{12} . Draw them.

Answer:

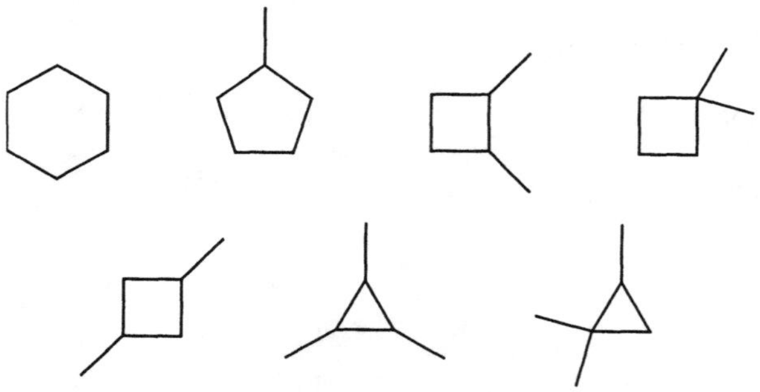

Cipro® (Ciprofloxacin) is a synthetic broad spectrum antibacterial agent. It was most recently in the news as the antibiotic of choice for the treatment of anthrax. The structure of Cipro is shown below.

Cipro

22. ***Circle*** the functional groups in the Cipro representation above.

Answer:

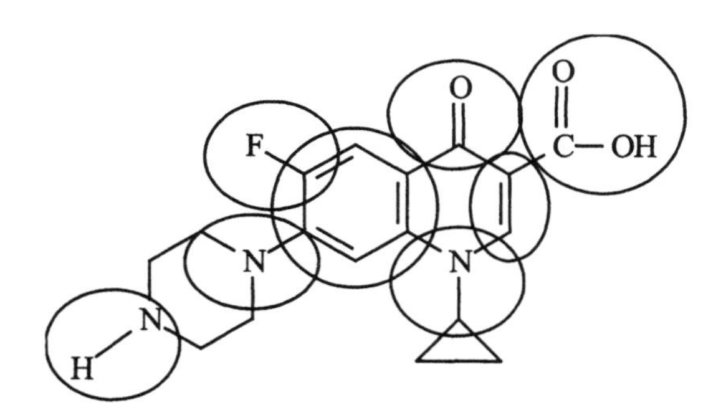

Predict the hybridization of the indicated atoms in Cipro.

24. __________

__________ **23.**

25. __________

23. The hybridization of this nitrogen atom is __________.

Answer: sp^3

24. The hybridization of this carbon atom is __________.

Answer: sp^2

25. The hybridization of this carbon atom is __________.

Answer: sp^3

Predict the indicated bond angles in Cipro.

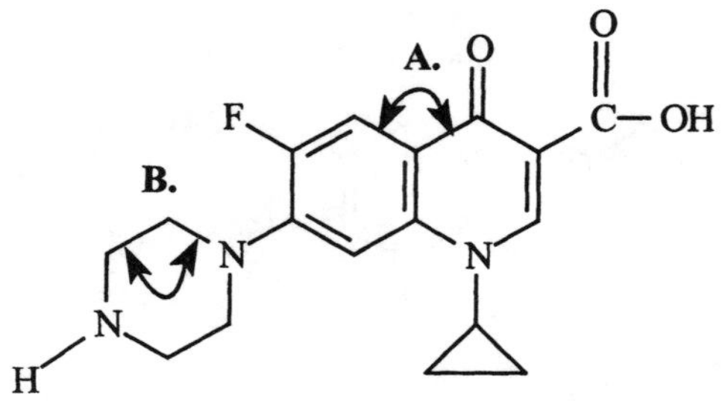

A. **B.**

26. Bond angle **A.** is __________ degrees.

Answer: 120°

27. Bond angle **B.** is __________ degrees.

Answer: 109.5°

28. Put a ***box*** around the **most polar** bond in Cipro.

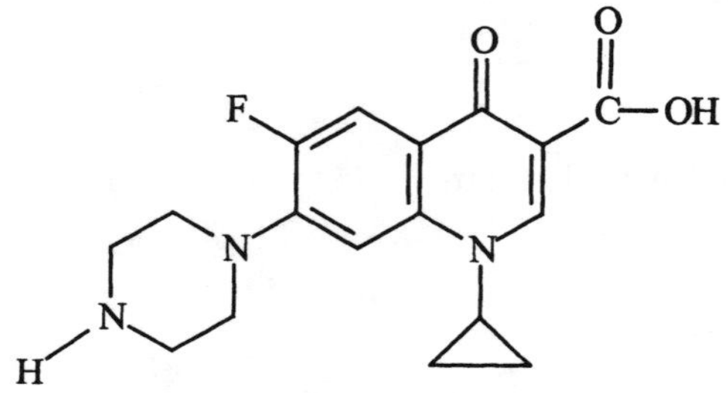

Cipro

Answer:

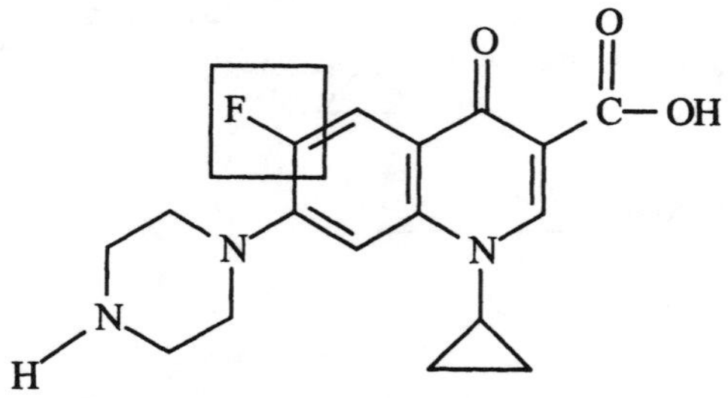

29. Draw the two stereoisomers of 1,3-dibromocyclobutane.

Answer:

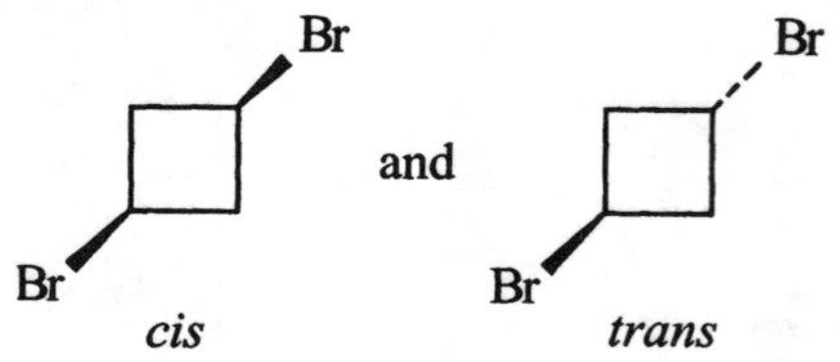

and

cis *trans*

Chapter 4 – Stereochemistry of Alkanes and Cycloalkanes

Experiments have shown that for 1,2-dichloroethane, $ClCH_2CH_2Cl$, in carbon tetrachloride solution at 25° C, 70% of the molecules are in the *anti* and 30% are in the *gauche* conformation.

1. Draw a Newman projection of the *anti* conformation of 1,2-dichloroethane.

Answer:

Cl
H H
H H
Cl

2. Draw a Newman projection of the *gauche* conformation of 1,2-dichloroethane.

Answer:

Cl
H Cl
H H
H

3. Draw a Newman projection of the *least* stable conformation of 1,2-dichloroethane.

Answer:

Cl Cl
H H
H H

Consider the conformations of 2-methylbutane shown below to answer the following questions.

A. CH_3 H H H_3C H CH_3

B. H_3C CH_3 H H H_3C H

C. CH_3 H CH_3 H CH_3 H

D. H CH_3 CH_3 H H_3C H

4. Which of the structures has two gauche interactions?

Answer: **C.**

5. Which of the structures represents the *most* stable conformation of 2-methylbutane?

Answer: **A.**

6. Which of the structures represents the *least* stable conformation of 2-methylbutane?

Answer: **B.**

MATCH the Newman projection for the conformation of 2-methylbutane to the indicated position on the potential energy diagram and place the letter corresponding to the correct projection in the blank.

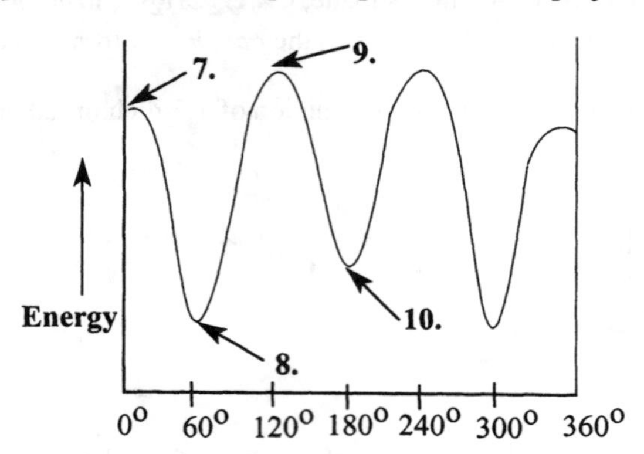

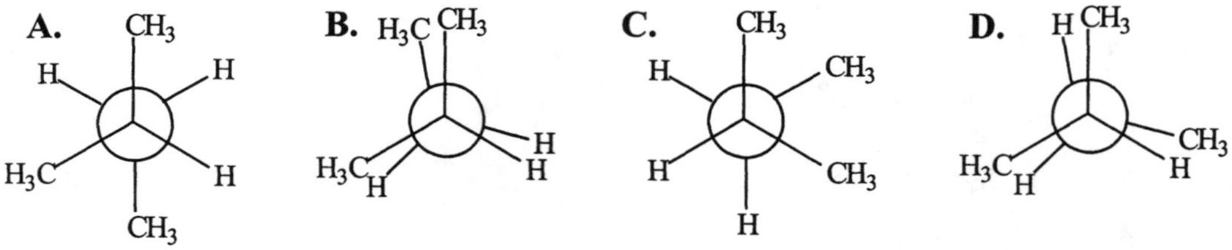

A. **B.** **C.** **D.**

7. This energy maximum corresponds to the Newman projection labeled _____ .

   Answer: **D.**

8. This energy minimum corresponds to the Newman projection labeled _____ .

   Answer: **A.**

9. This energy maximum corresponds to the Newman projection labeled _____ .

   Answer: **B.**

10. This energy minimum corresponds to the Newman projection labeled _____ .

    Answer: **C.**

Refer to the structure below to answer the following questions:

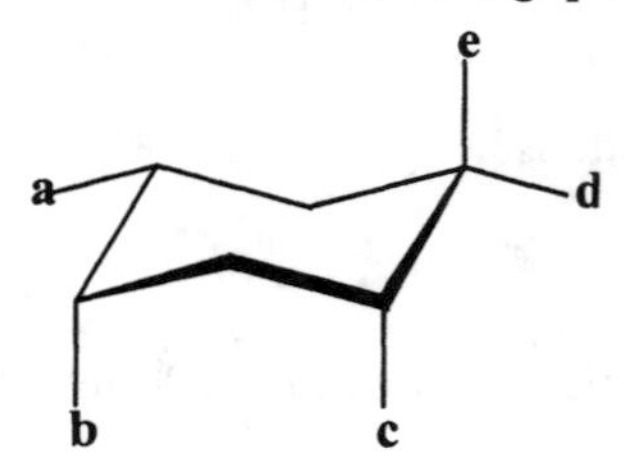

11. Which of the labeled bonds in the structure are *equatorial* bonds?

    Answer: **a** and **d**

12. Which of the labeled bonds is *trans* to bond **b**?

Answer: **e**

13. Which bonds have a 1,3-diaxial interaction with each other?

Answer: **b** and **c**

For each substituted cyclohexane below, draw its ring-flip isomer. *Circle* the *most* stable conformation.

14.

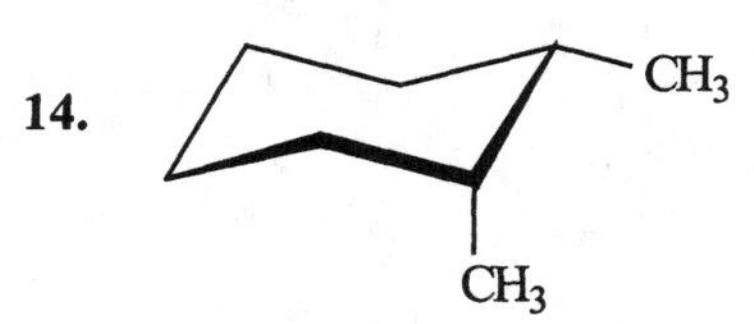

Answer:

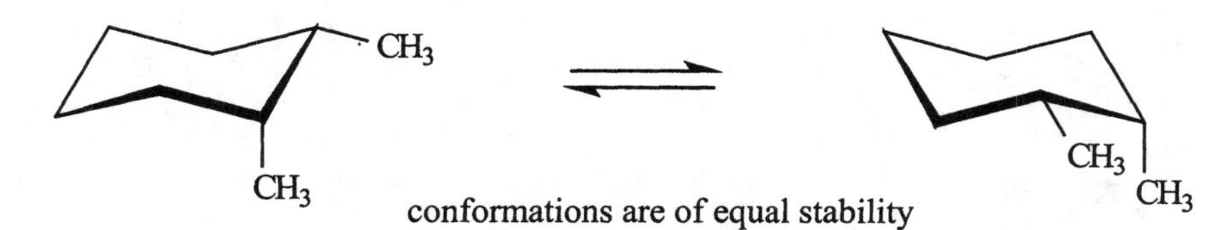

15. $(CH_3)_3C$

CH_3

Answer:

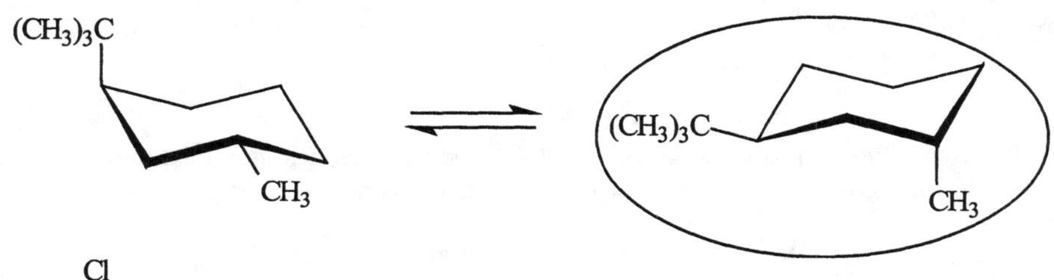

16. Cl

Answer:

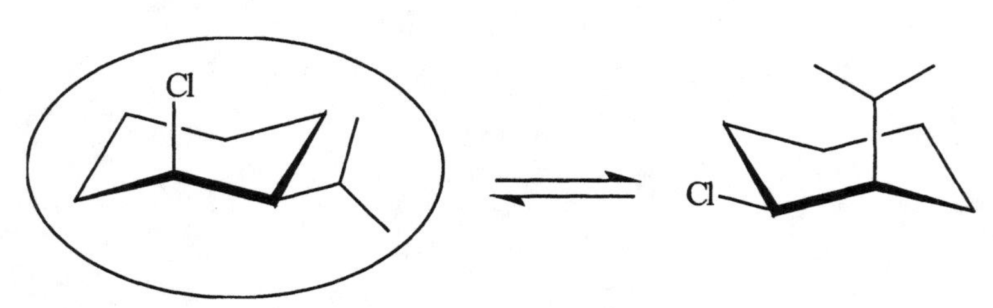

The following questions refer to the structure of camphor shown below.

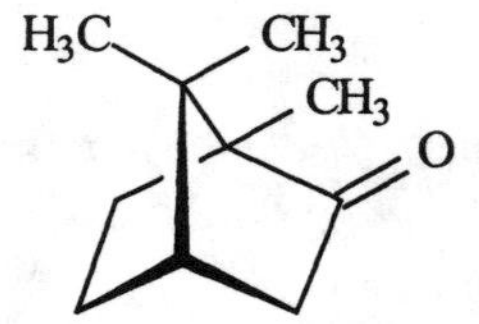

camphor

17. Circle all bridgehead carbons in camphor.

Answer:

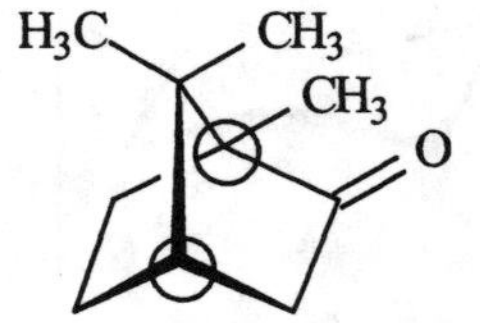

camphor

18. Camphor is an example of a:

a. fused bicyclic molecule.
b. bridged bicyclic molecule.
c. fused tricyclic molecule.
d. bridged tricyclic molecule.

Answer: b.

19. Below are the two chair conformations of a 1,2,4-trimethylcyclohexane. Estimate the amount of 1,3-diaxial strain in each conformer and predict which conformer is most stable.

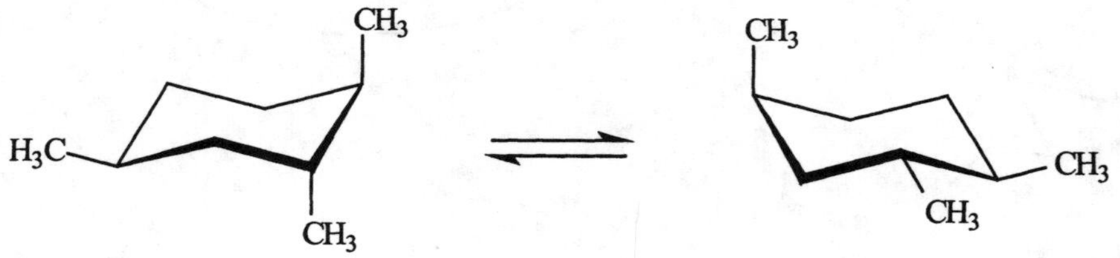

A. **B.**

Answer:

CH_3 1 H_3C 4 2 CH_3 ⇌ CH_3 4 2 CH_3 CH_3 1

A. **B.**

Conformer A		
$C1-CH_3$	2 (H-CH$_3$) = 2 x 6 kJ/mol	= 12 kJ/mol
$C2-CH_3$	2 (H-CH$_3$) = 2 x 6 kJ/mol	= 12 kJ/mol
$C4-CH_3$	no diaxial interactions	= 0 kJ/mol
	Strain energy in conformer A	= 24 kJ/mol

Conformer B		
$C1,C2-CH_3$	one gauche interactions	= 6 kJ/mol
$C4-CH_3$	2 (H-CH$_3$) = 2 x 6 kJ/mol	= 12 kJ/mol
	Strain energy in conformer B	= 18 kJ/mol

Conformer B is more stable than conformer A by 6 kJ/mol.

20. The energy difference of 3.8 kJ/mol between gauche and anti butane corresponds to an equilibrium constant, K_{eq}, of approximately 1.9. Calculate the percentage of each conformer at equilibrium.

Answer: $K_{eq} = (\text{anti})/(\text{gauche}) = 1.9$

$(\text{anti}) = 1.9(\text{gauche})$ *and* $(\text{anti}) + (\text{gauche}) = 100\%$

Substitute 1.9(gauche) for (anti) and you have:

$$1.9(\text{gauche}) + (\text{gauche}) = 100\%$$
$$2.9(\text{gauche}) = 100\%$$
$$(\text{gauche}) = 34.4\%$$
$$(\text{anti}) = 1.9(\text{gauche}) = 65.6\%$$

21. In general, 5-alkyl substituents in 1,3-dioxane exhibit a smaller equatorial preference than they do in cyclohexane. To what might you attribute this observation?

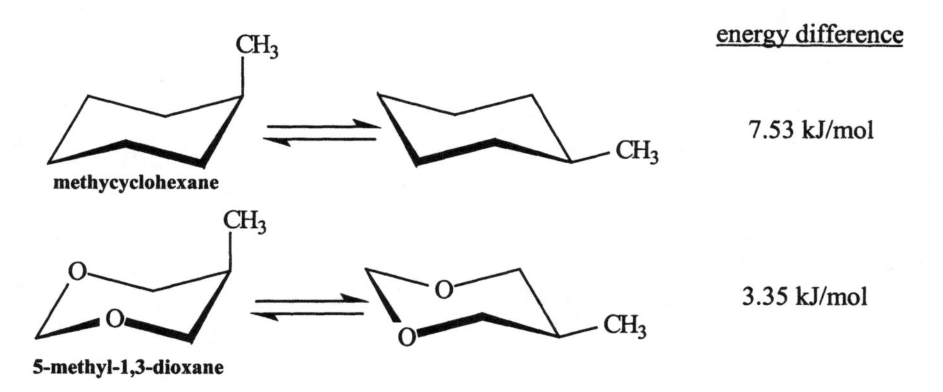

energy difference

7.53 kJ/mol

3.35 kJ/mol

Answer: The 5-alkyl substituted dioxanes do not suffer from 1,3-diaxial interactions since there are no hydrogens that are axial to the 5-substituent. Hence, the axial conformation is more stable in 5-substituted 1,3-dioxanes than it is in substituted cyclohexanes.

Label each pair of compounds below as:

a. conformational isomers
b. stereoisomers
c. constitutional isomers
d. identical

22. and

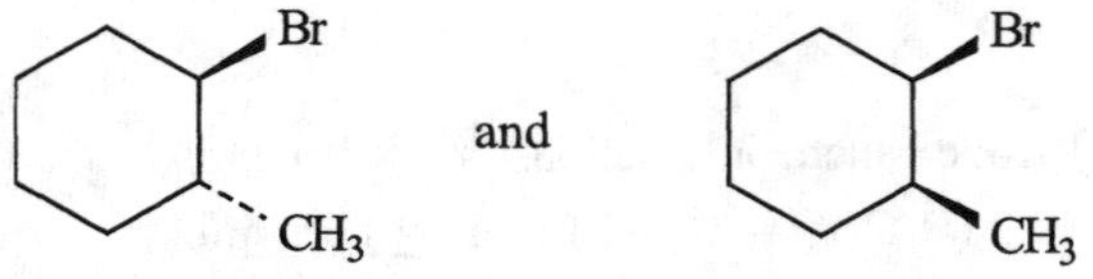

Answer: b

23. and

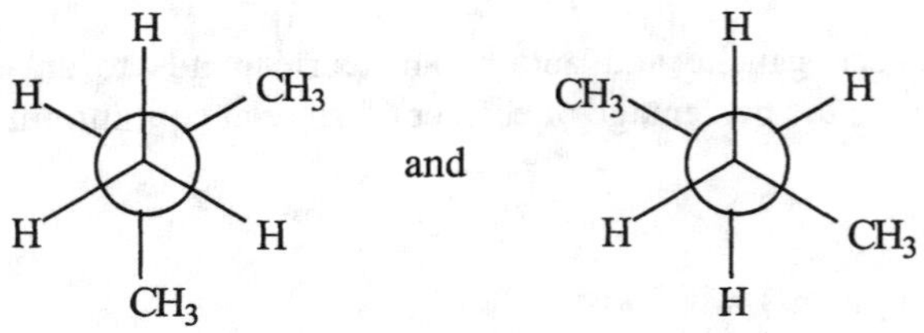

Answer: c

24. and

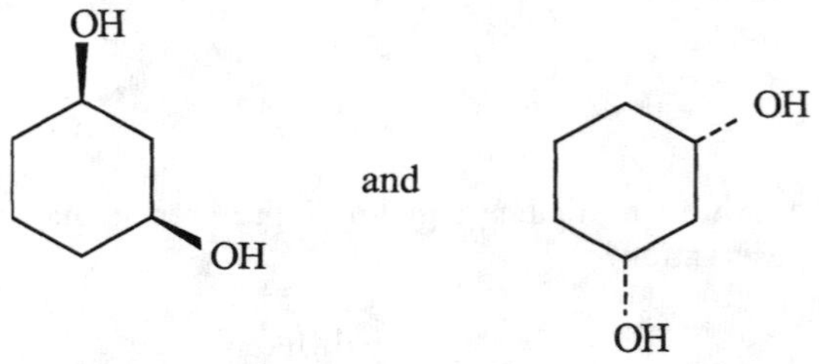

Answer: d

25. and

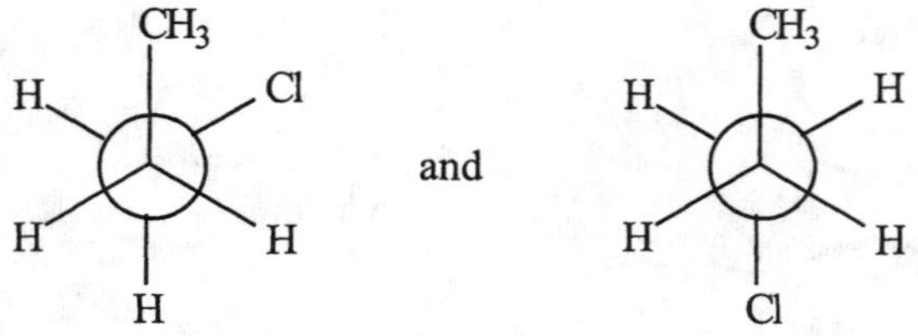

Answer: a

For each pair of molecules below, circle the **most** stable.

25.

Answer:

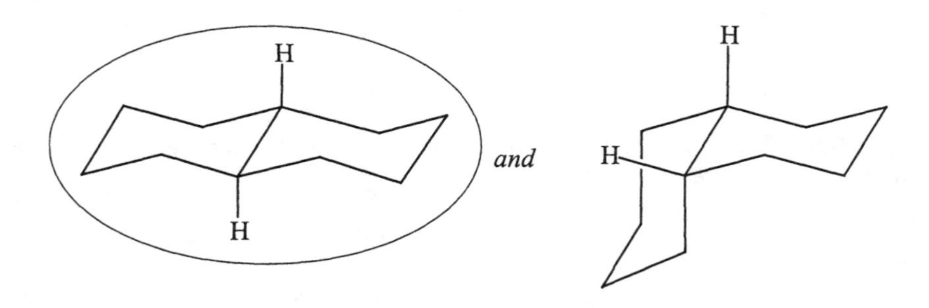

26.

Answer:

28.

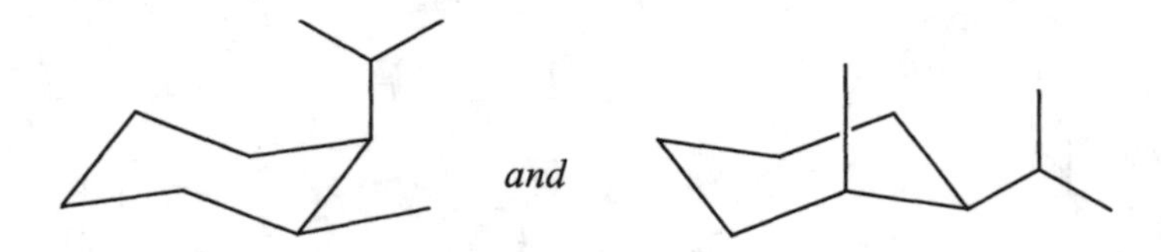

Answer:

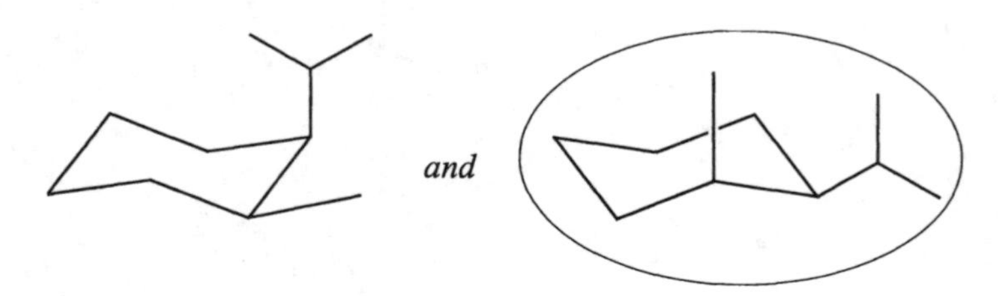

29. (-)-Menthol can be isolated from the peppermint plant and is responsible for the characteristic flavor and taste of peppermint. The structure of (-)-menthol is:

On the chair template provided below, draw the two chair conformations that are in equilibrium for (-)-menthol.

Answer:

30. D-Pinitol is an interesting hexahydroxy cyclohexane, whose structure is shown below.

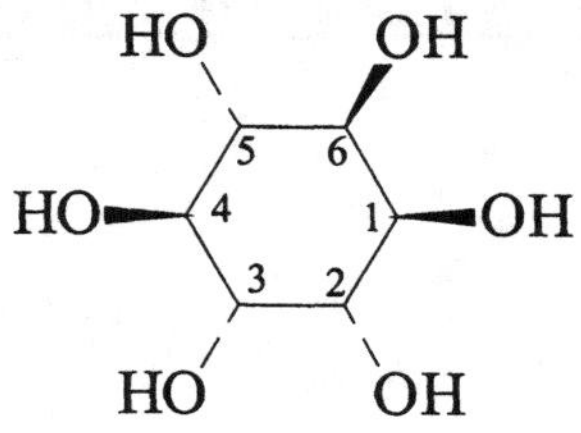

HO OH
5 6
HO 4 1 OH
3 2
HO OH

On the templates provided, draw the two chair conformations that are in equilibrium for D-pinitol. *Circle* the ***most*** stable conformation.

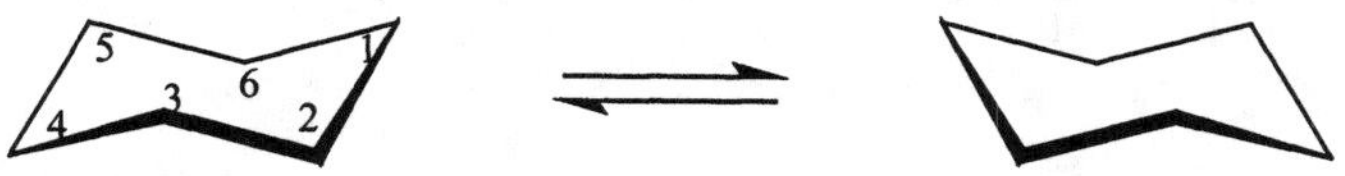

5 6 1
4 3 2

Answer:

OH OH HO 5 6 1 HO 4 3 2 HO OH

OH OH OH OH OH OH

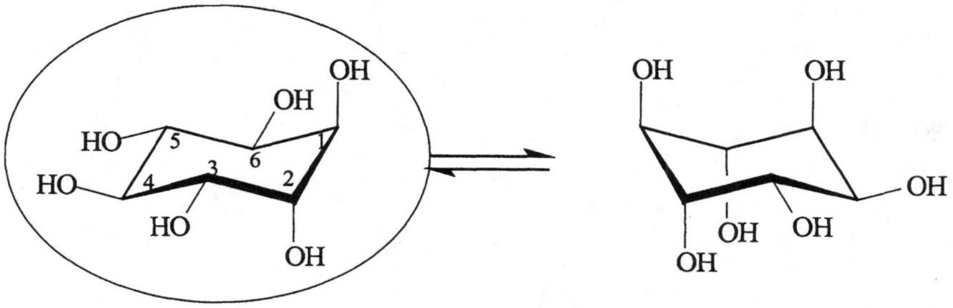

Chapter 5 – An Overview of Organic Reactions

Classify each reaction below as a(n):

a. addition
b. elimination
c. substitution
d. rearrangement

Place the letter corresponding to the correct answer in the blank to the left of the reaction.

1. ___ benzene $\xrightarrow[\text{catalyst}]{Cl_2}$ chlorobenzene + HCl

Answer: c

2. ___ isopropylidenecyclohexane $\xrightarrow[\text{catalyst}]{\text{acid}}$ 1-isopropylcyclohexene

Answer: d

3. ___ cyclopentene $\xrightarrow{Br_2}$ trans-1,2-dibromocyclopentane

Answer: a

Identify the functional groups present in each compound below and predict the direction of polarity in each.

4. mustard gas $Cl-CH_2CH_2-S-CH_2CH_2-Cl$

Answer:

halide sulfide

$\overset{\delta-}{Cl}-\overset{\delta+}{CH_2}\overset{\delta+}{CH_2}-\overset{\delta-}{S}-\overset{\delta+}{CH_2}\overset{\delta+}{CH_2}-\overset{\delta-}{Cl}$

5. amphetamine $C_6H_5CH_2CH(NH_2)CH_3$

Answer:

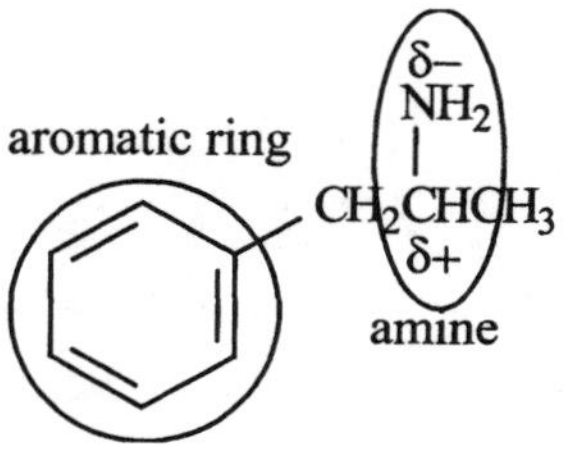

aromatic ring

$\delta-$

NH_2

CH_2CHCH_3

$\delta+$

amine

Classify each structure below as a nucleophile or electrophile and briefly explain your choice.

6. azide $:\ddot{N}=N=\ddot{N}:$ (charges: $-$ $+$ $-$)

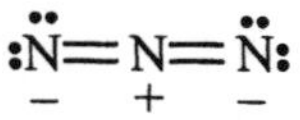

Answer: Azide is a nucleophile since it has a net negative charge (and lots of electron pairs!).

7. hydronium ion H_3O^+

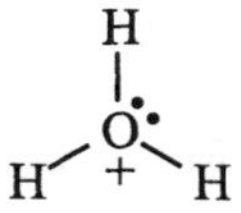

Answer: Hydronium ion is an electrophile since it has a positive charge.

8. phenol $C_6H_5\ddot{O}H$

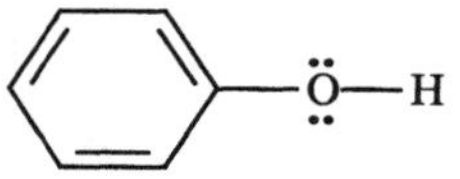

Answer: Phenol can be a nucleophile *or* an electrophile

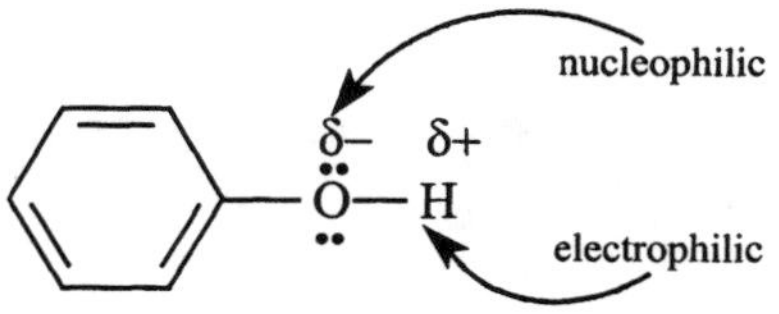

nucleophilic

$\delta-$ $\delta+$

O—H

electrophilic

Identify the nuclephile and electrophile in each reaction below and label them.

9. + H—Cl ⇌ + Cl^-

Answer:

+ H—Cl ⇌ H + Cl^-

nucleophile electrophile

10. 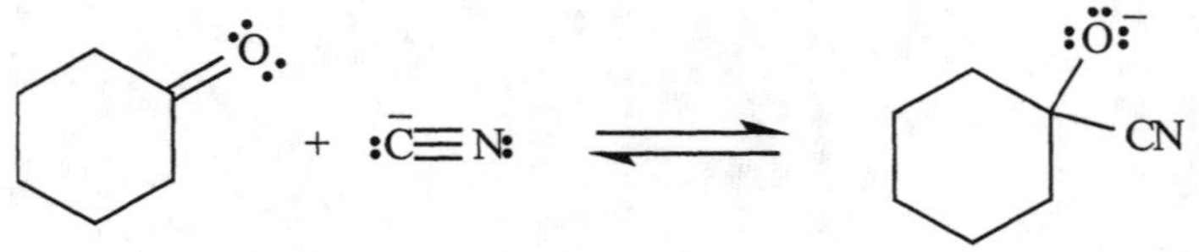 $\text{cyclohexanone} + :\bar{C}\equiv N: \rightleftharpoons$ (cyclohexane with $:\ddot{O}:^-$ and CN)

Answer:

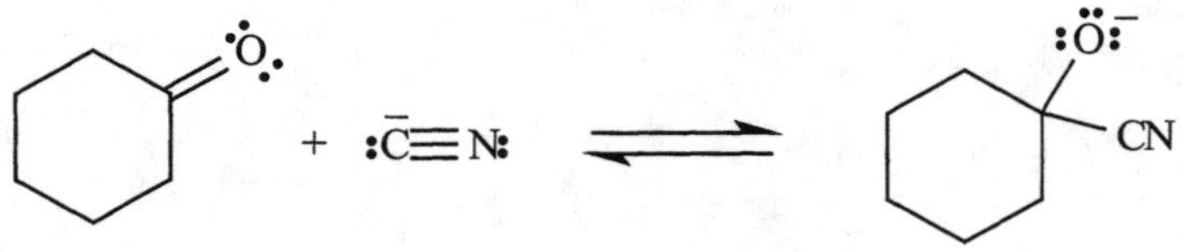

$\text{cyclohexanone} + :\bar{C}\equiv N: \rightleftharpoons$ (cyclohexane with $:\ddot{O}:^-$ and CN)

electrophile nucleophile

11. $H-\ddot{O}-H + H_3C-MgBr \longrightarrow CH_4 + H\ddot{O}:^- \; \overset{+}{M}gBr$

Answer:

$H-\ddot{O}-H + H_3C-MgBr \longrightarrow CH_4 + H\ddot{O}:^- \; \overset{+}{M}gBr$

electrophile nucleophile

Add curved arrows to the following reactions to indicate the flow of electrons in each.

12. 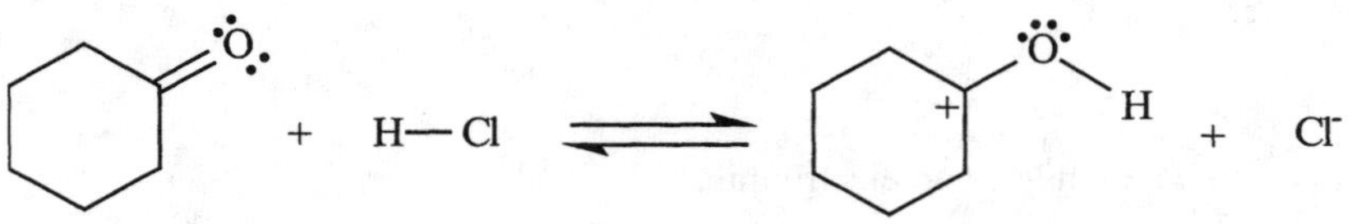 $\text{cyclohexanone} + H-Cl \rightleftharpoons$ (cyclohexyl cation with $\ddot{O}-H$) $+ Cl^-$

Answer:

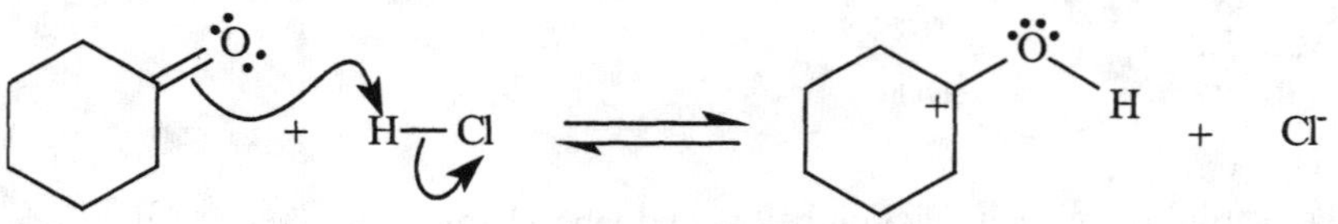

$\text{cyclohexanone} + H-Cl \rightleftharpoons$ (cyclohexyl cation with $\ddot{O}-H$) $+ Cl^-$

13. 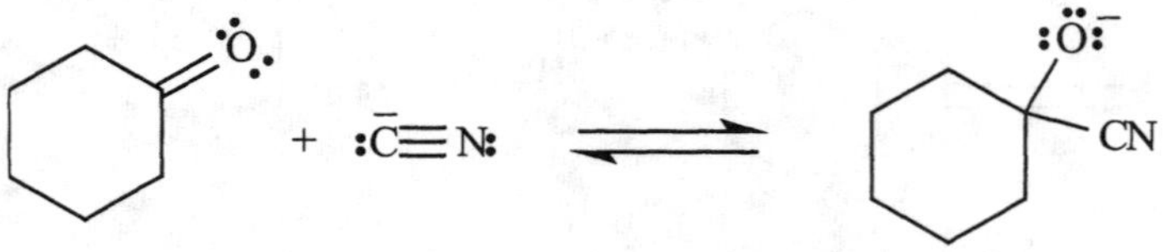 $\text{cyclohexanone} + :\bar{C}\equiv N: \rightleftharpoons$ (cyclohexane with $:\ddot{O}:^-$ and CN)

Answer:

$\text{cyclohexanone} + :\bar{C}\equiv N: \rightleftharpoons$ (cyclohexane with $:\ddot{O}:^-$ and CN)

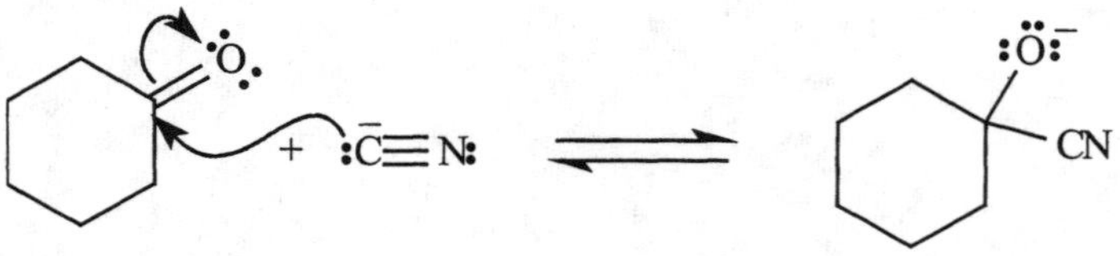

14. H—$\ddot{\underset{..}{O}}$—H + H_3C—MgBr ⟶ CH_4 + H$\ddot{\underset{..}{O}}$: $\overset{+}{Mg}$Br

Answer:

H—$\ddot{\underset{..}{O}}$—H + H_3C—MgBr ⟶ CH_4 + H$\ddot{\underset{..}{O}}$: $\overset{+}{Mg}$Br

15. Acidic ether cleavages are typical substitution reactions. Use the information in Table 5.3 of the textbook to calculate $\Delta H°$ for the reaction of ethyl methyl ether with hydrogen chloride and hydrogen iodide.

a. $CH_3CH_2OCH_3$ + HCl ⟶ CH_3CH_2OH + CH_3Cl

b. $CH_3CH_2OCH_3$ + HI ⟶ CH_3CH_2OH + CH_3I

Which acid would you predict to be most effective at ether cleavage?

Answer:

a. $CH_3CH_2OCH_3 + HCl$ $\quad$ $CH_3CH_2OH + CH_3Cl$

Bonds broken		Bonds formed	
$CH_3CH_2O-CH_3$	339 kJ/mol	CH_3CH_2O-H	436 kJ/mol
$H-Cl$	432 kJ/mol	CH_3-Cl	351 kJ/mol
	771 kJ/mol		787 kJ/mol

$$\Delta H° = \Delta H° \text{ bonds broken} - \Delta H° \text{ bonds formed} = 771 - 787 \text{ kJ/mol}$$
$$= -16 \text{ kJ/mol}$$

b. $CH_3CH_2OCH_3 + HI$ $\quad$ $CH_3CH_2OH + CH_3I$

Bonds broken		Bonds formed	
$CH_3CH_2O-CH_3$	339 kJ/mol	CH_3CH_2O-H	436 kJ/mol
$H-I$	298 kJ/mol	CH_3-I	234 kJ/mol
	637 kJ/mol		670 kJ/mol

$$\Delta H° = \Delta H° \text{ bonds broken} - \Delta H° \text{ bonds formed} = 637 - 670 \text{ kJ/mol}$$
$$= -33 \text{ kJ/mol}$$

Since cleavage with HI is the most exothermic we would predict that HI would be most effective at ether cleavage.

MATCH each definition to one of the terms below. Place the letter of the term in the blank to the left of the definition.

a. polarization
b. addition reaction
c. homolytic bond breakage
d. electrophile
e. polar reaction
f. substitution
g. nucleophile
h. radical reaction
i. elimination reaction
j. heterolytic bond breakage

16. _____ A process involving symmetrical bond breaking and bond making.

Answer: h

17. _____ This occurs when both bonding electrons remain with one product fragment.

Answer: j

18. _____ A reaction where two reactants exchange parts to give two new products.

Answer: f

19. _____ A general term for species which have electron rich sites that can form a bond by donating a pair of electrons to an electron poor site.

Answer: g

Consider this reaction when answering the following questions:

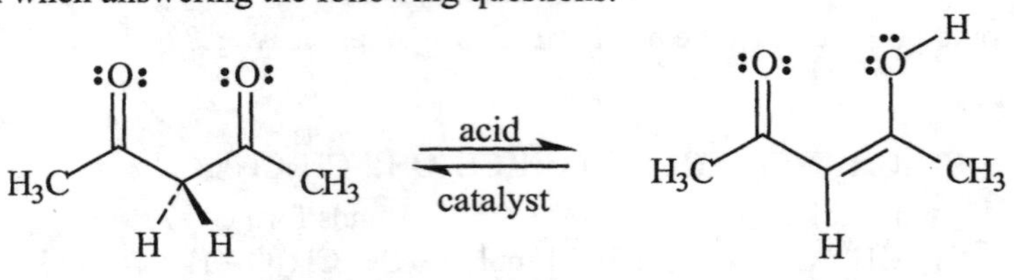

:O: :O: H₃C CH₃ H H — acid catalyst ⇌ — :O: :Ö—H H₃C CH₃ H

76%

20. This reaction is an example of:

a. a substitution reaction.
b. a rearrangement reaction.
c. an addition reaction.
d. an elimination reaction.

Answer: b

21. The structures below show the step-wise bond making and bond breaking in this reaction. Draw curved arrows to show the electron flow that has occurred in each step.

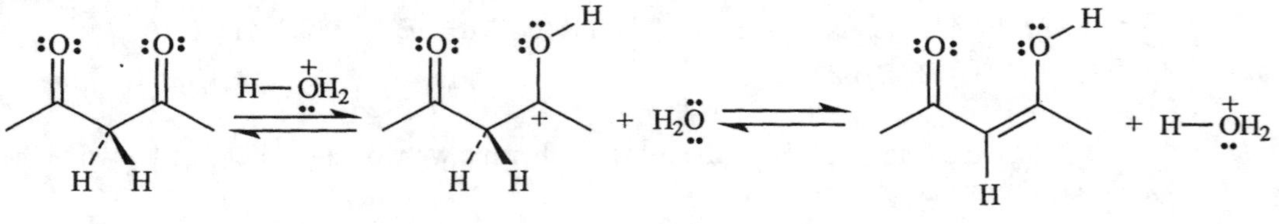

:O: :O: H H — $H—\overset{+}{O}H_2$ ⇌ — :O: :Ö—H + H H + $H_2\ddot{O}$ ⇌ :O: :Ö—H H + $H—\overset{+}{O}H_2$

76%

Answer:

:O: :O: H H — $H—\overset{+}{O}H_2$ ⇌ — :O: :Ö—H + H H + $H_2\ddot{O}$ ⇌ :O: :Ö—H H + $H—\overset{+}{O}H_2$

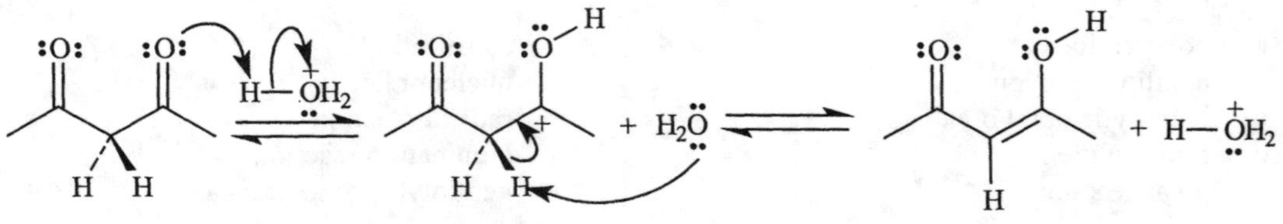

76%

22. Calculate K_{eq} for the reaction.

Answer: K_{eq} = [products]/[reactants] = 76/24 = 3.17

23. Draw a qualitative energy diagram for the reaction (assume that the first step is slower than the second step). Label fully.

Answer:

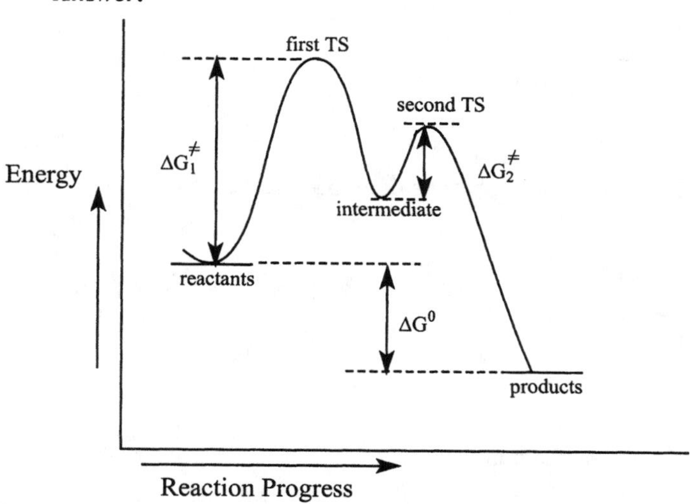

MATCH each definition to one of the terms below. Place the letter corresponding to the term in the blank to the left of the definition.

a. transition state
b. endergonic reaction
c. activation energy
d. standard Gibbs free energy change
e. exergonic reaction
f. reaction intermediate

24. _____ A species that lies at an energy minimum between steps on a reaction.

Answer: f

25. _____ The energy needed by reactants to reach the transition state.

Answer: c

26. _____ A reaction where $\Delta G°$ is negative.

Answer: e

27. _____ $\Delta G° = -RT \ln K_{eq}$

Answer: d

Use the reaction energy diagram below to answer the following questions.

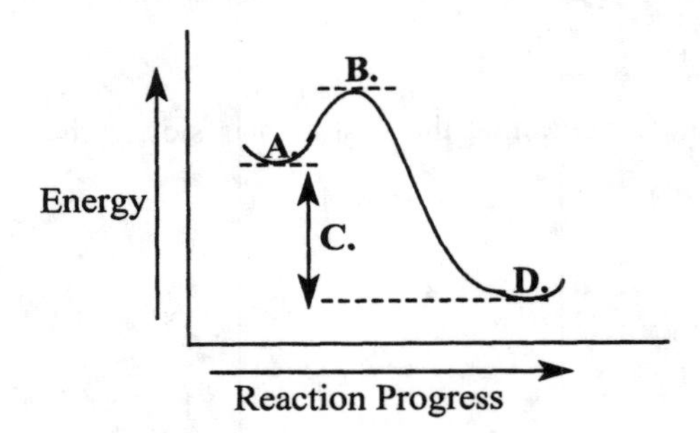

28. The reaction depicted in this reaction energy diagram can best be described as:

a. a slow exothermic reaction
b. a fast exothermic reaction
c. a slow endothermic reaction
d. a fast endothermic reaction

Answer: b

29. The transition state is found at point _____ on the diagram.

Answer: B.

30. The products are found at point _____ on the diagram.

Answer: D.

31. The free-energy change for the reaction is indicated at point _____ on the diagram.

Answer: C.

32. The reactants are found at point _____ on the diagram.

Answer: A.

Consider the reaction of 2-bromo-2-methylpropane with water, shown below, to answer the following questions.

$$H_3C-C(CH_3)_2-Br \xrightarrow{H_2O} H_3C-C(CH_3)_2-OH + HBr$$

33. This reaction is an example of:

a. a substitution reaction.
b. a rearrangement reaction.
c. an elimination reaction.
d. an addition reaction.

Answer: a.

The first step of this reaction is shown below.

$$H_3C-C(CH_3)_2-Br \rightleftharpoons H_3C-C^+(CH_3)_2 + Br^-$$

A — *B*

34. Species ***B*** is:

a. a carbene
b. a carbanion
c. a carbocation
d. a radical

Answer: c

35. Add curved arrows to indicate electron flow in the first step.

Answer:

$$H_3C-C(CH_3)_2-Br \rightleftharpoons H_3C-C^+(CH_3)_2 + Br^-$$

A — *B*

The second and third steps of the reaction are shown below.

$$H_3C-C^+(CH_3)_2 \quad :\ddot{O}H_2 \rightleftharpoons H_3C-C(CH_3)_2-\ddot{O}^+H_2 \quad :\ddot{O}H_2 \rightleftharpoons H_3C-C(CH_3)_2-\ddot{O}H + H_3O^+$$

________ ________

36. Label the nucleophile, Nu, and the electrophile, E^+, in the blanks provided under the structures.

Answer:

$$H_3C-C^+(CH_3)_2 \quad :\ddot{O}H_2 \rightleftharpoons H_3C-C(CH_3)_2-\ddot{O}^+H_2 \quad :\ddot{O}H_2 \rightleftharpoons H_3C-C(CH_3)_2-\ddot{O}H + H_3O^+$$

electrophile — nucleophile

37. Draw arrows on the structures above showing electron flow in steps two and three of this reaction.

Answer:

$$H_3C-C^+(CH_3)_2 \quad :\ddot{O}H_2 \rightleftharpoons H_3C-C(CH_3)_2-\ddot{O}^+H_2 \quad :\ddot{O}H_2 \rightleftharpoons H_3C-C(CH_3)_2-\ddot{O}H + H_3O^+$$

38. This reaction is an example of:

a. a pericyclic reaction.
b. a radical reaction.
c. a concerted reaction.
d. a polar reaction.

Answer: d

39. Using the bond dissociations values in the table below, calculate the ΔH° for this reaction. Show your calculations for full credit.

Bond	D (kJ/mol
$(CH_3)_3C—Br$	263
$(CH_3)_3C—OH$	380
HO—H	498
H—Br	366

Answer:

Bonds Broken		Bonds Formed	
$(CH_3)_3C—Br$	263 kJ/mol	$(CH_3)_3C—OH$	380 kJ/mol
HO—H	498 kJ/mol	H—Br	366 kJ/mol
	761 kJ/mol		746 kJ/mol

$\Delta H° = \Delta H°$ bonds broken $-$ $\Delta H°$ bonds formed
= 761 kJ/mol - 746 kJ/mol
= +15 kJ/mol

40. Based on all of the data presented above, draw a qualitative reaction energy diagram for the reaction of 2-bromo-2-methylpropane with water. The first step is the slowest step of the reaction. Fully label the diagram, including the coordinates.

Answer:

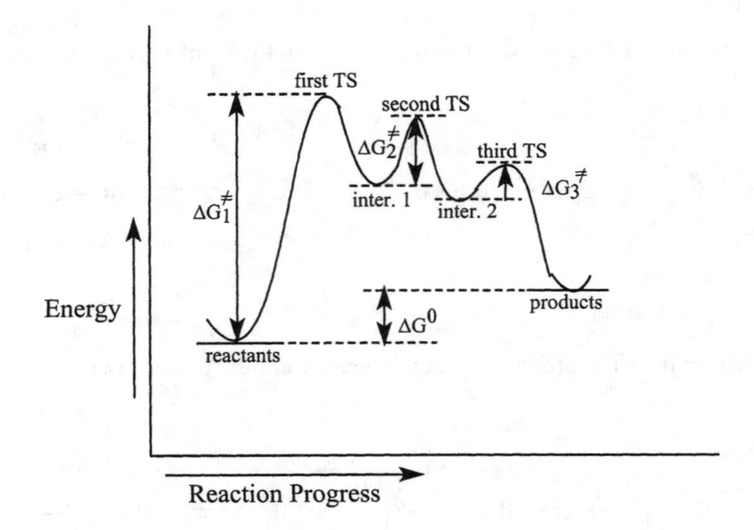

In each reaction below:

a) Label the nucleophile (Nu) and the electrophile (E).
b) Draw arrows on the structures showing electron flow in the reaction

41. $CH_3-\overset{\oplus}{C}H-CH_3 + :\ddot{Cl}:^{\ominus} \longrightarrow CH_3-CH(Cl)-CH_3$

Answer:

$CH_3-\overset{\oplus}{C}H-CH_3 + :\ddot{Cl}:^{\ominus} \longrightarrow CH_3-CH(Cl)-CH_3$

E Nu

42. $CH_3-CH=CH_2 + H-Cl \longrightarrow CH_3-\overset{\oplus}{C}H-CH_2(H) + :\ddot{Cl}:^{\ominus}$

Answer:

$CH_3-CH=CH_2 + H-Cl \longrightarrow CH_3-\overset{\oplus}{C}H-CH_2(H) + :\ddot{Cl}:^{\ominus}$

Nu E

Chapter 6 – Alkenes: Structure and Reactivity

Calculate the degree of unsaturation in each formula below. Show your calculations.

1. pinene, $C_{10}H_{18}$

Answer: The saturated ten carbon compound would have 22 hydrogens so the number of degrees of unsaturation is: $(22-18) \div 2 = 4 \div 2 = 2$.

2. eicosapentaenoic acid, $C_{20}H_{30}O_2$, a constituent of fish oil

Answer: Oxygen does not affect the base formula which in this case is $C_{20}H_{30}$. The saturated 20 carbon compound would have 42 hydrogens so the number of degrees of unsaturation for eiscosapentaenoic acid is: $(42 - 30) \div 2 = 12 \div 2 = 6$.

3. diazepam (Valium), $C_{16}H_{13}N_2OCl$

Answer: Oxygen does not affect the base formula. A hydrogen is added to the base formula for each halogen and subtracted for each nitrogen so the base formula for diazepam is $C_{16}H_{12}$. The saturated 16 carbon compound would have 34 hydrogens so the number of degrees of unsaturation for diazepam is: $(34 - 12) \div 2 = 22 \div 2 = 11$.

Dieldrin, $C_{12}H_8Cl_6O$, is a pentacyclic compound formerly used as an insecticide.

4. Calculate the degree of unsaturation for Dieldrin. Show calculations for credit.

Answer: Oxygen does not affect the base formula. A hydrogen is added to the base formula for each halogen so the base formula for dieldrin is $C_{12}H_{14}$. The saturated 12 carbon compound would have 26 hydrogens so the number of degrees of unsaturation for dieldrin is $(26 - 14) \div 2 = 12 \div 2 = 6$.

5. How many double bonds does dieldrin have?

Answer: Dieldrin has 6 degrees of unsaturation and it is pentacyclic, meaning it has 5 rings. Therefore, dieldrin must have one double bond.

Draw structures corresponding to each name below. Either condensed or line structures may be used.

6. (3*E*)-3,7-dimethyl-1,3,6-octatriene

Answer:

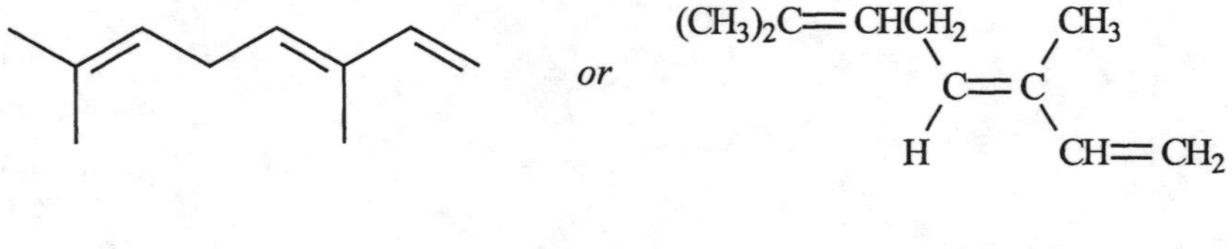

or

$(CH_3)_2C{=}CHCH_2$ CH_3

C=C

H $CH{=}CH_2$

7. 3,6-dimethyl-1,4-cyclohexadiene

Answer:

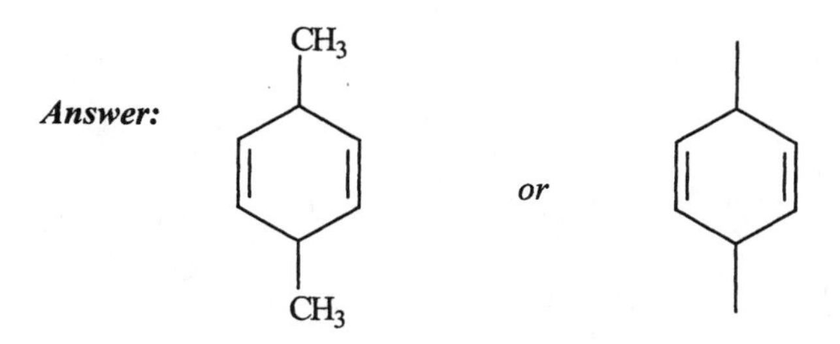

8. *cis*-2-hexene

Answer:

or

H_3C $CH_2CH_2CH_3$

C=C

H H

9. *trans*-4,4-dimethyl-2-pentene

Answer:

or

H_3C H

C=C

H $C(CH_3)_2CH_3$

2-Pentene is an example of a *disubstituted* alkene.

$$CH_3CH{=}CHCH_2CH_3$$

10. Draw the cis and trans isomers of 2-pentene and label them.

Answer:

H_3C CH_2CH_3 H_3C H

C=C C=C

H H H CH_2CH_3

cis *trans*

11. *Circle* the isomer which is ***most*** stable.

Answer:

H_3C CH_2CH_3 H_3C H

C=C C=C

H H H CH_2CH_3

cis *trans*

Provide names for each structure below. Be sure to include the *cis,trans* or *E,Z* designations where applicable.

12.

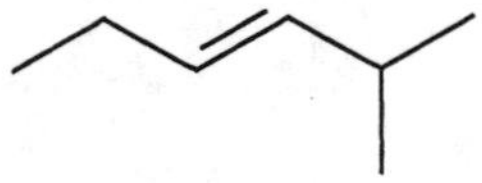

Answer: *trans*-2-methyl-3-hexene *or* (*E*)-2-methyl-3-hexene

13.

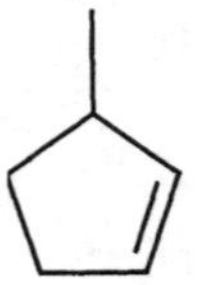

Answer: 3-methylcyclopentene

14.

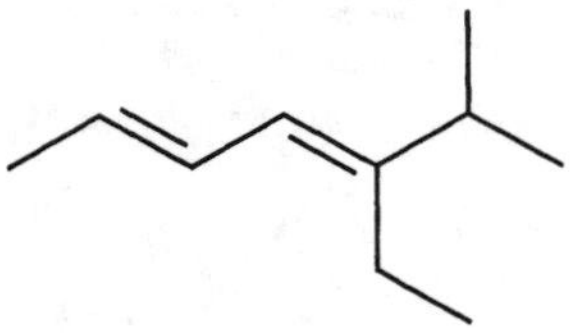

Answer: (2*E*,4*E*)-5-ethyl-6-methyl-2,4-heptadiene

15. 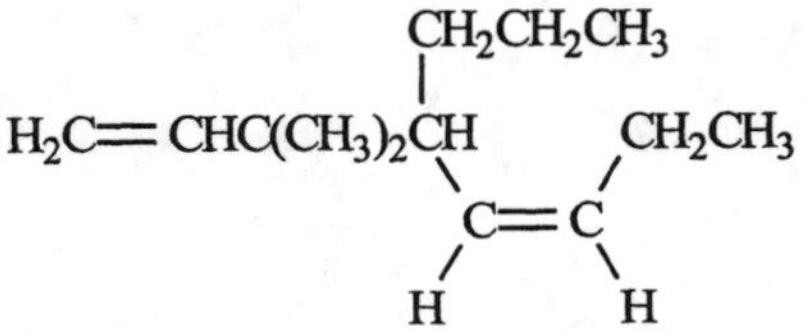 $H_2C{=}CHC(CH_3)_2CH(CH_2CH_2CH_3)CH{=}CHCH_2CH_3$ (H and H on the same side of the C=C)

Answer: *cis*-3,3-dimethyl-4-propyl-1,5-octadiene or *(Z)*-3,3-dimethyl-4-propyl-1,5-octadiene

Rank each set of substituents using the Cahn-Ingold-Prelog sequence rules by numbering the highest priority substituent 1 and numbering the lowest priority substituent 4. Place the number in the blank below the substituent.

16. $-CHO$ (—C(=O)—H) ______ $-CH{=}CHCH_3$ ______ $-CH{=}NCH_3$ ______ $-C{\equiv}C{-}CH_3$ ______

Answer:

$-CHO$ (—C(=O)—H)	$-CH{=}CHCH_3$	$-CH{=}NCH_3$	$-C{\equiv}C{-}CH_3$
1	4	2	3

17. $—NHCCH_3$ (with C=O) ____ $—C\equiv C—H$ ____ $—CH(CH_3)—CH_3$ ____ $—CH(CH_3)—OH$ ____

Answer:

$—NHC(=O)CH_3$	$—C\equiv C—H$	$—CH(CH_3)—CH_3$	$—CH(CH_3)—OH$
1	3	4	2

18. $—CH_2—I$ ____ $—C{=}N—OH$ ____ $—C(=O)—OCH_3$ ____ $—CH{=}CHCH_3$ ____

Answer:

$—CH_2—I$	$—C{=}N—OH$	$—C(=O)—OCH_3$	$—CH{=}CHCH_3$
1	3	2	4

19. $—CH_2—OH$ ____ $—C\equiv N$ ____ $—CH_2—Cl$ ____ $—CH{=}CH_2$ ____

Answer:

$—CH_2—OH$	$—C\equiv N$	$—CH_2—Cl$	$—CH{=}CH_2$
2	3	1	4

MATCH each alkene below with the appropriate heat of hydrogenation. Place the letter of the correct answer in the blank to the left of the alkene.

a. 125.9 kJ/mol
b. 118.4 kJ/mol
c. 115.5 kJ/mol

20. ____ H_3C, H / H, CH_3 (alkene)

Answer: c

21. ____ H, H / H, CH_3 (alkene)

Answer: a

22. _____

H_3C CH_2CH_3

H H

Answer: b

23. Arrange the following bicyclic alkenes in order of increasing stability (least stable to most stable).

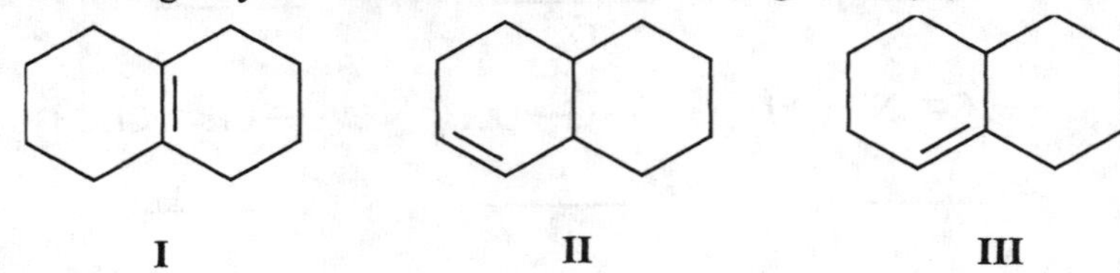

I II III

a. III < II < I
b. I < II < III
c. I < III < II
d. II < III < I

Answer: d

Assign *E* or *Z* configurations to each alkene below.

24.

H_3C CH_3

Br CH_2CH_3

Answer: *Z*

25.

CN

CH_2CH_2OH

CH_3

Answer: *E*

26.

O CH_3

H_3COC $C{=}CH_2$

$O{=}C$ $C{\equiv}CH$

OH

Answer: *E*

MATCH each definition to the term it describes. Place the letter corresponding to the term in the blank to the left of the definition.

a. Hammond Postulate
b. Cahn-Ingold-Prelog Rules
c. Markovnikov's Rule

27. ______ Predicts that the more stable carbocation intermediate is formed in electrophilic additions to alkenes.

Answer: c

28. ______ Predicts that the transition state of an exergonic reaction step structurally resembles the reactant.

Answer: a

29. ______ Assigns priorities to the substituent groups on a carbon.

Answer: b

30. ______ Predicts that the transition state of an endergonic reaction step structurally resembles the product.

Answer: a

31. ______ Predicts that in additions of HX to alkenes, the H adds to the less substituted alkene carbon and the X adds to the more substituted alkene carbon.

Answer: c

32. Rank the carbocations below in order of increasing stability (least stable = 1; most stable = 3). Place the number corresponding to the carbocation's relative stability in the blank below the structure.

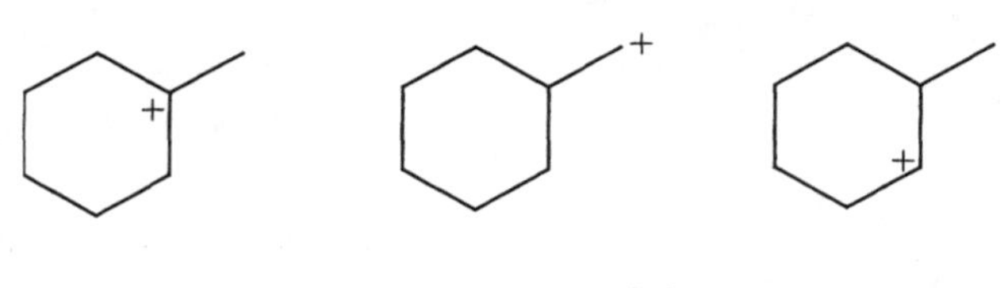

___ ___ ___

Answer:

3 1 2

Consider the following reaction:

1-methylcyclohexene + HCl ⟶ 1-chloro-1-methylcyclohexane

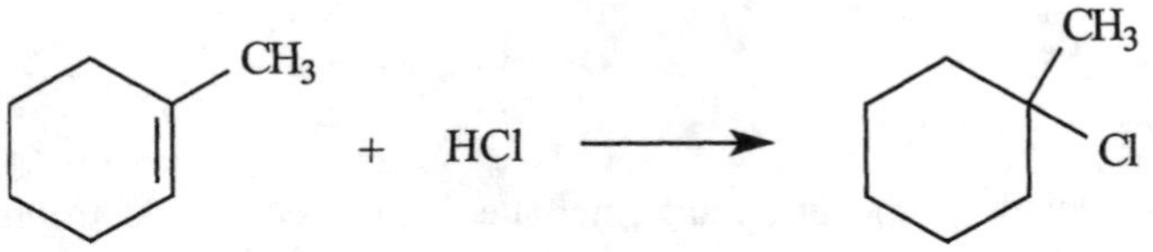

33. Write the complete stepwise mechanism for this reaction. Show all intermediate structures and show all electron flow using the curved arrow convention.

Answer:

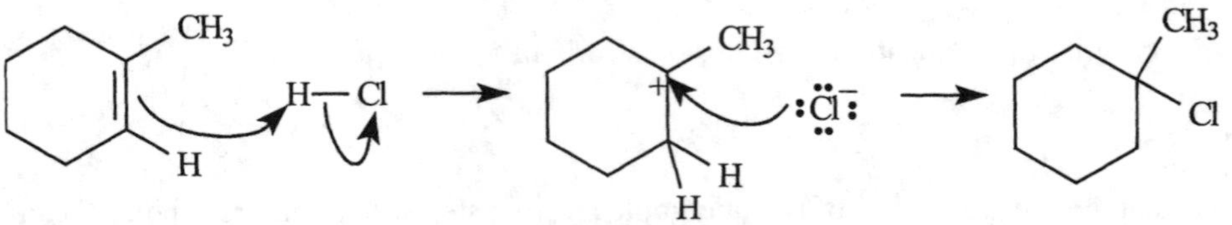

34. Draw a qualitative reaction energy diagram for this reaction. Label the positions of all reactants, intermediates and products.

Answer:

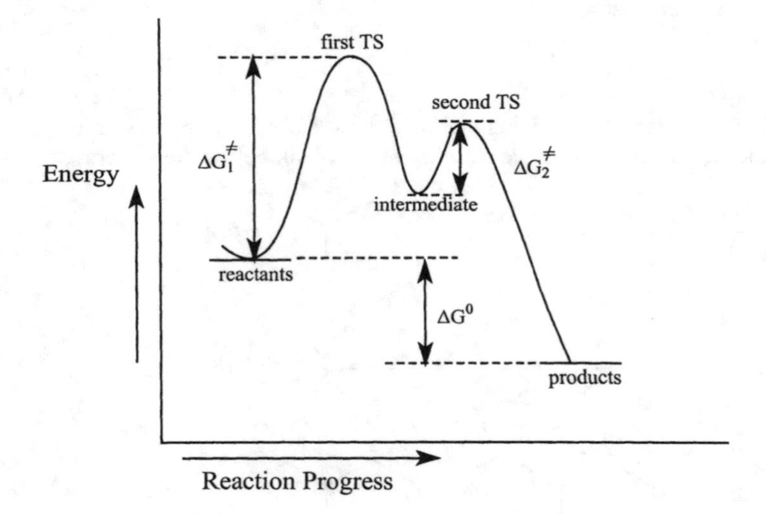

Consider the following reaction:

$$(CH_3)_3CCH{=}CH_2 \;+\; HCl \longrightarrow (CH_3)_3CCH(Cl)CH_3 \;+\; (CH_3)_2C(Cl)CH(CH_3)CH_3$$

A 50% **B** 50%

35. Below are all the chemical structures and intermediates involved in this reaction. On the structures provided, show all electron flow using the arrow formalism for the complete stepwise mechanism for this reaction.

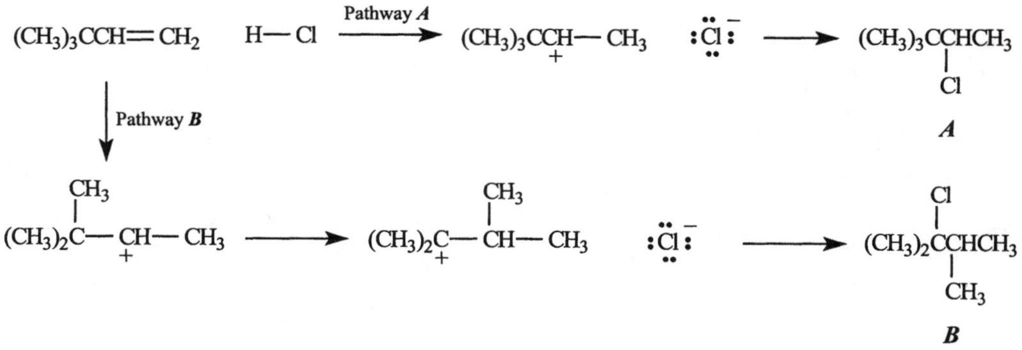

$(CH_3)_3CCH{=}CH_2$ H—Cl —Pathway *A*→ $(CH_3)_3CCH{-}CH_3$ (+) $:\ddot{Cl}:^-$ → $(CH_3)_3CCHCH_3$ | Cl

A

Pathway *B* ↓

CH_3 | $(CH_3)_2C{-}CH{-}CH_3$ (+) → CH_3 | $(CH_3)_2C{-}CH{-}CH_3$ (+) $:\ddot{Cl}:^-$ → Cl | $(CH_3)_2CCHCH_3$ | CH_3

B

Answer:

$(CH_3)_3CCH{=}CH_2$ H—Cl —Pathway *A*→ $(CH_3)_3CCH{-}CH_3$ (+) $:\ddot{Cl}:^-$ → $(CH_3)_3CCHCH_3$ | Cl

A

Pathway *B* ↓

CH_3 | $(CH_3)_2C{-}CH{-}CH_3$ (+) → CH_3 | $(CH_3)_2C{-}CH{-}CH_3$ (+) $:\ddot{Cl}:^-$ → Cl | $(CH_3)_2CCHCH_3$ | CH_3

B

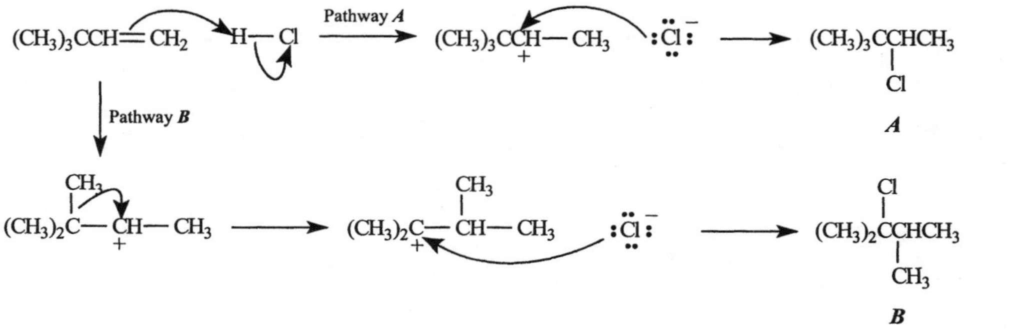

36. Why does the rearrangement that results in the formation of product B occur?

Answer: The 1,2-alkyl shift is the rearrangement of a secondary carbocation to a more stable tertiary carbocation.

37. Write the complete stepwise mechanism for the following reaction. Show all intermediate structures and all electron flow with arrows.

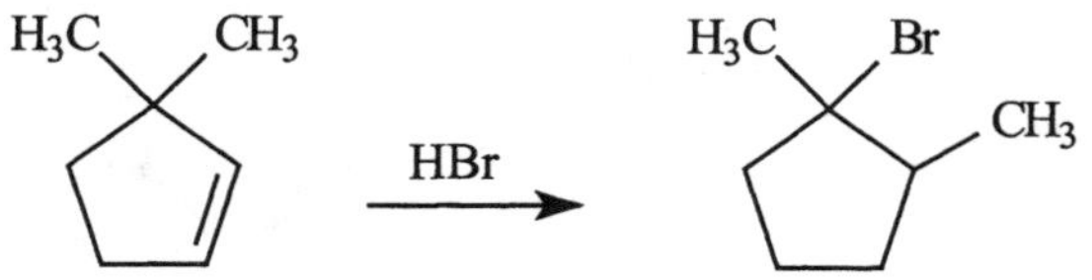

H_3C CH_3 —HBr→ H_3C Br CH_3

Answer:

H_3C CH_3 H—Br → H_3C CH_3 (+) H + $:\ddot{Br}:^-$ → CH_3 (+) CH_3 $:\ddot{Br}:^-$ → H_3C Br CH_3

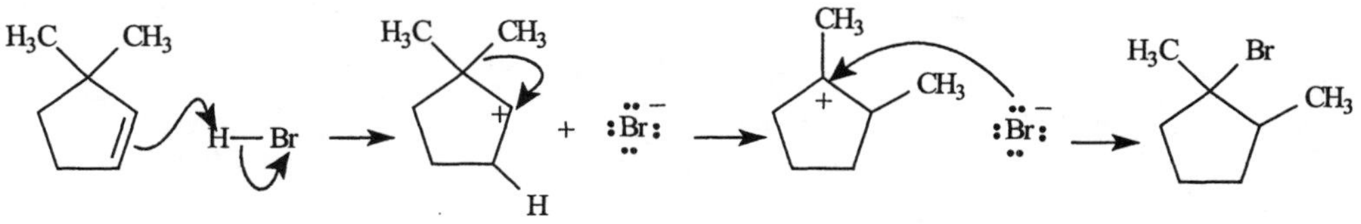

Predict the major organic product(s) in each reaction below. If more than one major organic product is expected draw each one.

38. 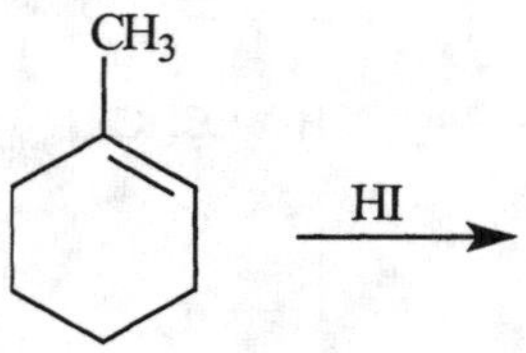 CH_3 HI

Answer:

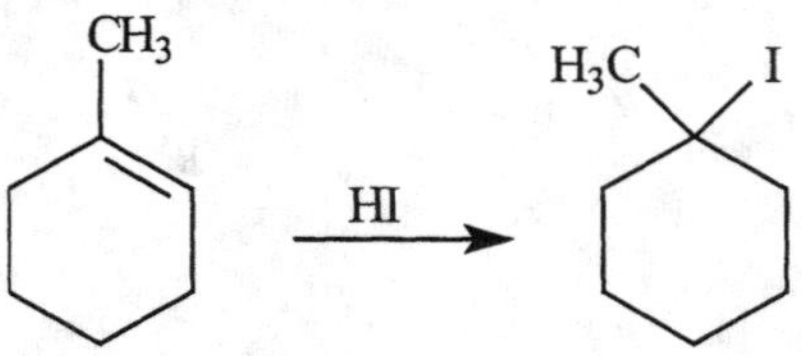

CH_3 HI H_3C I

39. 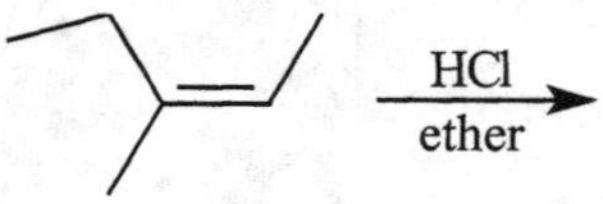 HCl ether

Answer:

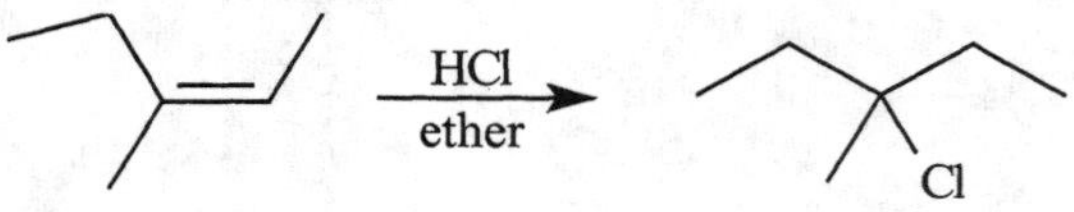

HCl ether Cl

40. HBr

Answer:

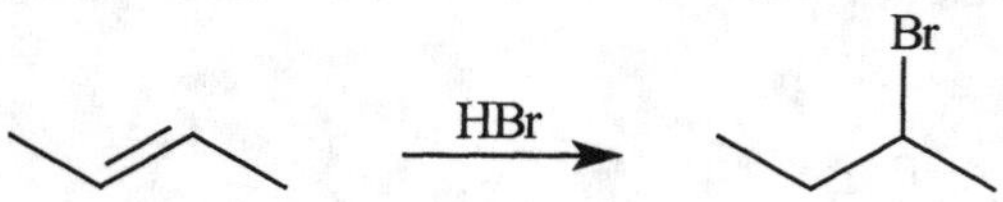

HBr Br

41. 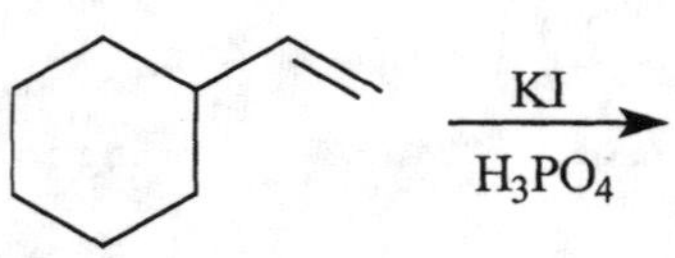 KI H_3PO_4

Answer:

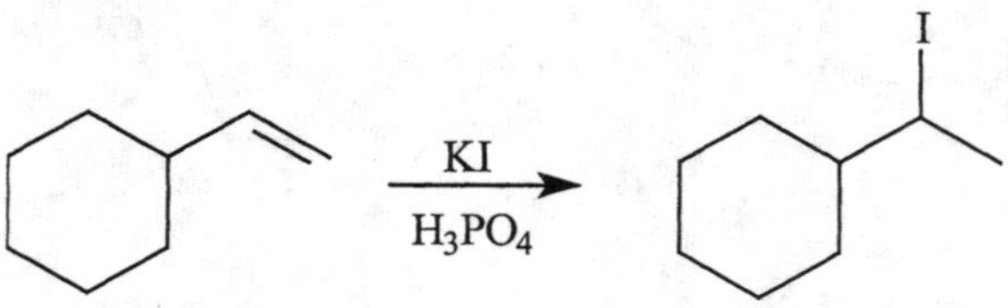

KI H_3PO_4 I

Predict the structure of the alkene you would use to prepare each alkyl halide below.

42. 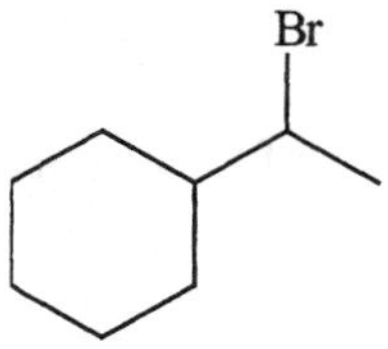 (only product)

Answer:

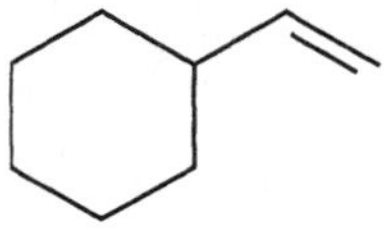

43. 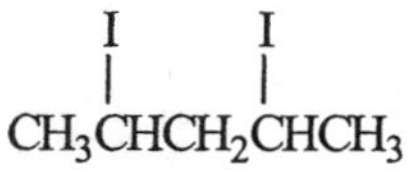 $CH_3CHICH_2CHICH_3$

Answer:

The reaction of isobutene with HBr in ether gives one of the two products below as the major product. Answer the following questions about this reaction.

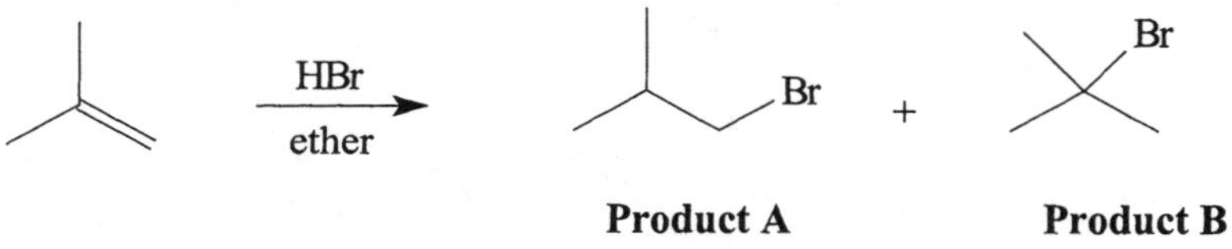

HBr / ether → Br + Br

Product A **Product B**

44. Which product would be the major product?

Answer: Product B

45. Which product would be formed via a primary carbocation?

Answer: Product A

46. Which product would have a higher energy transition state for the formation of the intermediate leading to it?

Answer: Product A

47. Which product is the non-Markovnikov product?

Answer: Product A

48. According to Hammond's Postulate, which product would have a transition state structure most closely resembling the carbocation intermediate?

Answer: Product A

49. Which product would be formed by a carbocation experiencing the greatest degree of hyperconjugative stabilization?

Answer: Product B

50. Increasing the temperature at which the reaction is run would lead to an increase in the percentage of which product relative to the other product?

Answer: Product A

Chapter 7 – Alkenes: Reactions and Synthesis

To answer the questions below consider the following reaction:

When cyclohexene reacts with chlorine in carbon tetrachloride the *trans*-dihalide is formed.

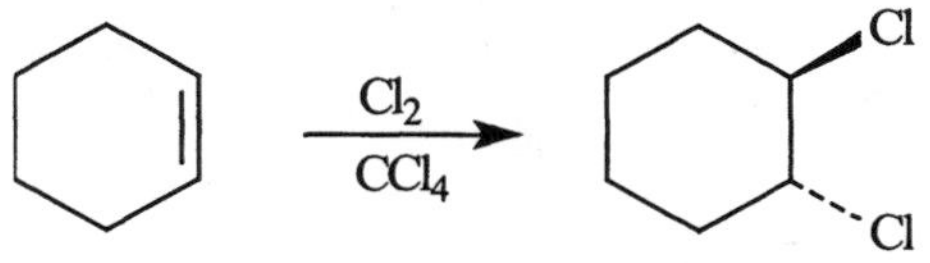

1. Write the complete stepwise mechanism for this reaction. Be sure to show all intermediate structures and all electron flow using arrows.

Answer:

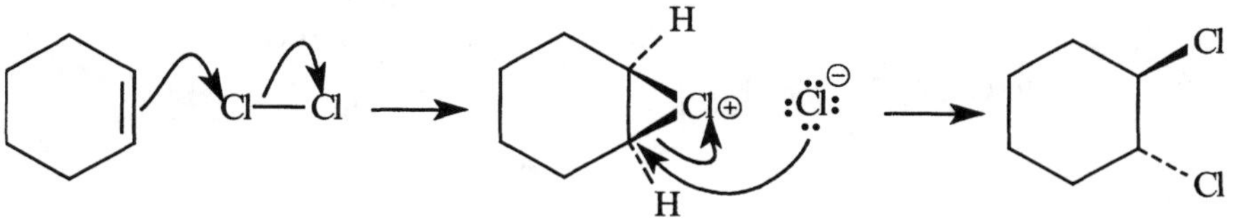

2. Since the two chlorine atoms add to opposite faces of the cyclohexene double bond, we say that the reaction occurs with:

a. syn stereochemistry
b. cis stereochemistry
c. anti stereochemistry
d. retention of stereochemistry

Answer: c

3. The observed stereochemistry of addition of chlorine to cyclohexene is explained by the intermediacy of a:

a. cyclonium ion
b. carbocation
c. carbene
d. chloronium ion

Answer: d

4. Provide the IUPAC name for the product of the reaction of cyclohexene with bromine.

Answer: *trans*-1,2-dichlorocyclohexane

5. Draw both chair conformations of *trans*-1,2-dichlorocyclohexane on the templates provided below. Circle the *least* stable conformation.

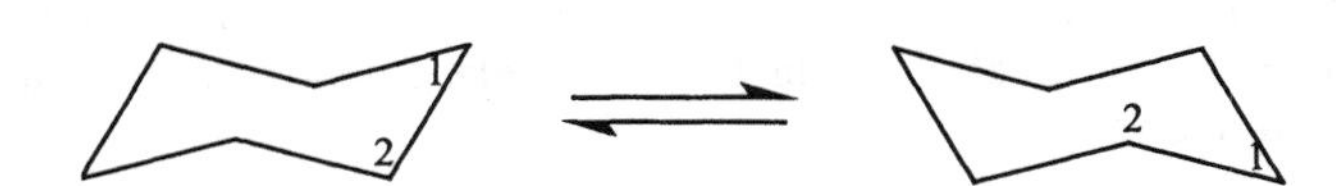

Answer:

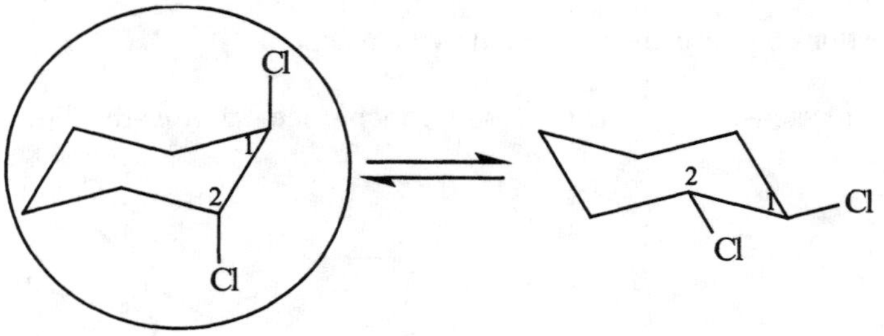

Consider the reaction sequence below to answer the following questions:

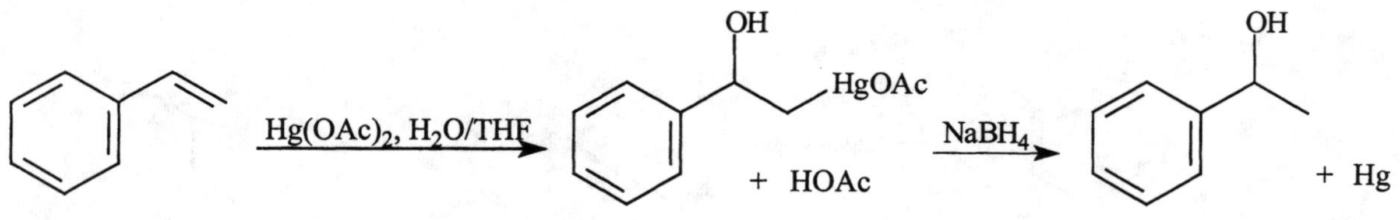

6. Write the complete reaction mechanism for the first step of this reaction sequence. Show all electron flow with arrows and show all intermediate structures.

Answer:

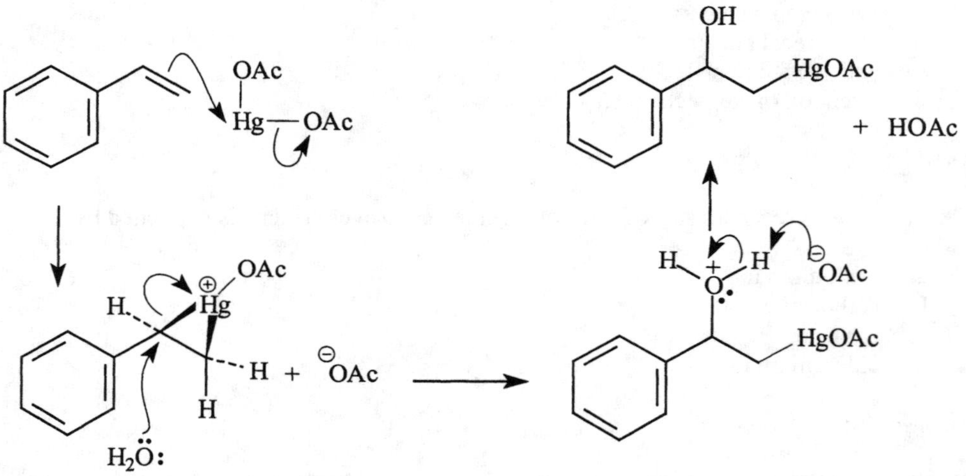

7. The intermediate in the first step of this reaction sequence is called a:

a. carbocation b. cyclonium ion c. mercurinium ion d. mercapto species.

Answer: c

8. In the second step of this reaction sequence, the organomercury compound is treated with sodium borohydride, $NaBH_4$, to yield the alcohol product. This replacement of a carbon-mercury bond with a carbon-hydrogen bond is termed:

a. an oxidation b. a reduction c. a hydroxylation d. a cycloaddition

Answer: b.

Consider the reaction below to answer the following questions.

Alkenes may be hydrated by the hydroboration/oxidation procedure shown.

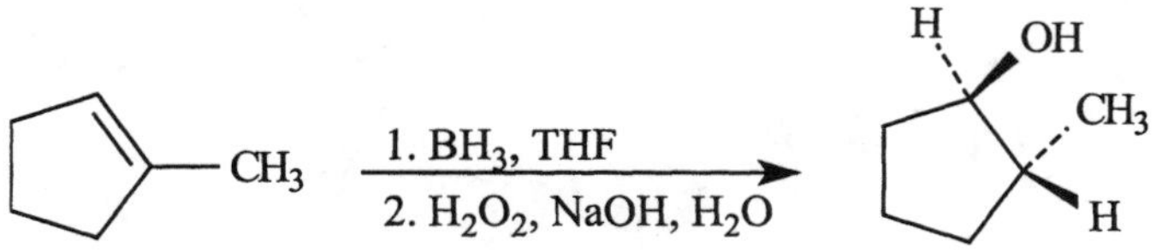

1. BH_3, THF
2. H_2O_2, NaOH, H_2O

9. The intermediate formed in the first step of this reaction is:

a.

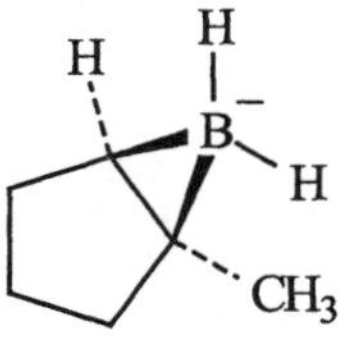

b.

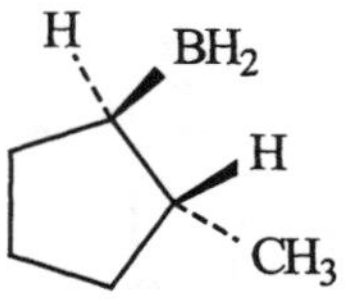

c.

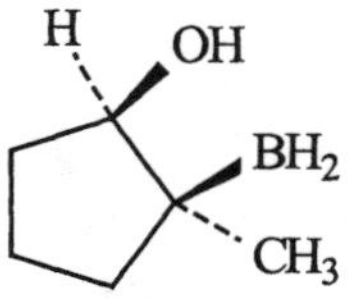

d.

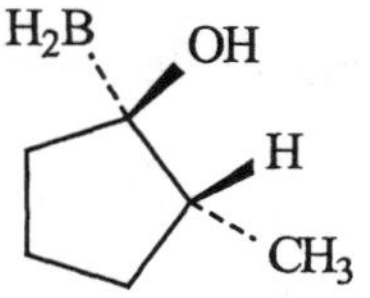

Answer: b

10. Hydroboration of alkenes is an example of:

a. a rearrangement reaction.
b. a substitution reaction.
c. an elimination reaction.
d. an addition reaction.

Answer: d

11. Hydroboration/oxidation of alkenes occurs with:

a. *anti* stereochemistry.
b. *trans* stereochemistry.
c. *syn* stereochemistry.
d. unpredictable stereochemistry.

Answer: c

12. The regiochemistry of hydroboration/oxidation of alkenes is:

a. Markovnikov.
b. non-Markovnikov
c. subject to solvent effects.
d. unrelated to alkene structure.

Answer: b

Consider the reaction below to answer the following questions.

When dichlorocarbene is generated in the presence of an alkene, a dichlorocyclopropane is formed.

$H_3C(H)C=C(H)CH_3$ + $CHCl_3$ $\xrightarrow{KOH}$ 1,1-dichloro-2,3-dimethylcyclopropane

13. Write the complete stepwise mechanism for the formation of dichlorocarbene, $:CCl_2$. Show all intermediate structures and show all electron flow with arrows.

Answer:

$Cl_3C–H + K^+ \ ^-:\ddot{O}H \longrightarrow Cl_3C:^- K^+ + H_2O \longrightarrow Cl_2C: + KCl$

14. Draw the complete Lewis electron dot structure for dichlorocarbene, $:CCl_2$.

Answer: $:\ddot{Cl}:\ddot{C}:\ddot{Cl}:$

15. In the reaction of an alkene with dichlorocarbene, the dichlorocarbene is the:

a. electrophile. b. Lewis base. c. nucleophile. d. both b and c.

Answer: a

16. The reaction of an alkene with dichlorocarbene is:

a. regiospecific. b. Markovnikov. c. stereospecific. d. non-Markovnikov.

Answer: c

The sequence of (1) alkene hydroxylation followed by (2) diol cleavage is often an excellent alternative to direct alkene cleavage with ozone. For this sequence below, answer the following questions.

1-methylcyclohexene $\xrightarrow[\text{2. NaHSO}_3\text{, H}_2\text{O}]{\text{1. OsO}_4\text{, pyridine}}$ **A** $\xrightarrow{\textbf{B}}$ $CH_3CO(CH_2)_4CHO$

17. Draw the structure of **A**.

Answer: cis-1-methylcyclohexane-1,2-diol (OH, CH_3, OH, H)

18. Give the formula for reagent **B**.

Answer: HIO_4

Predict the products of each reaction below. Indicate regiochemistry and stereochemistry when relevant.

19. 1,2-dimethylcyclohexene $\xrightarrow[\text{Pd}]{H_2}$

Answer:

1,2-dimethylcyclohexene $\xrightarrow[\text{Pd}]{H_2}$ cis-1,2-dimethylcyclohexane (CH_3, H, CH_3, H)

20. H_3C(H)C=C(H)CH_3 $\xrightarrow[\text{KOH}]{CHCl_3}$

Answer:

H_3C(H)C=C(H)CH_3 $\xrightarrow[\text{KOH}]{CHCl_3}$ 1,1-dichloro-2,3-dimethylcyclopropane (Cl, Cl, H_3C, H, H, CH_3)

21. methylcyclohexane (CH_3, H) $\xrightarrow[\text{THF, heat}]{H_3O^+}$

Answer:

methylcyclohexane (CH_3, H) $\xrightarrow[\text{THF, heat}]{H_3O^+}$ 1-methylcyclohexene (CH_3)

22. $C_6H_5CH{=}CH_2$ $\xrightarrow[H_2O]{Cl_2}$

Answer:

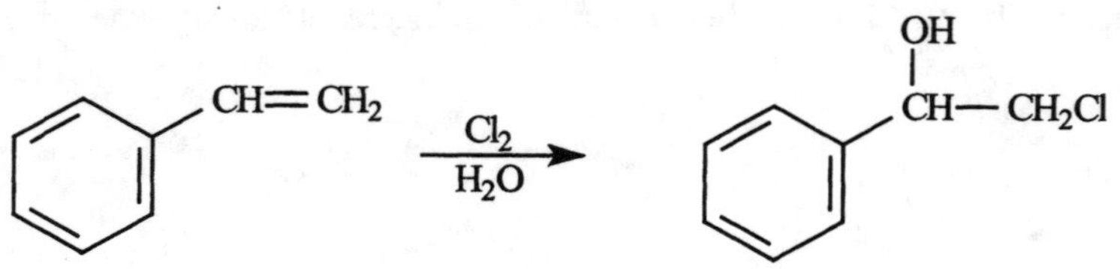

CH=CH$_2$ $\xrightarrow[H_2O]{Cl_2}$ OH | CH—CH$_2$Cl

23. H, H, C=C $\xrightarrow[\text{2. NaHSO}_3\text{, H}_2\text{O}]{\text{1. OsO}_4\text{, pyridine}}$

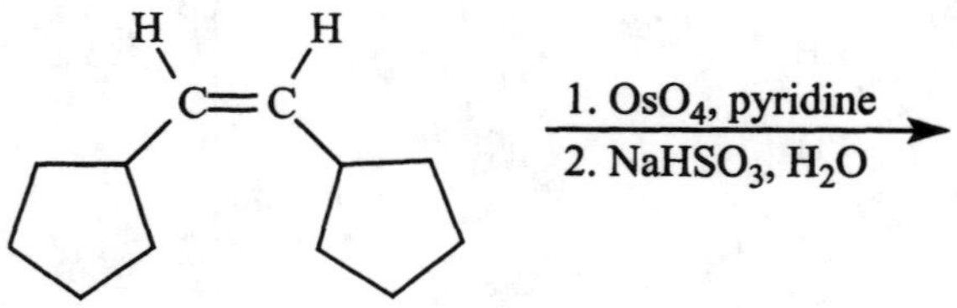

Answer:

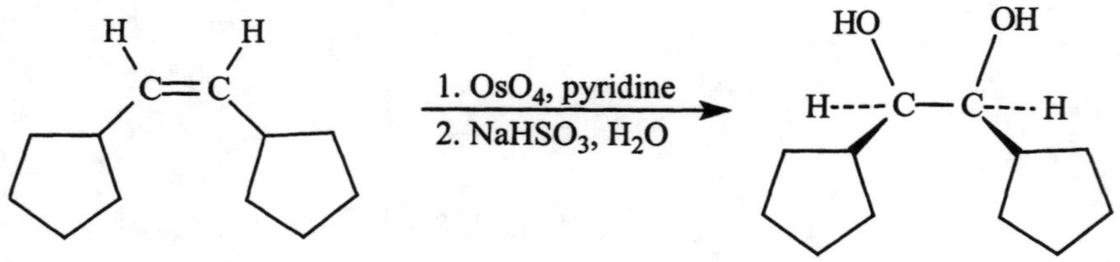

H, H, C=C $\xrightarrow[\text{2. NaHSO}_3\text{, H}_2\text{O}]{\text{1. OsO}_4\text{, pyridine}}$ HO, OH, H----C—C----H

24. OH, OH $\xrightarrow[H_2O]{HIO_4}$

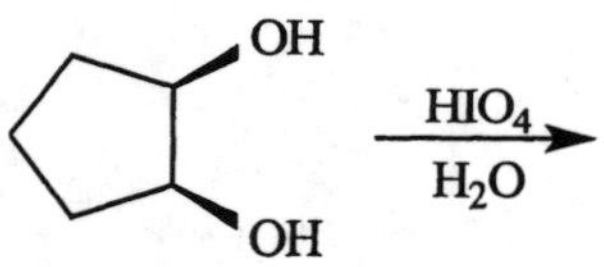

Answer:

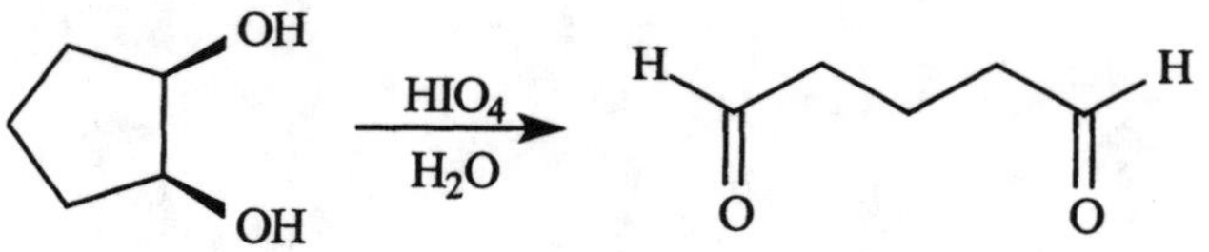

OH, OH $\xrightarrow[H_2O]{HIO_4}$ H, O, O, H

25. CH$_3$ $\xrightarrow[CCl_4]{Cl_2}$

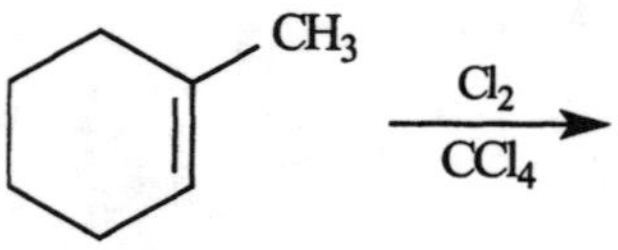

Answer:

CH$_3$ $\xrightarrow[CCl_4]{Cl_2}$ CH$_3$, Cl, H, Cl

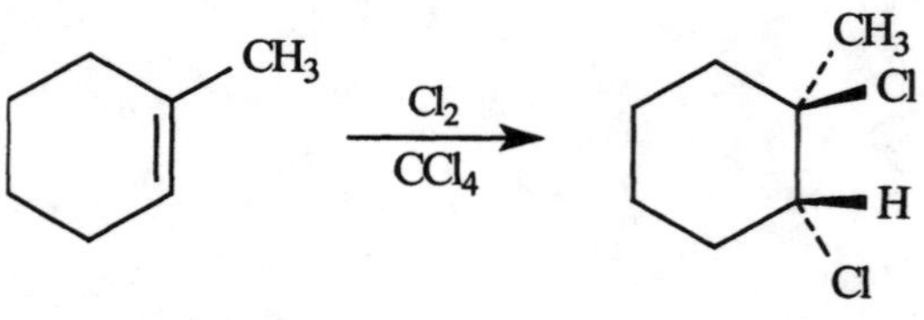

26. 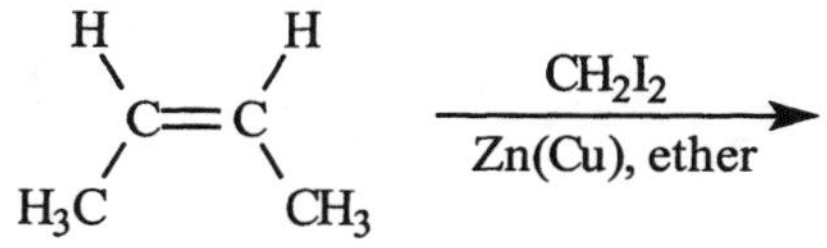 $H(H_3C)C{=}C(H)CH_3$ $\xrightarrow[\text{Zn(Cu), ether}]{CH_2I_2}$

Answer:

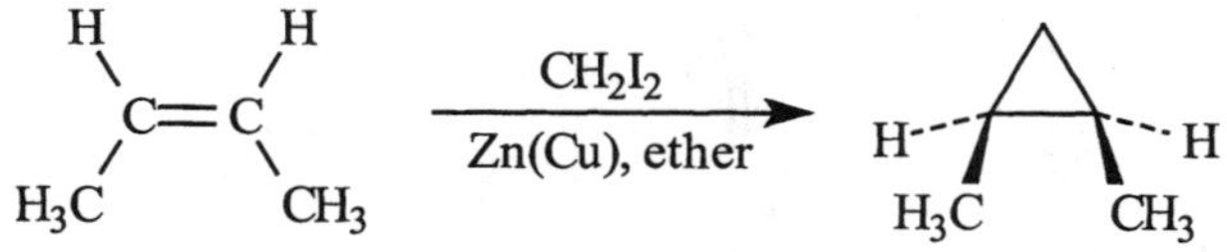

$H(H_3C)C{=}C(H)CH_3$ $\xrightarrow[\text{Zn(Cu), ether}]{CH_2I_2}$ cyclopropane with H, H_3C and H, CH_3

27. 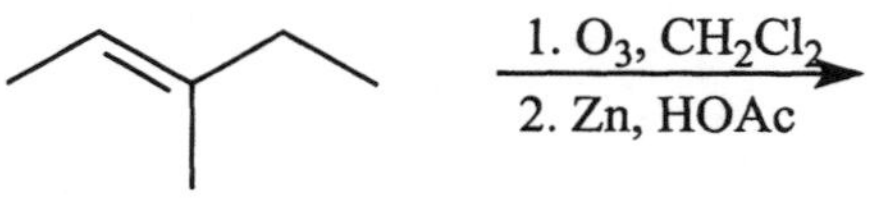 $\xrightarrow[\text{2. Zn, HOAc}]{\text{1. } O_3, CH_2Cl_2}$

Answer:

$\xrightarrow[\text{2. Zn, HOAc}]{\text{1. } O_3, CH_2Cl_2}$ O + O, H

28. 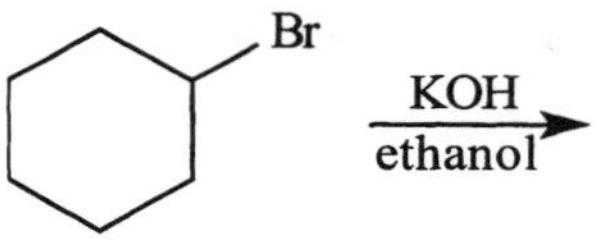 Br $\xrightarrow[\text{ethanol}]{\text{KOH}}$

Answer:

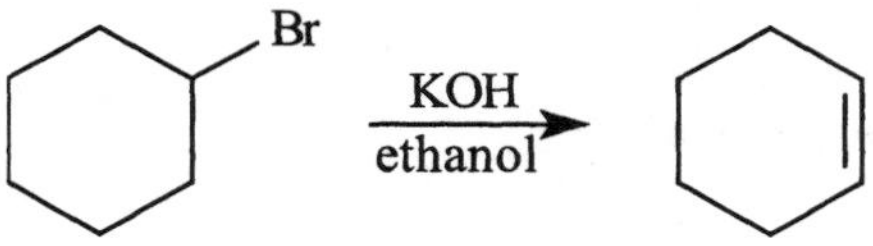

Br $\xrightarrow[\text{ethanol}]{\text{KOH}}$

29. 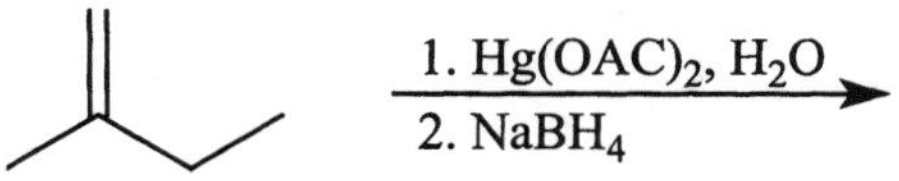 $\xrightarrow[\text{2. } NaBH_4]{\text{1. } Hg(OAC)_2, H_2O}$

Answer:

$\xrightarrow[\text{2. } NaBH_4]{\text{1. } Hg(OAC)_2, H_2O}$ OH

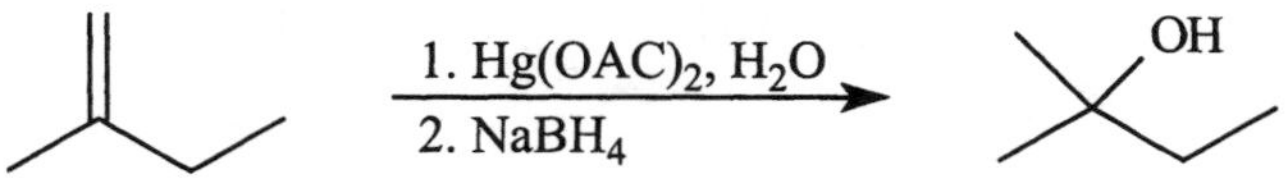

30. 1-methylcyclohexene $\xrightarrow[H_3O^+]{KMnO_4}$

Answer:

1-methylcyclohexene $\xrightarrow[H_3O^+]{KMnO_4}$ $HO_2C-CH_2CH_2CH_2CH_2-C(=O)-CH_3$

31. $H_2C{=}CHCl$ $\xrightarrow[heat]{ROOR}$ (polymer segment)

Answer:

$H_2C{=}CHCl \xrightarrow[heat]{ROOR} -\!\!(CH_2-CH(Cl)-CH_2-CH(Cl)-CH_2-CH(Cl))\!\!-$

Choose the *best* reagent from the list below for carrying out each transformation. Place the letter of the reagent in the blank to the left of the reaction.

a. 1. O_3
   2. Zn, H_3O^+

b. 1. BH_3, THF
   2. H_2O_2, NaOH, H_2O

c. $CHCl_3$, KOH

d. H_2O, H_2SO_4, heat

e. 1. OsO_4
   2. $NaHSO_3$, H_2O

f. $KMnO_4$, acid

g. CH_2I_2, Zn(Cu)

h. 1. $Hg(OAc)_2$, H_2O
   2. $NaBH_4$

32. ___ 1-methylcyclohexene ⟶ trans-2-methylcyclohexanol (CH_3, OH)

Answer: b

33. ___ 1-methylcyclohexene ⟶ $H-C(=O)-CH_2CH_2CH_2CH_2-C(=O)-CH_3$

Answer: a

34. ___

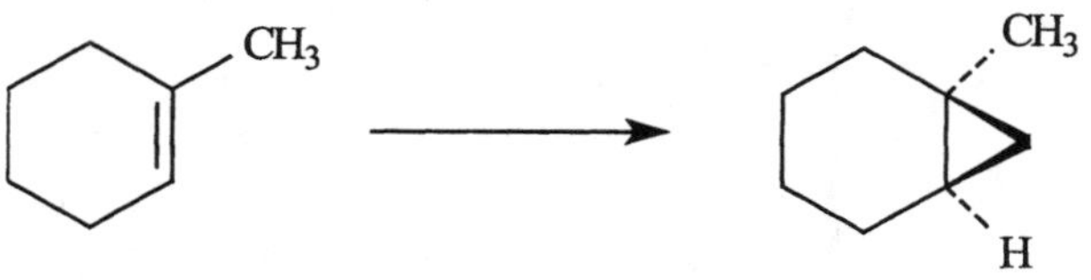

CH_3 → CH_3 H

Answer: g

35. ___

CH_3 → CH_3 OH

Answer: h

For each reaction below suggest structures for alkenes that give the indicated reaction products. There may be more than one answer in some cases.

36. ___

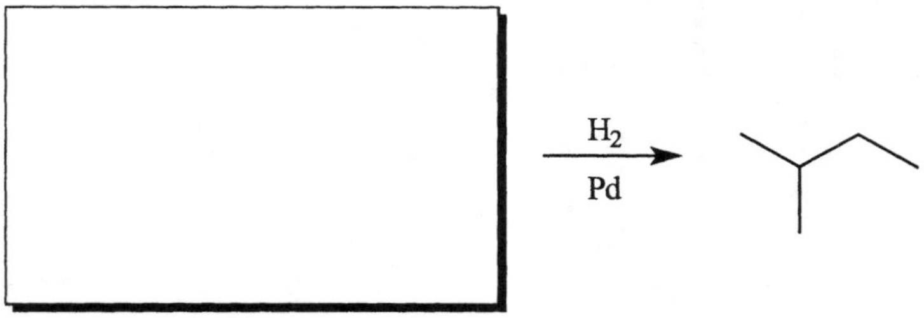

H_2 Pd

Answer:

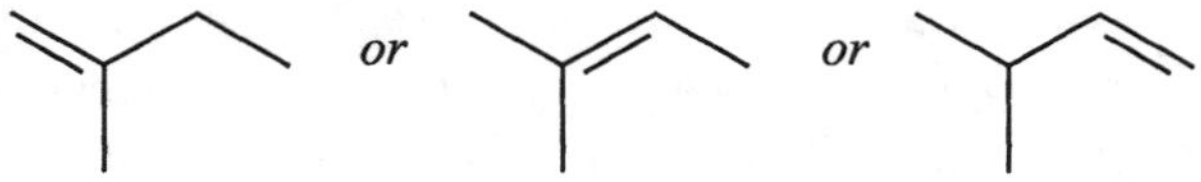

or *or*

37. ___

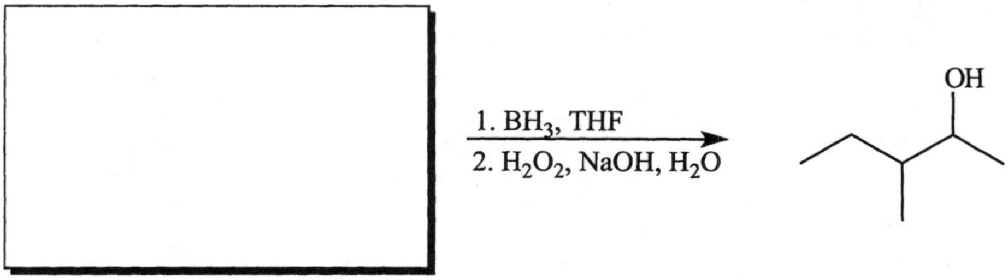

1. BH_3, THF
2. H_2O_2, NaOH, H_2O

OH

Answer:

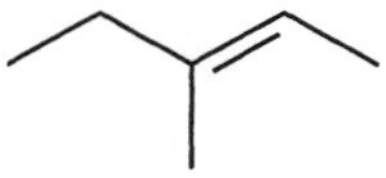

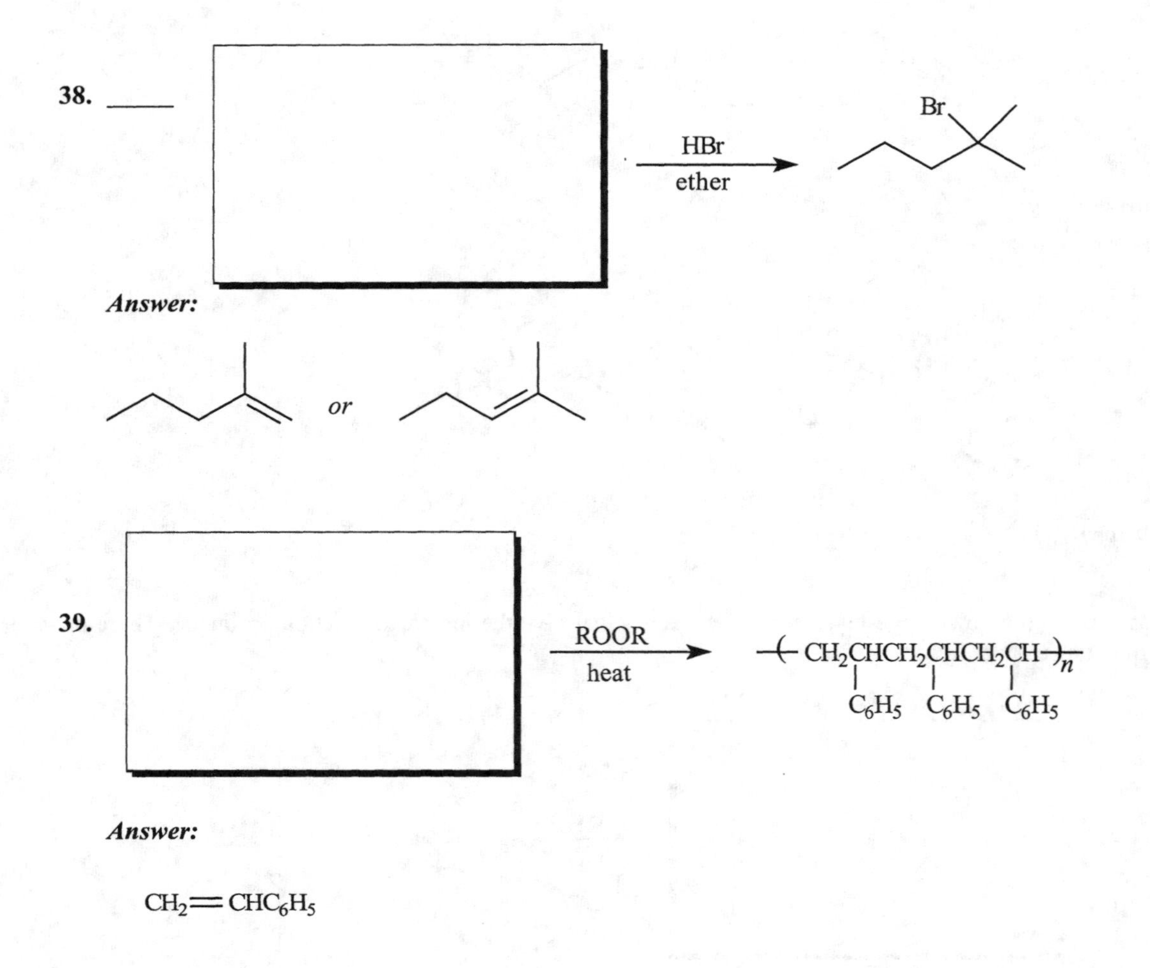

To answer the questions below consider the following information:

In an abandoned laboratory has been found a flammable liquid, A, in a bottle bearing only the label "Compound **A**: C_7H_{12}." Government agents have offered you a considerable sum to determine the structure of this compound. After verifying the molecular formula by elemental analysis, you find that Compound **A** reacts with 1 mol equiv of hydrogen and, after treatment with acidic $KMnO_4$, gives the dicarboxylic acid **C** (see below). Another bottle from the same laboratory is labeled "Compound **B** (isomer of **A**)." Compound **B** also reacts with 1 mol equiv of hydrogen, but yields cyclohexanone after treatment with acidic $KMnO_4$.

$$HO{-}\overset{O}{\overset{\|}{C}}{-}\underset{CH_3}{\underset{|}{C}}HCH_2CH_2CH_2{-}\overset{O}{\overset{\|}{C}}{-}OH$$

Compound **C**

cyclohexanone

40. How many degrees of unsaturation does Compound **A** possess?

Answer: A saturated seven carbon compound should have the formula C_7H_{16} so compound A has $(16-12)\div 2 = 2$ degrees of unsaturation.

41. Suggest structures for **A** and **B**.

Answer:

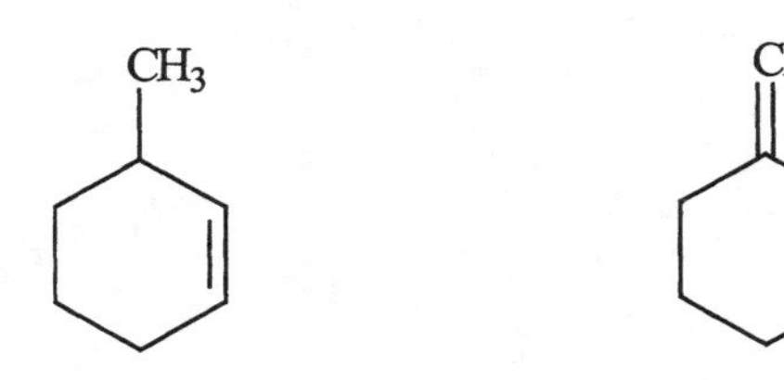

Compound **A** Compound **B**

42. What was the other product formed in the $KMnO_4$ oxidation of B?

Answer: CO_2

43. Lyapolate Sodium, whose structure is shown below, is used as an anticoagulant. Identify the monomer unit(s) in lyapolate sodium.

$$-\!\!(CH_2-\underset{SO_3Na}{\underset{|}{CH}}-CH_2-\underset{SO_3Na}{\underset{|}{CH}})\!\!-_n$$

Answer:

$$H_2C{=}CH-SO_3Na$$

44. Povidone is produced commercially as a series of products having mean molecular weights ranging from about 10,000 to 700,000. Complexed with iodine, povidone yields an iodophor, marketed under the tradename Betadine, which is used as a topical anti-infective.

N O N O

$$-\!\!(CH-CH_2-CH-CH_2)\!\!-_n$$

Identify the monomer unit(s) in povidone.

Answer:

N O

$$CH{=}CH_2$$

Chapter 8 - Alkynes: An Introduction to Organic Synthesis

Draw structures corresponding to each of the following names.

1. ethynylcyclopropane

Answer: $-C\equiv C-H$

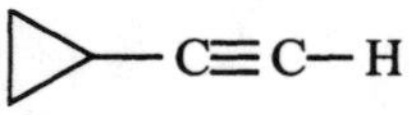

2. 3,10-dimethyl-6-*sec*-butylcyclodecyne

Answer:

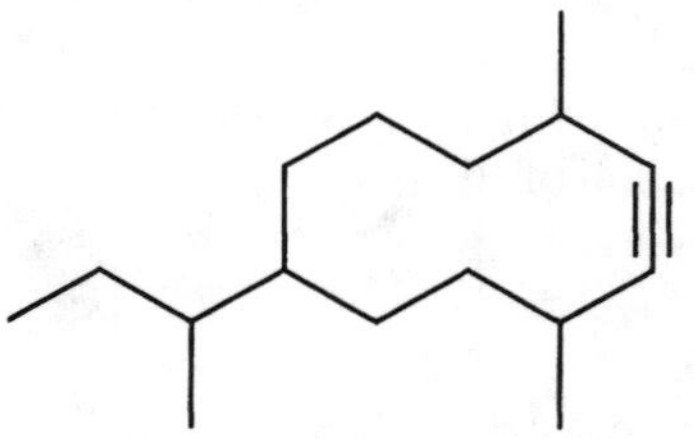

3. 4-bromo-3,3-dimethyl-1-hexen-5-yne

Answer: $H_2C{=}CH{-}C(CH_3)_2{-}CH(Br){-}C\equiv C{-}H$

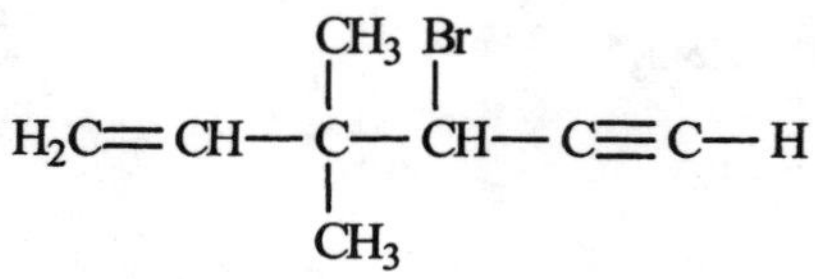

4. acetylene

Answer: $H-C\equiv C-H$

Provide names for each compound below.

5. $CH_3C\equiv CCH(CH_3)CH_2CH_2CH_3$

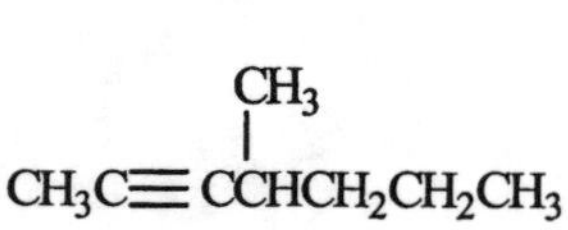

Answer: 4-methyl-2-heptyne

6. CH_3 $C\equiv CH$

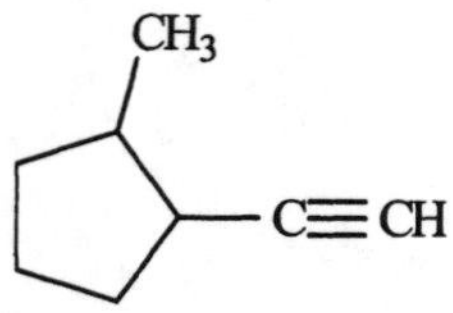

Answer: 1-ethynyl-2-methylcyclopentane

The compound below has been isolated from the safflower plant. Consider its structure to answer the following questions.

```
          H                                        H
           \                                      /
            C—C≡C—C≡C—C≡C—C≡C—C
           //                                     \\           H
   H3C—C                                           C—C       /
           \                                       /      \\
            H                                     H        C—H
                                                           /
                                                          H
```

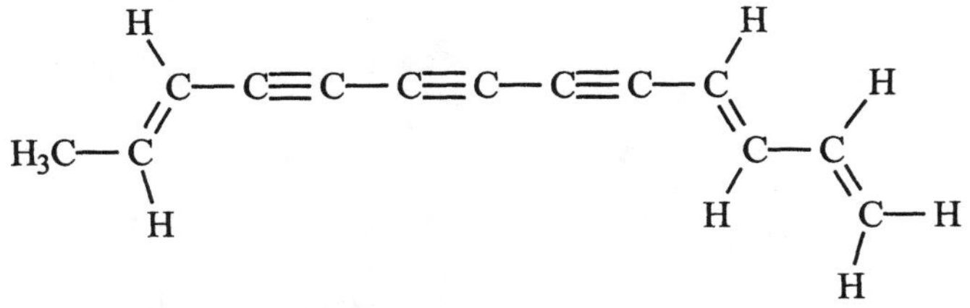

7. What is the molecular formula for this natural product?

Answer: $C_{13}H_{10}$

8. What is the degree of unsaturation for this compound?

Answer: We can arrive at the degree of unsaturation for a *structure* in two ways. Since we know that the degree of unsaturation is the number of rings and/or multiple bonds in a compound, we can simply count them. There are three double bonds (3 degrees) and three triple bonds (six degrees), so the degree of unsaturation is 9.

We can verify this by using the molecular formula, $C_{13}H_{10}$, to *calculate* a degree of unsaturation. The saturated 13-carbon compound should have the base formula $C_{13}H_{28}$, so $(28 - 10) \div 2 = 18 \div 2 = 9$.

9. Assign *E* or *Z* configuration to each of the double bonds in the compound.

Answer:

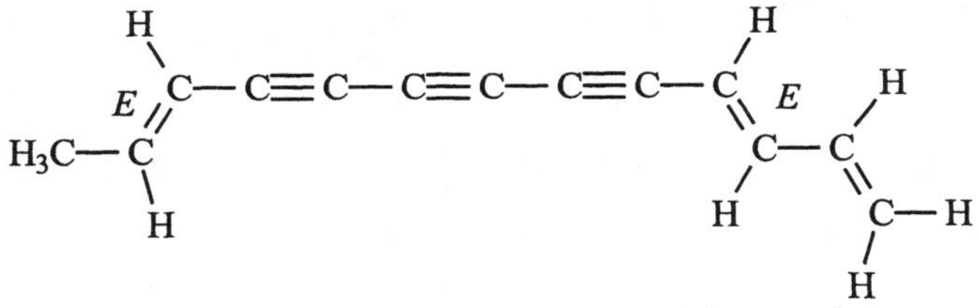

```
          H                                        H
           \                                      /
         E  C—C≡C—C≡C—C≡C—C≡C—C   E        H
           //                                     \\          /
   H3C—C                                           C—C
           \                                       /      \\
            H                                     H        C—H
                                                           /
                                                          H
```

10. Provide the name for this unusual natural product.

Answer: (3*E*, 11*E*)-1,3,11-tridecatrien-5,7,9-triyne

To answer the following questions, consider the information below:

The heat of hydrogenation of 1,4-pentadiene is 254.4 kJ/mol. The heat of hydrogenation of 1-pentyne is approximately 292.9 kJ/mol.

11. Which structure is ***more stable***, 1,4-pentadiene or 1-pentyne?

Answer: 1,4-pentadiene

12. Show the energy differences between the hydrogenation of 1,4-pentadiene and 1-pentyne on a reaction energy diagram.

Answer:

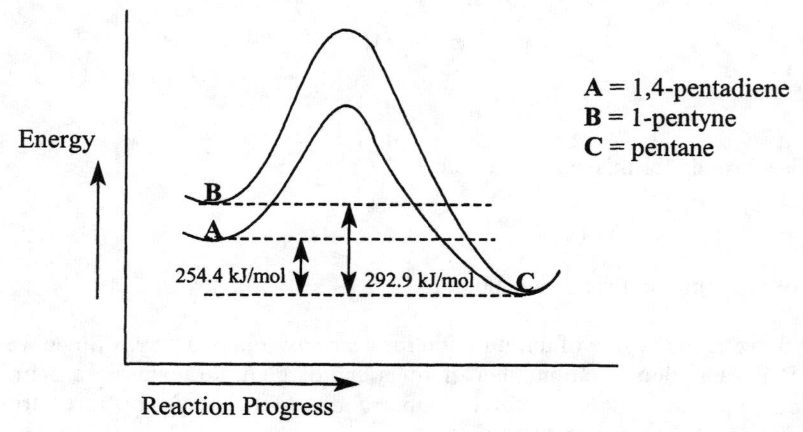

Consider an unknown with the molecular formula C_4H_6.

13. How many degrees of unsaturation are present?

Answer: A saturated four carbon compound has the formula C_4H_{10}. Therefore this compound has $(10-6) \div 2 = 2$ degrees of unsaturation.

14. Draw *six* of the nine possible structures with this formula.

Answer:

$H-C\equiv CCH_2CH_3$ $CH_3C\equiv CCH_3$ $H_2C=CHCH=CH_2$

$H_2C=C=CHCH_3$

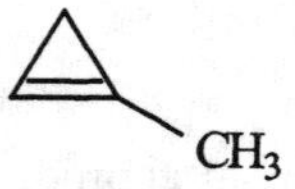

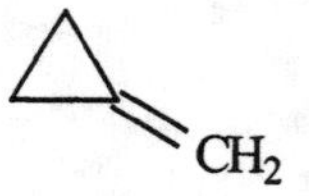

CH_3

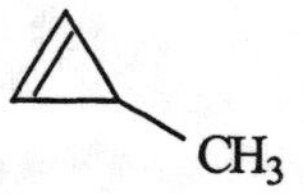

CH_3 CH_2

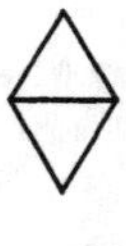

Predict the product of each reaction below. Be sure to indicate stereochemistry when appropriate.

15.

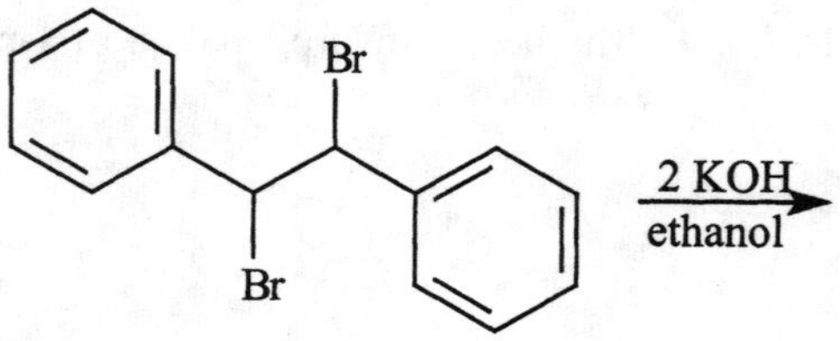

Br

Br

2 KOH / ethanol →

Answer:

$$\text{PhCHBr–CHBrPh} \xrightarrow[\text{ethanol}]{\text{2 KOH}} \text{Ph–C}\equiv\text{C–Ph}$$

16. $CH_3CH_2—C\equiv C—CH_3 \xrightarrow[\text{Lindlar catalyst}]{D_2}$

Answer:

$$CH_3CH_2—C\equiv C—CH_3 \xrightarrow[\text{Lindlar catalyst}]{D_2} (CH_3CH_2)(D)C=C(CH_3)(D)$$

17. $CH_3CH_2—C\equiv C—CH_3 \xrightarrow[CH_3COOH]{HCl,\ NH_4Cl}$

Answer:

$$CH_3CH_2—C\equiv C—CH_3 \xrightarrow[CH_3COOH]{HCl,\ NH_4Cl} (CH_3CH_2)(H)C=C(Cl)(CH_3) + (CH_3CH_2)(Cl)C=C(H)(CH_3)$$

18. $C_6H_5—C\equiv C—H \xrightarrow[\text{2. } H_2O_2,\ NaOH,\ H_2O]{\text{1. } BH_3,\ THF}$

Answer:

$$C_6H_5—C\equiv C—H \xrightarrow[\text{2. } H_2O_2,\ NaOH,\ H_2O]{\text{1. } BH_3,\ THF} C_6H_5—CH_2—C(=O)—H$$

19. $C_6H_5—C\equiv C—H \xrightarrow[\text{2. } CH_3CH_2I]{\text{1. } NaNH_2,\ NH_3}$

Answer:

$$C_6H_5—C\equiv C—H \xrightarrow[\text{2. } CH_3CH_2I]{\text{1. } NaNH_2,\ NH_3} C_6H_5—C\equiv C—CH_2CH_3$$

20. (cyclodecyne) $\xrightarrow[H_3O^+]{KMnO_4}$

Answer:

(cyclodecyne) $\xrightarrow[H_3O^+]{KMnO_4}$ HOOC(CH₂)₈COOH

21. $CH_3CH_2C{\equiv}CH \xrightarrow[H_2O]{HgSO_4,\ H_2SO_4}$

Answer:

$CH_3CH_2C{\equiv}CH \xrightarrow[H_2O]{HgSO_4,\ H_2SO_4} CH_3CH_2\overset{O}{\overset{\|}{C}}CH_3$

22. $C_6H_5-CH{=}CH-C{\equiv}C-H \xrightarrow[Pd/C]{excess\ H_2}$

Answer:

$C_6H_5-CH{=}CH-C{\equiv}C-H \xrightarrow[Pd/C]{excess\ H_2} C_6H_5-CH_2CH_2CH_2CH_3$

To answer the following questions consider this reaction:

$$CH_3CH_2CH_2CH_2-C{\equiv}C-H \xrightarrow[CH_3COOH]{HBr} CH_3CH_2CH_2CH_2-\overset{Br}{\overset{|}{C}}{=}CH_2$$

23. On the structures provided, draw arrows showing the electron flow for the reaction mechanism for the electrophilic addition of hydrogen bromide to 1-hexyne

$$CH_3CH_2CH_2CH_2-C{\equiv}C-H \quad H-Br \longrightarrow CH_3CH_2CH_2CH_2-\overset{+}{C}{=}CH_2 \; + \; :\ddot{\underset{..}{Br}}:^-$$

$$\downarrow$$

$$CH_3CH_2CH_2CH_2-\overset{Br}{\overset{|}{C}}{=}CH_2$$

Answer:

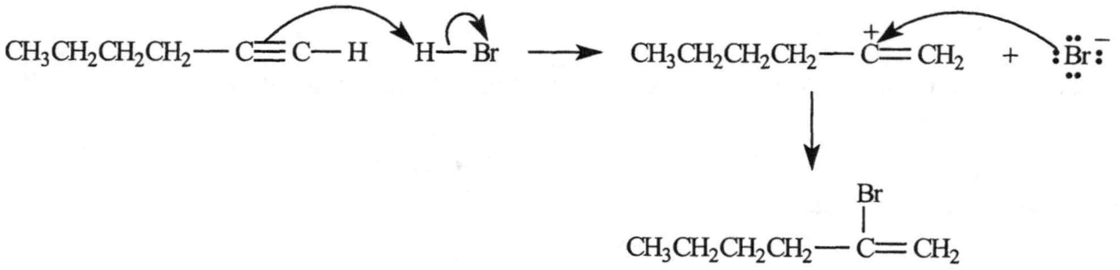

$$CH_3CH_2CH_2CH_2-C\equiv C-H \quad H-Br \longrightarrow CH_3CH_2CH_2CH_2-\overset{+}{C}=CH_2 \quad + \quad :\ddot{Br}:^-$$

$$\downarrow$$

$$CH_3CH_2CH_2CH_2-\underset{}{\overset{Br}{\overset{|}{C}}}=CH_2$$

24. The key intermediate in the electrophilic addition reaction shown above is called:

a. an acetylenic carbocation
b. a vinylic bromide
c. a secondary carbocation
d. a vinylic carbocation

Answer: d

Select the *best* reagent or sequence of reagents from the list provided which would best accomplish each transformation below. Place the letter corresponding to the reagent(s) in the blank to the left of each reaction. Each transformation requires only one answer.

a. H_2SO_4, H_2O, $HgSO_4$
b. H_2, Lindlar
c. 1. BH_3, THF
   2. H_2O_2
d. 1. $NaNH_2$, NH_3
   2. CH_3CH_2I
e. 1. Br_2, CCl_4
   2. 2 $NaNH_2$, NH_3
f. 1. HCl
   2. $NaNH_2$, NH_3
g. Li/NH_3
h. 1. $NaNH_2$, NH_3
   2. $CH_3CH_2CH_2I$

25. _____ $CH_3C\equiv CCH_3 \longrightarrow$ (H₃C)(H)C=C(H)(CH₃) [trans: H_3C and H on the left carbon, H and CH_3 on the right carbon]

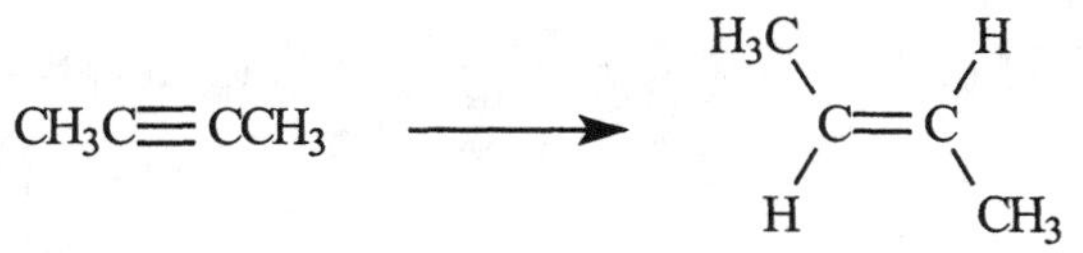

Answer: g

26. _____ cyclohexyl–$CH_2-C\equiv CH \longrightarrow$ cyclohexyl–$CH_2-\overset{O}{\overset{||}{C}}-CH_3$

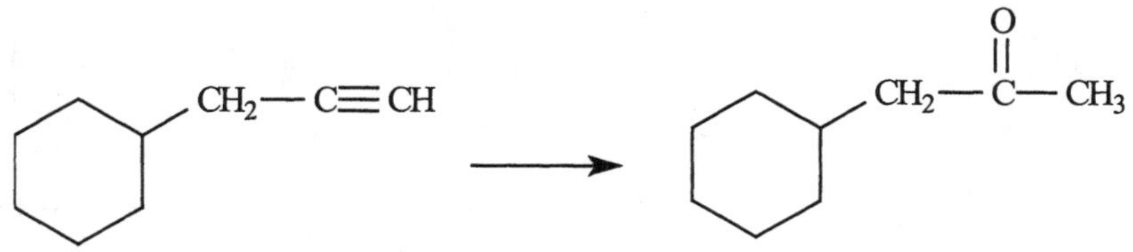

Answer: a

27. _____ $H-C\equiv C-H \longrightarrow CH_3CH_2CH_2C\equiv C-H$

Answer: h

28. ____ $C_6H_5-CH=CH-C_6H_5 \longrightarrow C_6H_5-C\equiv C-C_6H_5$

Answer: e

Show all reagents and intermediates necessary to carry out the following conversions.

29. $(CH_3)_2CHCH_2C\equiv CH \longrightarrow$ (E)-alkene: H and $(CH_3)_2CHCH_2$ on one carbon, CH_2CH_3 and H on the other ($(CH_3)_2CHCH_2CH=CHCH_2CH_3$, trans)

Answer:

$(CH_3)_2CHCH_2C\equiv CH$

1. $NaNH_2$, NH_3
2. CH_3CH_2Br

$(CH_3)_2CHCH_2C\equiv CCH_2CH_3 \xrightarrow{Li/NH_3}$ trans-$(CH_3)_2CHCH_2CH=CHCH_2CH_3$ (H and $(CH_3)_2CHCH_2$ on one carbon; CH_2CH_3 and H on the other)

30. $CH_3CH_2C\equiv C-H \longrightarrow CH_3CH_2CH(OH)CH_2CH_2CH_3$

Answer:

$CH_3CH_2C\equiv C-H \xrightarrow[2.\ CH_3CH_2Br]{1.\ NaNH_2,\ NH_3} CH_3CH_2C\equiv CCH_2CH_3 \xrightarrow[\text{or } Li/NH_3]{H_2,\ Pd/C} CH_3CH_2CH=CHCH_2CH_3$

1. $Hg(OAc)_2$, H_2O,/THF
2. $NaBH_4$

or

1. BH_3, THF
2. H_2O_2, NaOH, H_2O

$\downarrow$

$CH_3CH_2CH(OH)CH_2CH_2CH_3$

Using acetylene and any alkyl halides as starting materials, synthesize the following compounds. More than one step may be required. Show all reagents and all intermediate compounds in your synthetic scheme.

31. $CH_3C(=O)CH_2CH_2CH_2CH_2CH_3$

2-heptanone
(responsible for the odor of cheddar cheese)

Answer:

$$HC\equiv CH \xrightarrow[2.\ CH_3CH_2CH_2CH_2CH_2I]{1.\ NaNH_2,\ NH_3} HC\equiv CCH_2CH_2CH_2CH_2CH_3$$

$$\xrightarrow{HgSO_4,\ H_2SO_4,\ H_2O} CH_3C(=O)CH_2CH_2CH_2CH_2CH_3$$

32. $C_6H_5CH_2CH=CHCH_2C_6H_5$

Answer:

$$HC\equiv CH \xrightarrow[2.\ C_6H_5CH_2I]{1.\ NaNH_2,\ NH_3} C_6H_5CH_2C\equiv CH \xrightarrow[2.\ C_6H_5CH_2I]{1.\ NaNH_2,\ NH_3}$$

$$C_6H_5CH_2C\equiv CCH_2C_6H_5 \xrightarrow{Li/NH_3} C_6H_5CH_2CH=CHCH_2C_6H_5$$

33. $ClCH_2CH(Cl)CH_3$

1,2-dichloropropane
(a degreasing solvent used in dry cleaning)

Answer:

$$HC\equiv CH \xrightarrow[2.\ CH_3I]{1.\ NaNH_2,\ NH_3} HC\equiv CCH_3 \xrightarrow[\text{or } Li/NH_3]{H_2/\text{Lindlar}} H_2C=CHCH_3$$

$$\xrightarrow{Cl_2,\ CCl_4} ClCH_2CH(Cl)CH_3$$

34. $H_3C{-}C(=O){-}OH$ acetic acid (raw material for the vinyl acetate polymer used in paints and adhesives)

Answer:

$$HC{\equiv}CH \xrightarrow[\text{2. } CH_3I]{\text{1. } NaNH_2,\ NH_3} CH_3C{\equiv}CH \xrightarrow[\text{2. } CH_3I]{\text{1. } NaNH_2,\ NH_3} CH_3C{\equiv}CCH_3$$

$$CH_3C{\equiv}CCH_3 \xrightarrow{KMnO_4,\ H_3O^+} 2\ H_3C{-}C(=O){-}OH$$

35. $CH_3CH(Br)CH_2CH_2CH_3$

Answer:

$$HC{\equiv}CH \xrightarrow[\text{2. } CH_3CH_2CH_2I]{\text{1. } NaNH_2,\ NH_3} HC{\equiv}CCH_2CH_2CH_3 \xrightarrow[\text{Lindlar catalyst}]{H_2} H_2C{=}CHCH_2CH_2CH_3$$

$$H_2C{=}CHCH_2CH_2CH_3 \xrightarrow{HBr,\ ether} CH_3CH(Br)CH_2CH_2CH_3$$

Chapter 9 – Stereochemistry

For the following questions MATCH each definition to a term from the list below. Place the letter of the term in the blank to the left of the definition.

a. racemates
b. chirality center
c. chirality
d. diastereomers
e. enantiomers
f. meso compounds
g. optically active
h. prochirality center
i. optically inactive
j. achiral

1. ____ describes organic molecules which rotate plane-polarized light.

Answer: g

2. _____ is the property of "handedness"; the property of an object that causes it to be nonsuperimposable on its mirror image.

Answer: c

3. _____ are stereoisomers that are not mirror images.

Answer: d

4. _____ is an atom in a molecule that is bonded to four different atoms or groups of atoms.

Answer: b

5. _____ are molecules which contain chirality centers and a plane of symmetry.

Answer: f

6. _____ describes an sp^3-hybridized atom that can become a chirality center by changing one of its attached groups.

Answer: h

7. The specific rotation of a compound is denoted by the symbol:

a. R
b. S
c. α
d. $[\alpha]_D$

Answer: d

Place asterisks at all the chirality centers in each molecule below.

8.

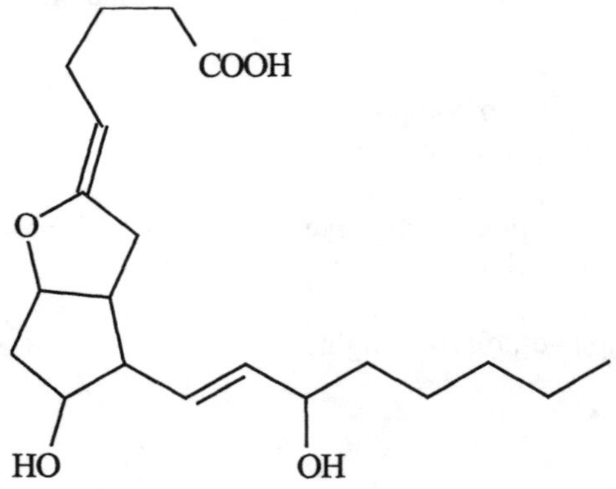

COOH

O

HO

OH

prostacyclin

Answer:

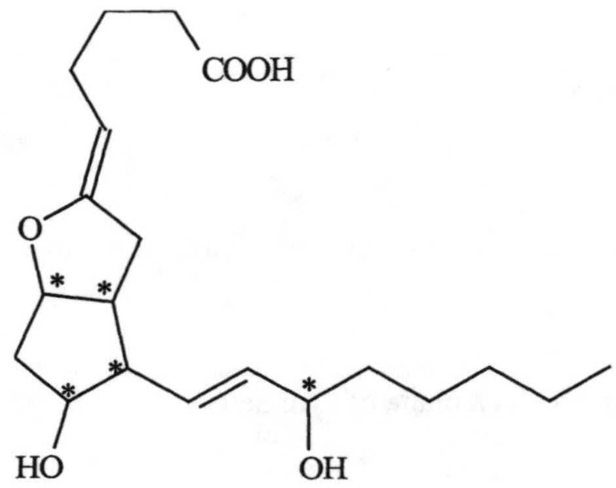

COOH

O

HO

OH

9.

CH_3O

O

H

H

N

CH_3

HO

H

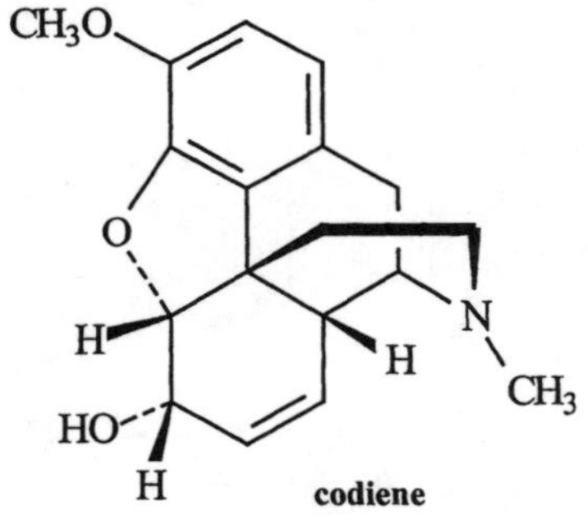

codiene

Answer:

CH_3O

O

H

H

N

CH_3

HO

H

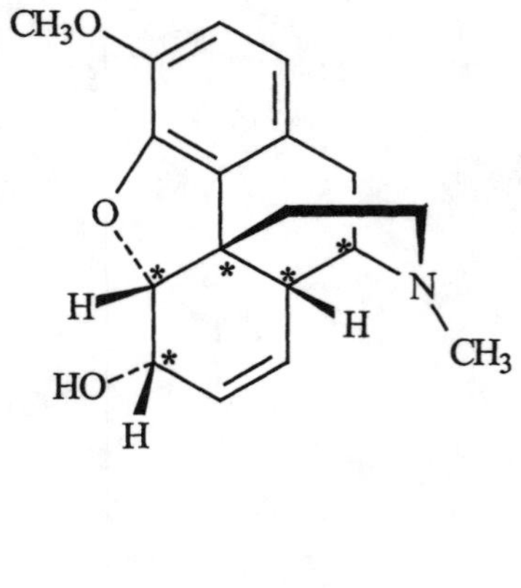

10.

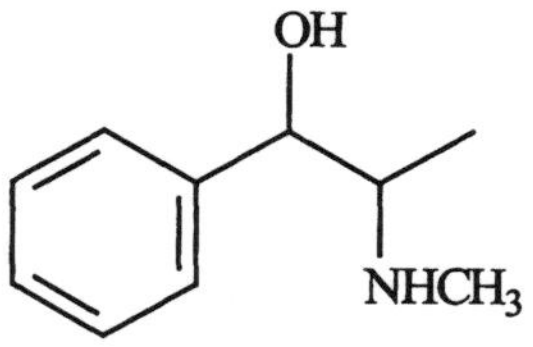

ephedrine

Answer:

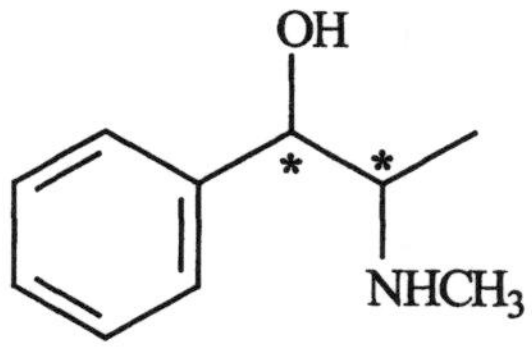

11.

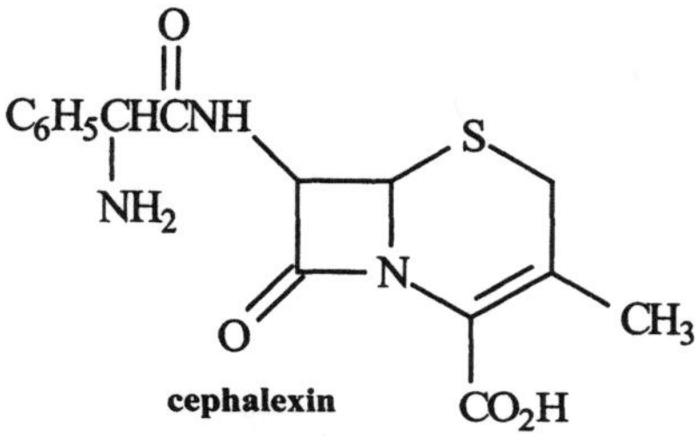

cephalexin

Answer:

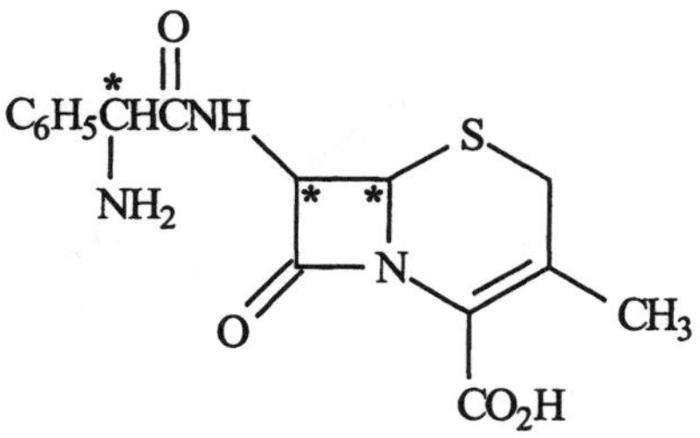

12.

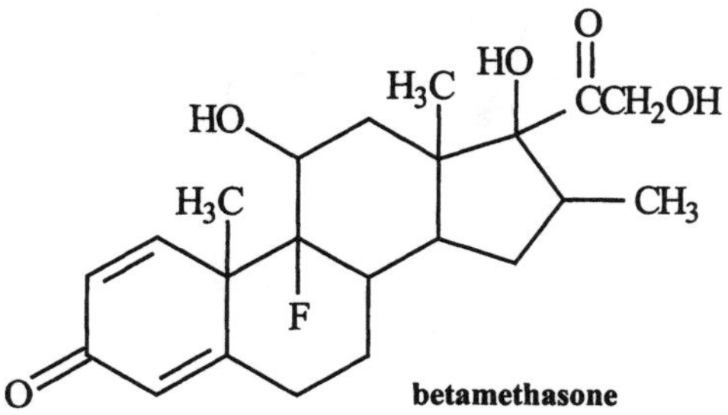

betamethasone

Answer:

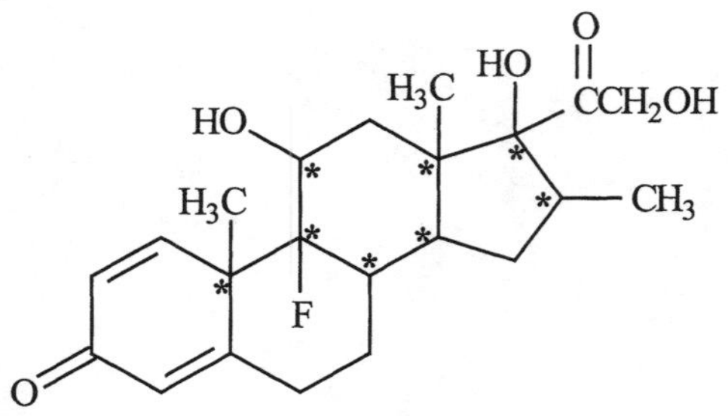

HO, H_3C, H_3C, HO, O, CCH_2OH, CH_3, F, O

13.

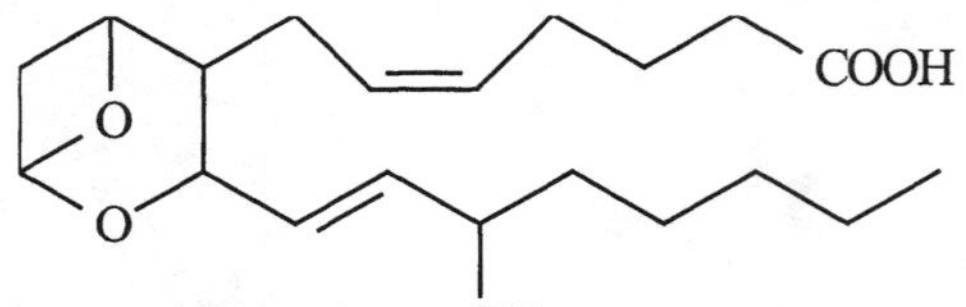

COOH, O, O, thromboxane A_2, OH

Answer:

COOH, O, O, OH

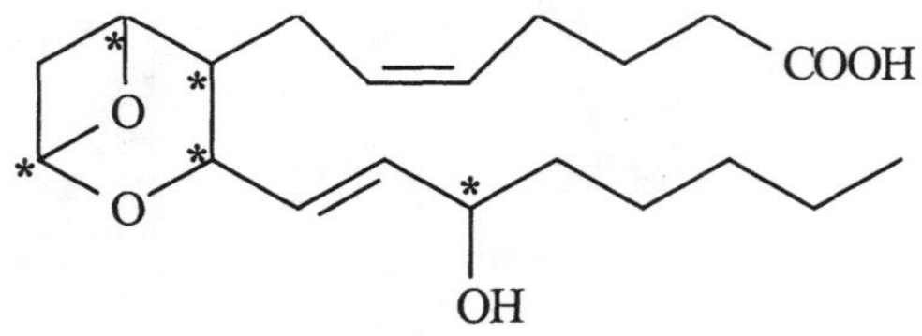

Assign *R*, *S* configurations to each indicated chirality center in the molecules below.

14. OH, HO, H, CH_2NH_2, HO, **norepinephrine**

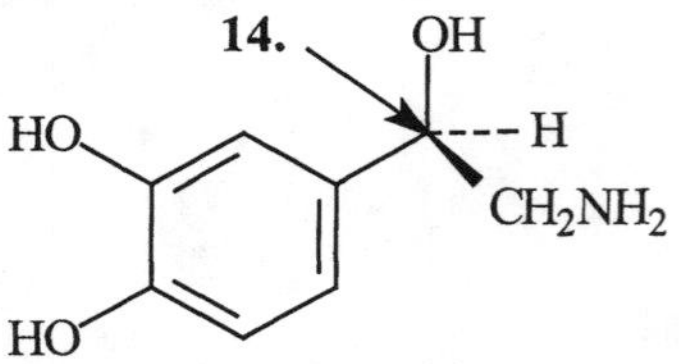

15. COOH, C, CH_3, H_2N, H, **alanine**

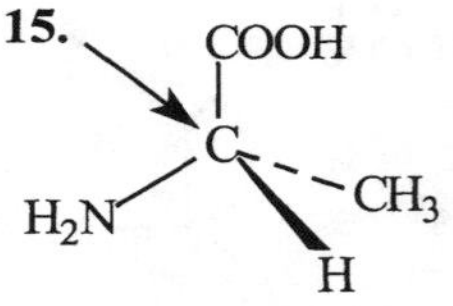

16. HO_2C, OH, H, H, HO, CO_2H, **tartaric acid**

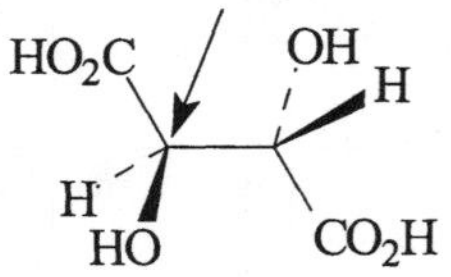

17. O, H, **18.** H, CH_3, H_3C, CH_2, **dihydrocarvone**

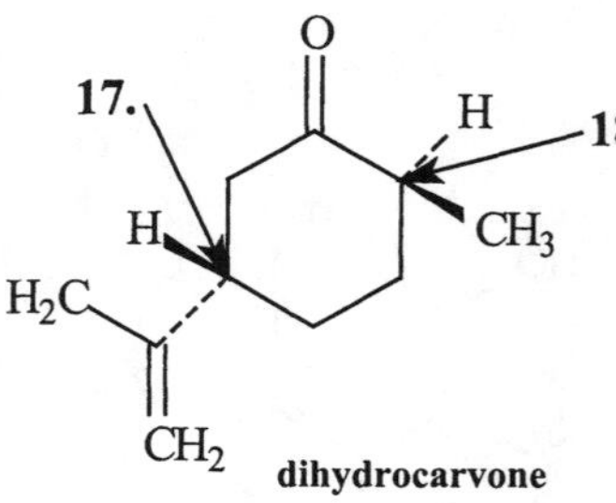

14. The configuration of this carbon atom is _____.

Answer: *R*

15. The configuration of this carbon atom is _____.

Answer: *S*

16. The configuration of this carbon atom is _____ .

Answer: *R*

17. The configuration of this carbon atom is _____ .

Answer: *S*

18. The configuration of this carbon atom is _____ .

Answer: *S*

Consider the structure of streptimidone to answer the following questions.

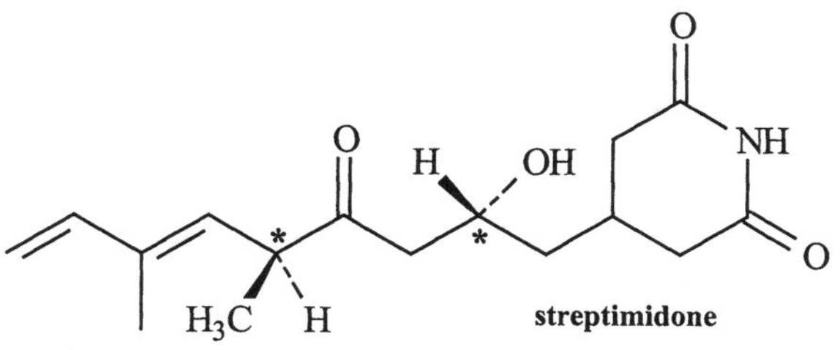

streptimidone

19. Assign *R* or *S* configuration to each chirality center indicated in streptimidone.

Answer:

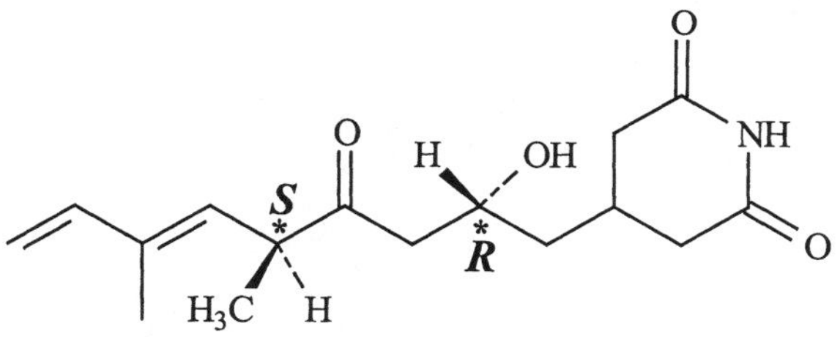

20. Based on the number of chirality centers, how many stereoisomers of streptimidone are possible?

Answer: Streptimidone has two chirality centers so there are 2^2, or 4, possible stereoisomers.

21. Will streptimidone have a *meso* stereoisomer? Explain your answer.

Answer: No. *Meso* compounds are compounds that contain chirality centers, but possess a plane of symmetry. Because the substituents on the chiral carbons are different in streptimidone it is impossible for any stereoisomer to have a plane of symmetry.

Label each pair of stereoisomers below as:

a. enantiomers
b. diastereomers
c. identical

Place the letter of the correct answer in the blank to the left of the pair of stereoisomers.

22. ____ H_3C H OH HO H CH_2OH H_3C OH H H HO CH_2OH

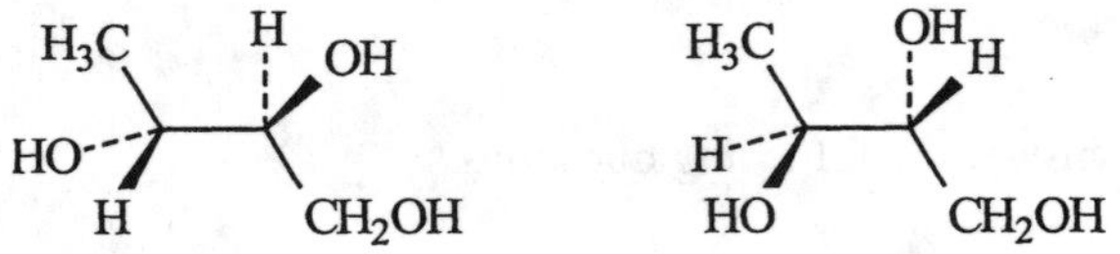

Answer: a

23. ____ CO_2H HO H CH_3 H HO H_2OC CH_3

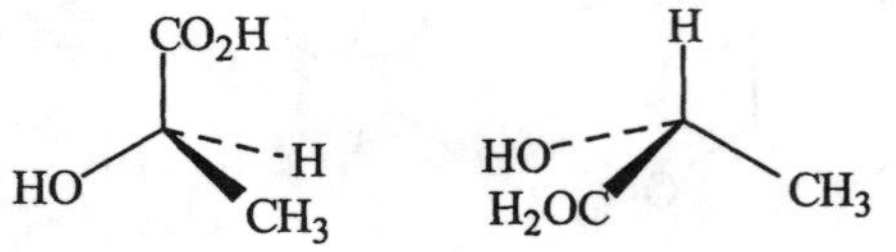

Answer: c

24. ____ HO_2C CO_2H HO_2C CO_2H

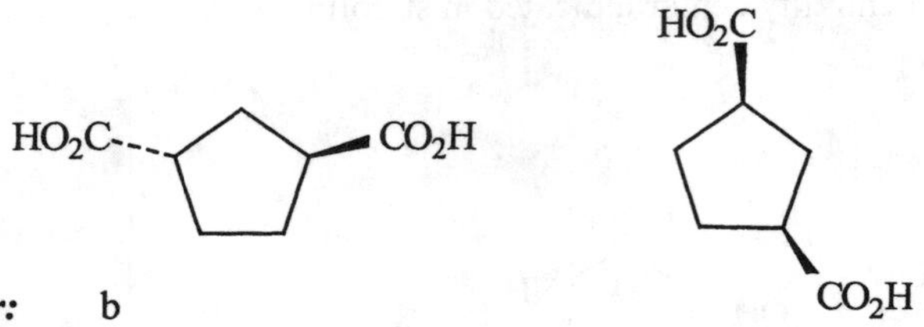

Answer: b

25. ____ H OH HOH_2C CHO H OH HO H HO H OHC CH_2OH H OH HO H

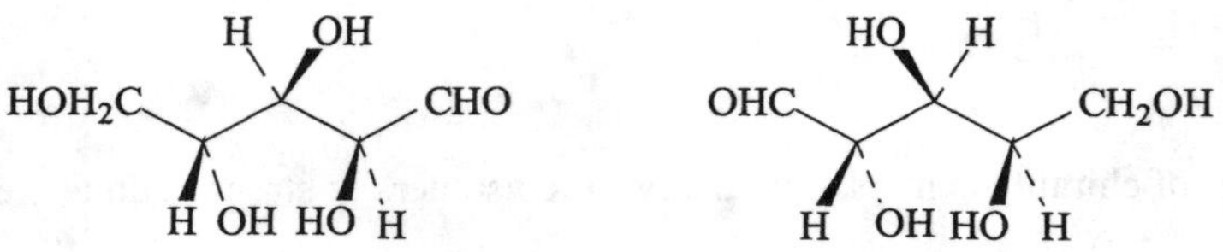

Answer: b

26. ____ Br H_3C Br Br H_3C Br

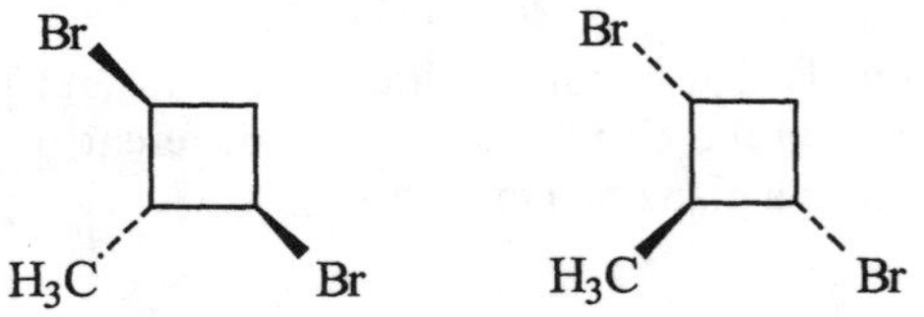

Answer: c

27. ____ H CH_3CH_2 C CH_3 Cl CH_2CH_3 H C CH_3 Cl

Answer: a

28. ____

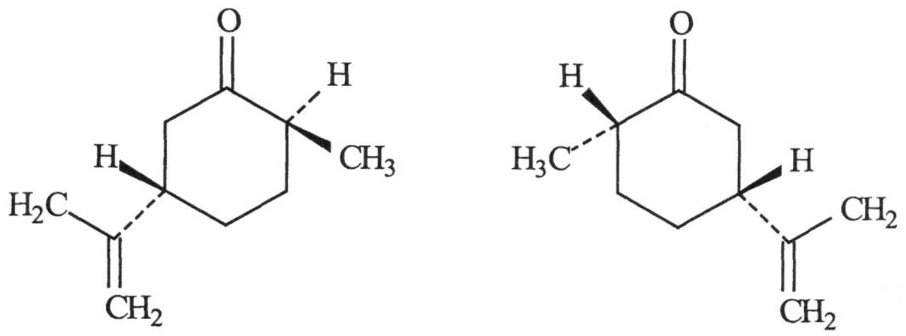

Answer: b

29. Draw a wedge-dash projection of (*2R,3S*)-dibromobutane.

Answer:

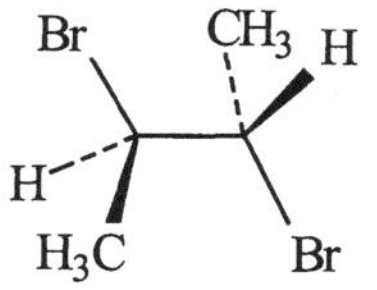

30. Draw a Newman projection of the most stable conformation of (*2R,3S*)-dibromobutane sighting down the C2-C3 bond.

Answer:

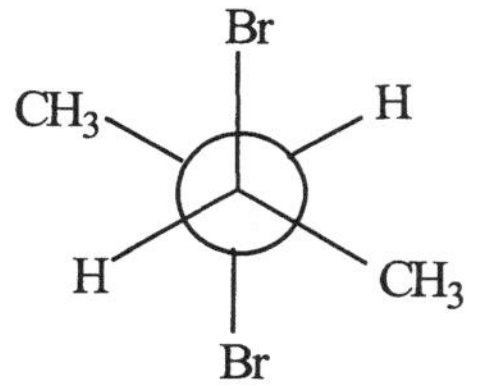

31. (*2R,3S)*-Dibromobutane is:

a. optically active.
b. racemic.
c. dextrorotatory.
d. a *meso* compound.

Answer: d

32. The alkane formed by hydrogenation of (*S*)-4-methyl-1-hexene is optically active while the one formed by hydrogenation of (*S*)-3-methyl-1-pentene is not. Explain.

Answer: Each starting alkene is optically active because it contains a stereogenic center—a carbon with four different groups bonded to it. The alkane formed by the hydrogenation of (*S*)-4-methyl-1-hexene is optically because carbon four is still chiral. The product of hydrogenation of (*S*)-3-methyl-1-pentene is not optically active because two of the groups on carbon three are the same now—they are ethyl groups.

33. Estriol, a potent estrogenic hormone, has been isolated from the urine of pregnant women. When 40 mg of estriol is dissolved in 1.0 mL of dioxane and placed in a sample tube with 1 dm path length a rotation of +2.32° is observed. Calculate the specific rotation for estriol.

Answer: $[\alpha]_D = \dfrac{+2.32°}{1\ \text{dm} \times 0.040\ \text{g/mL}} = +58°$

34. Compound A, C_9H_{16}, was found to be optically active. On catalytic reduction over a palladium catalyst, 2 equivalents of hydrogen were absorbed to yield compound B. Ozonolysis of A gave two compounds. One was identified as acetaldehyde, CH_3CHO. The other compound, C, was an optically active dialdehyde, $C_5H_8O_2$. Formulate the reactions and draw structures for compounds A, B and C.

Answer:

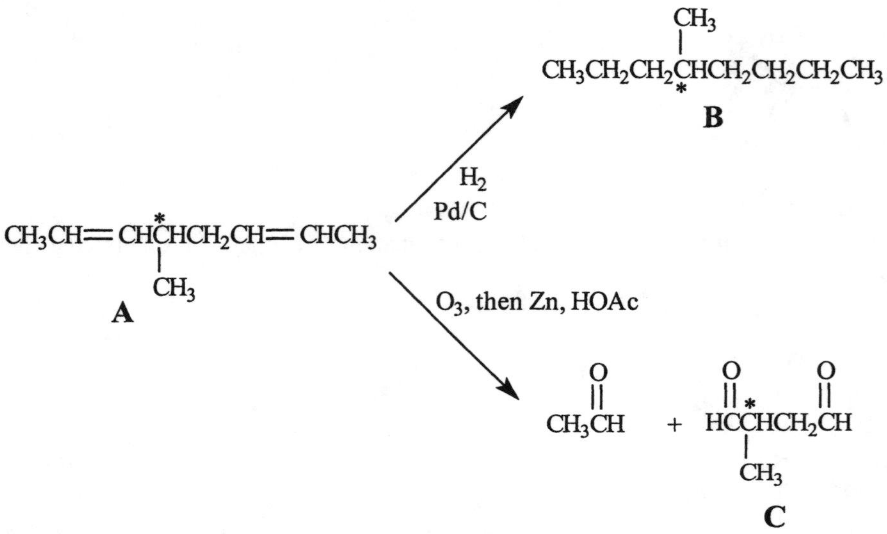

A: $CH_3CH{=}CH\overset{*}{C}H(CH_3)CH_2CH{=}CHCH_3$

A → (H_2, Pd/C) → B: $CH_3CH_2CH_2\underset{*}{C}H(CH_3)CH_2CH_2CH_2CH_3$

A → (O_3, then Zn, HOAc) → CH_3CHO + C: $HC(=O)\overset{*}{C}H(CH_3)CH_2CH(=O)$

Refer to the structure below to answer the following questions.

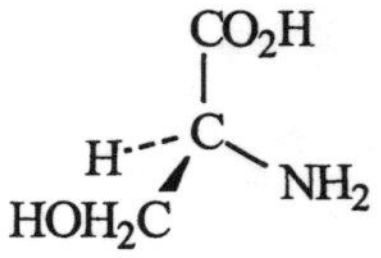

(S)-(-)-Serine: CO_2H on top; H (dash), HOH_2C (wedge), NH_2 on the stereocenter C

35. (*S*)-(−)-Serine:

a. is dextrorotatory
b. rotates plane-polarized light in a counterclockwise direction
c. rotates plane-polarized light in a clockwise direction
d. is racemic

Answer: b

36. Draw the enantiomer of (*S*)-(−)-serine in a wedge-dash projection.

Answer:

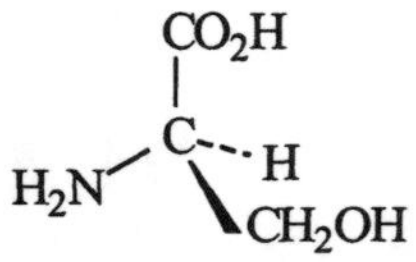

CO_2H on top; H_2N, H (dash), CH_2OH (wedge) on the stereocenter C

37. Give the complete name of the enantiomer of (*S*)-(−)-serine.

Answer: (*R*)-(+)-serine

A natural product having $[\alpha]_D = +40.3°$ has been isolated and purified

38. This information indicates that the natural product:

a. is racemic.
b. does not rotate plane-polarized light.
c. is levorotatory.
d. is dextrorotatory.

Answer: d

39. Two structures have been proposed for this natural product. *Circle* the structure that is consistent with the information presented and briefly explain your choice.

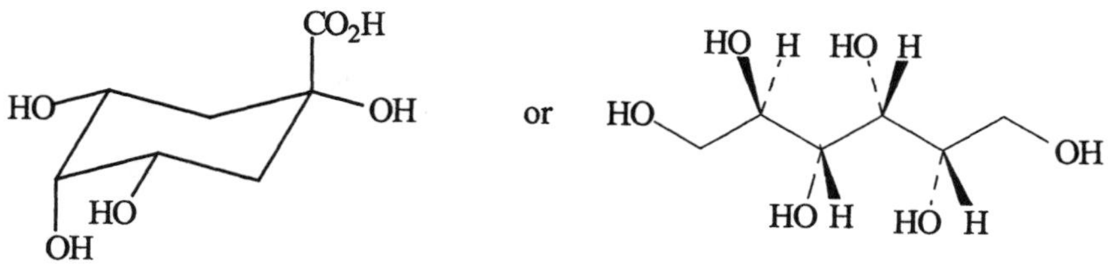

CO_2H HO OH HO OH or HO HO H HO H OH HO H HO H

Answer:

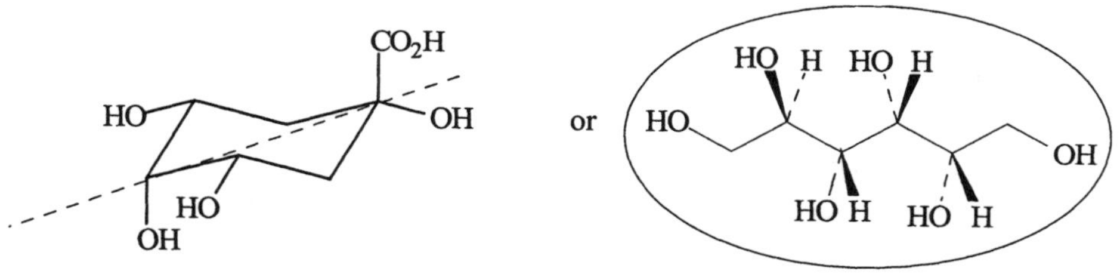

CO_2H HO OH HO OH or HO HO H HO H OH HO H HO H

The information presented indicates that the natural product is optically active. To be optically active molecules must be chiral - that is, they must *not* have a plane of symmetry. The cyclic structure, although is has chirality centers, has a plane of symmetry, indicated by the dashed line on the structure, and can, therefore, not be optically active. The circled structure has four chirality centers, and is not symmetric. We would expect it to be optically active.

40. The enzyme aconitase catalyzes the hydration of the alkene functional group of aconitic acid to give two products, citric acid and isocitric acid. Isocitric acid is optically active; citric acid is not optically active. Based on your knowledge of alkene hydration and optical activity, the structure of citric acid is:

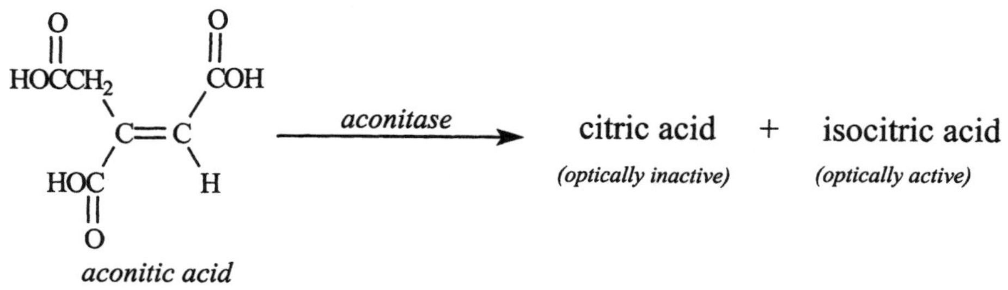

$HOCCH_2(C{=}O)$, $COOH$, $C{=}C$, HOC(=O), H

aconitic acid —*aconitase*→ citric acid *(optically inactive)* + isocitric acid *(optically active)*

Answer:

a. 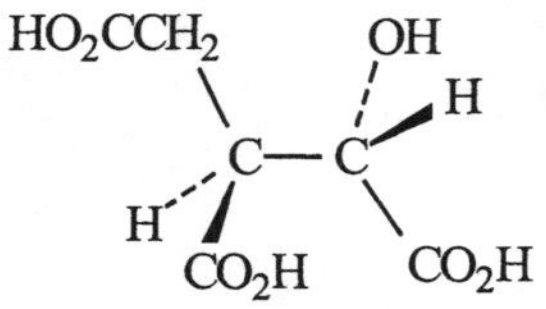 HO_2CCH_2 OH H C— C H CO_2H CO_2H

b. 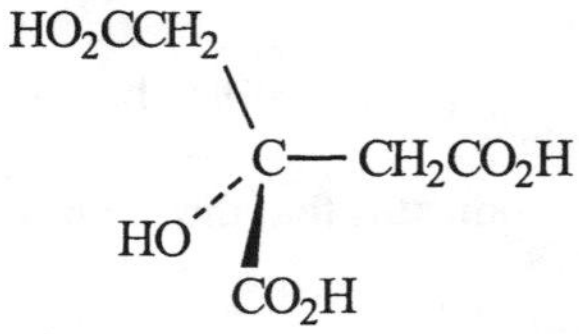 HO_2CCH_2 C— CH_2CO_2H HO CO_2H

c. HO_2CCH_2 H OH C— C HO_2C H CO_2H

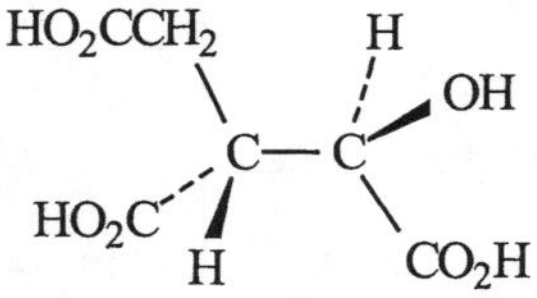

d. cannot be determined

Answer: b

Identify the indicated hydrogens in the following molecules as *pro-R* or *pro-S*.

41.

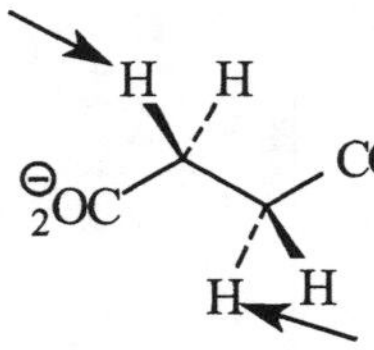

H H $^{\ominus}{}_2OC$ $CO_2^{\ominus}$ H H

succinate

Answer:

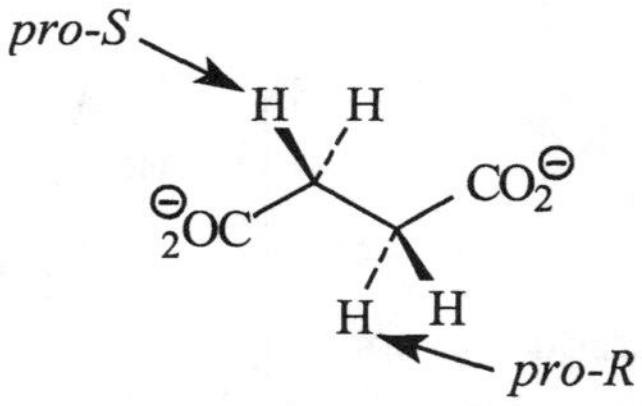

pro-S H H $^{\ominus}{}_2OC$ $CO_2^{\ominus}$ H H *pro-R*

42.

H H $CO_2^{\ominus}$ O

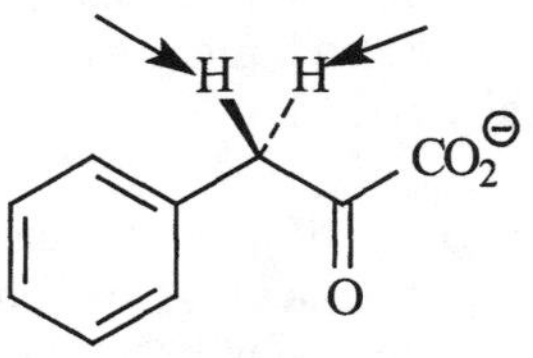

phenylpyruvate

Answer:

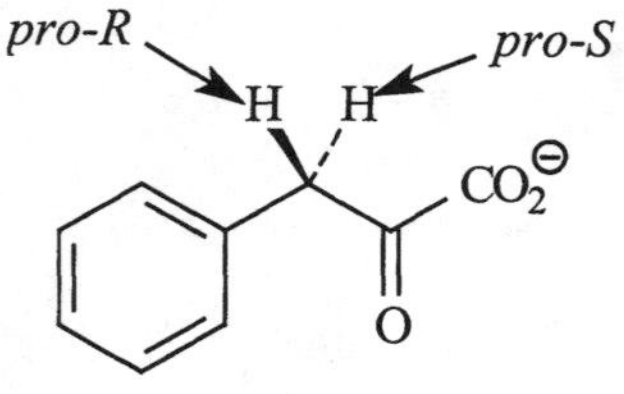

pro-R H H *pro-S* $CO_2^{\ominus}$ O

phenylpyruvate

Identify the indicated faces in the following molecules as *re* or *si*.

43.

Ph, $^{\ominus}O_2C$, C=O

phenylpyruvate

Answer:

re

Ph, $^{\ominus}O_2C$, C=O

si

44.

$^{\ominus}O_3POH_2C$, HOH_2C, C=O

dihydroxyacetone phosphate

Answer:

si

$^{\ominus}O_3POH_2C$, HOH_2C, C=O

re

45. Acetoacetate synthase catalyzes the addition of pyruvate to α-ketobutyrate to yield α-aceto-α-hydroxybutyrate. If the addtion occurs from the *si* face of α-ketobutyrate, what is the stereochemistry of the product?

$$CH_3COCO_2^{\ominus} + CH_3CH_2COCO_2^{\ominus} \xrightarrow[\text{thiamine pyrophosphate}]{\text{acetoacetate synthase}} CH_3CO\text{—}C(OH)(CH_2CH_3)CO_2^{\ominus} + CO_2$$

α-aceto-α-hydroxybutyrate

Answer: Addition of the aceto group to the *si* face results in the *R* enantiomer of α-aceto-α-hydroxybutyrate.

addition → $^{\ominus}O_2C$, CH_3CH_2, C=O ⟶ $COCH_3$, *R*, $^{\ominus}O_2C$, OH, CH_3CH_2

Chapter 10 - Alkyl Halides

Give the name for each of the following alkyl halides.

1. 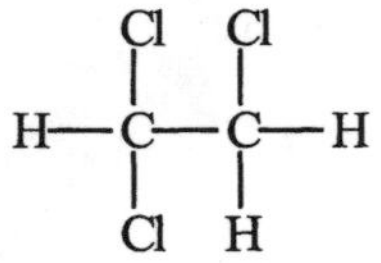
```
    Cl  Cl
    |   |
H—C—C—H
    |   |
    Cl  H
```

Answer: 1,1,2-trichloroethane

2. CHI_3

Answer: 1,1,1-triiodomethane

3. 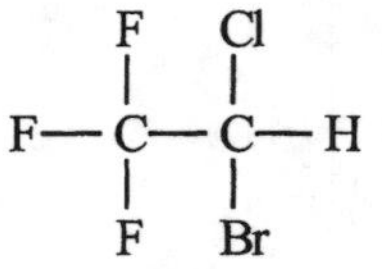
```
   F   Cl
   |   |
F—C—C—H
   |   |
   F   Br
```
, Halothane

Answer: 2-bromo-2-chloro-1,1,1-trifluoroethane

4. CH_2Cl_2

Answer: dichloromethane

Draw structures corresponding to these names.

5. 3-iodopropene

Answer:

I

6. *trans*-1-chloro-3-*sec*-butylcyclohexane

Answer:

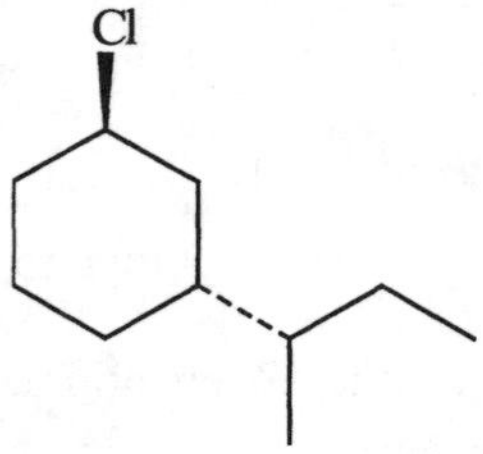

Cl

7. 1,2-dichloro-1,1,2,2-tetrafluoroethane (Cryofluorane)

Answer:
```
   Cl  Cl
   |   |
F—C—C—F
   |   |
   F   F
```

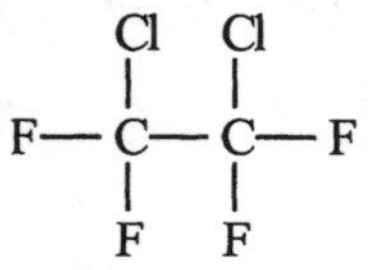

8. (*S*)-2-bromobutane

Answer:

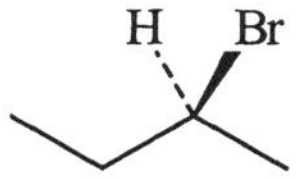

H Br

To answer the following questions consider the reaction below:

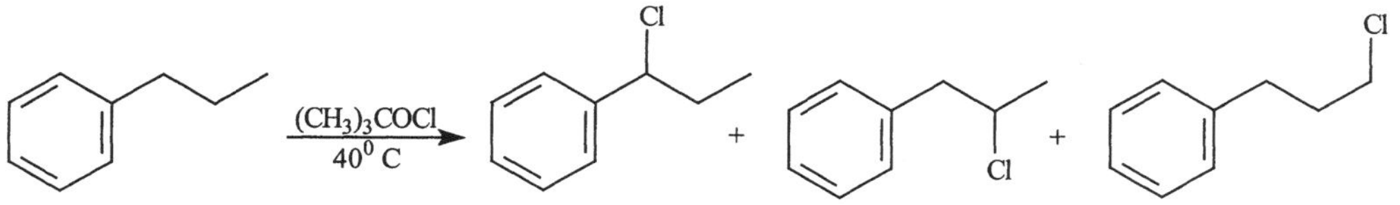

(CH3)3COCl
40° C

Cl + Cl + Cl

65% 25% 10%

9. When propylbenzene reacts with *tert*-butylhypochlorite three monochlorinated products are formed in the ratios indicated. Calculate a reactivity order for each type of hydrogen atom in propylbenzene.

Answer: $Ar-CH_{2}- = 65\% \div 2 = 32.5\%$ product $\div 3.3 = 9.85$

$-CH_{2}- = 25\% \div 2 = 12.5\%$ product $\div 3.3 = 3.8$

$-CH_{3}- = 10\% \div 3 = 3.3\%$ product $\div 3.3 = 1$

Therefore the Relative Reactivity for CH_3:CH_2:$ArCH_2$ is 1:3.8:9.85.

10. The reaction of propylbenzene with *tert*-butylhypochlorite proceeds by a radical substitution pathway. Draw the structure of the radical intermediate leading to each product.

Answer:

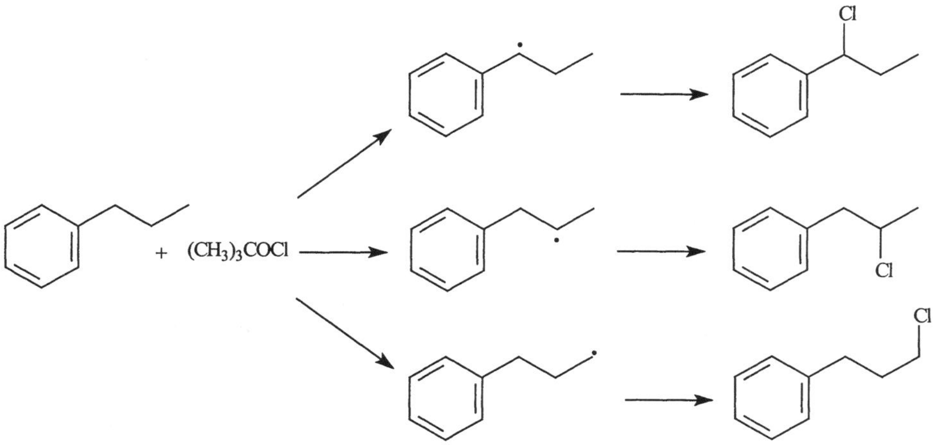

Cl

+ (CH3)3COCl

Cl

Cl

11. Based on your answers to the two questions above explain why (1-chloropropyl)benzene is the major product of this reaction.

Answer: In question 9 we calculated that the hydrogens next to the aryl group, the benzylic hydrogens, are about 2.5 times more reactive than the methylene hydrogens and about 10 times more reactive than the methyl hydrogens. This means that the benzylic radical is more stable than a 2 ° or 1° radical. The reason the benzylic radical is more stable is because it is resonance stabilized. The resonance forms for the benzylic radical are:

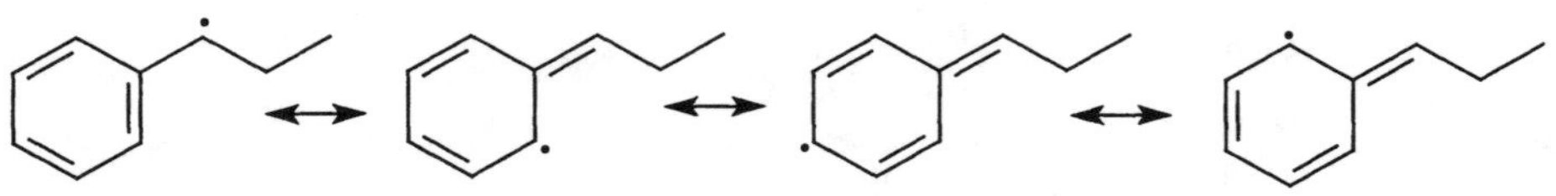

The 2° or 1° radicals have no other resonance forms.

12. Are any of the products of this reaction chiral? If so draw them and label the chirality center with an asterisk.

Answer: Yes!

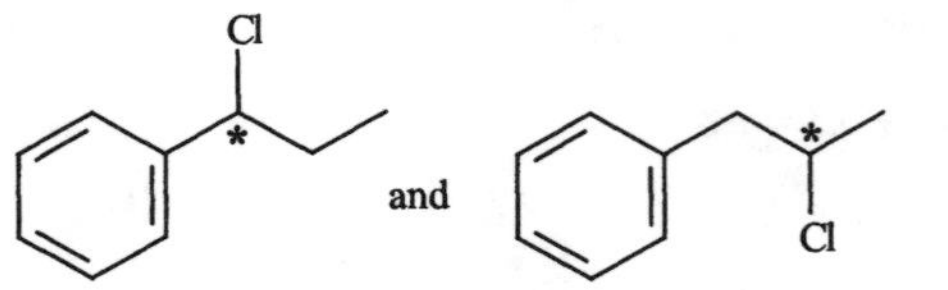

Cl * and * Cl

13. Will the product mixture of this reaction display optical activity?

Answer: No, the radical intermediates for the chiral products are symmetrical and the transition states leading to chiral products are of equal energy so racemic mixtures are formed.

14. In the discussion on relative reactivity of alkane hydrogens towards radical chlorination, we showed that the relative rate of 2° to 1° hydrogen atom abstratction is 3.5 : 1 for butane. Calculate the relative amounts of 1-chloropropane and 2-chloropropane obtained the radical chlorination of propane, using this relative rate of reactivity.

$$CH_3CH_2CH_3 \xrightarrow[\text{light}]{Cl_2} CH_3CH_2CH_2\text{—}Cl \quad + \quad CH_3\underset{}{\overset{Cl}{\overset{|}{C}}}HCH_3$$

Answer: Propane has six 1° hydrogrens, so 6 x 1 = 6; and two 2° hydrogens, so 2 x 3.5 = 7. The percentage of 1-chloropropane is therefore 6/13 or 46% and the percentage of 2-chloropropane is 7/13 or 54%.

Consider the reaction below to answer the following questions.

Methylcyclopentane (CH_3) $\xrightarrow[\text{light}]{Cl_2}$

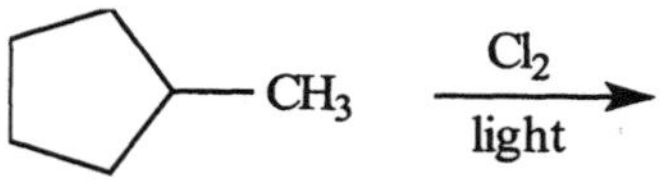

15. Draw all the monochlorination products of methylcyclopentane (ignore stereoisomers).

Answer:

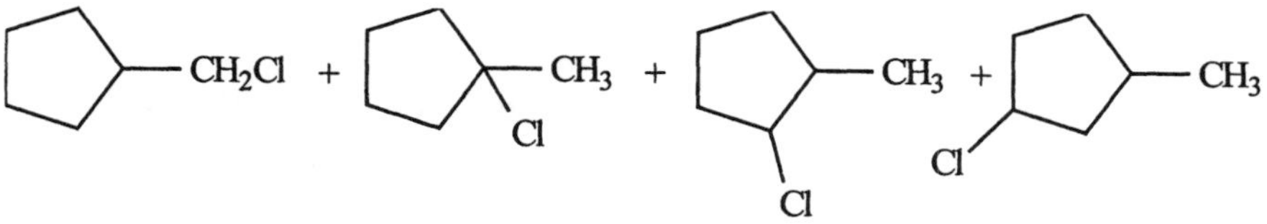

(chloromethyl)cyclopentane (CH_2Cl) + 1-chloro-1-methylcyclopentane (Cl, CH_3) + 1-chloro-2-methylcyclopentane (Cl, CH_3) + 1-chloro-3-methylcyclopentane (Cl, CH_3)

16. Label the chirality centers in the monochlorination products of methylcyclopentane with an asterisk.

Answer:

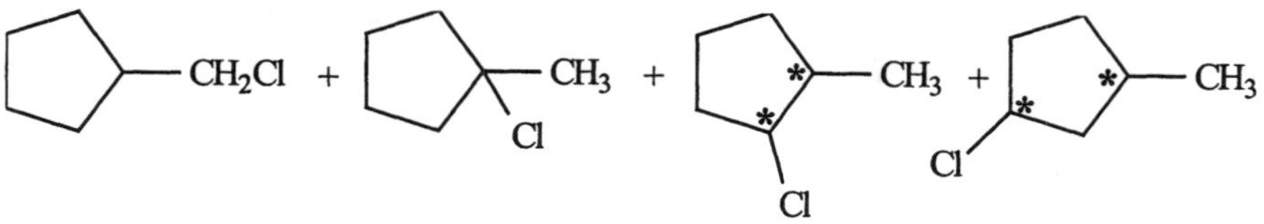

(chloromethyl)cyclopentane (CH_2Cl) + 1-chloro-1-methylcyclopentane (Cl, CH_3) + 1-chloro-2-methylcyclopentane (Cl, CH_3; C1* and C2*) + 1-chloro-3-methylcyclopentane (Cl, CH_3; C1* and C3*)

17. Tell whether radical chlorination of methylcyclopentane is an oxidation or a reduction process.

Answer: In the radical chlorination of methylcyclopentane a C-H bond is broken and a C-Cl bond is formed, so the process is an organic oxidation.

Consider the reaction below to answer the following questions.

$$CH_3CH{=}CHCH_2CH_2CH_3 \xrightarrow[h\nu]{NBS} CH_3CH{=}CHCH(Br)CH_2CH_3 + CH_3CH(Br)CH{=}CHCH_2CH_3$$

<u>**A**</u> (reactant)   <u>**B**</u> (first product)   <u>**C**</u> (second product)

18. Place asterisks(*) at all *allylic* positions in compound <u>**A**</u>.

Answer:

$$\overset{*}{C}H_3CH{=}CH\overset{*}{C}H_2CH_2CH_3$$

<u>**A**</u>

19. Draw the resonance forms of the allylic radical intermediate that accounts for the formation of <u>**B**</u> and <u>**C**</u>.

Answer:

$$CH_3CH{=}CH{-}\dot{C}HCH_2CH_3 \longleftrightarrow CH_3\dot{C}H{-}CH{=}CHCH_2CH_3$$

20. D and E, below, are minor products in this reaction. Explain why.

$$\underset{\textbf{D}}{BrCH_2CH{=}CHCH_2CH_2CH_3} \quad + \quad \underset{\textbf{E}}{CH_2{=}CHCH(Br)CH_2CH_2CH_3}$$

Answer: Products D and E are formed from the other allylic radical, whose resonance forms are shown below.

$$\underset{1^\circ \text{ allylic}}{\dot{C}H_2CH{=}CHCH_2CH_2CH_3} \longleftrightarrow \underset{2^\circ \text{ allylic}}{CH_2{=}CH\dot{C}HCH_2CH_2CH_3}$$

This allylic radical forms more slowly than the radical for products A and B because is has some 1° character, and thus, is less stable. The allylic radical intermediate for products A and B is 2° allylic.

Choose the *best* reagent or sequence of reagents from the list provided below for carrying out the following transformations. Place the letter of your response to the left of the reaction.

a. PBr_3
b. HCl (gas), ether
c. 1. Mg, ether
 2. D_2O
d. $SOCl_2$, pyridine
e. HBr (gas), ether
f. 1. Mg, ether
 2. NBS

21. ____ $(CH_3)_3C{-}OH \longrightarrow (CH_3)_3C{-}Br$

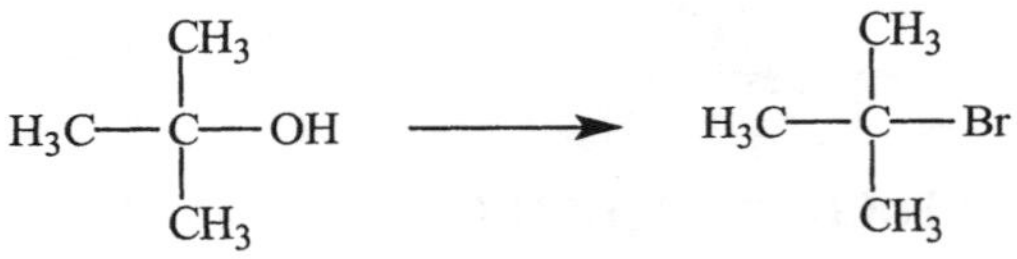

Answer: e

22. ____ 1-bromo-1-methylcyclohexane $\longrightarrow$ 1-deuterio-1-methylcyclohexane (CH3, Br on ring carbon → CH3, D)

Answer: c

23. ____ 3-methylbutan-1-ol (OH) $\longrightarrow$ 1-chloro-3-methylbutane (Cl)

Answer: d

Provide structures for the reactants, intermediates, or products, as indicated, in the following reactions. Draw the structures in the boxes provided.

24.

CH_3CH_2I —(1. Li, pentane; 2. CuI)→ [ ] —(CH_3I)→ [ ]

Answer:

CH_3CH_2I —(1. Li, pentane; 2. CuI)→ $(CH_3CH_2)_2CuLi$ —(CH_3I)→ $CH_3CH_2CH_3$

25.

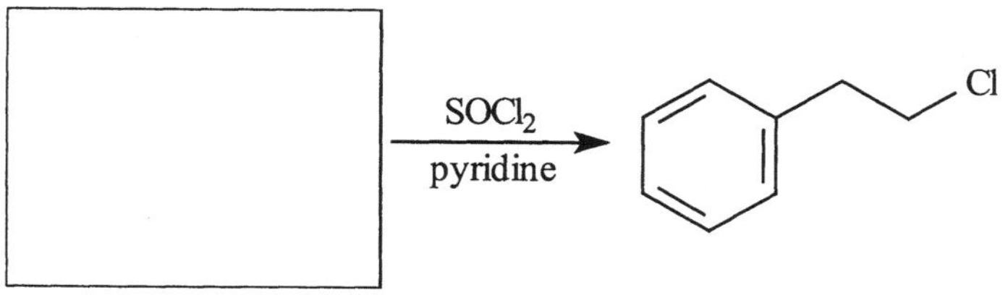

[ ] —($SOCl_2$, pyridine)→ (2-phenylethyl chloride) Cl

Answer:

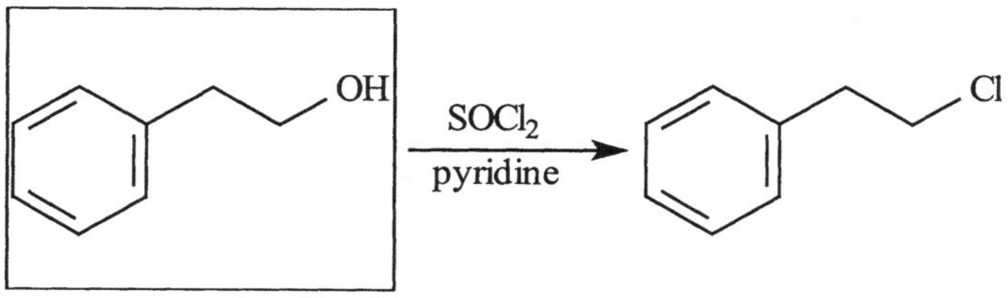

(2-phenylethanol) OH —($SOCl_2$, pyridine)→ (2-phenylethyl chloride) Cl

26.

(2-butene) —(NBS, CCl_4)→ [ ] + [ ]

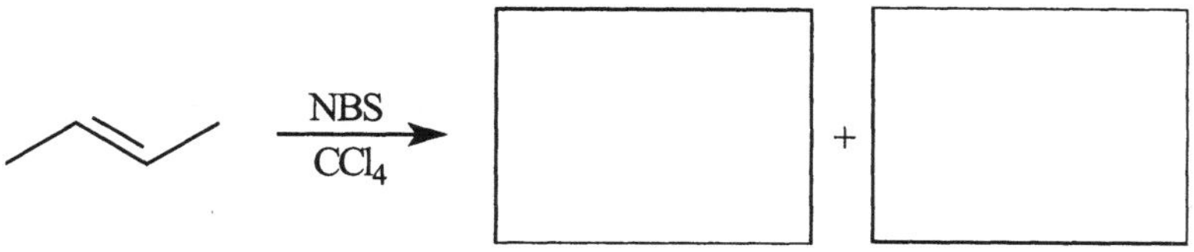

Answer:

(2-butene) —(NBS, CCl_4)→ (1-bromo-2-butene) Br + (3-bromo-1-butene) Br

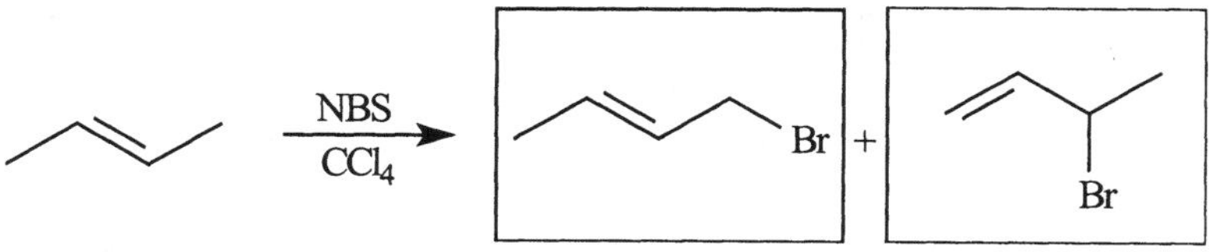

27.

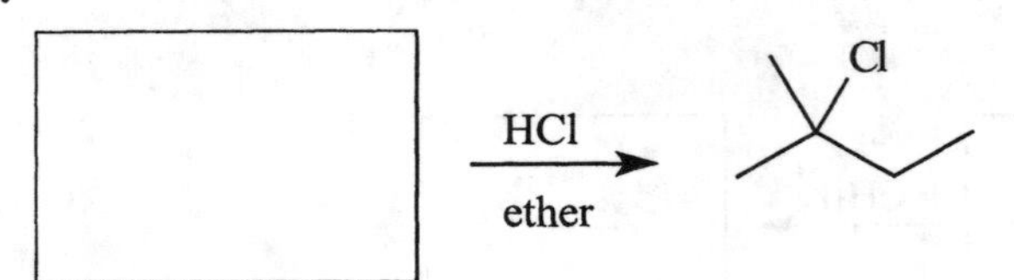

Answer:

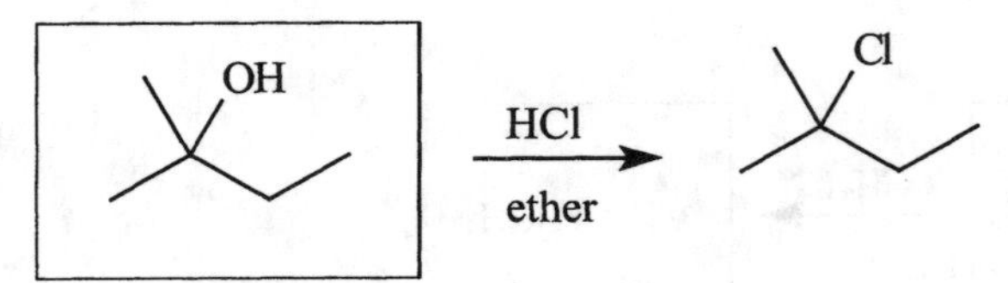

28.

Br

+ $(CH_3CH_2)_2CuLi$ $\xrightarrow{\text{ether}}$

Answer:

Br

+ $(CH_3CH_2)_2CuLi$ $\xrightarrow{\text{ether}}$ CH_2CH_3

29.

1. NBS, CCl_4
2. KOH, ethanol

Answer:

1. NBS, CCl_4
2. KOH, ethanol

30.

Br $\xrightarrow[\text{ether}]{\text{Mg}}$

Answer:

2-bromopropene + Mg, ether → [2-propenylmagnesium bromide] (MgBr)

31.

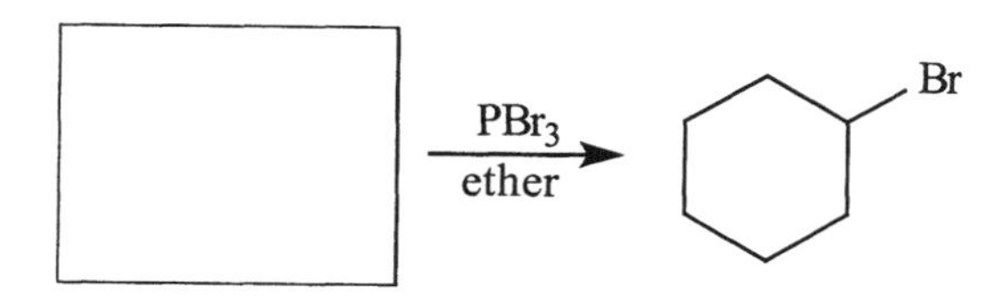

Answer:

[cyclohexanol] (OH) $\xrightarrow[\text{ether}]{PBr_3}$ bromocyclohexane (Br)

Propose a synthesis of each of the following compounds from the given starting material and any inorganic reagents necessary.

32.

$CH_3CH(CH_3)CH{=}CH_2$ from $CH_3CH(CH_3)CH_2CH_2OH$

Answer:

$CH_3CH(CH_3)CH_2CH_2OH \xrightarrow[\text{ether}]{PBr_3} CH_3CH(CH_3)CH_2CH_2Br \xrightarrow[\text{ethanol}]{KOH} CH_3CH(CH_3)CH{=}CH_2$

33.

$(H_3C)_2CH{-}CH(CH_3)_2$ from $(H_3C)_2CH{-}Br$ (only source of carbon)

Answer:

$2\ (H_3C)_2CH{-}Br \xrightarrow[\text{pentane}]{4\ Li} 2\ (H_3C)_2CH{-}Br \xrightarrow[\text{ether}]{CuI} [(CH_3)_2C]_2{-}CuLi \xrightarrow[\text{ether}]{(CH_3)_2CHBr} (H_3C)_2CH{-}CH(CH_3)_2$

34. Identify the reagents **a** and **b** in the following scheme.

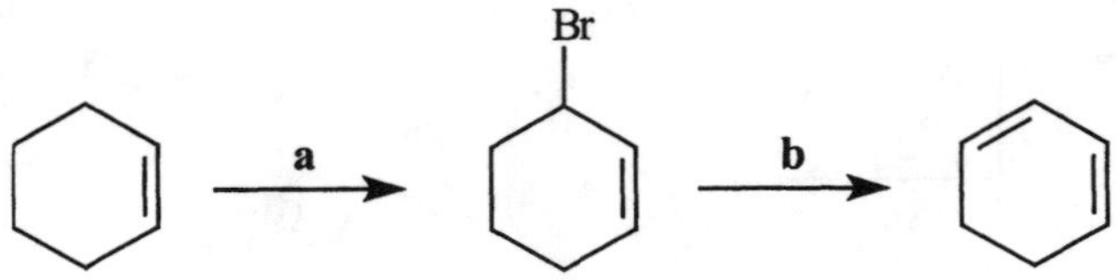

Answer: **a** = NBS, *hv* **b** = KOH

Label each transformation below as:

a. an oxidation
b. a reduction
c. neither oxidation nor reduction

Place the letter corresponding to the correct answer in the blank to the left of the transformation.

35. ____

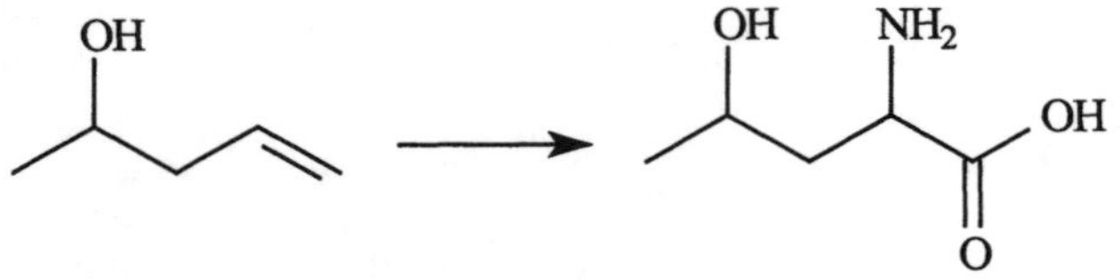

Answer: a

36. ____

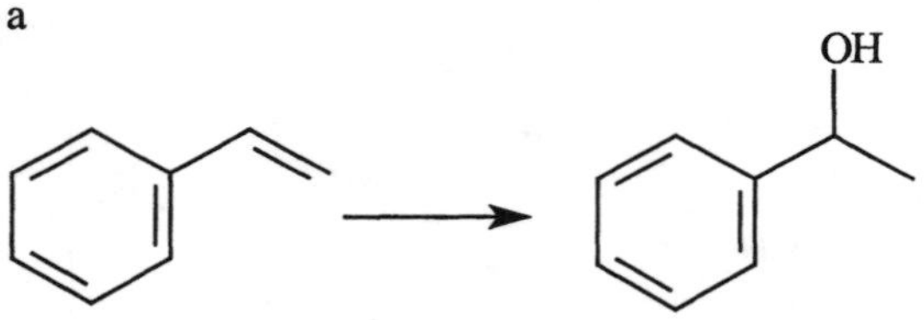

Answer: c

37. ____

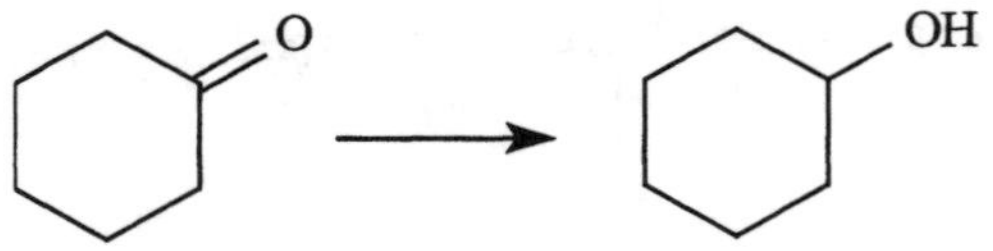

Answer: b

38. ____ $CH_3CH(CH_3)CH_3 \longrightarrow CH_3C(CH_3)(Br)CH_3$

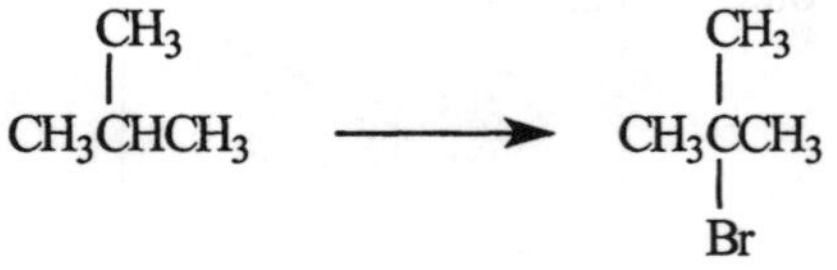

Answer: a

39. Rank the following compounds in order of *increasing* oxidation level. Place the number rank (1 = lowest; 4 = highest) in the blank below the structure.

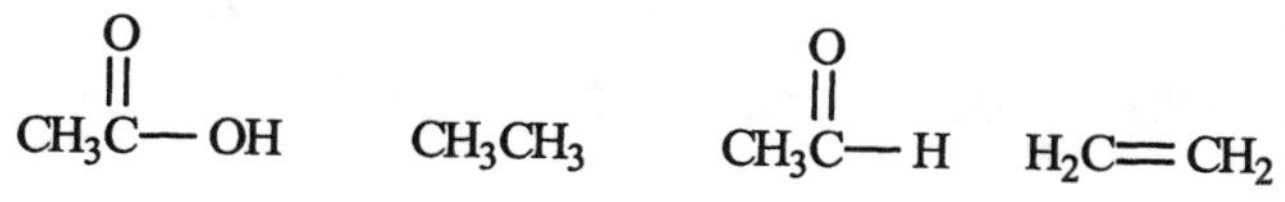

$CH_3C(=O)-OH$	CH_3CH_3	$CH_3C(=O)-H$	$H_2C=CH_2$
____	____	____	____

Answer:

$CH_3C(=O)-OH$	CH_3CH_3	$CH_3C(=O)-H$	$H_2C=CH_2$
4	1	3	2

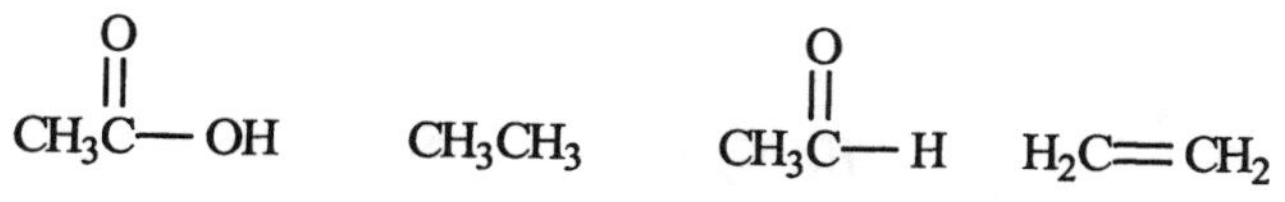

Chapter 11 - Reactions of Alkyl Halides: Nucleophilic Substitutions and Eliminations

Circle your response in each set below.

1. The *least* reactive compound in an S_N2 reaction.

$C_6H_5CH_2I$ (benzyl iodide)   H, I (stereo structure) CH_3CH_2OTos H, Br (stereo structure)

Answer:

$C_6H_5CH_2I$ (circled: H, I structure) CH_3CH_2OTos H, Br

2. The *best* leaving group in an elimination reaction.

$^{\ominus}OTos$ $^{\ominus}OC(=O)CH_3$ H_2O $F^{\ominus}$

Answer:

(circled: $^{\ominus}OTos$) $^{\ominus}OC(=O)CH_3$ H_2O $F^{\ominus}$

3. The *best* nucleophile in a substitution reaction at a primary carbon.

$CH_3CO_2^{\ominus}$ $HO^{\ominus}$ H_2O $(CH_3)_3CO^{\ominus}$

Answer:

$CH_3CO_2^{\ominus}$ (circled: $HO^{\ominus}$) H_2O $(CH_3)_3CO^{\ominus}$

4. The *least* reactive compound in a S_N1 reaction.

Cl (allylic chloride structure) CH_3CHFCH_3 $PhCHBrCH_3$ $(CH_3)_3C—I$

Answer:

Cl (allylic chloride structure)   (circled: CH_3CHFCH_3) $PhCHBrCH_3$ $(CH_3)_3C—I$

5. The *best* solvent for an S_N2 reaction.

HMPA $\quad$ $CHCl_3$ $\quad$ H_2O $\quad$ CH_3CH_2OH

Answer:

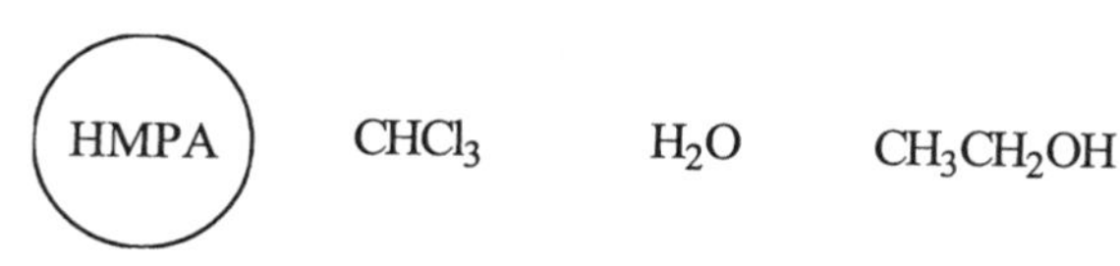

Consider the pair of reactions below to answer the following questions.

a. $CH_3CH_2CH_2Br \xrightarrow{^-OH,\ H_2O} CH_3CH_2CH_2OH + Br^-$

or

b. $CH_3CH_2CH_2Br \xrightarrow{^-SH,\ RSH} CH_3CH_2CH_2SH + Br^-$

6. Which reaction would be predicted to be faster?

Answer: b

7. Explain your answer to the question above.

Answer: –SH is a better nucleophile than –OH because nucleophilicity usually increases in going down a column of the periodic table and sulfur is below oxygen in group 6A.

8. The mechanism for these reactions is:

a. S_N1
b. S_N2
c. E1
d. E2

Answer: b

Consider the pair of reactions below to answer the following questions.

a. $(CH_3)_3C\text{—}Cl \xrightarrow[30\%\ CH_3OH]{70\%\ H_2O} (CH_3)_3C\text{—}OH + HCl$

or

b. $(CH_3)_3C\text{—}Cl \xrightarrow[50\%\ \text{acetone}]{50\%\ H_2O} (CH_3)_3C\text{—}OH + HCl$

9. Which reaction above is faster?

Answer: a

10. Explain your answer to the question above.

Answer: The conversion of *tert*-butyl chloride to *tert*-butyl alcohol proceeds faster in 70% H_2O/30% CH_3OH than in 50% H_2O/50% acetone because S_N1 reactions are faster in more polar solvents. Acetone (dielectric polarization, $P = 20.7$) is less polar than CH_3OH ($P = 33.6$), and the percentage of H_2O is higher in the water/methanol system.

11. The kinetics of these reactions are:

a. second-order
b. first-order in nucleophile
c. not measurable
d. first-order in alkyl halide

Answer: d

Consider the pair of reactions below to answer the following questions.

a. 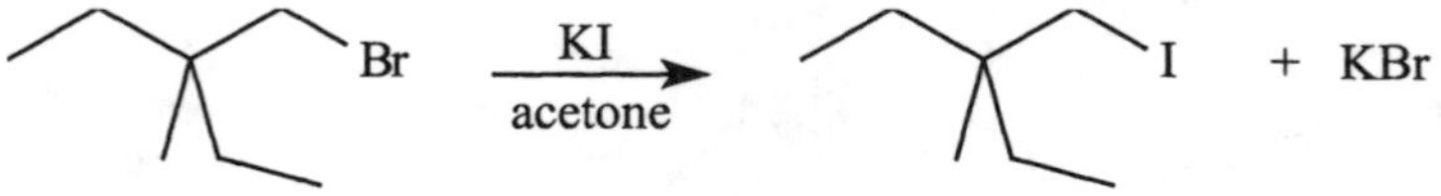 [1-bromo-2,2-diethyl alkyl bromide] Br $\xrightarrow[\text{acetone}]{\text{KI}}$ [corresponding alkyl iodide] I + KBr

or

b. 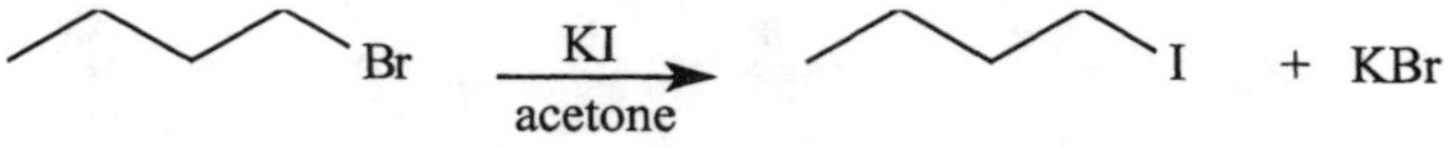 [1-bromopentane] Br $\xrightarrow[\text{acetone}]{\text{KI}}$ [1-iodopentane] I + KBr

12. The alkyl bromide starting materials in these reactions are classified as:

a. 3°
b. 2°
c. 1°
d. 4°

Answer: c

13. The solvent in these reactions is:

a. nonpolar aprotic
b. polar aprotic
c. polar protic
d. nonpolar protic

Answer: b

14. The nucleophile in these reactions is:

a. K^+
b. alkyl group
c. Br^-
d. I^-

Answer: d

15. Which reaction is *faster*?

Answer: b

16. The mechanism for these reactions is:

a. S_N2
b. E2
c. S_N1
d. E1

Answer: a

Consider the pair of reactions below to answer the following questions.

a. C_6H_5–$CH_2CH_2NH_2$ $\xrightarrow[\text{heat}]{\text{KOH}}$ C_6H_5–$CH{=}CH_2$

or

b. C_6H_5–CH_2CH_2OTos $\xrightarrow[\text{heat}]{\text{KOH}}$ C_6H_5–$CH{=}CH_2$

17. Which reaction above is faster?

Answer: b

18. Explain your answer to the question above.

Answer: Tosylate anion is a better leaving group than amide ion; tosylate is the weak conjugate base of a strong acid, while amide is the strong conjugate base of a weak acid.

19. Doubling the concentration of potassium hydroxide in these reactions:

a. causes the reaction mechanism to change
b. halves the rate of reaction
c. has no effect on the rate of reaction
d. doubles the rate of reaction

Answer: d

20. The mechanism for these reactions is:

a. S_N2
b. E2
c. S_N1
d. E1

Answer: b

Consider the reaction below to answer the following questions.

$$\underset{\textbf{A}}{H_3C-C(CH_3)_2-Cl} \xrightarrow[\text{ethanol}]{H_2O} \underset{\textbf{B}}{H_3C-C(CH_3)_2-OH} + \underset{\textbf{C}}{(H_3C)_2C=CH_2}$$

21. The substrate in the reaction is:

Answer: A

22. Compound B is the:

a. S_N2 product
b. S_N1 product
c. E2 product
d. E1 product

Answer: b

23. Compound C is the:

a. S_N2 product
b. S_N1 product
c. E2 product
d. E1 product

Answer: d

24. Write the complete reaction mechanism for the formation of Compound C in this reaction.

Answer:

$$H_3C-C(CH_3)_2-Cl \longrightarrow H_3C-\overset{\oplus}{C}(CH_3)-CH_2-H \quad :\ddot{O}H_2 \longrightarrow (H_3C)_2C=CH_2$$

To answer the following questions consider the data below:

Reaction of bromomethane with sodium hydroxide in water forms methanol. If sodium iodide is added to the reaction mixture, the rate of methanol formation is dramatically increased (i.e. sodium iodide is a catalyst).

25. The mechanism involved in the reaction of CH_3Br and NaOH is:

a. S_N1
b. S_N2
c. E1
d. E2

Answer: b

26. Write a reaction pathway that accounts for the effect of added NaI.

Answer:

$$CH_3Br + I^- \longrightarrow CH_3I + Br^- \xrightarrow{^-OH} CH_3OH + I^-$$

27. Draw a reaction energy diagram showing the two different reaction pathways (i.e. catalyzed and uncatalyzed). Indicate structures for all energy minima in the diagram.

Answer:

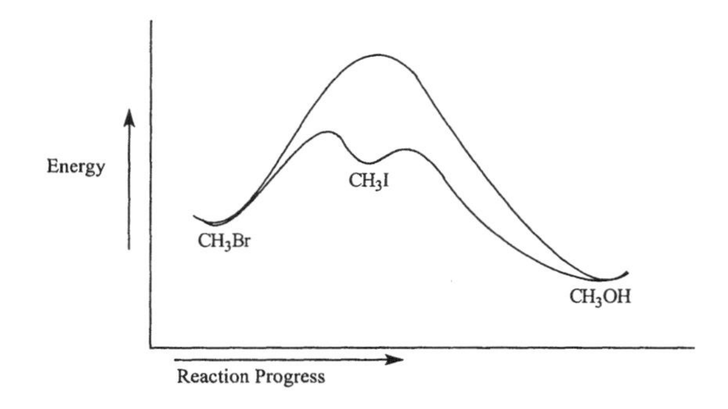

28. Explain why adding NaI increases the reaction rate.

Answer: Iodide is a better nucleophile than hydroxide so we expect reaction between CH_3Br and iodide to proceed faster than the reaction between CH_3Br and hydroxide. CH_3I is a more reactive alkyl halide than CH_3Br because iodide is a better leaving group than bromide so when CH_3I forms it reacts with hydroxide faster than CH_3Br to form CH_3OH. The overall result is faster formation of CH_3OH from CH_3Br when NaI is added.

29. Would you expect the same catalytic effect on this reaction if you added NaCl instead? Explain your answer.

Answer: No. Chloride ion is a poorer nucleophile as well as a poorer leaving group than bromide ion.

Consider the reaction below to answer the following questions:

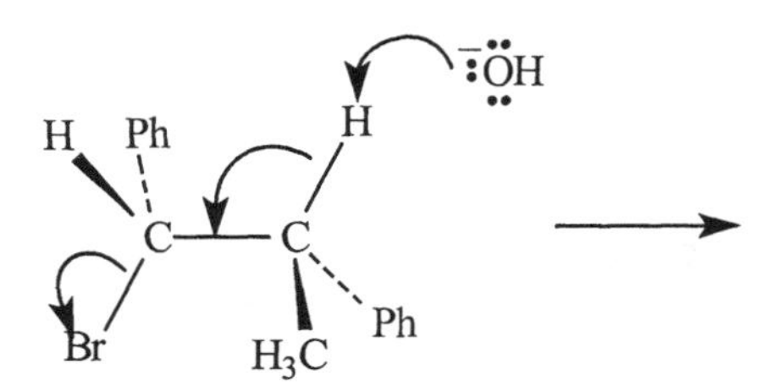

30. Write the product that results from the electron flow in the reaction, clearly indicating any stereochemistry

Answer:

Ph Ph

C=C

H CH_3

31. Draw a Newman projection of the reactive conformation of the starting material.

Answer:

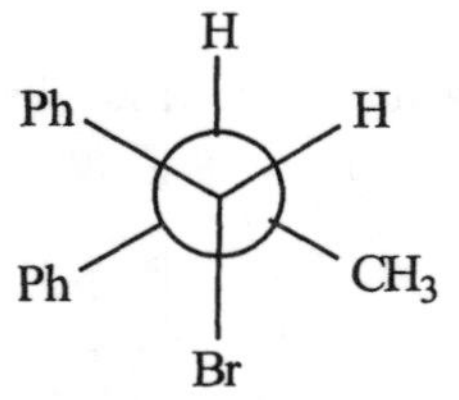

H
Ph H
Ph CH_3
Br

32. The mechanism of this reaction is:

a. S_N1
b. S_N2
c. E1
d. E2

Answer: d

Consider the reaction below to answer the following questions.

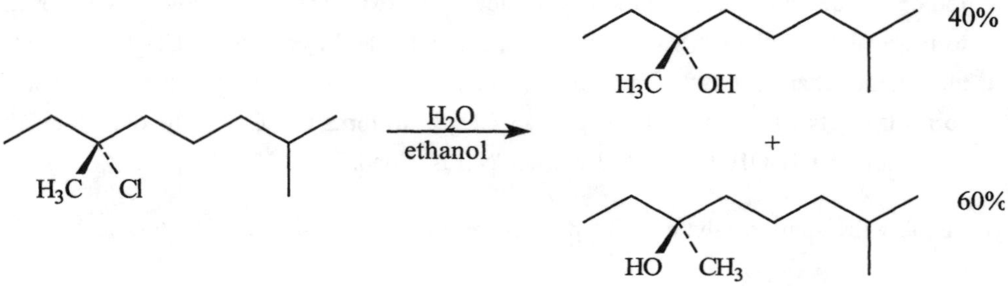

H_3C Cl → (H_2O, ethanol) → H_3C OH 40% + HO CH_3 60%

33. Write the complete stepwise mechanism for this reaction. Clearly show the formation of both products. Show all electron flow with arrows and draw all intermediate structures.

Answer:

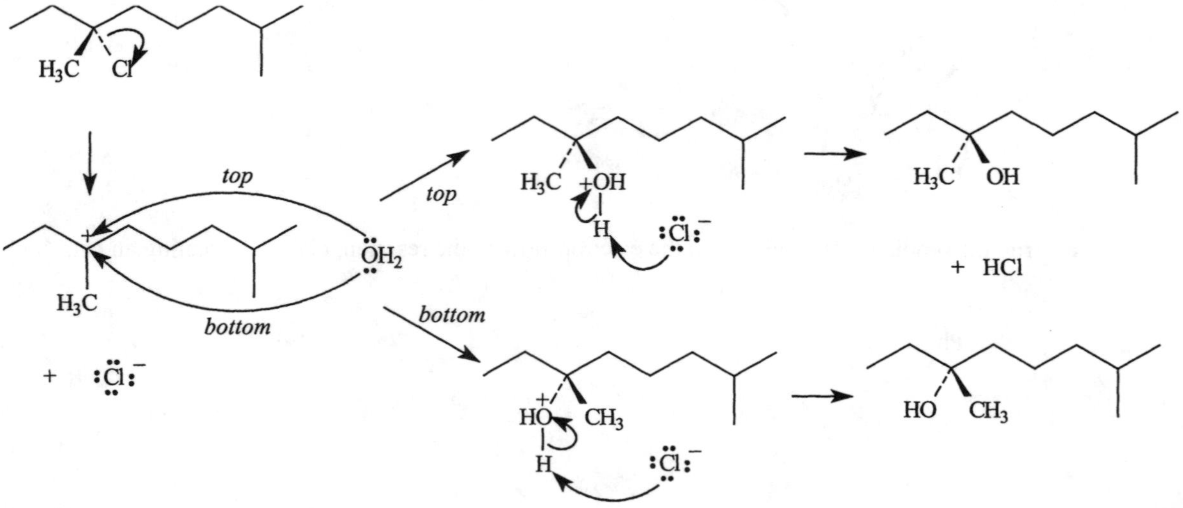

H_3C Cl

H_3C + :Cl:⁻   top   bottom $\ddot{O}H_2$

top: H_3C +OH, H, :Cl:⁻ → H_3C OH

\+ HCl

bottom: HO+ CH_3, H, :Cl:⁻ → HO CH_3

34. This reaction obeys a rate law of the form:

a. rate = k[RCl][CH_3CH_2OH]
b. rate = k[RCl][H_2O][CH_3CH_2OH]
c. rate = k[RCl]
d. rate = k[RCl][H_2O]

Answer: c

Draw the structure of the major organic products(s) for each of the following reations. Indicate the stereochemistry for each reaction when appropriate.

35. Br, H; NaCN / HMPA →

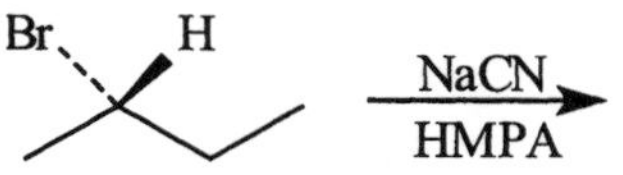

Answer:

Br, H; NaCN / HMPA → H, CN

36. Cl, H; CH_3OH →

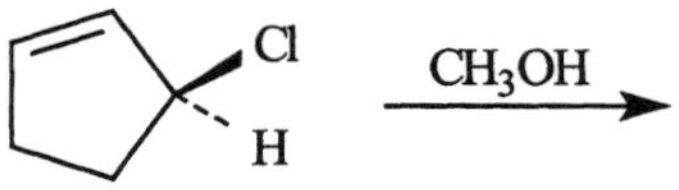

Answer:

Cl, H; CH_3OH → OCH_3, H + H, OCH_3

37. H_3C, OH; HCl →

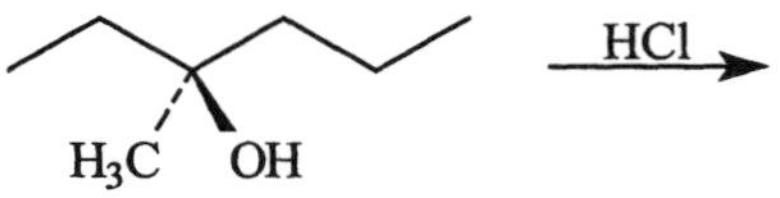

Answer:

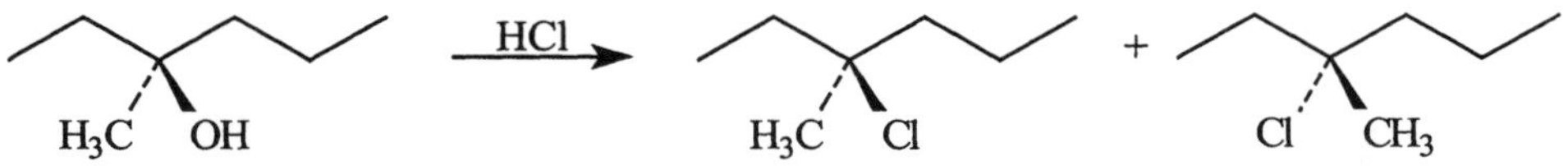

H_3C, OH; HCl → H_3C, Cl + Cl, CH_3

38. Br, $C(CH_3)_3$; NaSH / acetonitrile →

Answer:

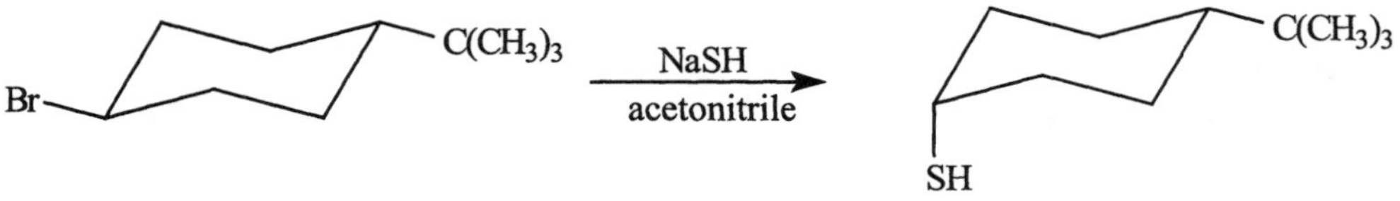

Br, $C(CH_3)_3$; NaSH / acetonitrile → $C(CH_3)_3$, SH

39. 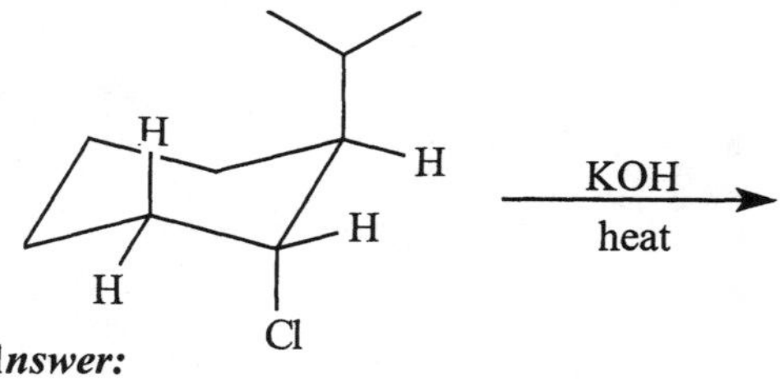 H, H, H, H, Cl; $\xrightarrow[\text{heat}]{\text{KOH}}$

Answer:

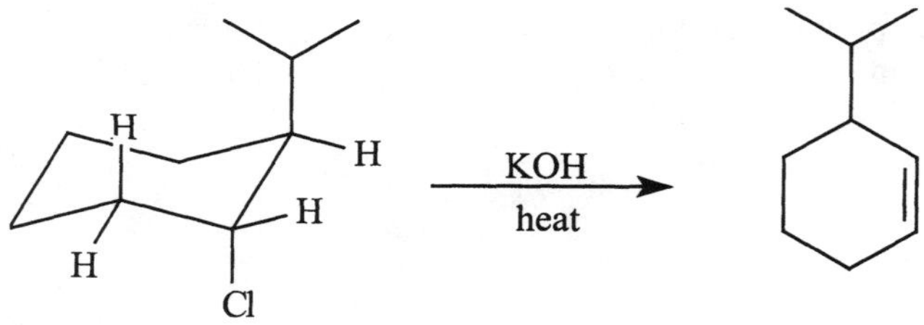

H, H, H, H, Cl; $\xrightarrow[\text{heat}]{\text{KOH}}$

40. 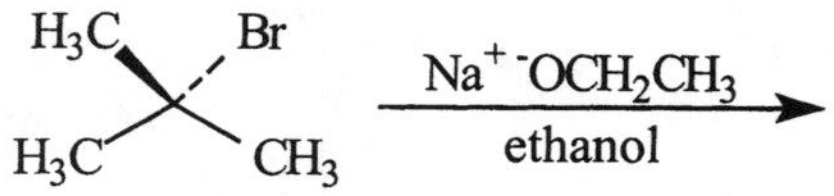 H_3C, Br, H_3C, CH_3; $\xrightarrow[\text{ethanol}]{Na^{+}\ {}^{-}OCH_2CH_3}$

Answer:

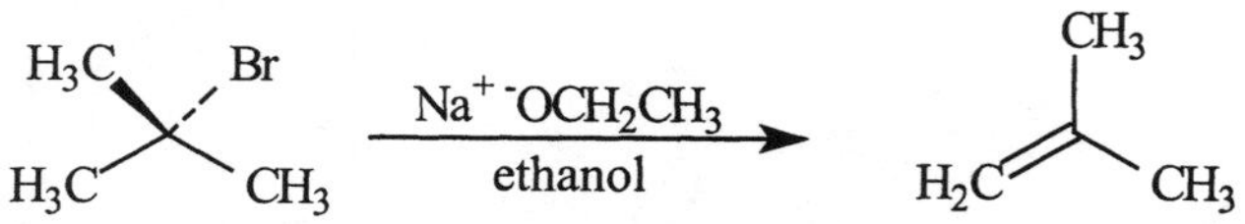

H_3C, Br, H_3C, CH_3; $\xrightarrow[\text{ethanol}]{Na^{+}\ {}^{-}OCH_2CH_3}$ CH_3, H_2C, CH_3

41. 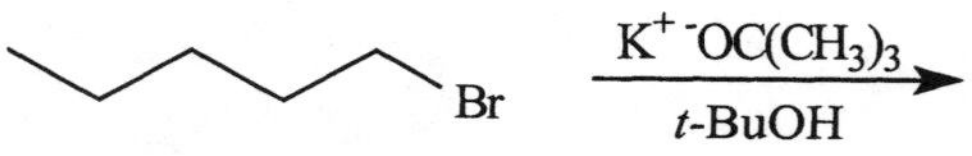 Br; $\xrightarrow[t\text{-BuOH}]{K^{+}\ {}^{-}OC(CH_3)_3}$

Answer:

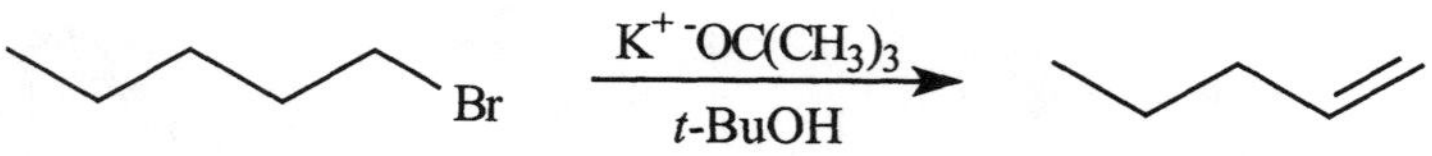

Br; $\xrightarrow[t\text{-BuOH}]{K^{+}\ {}^{-}OC(CH_3)_3}$

42. 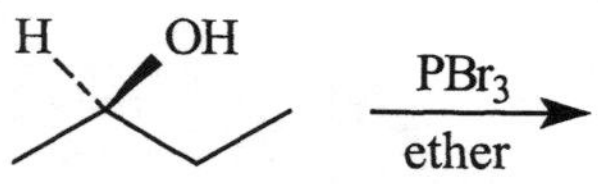 H, OH; $\xrightarrow[\text{ether}]{PBr_3}$

Answer:

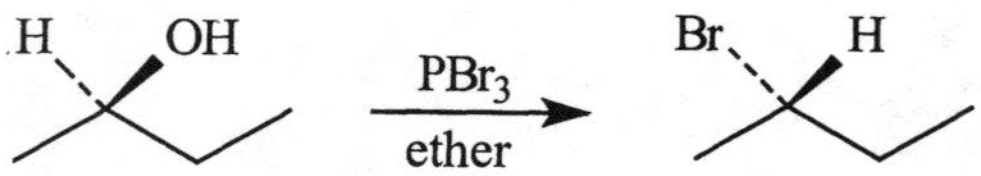

H, OH; $\xrightarrow[\text{ether}]{PBr_3}$ Br, H

43. 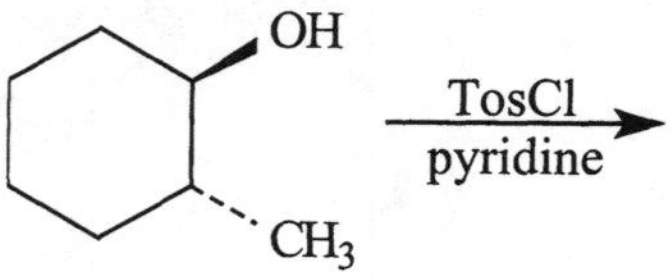 OH, CH_3; $\xrightarrow[\text{pyridine}]{\text{TosCl}}$

Answer:

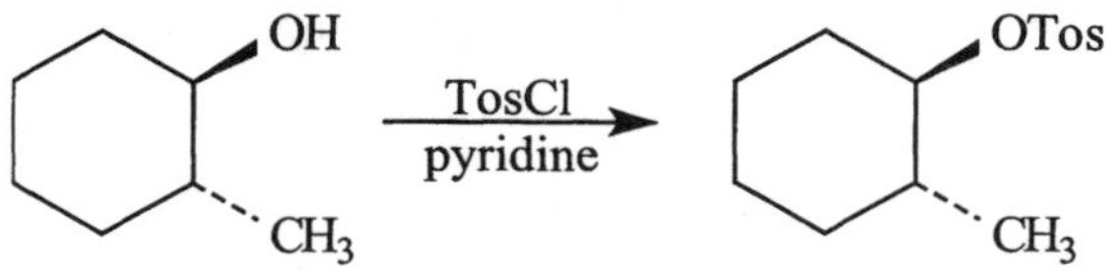

TosCl, pyridine

44.

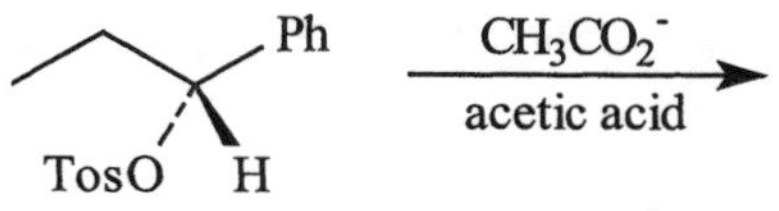

$CH_3CO_2^-$, acetic acid

Answer:

$CH_3CO_2^-$, acetic acid

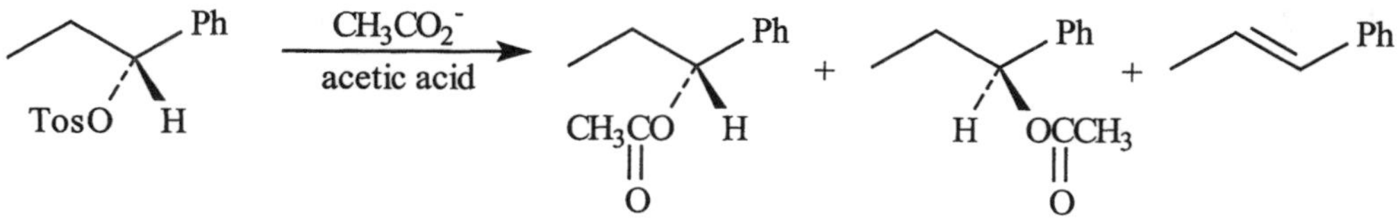

Consider the reaction below to answer the following questions.

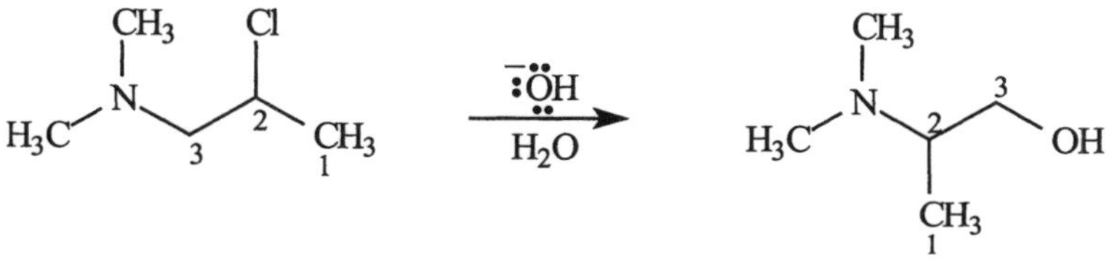

^-OH, H_2O

45. List all chirality centers in the starting material by number.

Answer: Carbon 2 is a chirality center.

46. As indicated by the carbon numbers, during the course of this reaction the bond between the nitrogen atom and carbon 3 is broken and a bond between the nitrogen atom and carbon 2 is formed. On the structures provided below, draw arrows showing electron flow for the mechanism which accounts for these bonding changes.

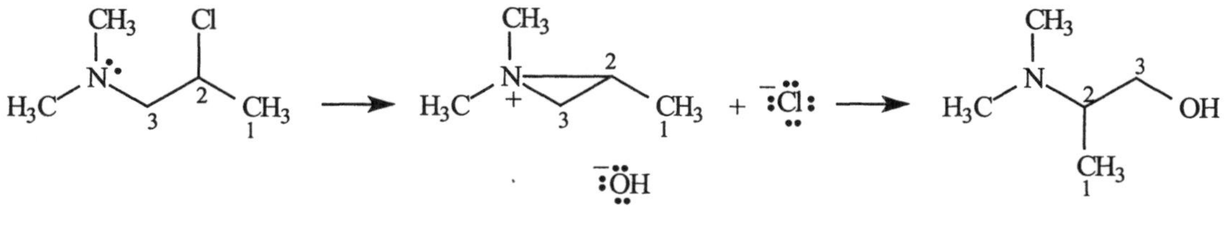

Answer:

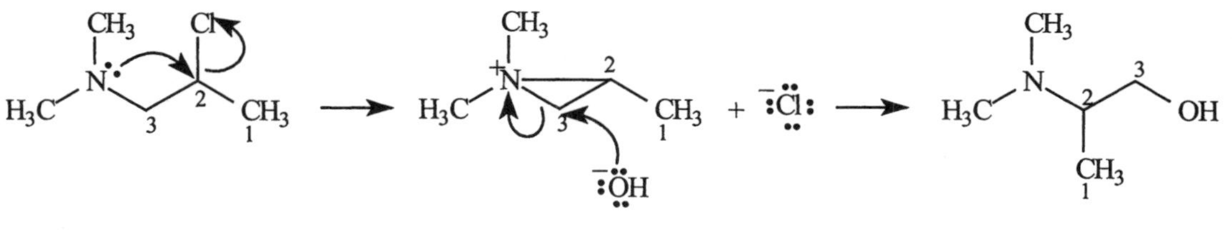

47. If the absolute configuration at carbon 2 in the starting material is *R*, what is the absolute configuration at carbon 2 in the product?

Answer: The absolute configuration at carbon 2 in the product is *S* because an intramolecular S_N2 reaction occurred in the first step of the reaction to invert the configuration at that carbon.

For each substrate below, choose which reaction type is favored. Place the letter of the reaction type in the blank to the left of the substrate.

a. S_N1
b. S_N2
c. E1
d. E2

48. ______ $R_3CX \xrightarrow[\text{solution}]{\text{acidic}}$

Answer: a

49. ______ $RCH_2X \xrightarrow{\text{Nu :}}$

Answer: b

50. ______ $R_2CHX \xrightarrow[\text{base}]{\text{strong}}$

Answer: d

Chapter 12 - Structure Determination: Mass Spectrometry and Infrared Spectroscopy

Select the most reasonable formula for the compounds with the following mass spectral data:

1. M^+ at $m/z = 101$ with a minor M+1 peak

a. C_5H_6Cl b. $C_5H_{12}N_2$ c. $C_6H_{15}N$ d. $C_9H_{12}O$

Answer: c

2. M^+ $m/z = 136$ and M^+ at $m/z = 138$ of approximately equal intensity

a. $C_6H_{13}OCl$ b. C_4H_9Br c. $C_{10}H_{16}$ d. $C_9H_{12}O$

Answer: b

3. The sugar glucose contains C, H, and O and has a mass of 180.0634 amu as determined by high-resolution mass spectrometry. Glucose contains an equal number of carbon and oxygen atoms. What is the molecular formula of glucose? (^1H = 1.00783 amu, ^{12}C = 12.00000 amu, ^{16}O = 15.99491 amu)

Answer: Since the number of carbons and oxygens is equal, we can add the masses of C and O and then divide 180.0634 by that number. The remainder should be the number of hydrogens.

$$12.0000 + 15.99491 = 27.99491$$

$$180.0634 \div 27.99491 = 6 \text{ carbons and 6 oxygens with} \sim 12 \text{ remaining}$$

So, the formula for glucose should be $C_6H_{12}O_6$. We can confirm this by doing the math.

$$(6 \times 12.0000) + (12 \times 1.00783) + (6 \times 15.99491) = 180.0634$$

Use the following data to answer the questions below:

Terfenedine is an amino diol that is the active ingredient in the antihistamine Seldane®. Mass spectral analysis of terfenedine shows a molecular ion at m/z = 471 and a peak at m/z = 472 which is 35.5% the height of the molecular ion. Terfenedine is known to contain C, H, O and N.

4. Suggest five molecular formulas for terfenedine.

Answer: Since we know that terfenedine is an amino diol, we know it has one nitrogen and two oxygens. By subtracting 46 (14 + 16 + 16) from the molecular weight of 471 we arrive at a weight of 425 for the carbon and hydrogen portion of the molecule. Possible formulas are: $C_{35}H_5NO_2$, $C_{34}H_{17}NO_2$, $C_{33}H_{29}NO_2$, $C_{32}H_{41}NO_2$, $C_{31}H_{53}NO_2$.

5. Terfenedine has an even number of carbons and contains nine double bonds and four rings. Based on this additional information, what is the formula for terfenedine?

Answer: An even number of carbons narrows the choices to the C_{34} and C_{32} formulas. Nine double bonds and four rings gives thirteen degrees of unsaturation. The formula $C_{34}H_{17}NO_2$ has 27 degrees of unsaturation, while the formula $C_{32}H_{41}NO_2$ has 13 degrees of unsaturation, so $C_{32}H_{41}NO_2$ must be the formula for terfenedine.

6. Explain the origin of the peak at *m/z* = 472.

Answer: The peak at *m/z* = 472 is the M+1 peak, which arises from the fact that each carbon atom has a 1.11% probability of being ^{13}C. The ratio of the height of the ^{13}C peak to the height of the ^{12}C peak for a one-carbon compound is 1.11%. For a 32-carbon compound, the contribution to M+1 is 35.5%.

Use the data below to answer the following questions.

Loratidine is the active ingredient in the antihistamine Claritin®. Mass spectral analysis of loratidine shows M^+ at *m/z* = 382 and M^+ at *m/z* = 384 in an approximate ratio of 3:1 in intensity.

7. The mass spectral data indicates that loratidine contains:

a. fluorine b. chlorine c. bromine d. iodine

Answer: b

8. Loratidine is known to contain nitrogen. What is the *minimum* number of nitrogens in loratidine?

Answer: Since the molecular ions are even numbers, loratidine must have an even number of nitrogen atoms. Therefore, the minimum number of nitrogen atoms in loratidine is two.

9. Which of the following statements best describes the base peak in a mass spectrum?

a. The peak from the most stable radical.
b. The peak from the species that has the isotope with the hightest atomic number.
c. The peak of highest intensity.
d. The peak from the molecule minus an electron.

Answer: c

For each compound below, what are the masses of the charged fragments produced by the indicated cleavage pathways?

10. Alpha cleavage of

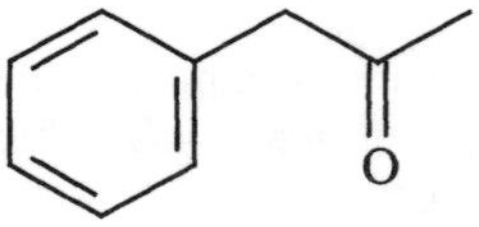

O

Answer: This compound, phenylacetone, has the formula $C_9H_{10}O$ and a nominal mass of 134. Alpha cleavage will result in charged fragments at *m/z* = 43 and *m/z* = 119.

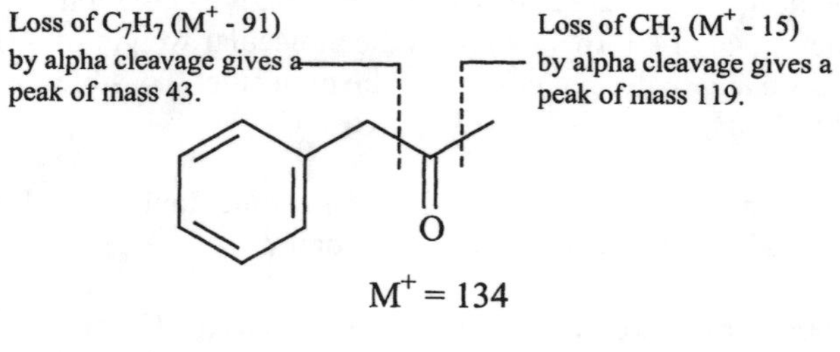

Loss of C_7H_7 (M^+ - 91) by alpha cleavage gives a peak of mass 43.

Loss of CH_3 (M^+ - 15) by alpha cleavage gives a peak of mass 119.

O

$M^+ = 134$

11. Alpha cleavage and dehydration of

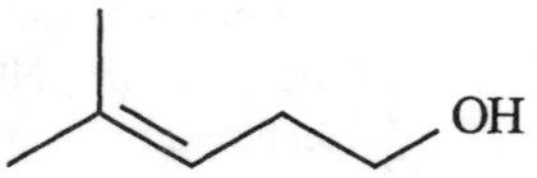

OH

Answer: This compound, 4-methyl-3-penten-1-ol, has the formula $C_6H_{12}O$ and a nominal mass of 100. Alpha cleavage will result in a charged fragment at m/z = 31. Dehydration (M^+ - 18) will result in a charged fragment at m/z = 82.

Loss of C_5H_9 (M^+ - 69) by alpha cleavage gives a peak of mass 31.

M^+ = 100

OH

12. Alpha cleavage of

N

H

Answer: This compound, diisopropylamine, has the formula $C_6H_{15}N$ and a nominal mass of 101. Alpha cleavage will result in a charged fragment at m/z = 58. Since both carbon groups are the same there is only one alpha cleavage product.

Loss of C_3H_7 (M^+ - 43) by alpha cleavage gives a peak of mass 58.

M^+ = 101

N

H

The following questions refer to the mass spectrum shown below.

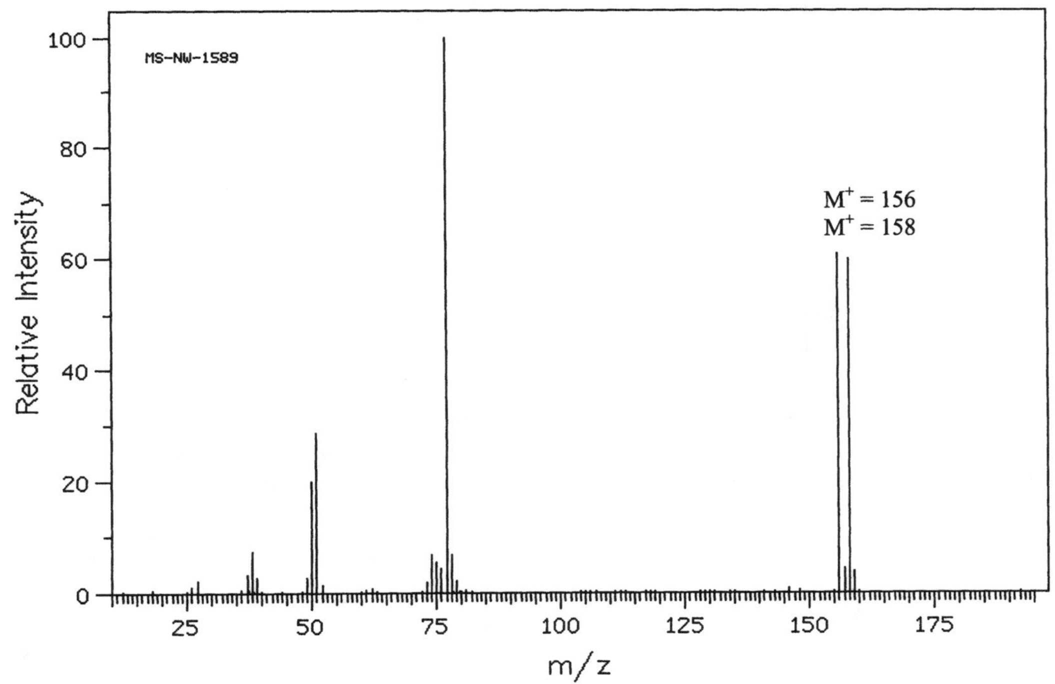

Spectrum obtained from: SDBSWeb: http://www.aist.go.jp/RIODB/SDBS/

13. This compound contains C, H, and one other atom. Identify the other atom from the mass spectrum and explain your reasoning.

Answer: There are two molecular ions identified in this spectrum of approximately equal intensity. This is characteristic for the presence of a bromine atom (^{79}Br = 50.7% and ^{81}Br = 49.3%).

14. Calculate a possible molecular formula for this compound.

Answer: The M^+ = 156 is due to the ^{79}Br, so the carbon and hydrogen portion of the molecule is 156 - 79 = 77. This mass corresponds to C_6H_5. A possible formula for this compound is C_6H_5Br.

15. Propose a structure for this compound.

Answer: C_6H_5Br contains four degrees of unsaturation, which is consistent with a benzene ring. A compatible structure is bromobenzene.

Refer to the mass spectrum of 2-methylbutane shown below to answer the following questions.

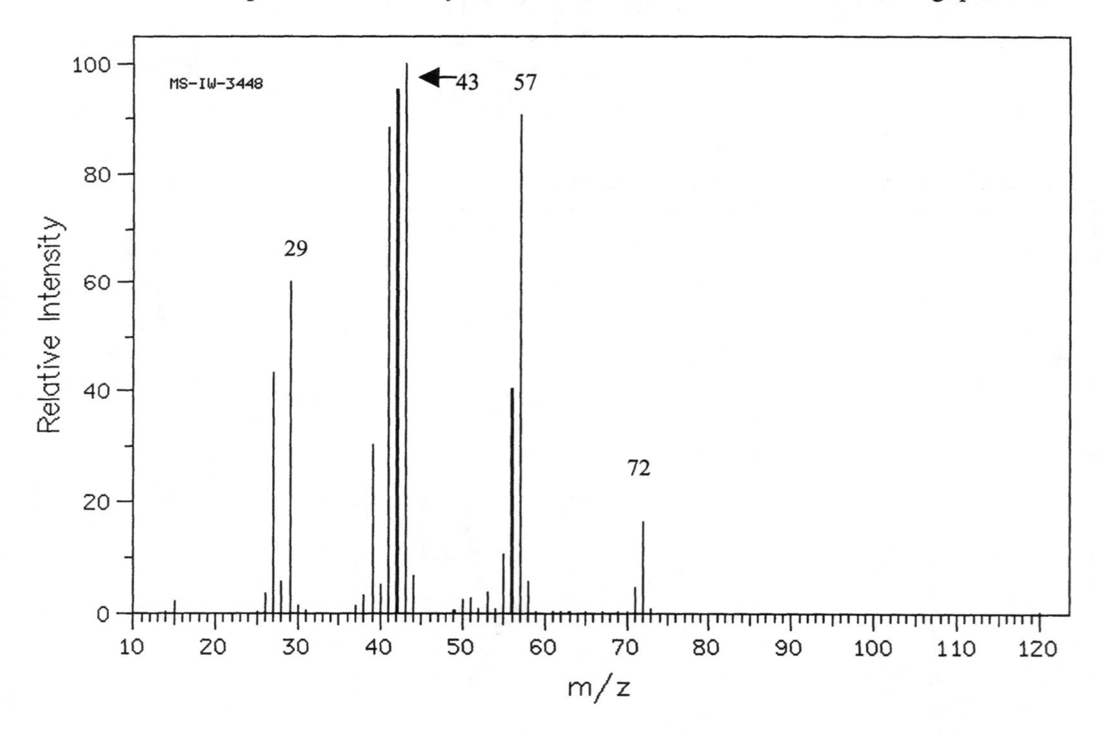

Spectrum obtained from: SDBSWeb: http://www.aist.go.jp/RIODB/SDBS/

16. What peak represents M^+?

Answer: The peak at *m/z* = 72 represents M^+.

17. What peak represents the base peak?

Answer: The peak at $m/z = 43$ is the base peak.

18. Propose structures for fragment ions at $m/z = 57$, 43, and 29.

Answer:

m/z	structure
57	$CH_3\overset{+}{C}HCH_2CH_3$
43	$CH_3\overset{+}{C}HCH_3$
29	$^{+}CH_2CH_3$

19. Below is the mass spectrum of an unknown hydrocarbon. In addition, this hydrocarbon shows characteristic absorption at 2100 cm^{-1} in its IR spectrum. Give the structure of this unknown.

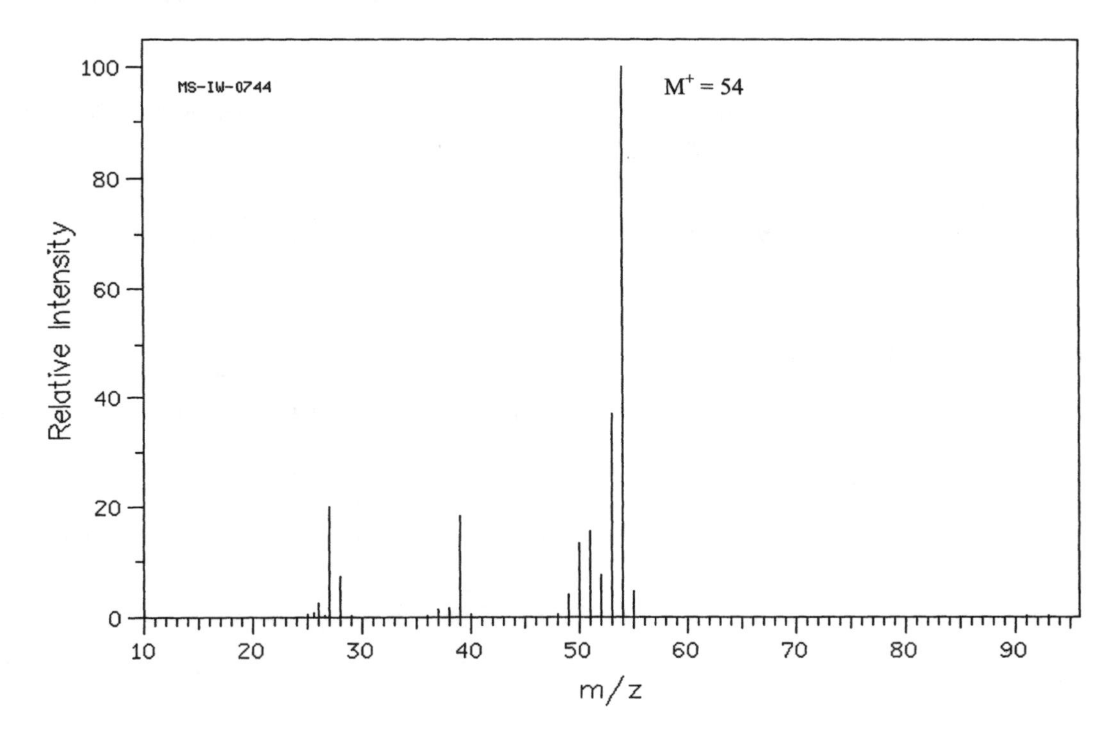

Spectrum obtained from: SDBSWeb: http://www.aist.go.jp/RIODB/SDBS/

Answer: The formula weight of 54 corresponds to a molecular formula of C_4H_6, which has two degrees of unsaturation. Possible structures for this formula are:

$CH_3CH_2C{\equiv}CH$ $CH_3C{\equiv}CCH_3$ $CH_3CH{=}C{=}CH_2$ (cyclopropene: ring CH_2 with H, H; $C{=}C$ bearing H and CH_3)

The IR data is consistent with an internal alkyne, so the compound is 2-butyne.

20. Could you distinguish 2,2-dimethylbutane from 2-methylpentane using mass spectrometry?

Answer: Yes, although M^+ at $m/z = 86$ for both compounds is identical, the fragmentation patterns of the two compounds should show two major differences. We would expect 2,2-dimethylbutane to have significant peaks at $m/z = 57$, corresponding to C_4H_9, and $m/z = 71$ corresponding to C_5H_{11}. Fragmentation of 2-methylpentane should produce significant peaks at $m/z = 43$, corresponding to C_3H_7, and $m/z = 57$, corresponding to C_4H_9.

21. Which of the following does ***not*** involve the interaction of molecules with electromagnetic energy?

a. mass spectrometry
b. infrared spectroscopy
c. ultraviolet spectroscopy
d. nuclear magnetic resonance spectroscopy

Answer: a

22. The amount of energy in electromagnetic raditation is related to the frequency and wavelength of the radiation. High energy radiation like gamma rays is of:

a. low frequency and short wavelength
b. low frequency and long wavelength
c. high frequency and short wavelength
d. high frequency and long wavelength

Answer: c

23. The amount of energy in infrared light corresponds to:

a. the amount of energy needed to promote one electron from a bonding to an antibonding molecular orbital
b. the amount of energy needed to "flip" the spin of a ^{13}C or ^{1}H nucleus
c. the amount of energy needed to strip a molecule of one electron to generate a cation radical
d. the amount of energy needed to increase certain molecular motions, such as bond vibrations, in organic molecules

Answer: d

24. Examining the infrared spectrum of a compound allows us to:

a. determine the types of functional groups present in the compound
b. determine the carbon-hydrogen framework of the compound
c. determine the molecular weight of the compound
d. determine the nature of the conjugated pi electron system in the compound

Answer: a

MATCH each of the following groups of bond-types to the region of the infrared spectrum in which their absorptions occur. Place the letter of the region in the blank to the left of the bond-type.

a. 4000 to 2500 cm^{-1}
b. 2500 to 2000 cm^{-1}
c. 2000 to 1500 cm^{-1}
d. below 1500 cm^{-1}

25. _____ $C-C$, $C-O$, $C-N$, and $C-X$ single-bond vibrations.

Answer: d

26. _____ C=O, C=N, and C=C bond absorptions.

Answer: c

27. _____ N – H , C – H , and O – H stretching and bending motions.

Answer: a

28. _____ triple bond stretching vibrations.

Answer: b

29. Cyclohexene and 2-hexyne both have the molecular formula C_6H_{10}. How would you use infrared spectroscopy to distinguish between the two compounds?

Answer: To use IR spectroscopy to distinguish between isomers, find a strong IR absorption present in one isomer that is absent in the other isomer.

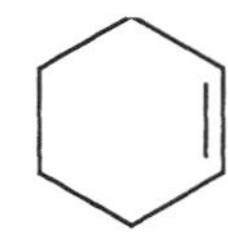

$H_3C—C \equiv C—CH_2CH_2CH_3$

alkene peak at 3020-3100 cm^{-1} and at 1650-1670 cm^{-1}	no alkene peaks
no alkyne peaks	alkyne peak of medium intensity at 2100-2260 cm^{-1}

30. When 2-bromopropane reacts with ethoxide ion, two products are formed; one is the product of S_N2 substitution and the other is the product of E2 elimination. Write the structures of both products, and tell how they could be distinguished using IR spectroscopy.

Answer:

S_N2 product	E2 product
$CH_3CH_2OCH(CH_3)_2$	$CH_3CH = CH_2$
no alkene bands	alkene bands at 3020–3100 cm^{-1} and 1650–1670 cm^{-1}
C – O stretch near 1100 cm^{-1}	no C – O stretch

31. Assume you are carrying out the conversion of 1-bromobutane to 1-butanol. How could you use IR spectroscopy to determine when the reaction is complete?

Answer: The infrared spectrum of the starting bromide contains only alkyl C – H absorptions between 2850–2960 cm^{-1} in the 4000–2500 cm^{-1} region. As the reaction progresses, a broad absorption at 3400–3640 cm^{-1}, due to the O – H stretch, should develop. When the relative intensity of this band no longer increases, the reaction is complete.

At what approximate positions might the compounds below show IR absorptions?

32. $N\equiv C-CH_2-\overset{\displaystyle O}{\overset{\|}{C}}-OCH_2CH_3$

Answer: This compound should show a medium absorption at 2210–2260 cm^{-1} for the nitrile, a strong absorption at about 1735 cm^{-1} for the ester carbonyl and a strong absorption at about 1100 cm^{-1} for the C-O of the ester.

33. (benzene ring)—OH

Answer: This compound should show a characteristic broad absorption at 3500 cm^{-1} due to the -OH group and a strong absorption at about 1200 cm^{-1} for the C-O, as well as the usual 1500 and 1600 cm^{-1} aromatic bands.

MATCH a structure from the list below to the following IR spectra. Place the letter of the structure in the blank to the left of the spectrum.

A. O

B. O

C. O

D. HO O

E. O OH

F. H O

34. _____

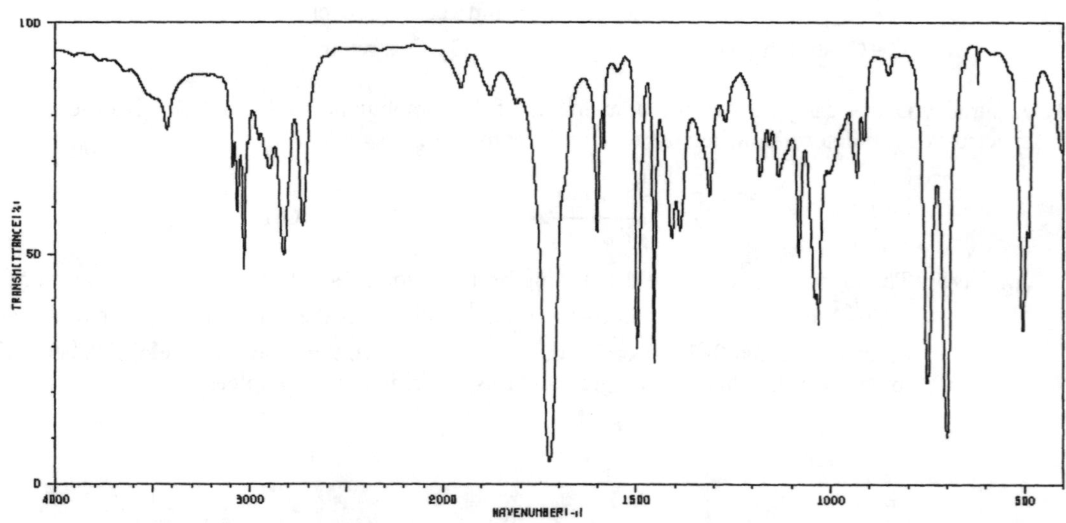

Spectrum obtained from: SDBSWeb: http://www.aist.go.jp/RIODB/SDBS/

Answer: F

35. 

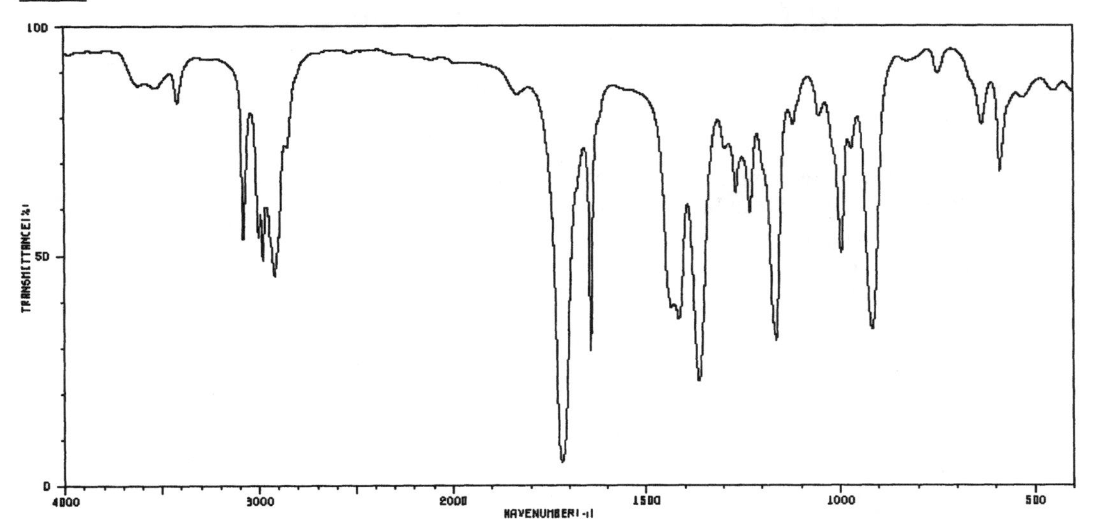

Spectrum obtained from: SDBSWeb: http://www.aist.go.jp/RIODB/SDBS/

Answer: A

36. ______

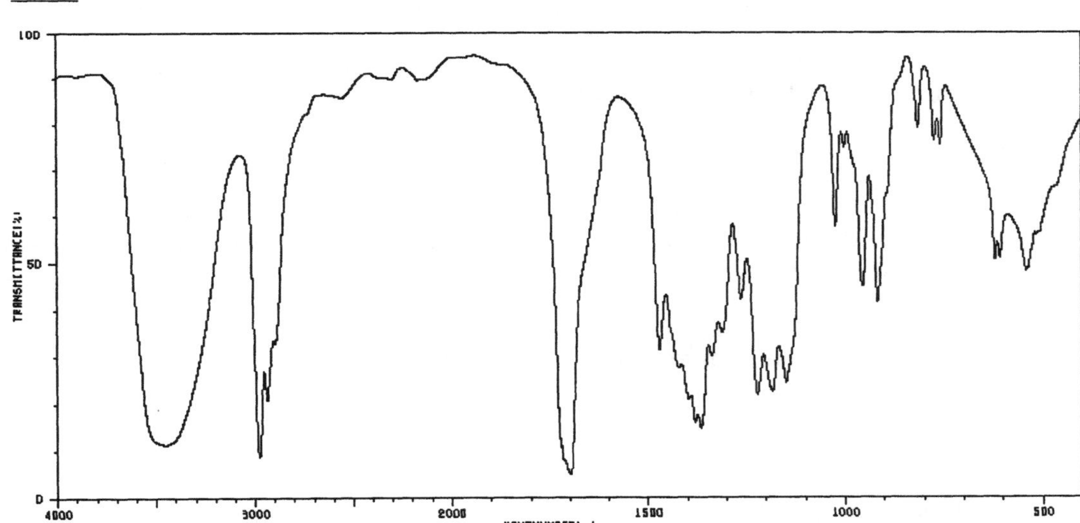

Spectrum obtained from: SDBSWeb: http://www.aist.go.jp/RIODB/SDBS/

Answer: D

Chapter 13 - Structure Determination: Nuclear Magnetic Resonance Spectroscopy

1. For a nucleus to exhibit the nuclear magnetic resonance phenomenon, it must be magnetic. Magnetic nuclei include:

a. all nuclei with even numbers of neutrons and protons
b. all nuclei with odd-numbers of protons
c. all nuclei with odd numbers of neutrons
d. both b and c

Answer: d

2. Nuclear magnetic resonance spectroscopy provides information about a molecule's:

a. conjugated pi electron system
b. size and formula.
c. carbon-hydrogen framework.
d. functional groups.

Answer: c

3. Explain why all protons in a molecule do not absorb rf energy at the same frequency.

Answer: All nuclei in molecules are surrounded by electron clouds. When a uniform external magnetic field is applied to a molecule, the circulating electron clouds set up tiny local magnetic fields of their own. These local magnetic fields act in opposition to the applied field, so that the effective field actually felt by a nucleus is a bit smaller than the applied field.

$$\boldsymbol{B}_{\text{effective}} = \boldsymbol{B}_{\text{applied}} - \boldsymbol{B}_{\text{local}}$$

This effect is termed shielding. Each nucleus is shielded to a slightly different extent, so each unique kind of proton in a molecule resonates at a slightly different frequency and gives rise to a unique NMR signal.

The following questions pertain to the charting of NMR spectra. MATCH a term to each description below. Place the letter of the term in the blank to the left of the description.

a. TMS
b. high-field or upfield side
c. MHz
d. delta (δ)
e. low-field or downfield side
f. chemical shift
g. specific absorption

4. _____ When looking at an NMR chart the right-hand part of the chart is the _____ .

Answer: b

5. _____ The exact place on the chart at which a nucleus absorbs is called its _____ .

Answer: f

6. _____ The calibration standard for ^{1}H and ^{13}C NMR is:

Answer: a

7. _____ The NMR charts are calibrated using an arbitrary scale that is divided into _____ units.

Answer: d

For each of the compounds below tell how many signals you would expect the molecule to have in its normal, broadband decoupled ^{13}C NMR spectra.

8.

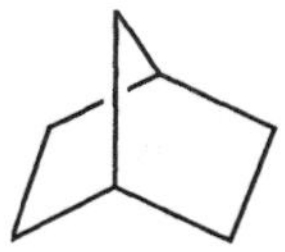

Answer: three

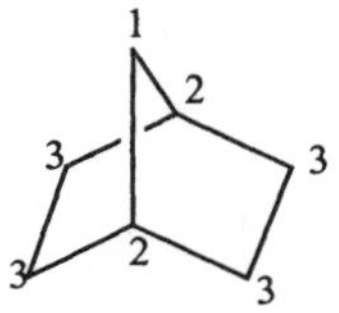

9. 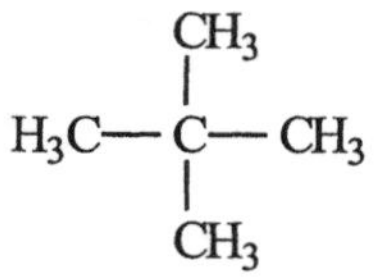 $H_3C-C(CH_3)_2-CH_3$

Answer: two $H_3C-C(CH_3)_2-CH_3$

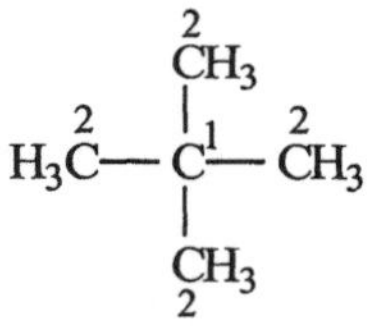

10.

plane of symmetry

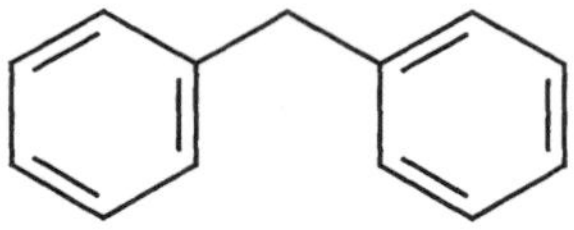

Answer: five

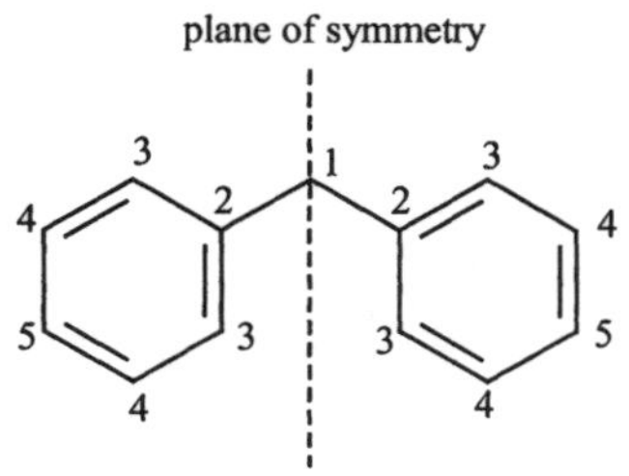

11.

Cl

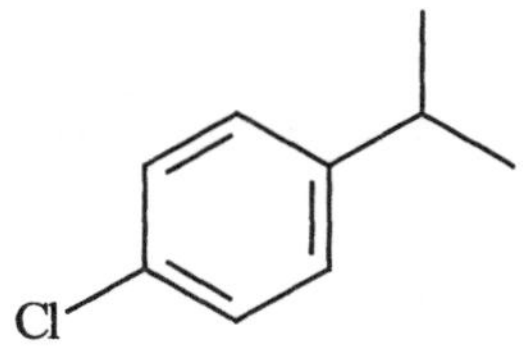

Answer: six

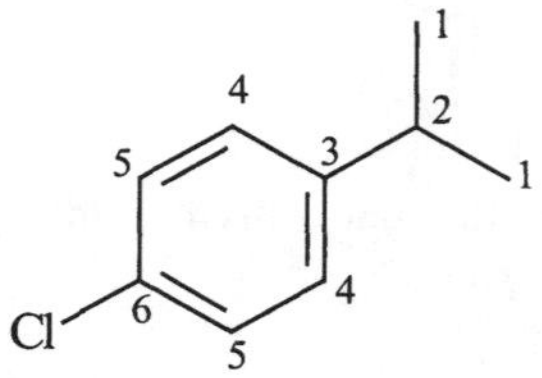

12.

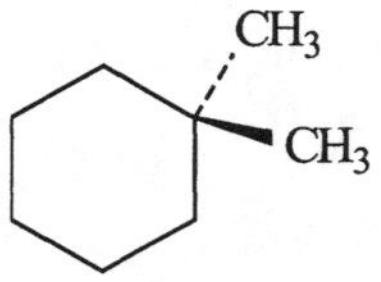

Answer: five

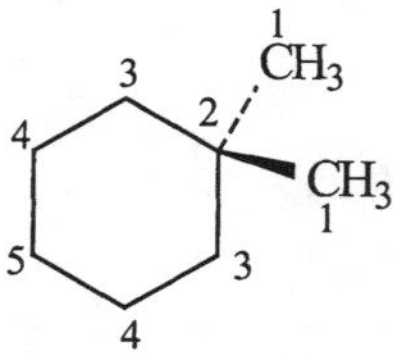

13.

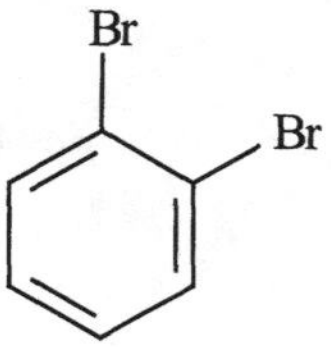

Answer: three

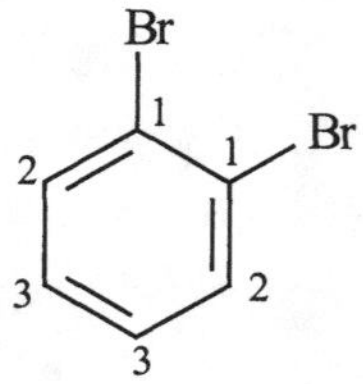

14.

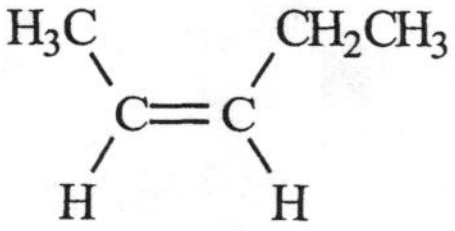

Answer: five

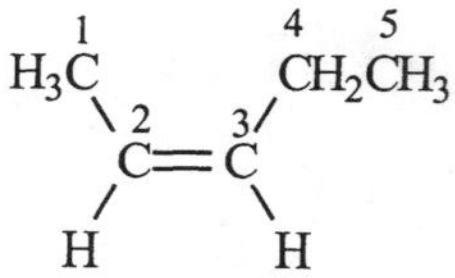

15.

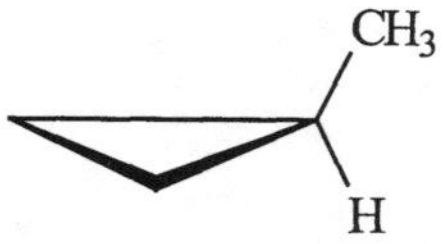

Answer: three

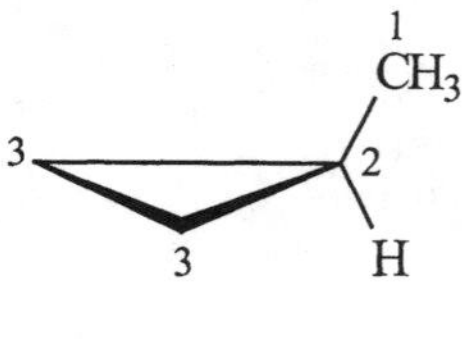

Identify the indicated sets of protons as unrelated, homotopic, enantiotopic, or diastereotopic.

16.

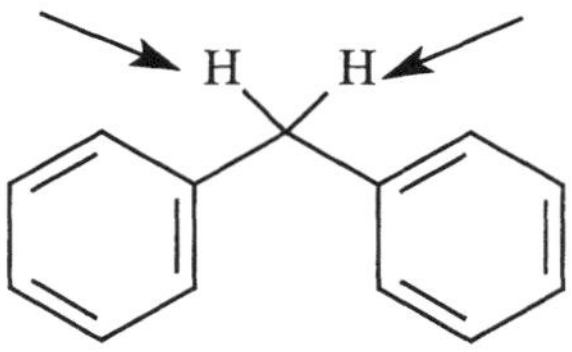

Answer: homotopic

17.

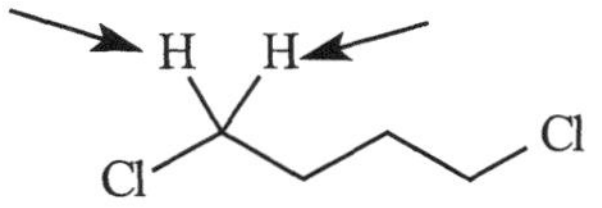

Answer: enantiotopic

18.

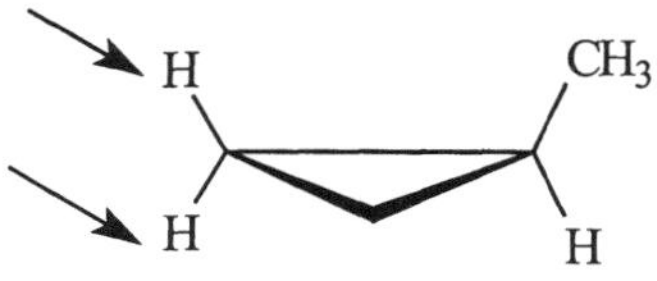

Answer: diastereotopic

19.

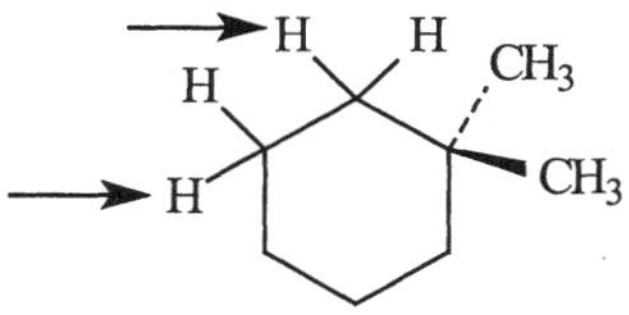

Answer: unrelated

For each compound below tell how many types of nonequivalent protons there are.

20.

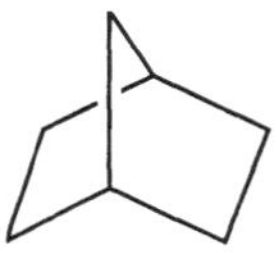

Answer: four

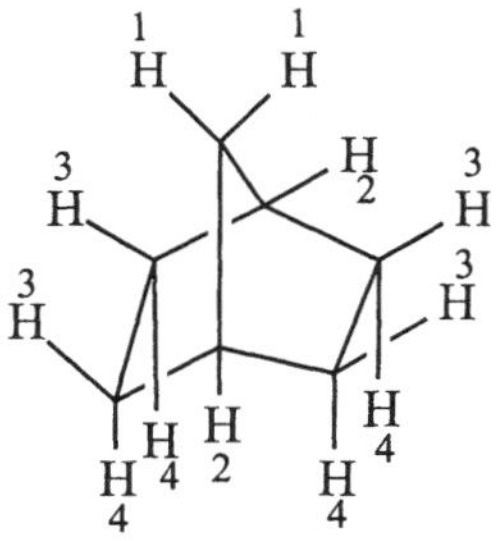

21.

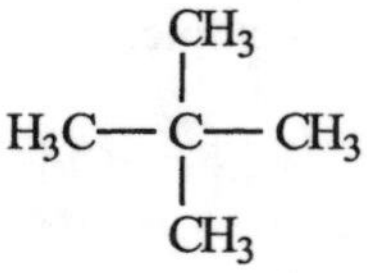

$$H_3C-\overset{\displaystyle CH_3}{\underset{\displaystyle CH_3}{C}}-CH_3$$

Answer: one

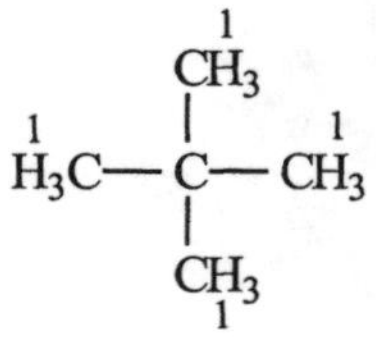

$$\overset{1}{H_3C}-\overset{\displaystyle \overset{1}{CH_3}}{\underset{\displaystyle \underset{1}{CH_3}}{C}}-\overset{1}{CH_3}$$

22.

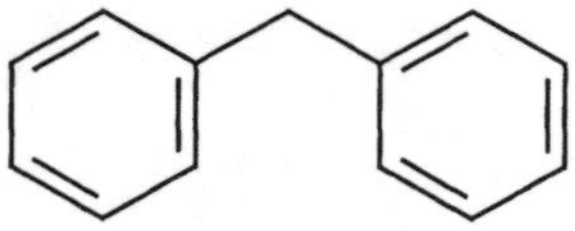

plane of symmetry

Answer: four

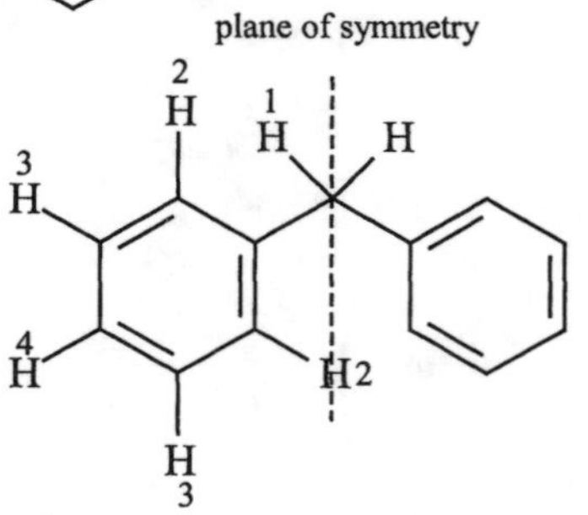

23.

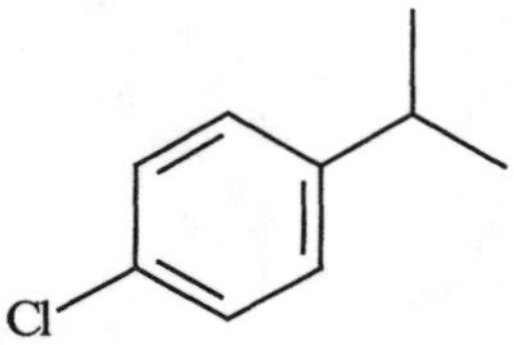

Cl

Answer: four

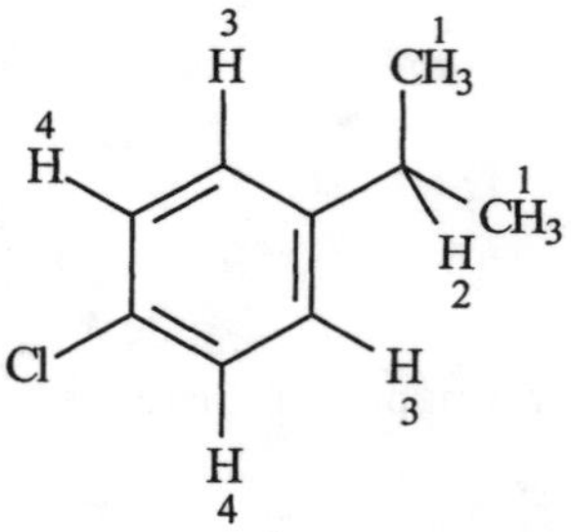

Cl

24.

CH_3 CH_3

plane of symmetry

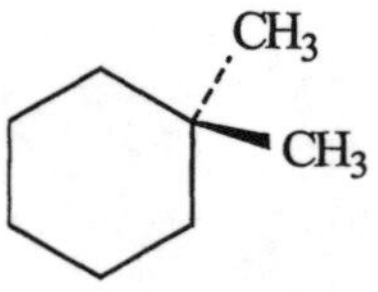

Answer: four

CH_3 CH_3

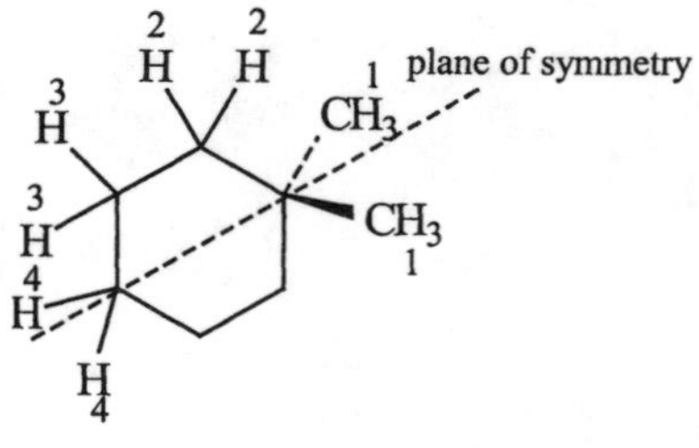

25. 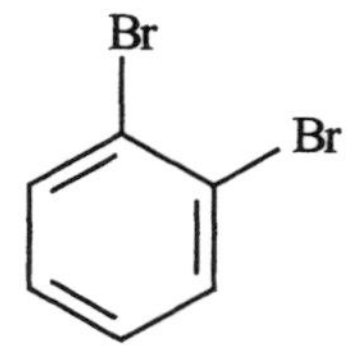 1,2-dibromobenzene structure: Br, Br

Answer: two

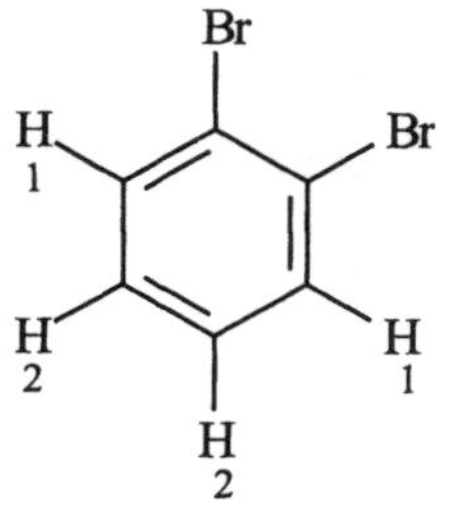

Br, Br, H 1, H 2, H 1, H 2

26. 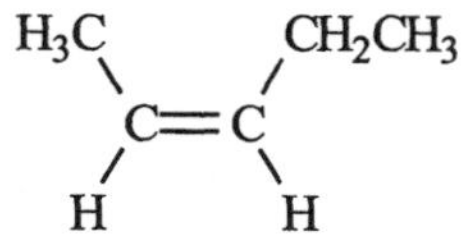 H_3C, CH_2CH_3, C=C, H, H

Answer: five

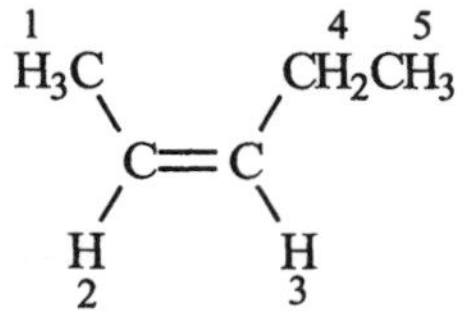

1 H_3C, 4 5 CH_2CH_3, C=C, H 2, H 3

27. 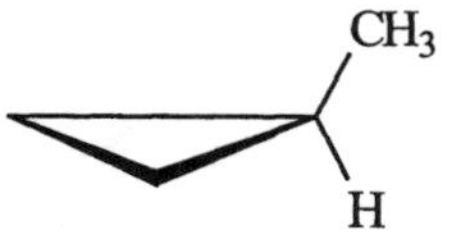 CH_3, H

Answer: four

3 H, 3 H, 1 CH_3, H 4, H 4, H 2

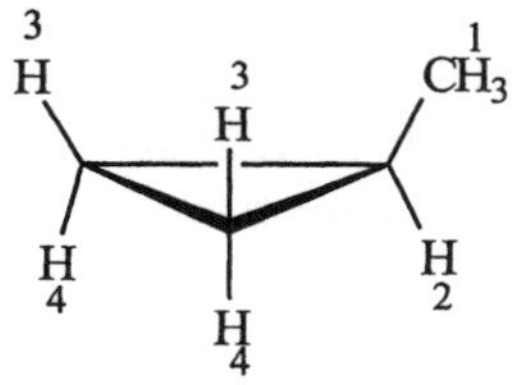

Predict the splitting patterns you would expect for each proton in the molecules below:

28. 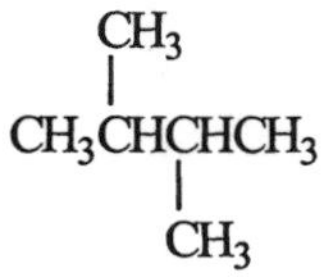 $CH_3CH(CH_3)CH(CH_3)CH_3$

Answer:

1 CH_3, 1 CH_3 2 CH 2 CH 1 CH_3, CH_3 1

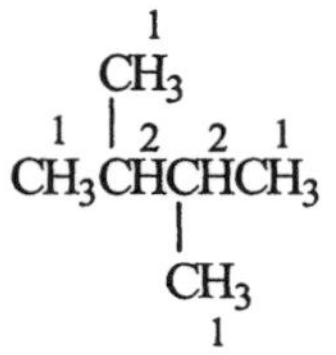

Proton	No. of adjacent Protons	Splitting
1	1	doublet
2	6	septet

29. 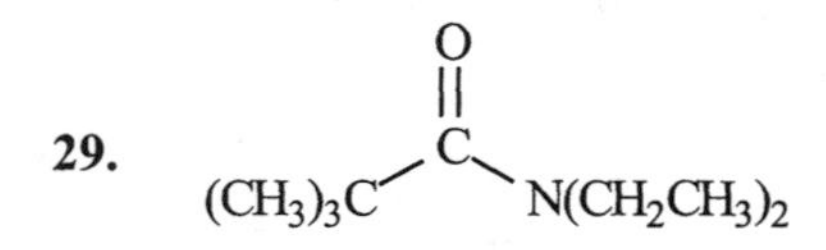

Answer:

$(CH_3)_3C-C(=O)-N(CH_2CH_3)_2$ (1 = $(CH_3)_3C$; 2 = CH_2; 3 = CH_3)

Proton	No. of adjacent Protons	Splitting
1	0	singlet
2	3	quartet
3	2	triplet

30. H(Cl)C=C(H)–C(=O)–CH_3

Answer:

Proton	No. of adjacent Protons	Splitting
1	0	singlet
2	1	doublet
3	1	doublet

31. The ^{1}H NMR spectrum of styrene oxide shows that protons 1, 2, and 3 all have different chemical shift values. Proton 1 is coupled to both proton 2 ($J = 5.8$ Hz) and proton 3 ($J = 2.5$ Hz). Draw a tree diagram for the proton 2 signal.

Answer:

Refer to the structure of 3-methyl-2-butanone below to answer the following questions.

$$\underset{\uparrow c.}{}\quad H_3C\text{—}\overset{O}{\overset{\|}{C}}\text{—}\underset{CH_3}{\underset{|}{\overset{H}{\overset{|}{C}}}}\text{—}CH_3$$

(Arrow a. points to the H_3C on the left; arrow b. points to the CH_3 on the right; arrow c. points to the carbonyl carbon.)

32. What is the splitting pattern for the hydrogens in 3-methyl-2-butanone labeled a.?

a. septet
b. quartet
c. doublet
d. singlet

Answer: d

33. What is the splitting pattern for the hydrogens in 3-methyl-2-butanone labeled b.?

a. septet
b. quartet
c. doublet
d. singlet

Answer: c

34. The carbonyl-carbon resonance of 3-methyl- 2-butanone occurs at 208.7 ppm downfield from TMS. How many hertz downfield from TMS would this carbonyl-carbon absorb is the spectrometer used to measure this absorption were operating at 200 MHz?

Answer:

$$\delta = \frac{\text{observed chemical shift (\# Hz from TMS)}}{\text{spectrometer frequency (in MHz)}}$$

$$208.7\text{ ppm} = \frac{\text{chemical shift}}{200\text{ MHz}};\ 208.7 \times 200\text{ MHz}$$

$$\text{chemical shift} = 4174\text{ Hz}$$

35. Treatment of *tert*-butyl alcohol with hydrogen chloride yields a mixture of *tert*-butyl chloride (S_N1 product) and 2-methylpropene (E1 product). After chromatographic separation, how would you use ^1H NMR to help you decide which was which?

$$(CH_3)_3COH \xrightarrow{HCl} (CH_3)_3CCl + (CH_3)_2C{=}CH_2$$

Answer: 2-Methylpropene has two kinds of hydrogens. It will have a vinylic absorption (4.5–6.5 δ) representing two hydrogens and an unsplit signal (1.0–1.5 δ) due to the six equivalent methyl hydrogens.

tert-Butyl chloride has only one kind of hydrogen, which results in one unsplit signal.

Below are three isomeric chlorobutanes and their ^{13}C NMR spectral data. MATCH the spectral data to the correct structures by placing the letter of the spectrum in the blank to the left of the corresponding structure.

a = δ, 55.4, 36.2, 19.3
b = δ, 56.2, 35.3
c = δ, 56.0, 36.0, 24.2, 8.2

36. ____ $H_3C-C(CH_3)_2-Cl$

Answer: b

37. ____ $H_3C-CH(Cl)-CH_2-CH_3$

Answer: c

38. ____ $H_3C-CH(CH_3)-CH_2-Cl$

Answer: a

Propose structures for compounds that fit the following ^1H NMR data:

39. C_8H_9Br
3H doublet at 2.0 δ, $J = 7$ Hz
1H quartet at 5.0 δ, $J = 7$ Hz
5H singlet at 7.3 δ

Answer: $C_6H_5-CH(Br)-CH_3$

40. $C_7H_{14}O$
6H triplet at 0.9 δ, $J = 7$ Hz
4H sextet at 1.6 δ, $J = 7$ Hz
4H triplet at 2.4 δ, $J = 7$ Hz

Answer: $CH_3CH_2CH_2C(=O)CH_2CH_2CH_3$

41. $C_3H_6Br_2$
2H quintet at 2.4 δ, $J = 6$ Hz
4H triplet at 3.5 δ, $J = 6$ Hz

Answer: $BrCH_2CH_2CH_2Br$

42. $C_{10}H_{14}$

6H doublet at 1.2 δ, $J = 7$ Hz
3H singlet at 2.3 δ
1H septet at 2.9 δ, $J = 7$ Hz
4H singlet at 7.0 δ

Answer:

CH_3
H_3C— (benzene ring) —CH
CH_3

43. C_6H_{14}

12H doublet at 0.8 δ
2H septet at 1.4 δ

Answer:

CH_3
$CH_3CHCHCH_3$
CH_3

To answer the following questions, consider the data and ^1H NMR spectrum below:

The mass spectrum of this compound shows a molecular ion at m/z = 113, the IR spectrum has characteristic absorptions at 2270 and 1735 cm^{-1}, and the ^{13}C NMR spectrum has five signals.

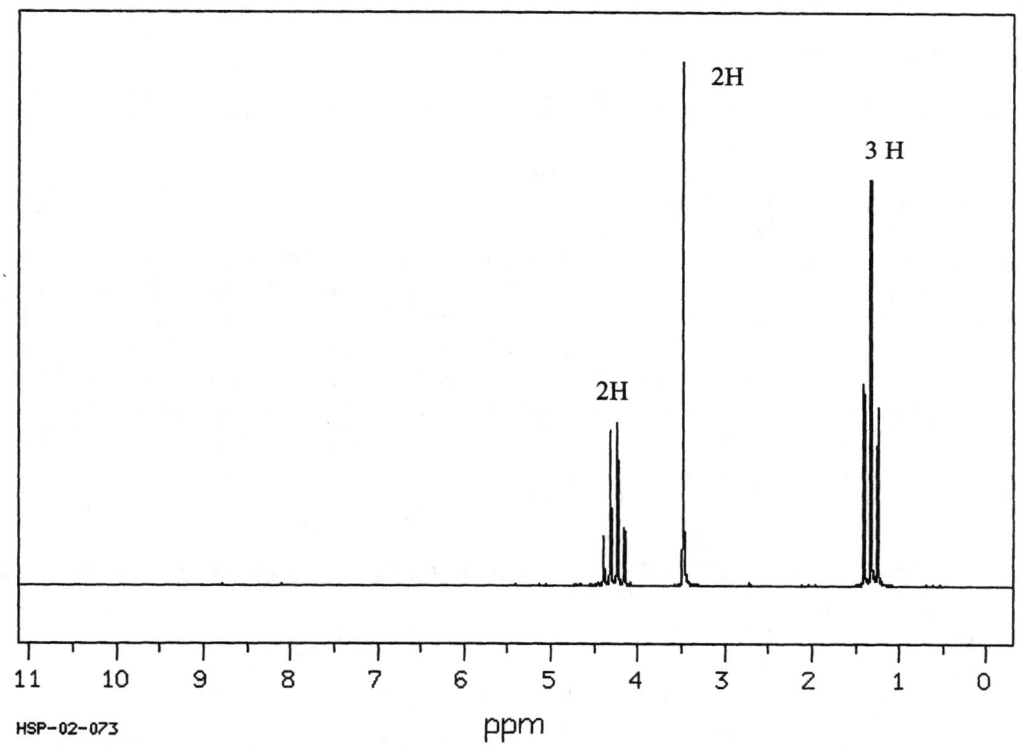

Spectrum obtained from: SDBSWeb: http://www.aist.go.jp/RIODB/SDBS/

44. Based on the mass spectral data and the IR data, what functional groups are present in this compound?

Answer: A molecular ion of mass 113 indicates an odd number of nitrogen atoms in the compound. Coupled with the IR absorption at 2270 cm^{-1}, a nitrile functional group is indicated. The IR absorption at 1735 cm^{-1} indicates a carbonyl group, possibly an ester.

45. How many types of nonequivalent protons are there in this molecule?

Answer: three

46. Describe the signal at 3.5 δ in terms of its integration, splitting pattern and chemical shift.

Answer: The integration of the signal at 3.5 δ indicates that it is due to two equivalent hydrogens, probably a $-CH_2-$ group. Since the signal is a singlet (not split) there are no nonequivalent hydrogens attached to the atoms adjacent to the carbon to which these two hydrogens are bonded. The chemical shift to 3.5 δ indicates that this $-CH_2-$ group has at least one electronegative atom or group bonded to it, possibly a carbonyl group

47. Describe the signals at 4.35 δ and 1.3 δ in terms of their integration, splitting and chemical shift.

Answer: The signal at 4.35 δ is owing to two equivalent hydrogens split by three adjacent hydrogens or a $-CH_2-$ next to a $-CH_3$. It is shifted by attachment to an electronegative atom like oxygen. The signal at 1.3 δ is three equivalent hydrogens split by two adjacent hydrogens of a $-CH_3$ next to a $-CH_2-$. It is shifted slightly downfield by the presence of an electronegative atom bonded to the adjacent $-CH_2-$

48. What is the significance of the ^{13}C NMR data?

Answer: The ^{13}C NMR has five signals, which means that there five differenct kinds of carbon in this compound.

49. Propose a structure for this compound.

Answer: By compiling all the information deduced from the data provided, we note that this compound is a) a nitrile and an ester [two carbons accounted for], and b) has two CH_2 groups and one CH_3 group [three more carbons accounted for]. One of the CH_2 groups is attached to the oxygen of the ester and one is attached to the carbonyl of the ester. The singlet CH_2 is also bonded to the nitrile. Based on the chemical shifts, the singlet CH_2 must be bonded to the carbonyl and the quartet CH_2 must be bonded to the oxygen of the ester. So the compound is ethyl cyanoacetate:

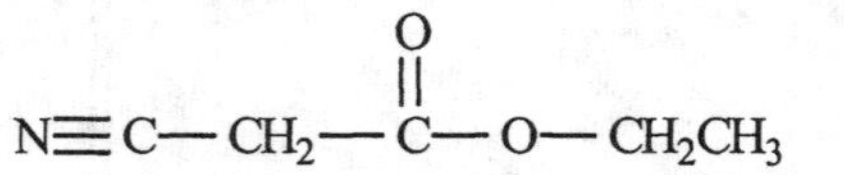

$$N{\equiv}C-CH_2-\overset{\overset{\displaystyle O}{||}}{C}-O-CH_2CH_3$$

50. How would you use ^1H and ^{13}C NMR to help you distinguish between these two isomeric structures?

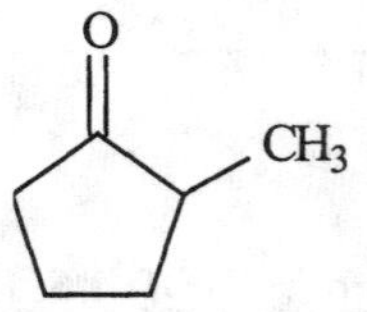

O CH3 and OCH3

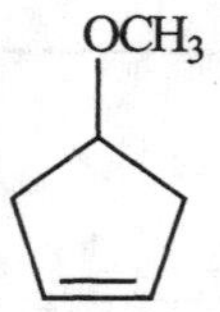

Answer:

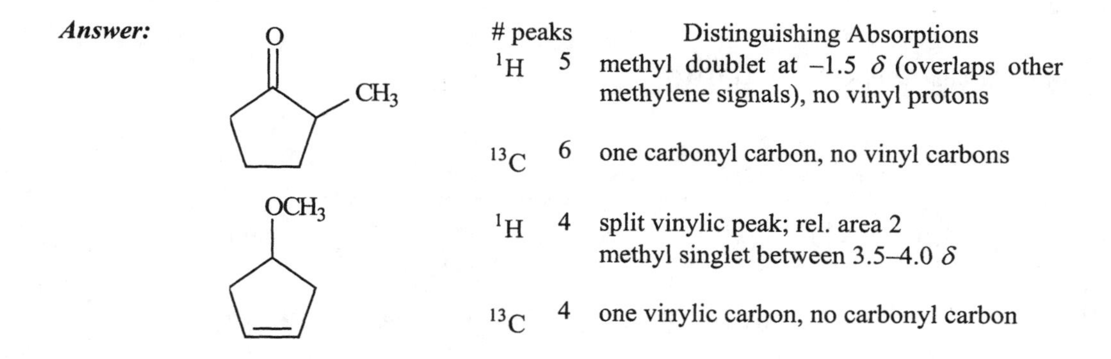

	# peaks	Distinguishing Absorptions
^1H	5	methyl doublet at –1.5 δ (overlaps other methylene signals), no vinyl protons
^{13}C	6	one carbonyl carbon, no vinyl carbons
^1H	4	split vinylic peak; rel. area 2 methyl singlet between 3.5–4.0 δ
^{13}C	4	one vinylic carbon, no carbonyl carbon

Answer the questions for each of the compounds whose ^1H NMR spectra are shown below.

C_4H_8O

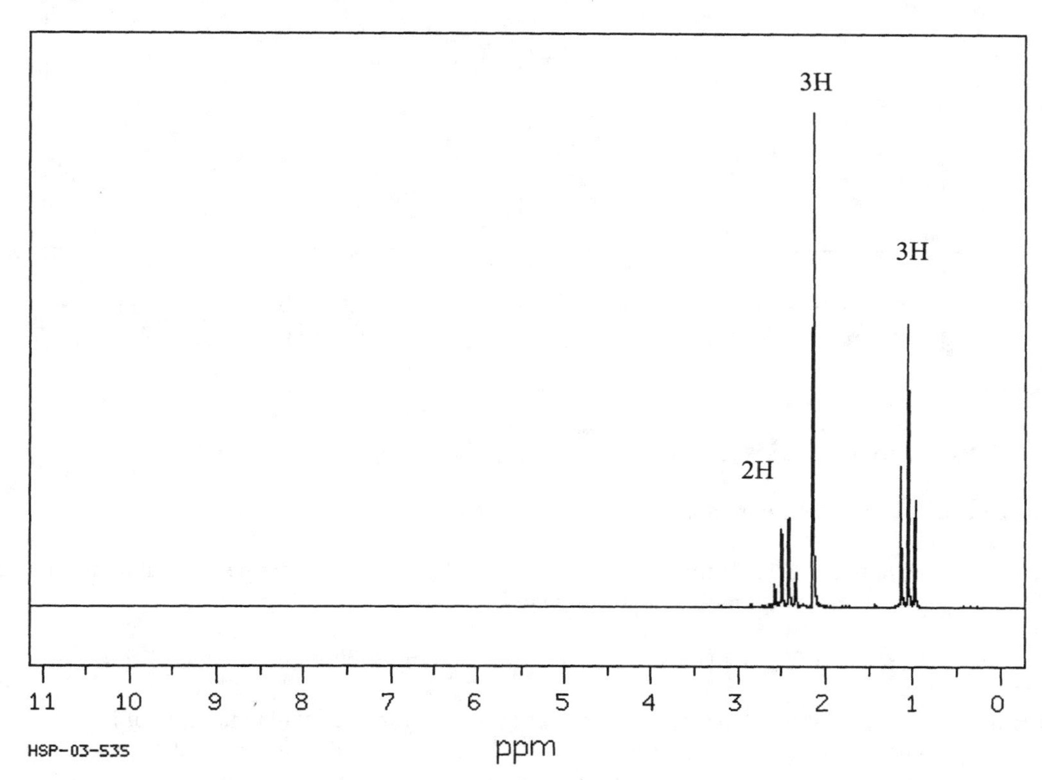

Spectrum obtained from: SDBSWeb: http://www.aist.go.jp/RIODB/SDBS/

51. Describe each signal in terms of its integration, splitting and chemical shift.

Answer: The signals at 1.05 and 2.45 δ are characteristic, in their integration and slitting (a 2H quartet and a 3H triplet), for an ethyl group. The shift of the CH_2 to 2.45 indicates that the ethyl group is attached to a carbonyl group. The signal at 2.1 δ, a 3H singlet, is characteristic for a CH_3 attached to a carbonyl group.

52. Propose a structure for this compound.

Answer: 2-butanone, $CH_3COCH_2CH_3$

$C_5H_{12}O$

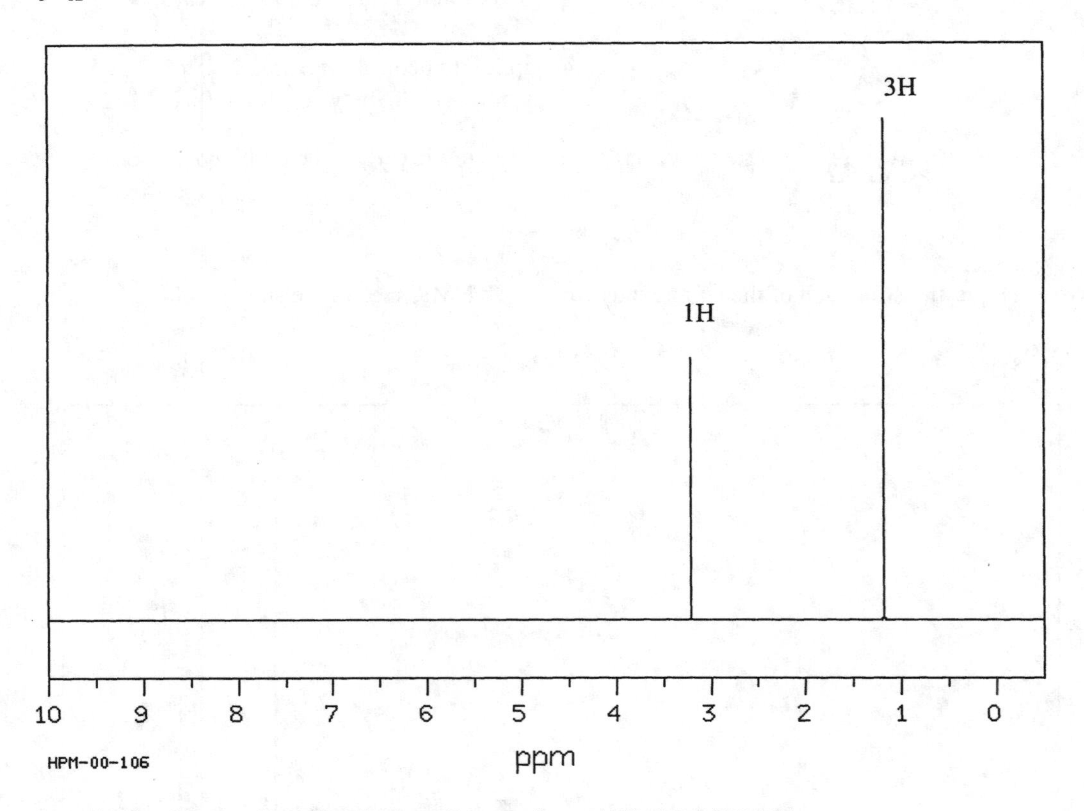

Spectrum obtained from: SDBSWeb: http://www.aist.go.jp/RIODB/SDBS/

53. Calculate the degree of unsaturation for this compound.

Answer: The base formula for this compound is C_5H_{12}, which is corresponds to a saturated compound, so there is no unsaturation in this compound.

54. Describe each signal in the ^{1}H NMR in terms of its integration, splitting and chemical shift.

Answer: In looking at the spectrum, it is important to note that the relative number of hydrogens for each signal adds up to four. The formula of the compound indicates that there are a total of 12 hydrogens. Therefore, the integration of 3:1 corresponds to 9H:3H. The signal at 1.2 δ is a 9H singlet, which is characteristic for a *tert*-butyl group. The slight downfield shifts indicates that this group is attached to an electronegative atom, in this case, oxygen. The signal at 3.2 δ is a 3H singlet which is characteristic of a methyl group bonded to an oxygen.

55. Propose a structure for this compound.

Answer: *tert*-butyl methyl ether, $(CH_3)_3COCH_3$

C_8H_7ClO

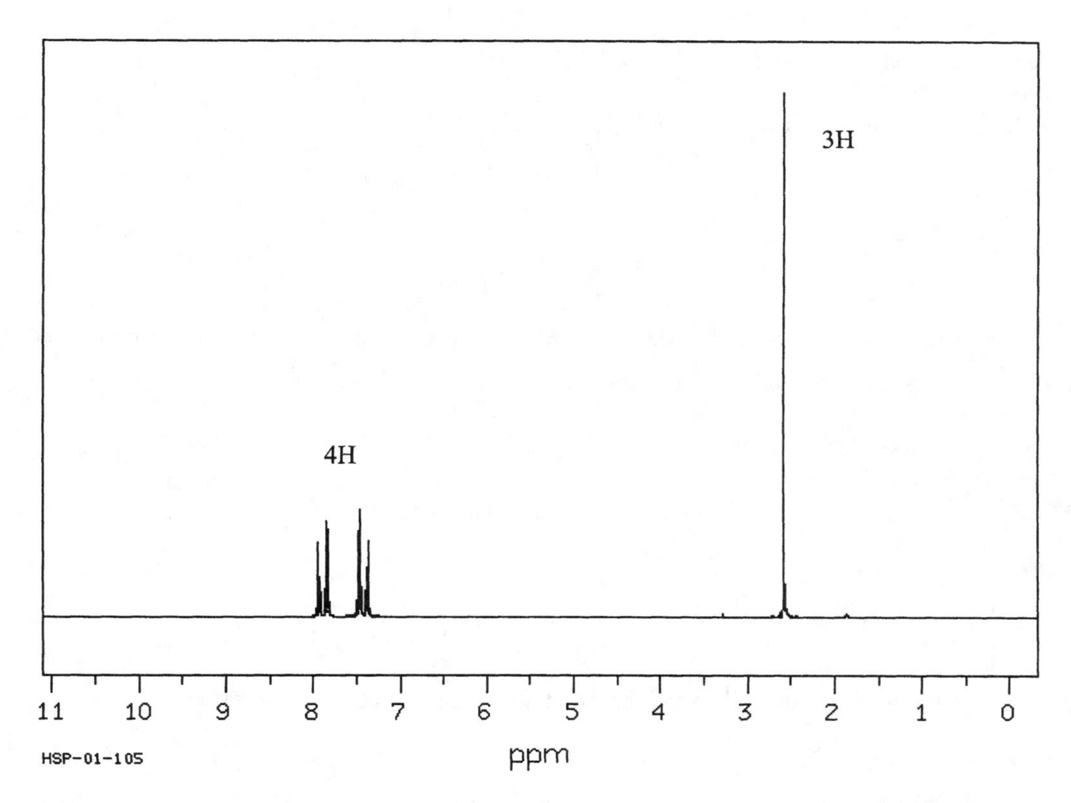

Spectrum obtained from: SDBSWeb: http://www.aist.go.jp/RIODB/SDBS/

56. Calculate the degree of unsaturation in this compound.

> ***Answer:*** The base formula for this compound is C_8H_8; the saturated formula is C_8H_{18}; the degree of unsaturation is five [(18 - 8) ÷ 2].

57. Describe the signals that occur between 7 and 8 δ in terms of integration, splitting and chemical shift.

> ***Answer:*** The chemical shift of the signals between 7 and 8 δ indicates that these hydrogens are aromatic. The integration of four hydrogens and the splitting pattern of two doublets is characteristic of a *para* disubstituted aromatic compound.

58. Describe the signal at 2.6 δ in terms of integration, splitting and chemical shift.

> ***Answer:*** This signal is a 3H singlet shifted by attachment to a carbonyl group; a methyl ketone, probably.

59. Propose a structure for this compound.

> ***Answer:*** 4-chloroacetophenone Cl—C_6H_4—$\overset{O}{\overset{\|}{C}}CH_3$

60. Propose a structure for a compound, $C_6H_{14}O$, with the following ^{13}C NMR spectral data:

Broadband decoupled ^{13}C NMR: 23.0, 68.4 δ
DEPT-90: 68.4 δ
DEPT-135: positive peaks at 23.0, 68.4 δ; no negative peaks

Answer:

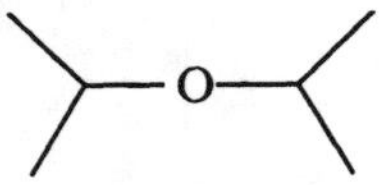

61. Propose a structure for Compound **X**, which has $\mathbf{M}^+ = 120$ and $(M+2) = 122$ of approximately equal intensity in its mass spectrum and has the following ^{13}C NMR spectral data:

Broadband decoupled ^{13}C NMR: 32.6, 118.8, 134.3 δ
DEPT-90: 134.3 δ
DEPT-135: positive peaks at 134.4 δ; negative peaks at 32.6, 118.8 δ

Answer:

Br

62. Propose a structure for Compound **Z**, which has the following spectroscopic properties:

MS: $M^+ = 88$
IR: 3380 cm^{-1}
^1H NMR: 0.85 δ (6H doublet); 1.40 δ (3H multiplier); 2.68 δ (1H singlet); 3.55 δ (2H triplet)

Broadband decoupled ^{13}C NMR: 322.7, 25.0, 41.8, 60.5 δ
DEPT-90: 25.0 δ
DEPT-135: positive peaks at 22.7, 25.0 δ; negative peaks at 41.8, 60.5 δ

Answer: $(CH_3)_2CHCH_2CH_2OH$

63. Describe how you could differentiate the following compounds using a DEPT NMR experiment.

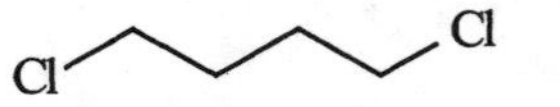

Cl Cl Cl Cl

1,4-dichlorobutane 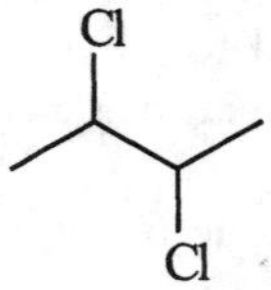 2,3-dichlorobutane

Answer: Both compounds contain two different kinds of carbon, so an ordinary broadband decoupled ^{13}C NMR spectrum of either compound will show two peaks. The DEPT-90 spectrum, however, will show no peaks for 1,4-dichlorobutane while the DEPT-90 sprectrum of 2,3-dichlorobutane will show one peak. The DEPT-135 spectrum for 1,4-dichlorobutane will show two negative peaks, while the DEPT-135 spectrum of 2,3-dichlorobutane will show two positive peaks.

64. Which structure of molecular formula $C_4H_8Cl_2$ fits both the ^{1}H NMR and ^{13}C NMR spectra shown below?

A. Cl Cl

B. Cl Cl

C. Cl Cl

D. Cl Cl

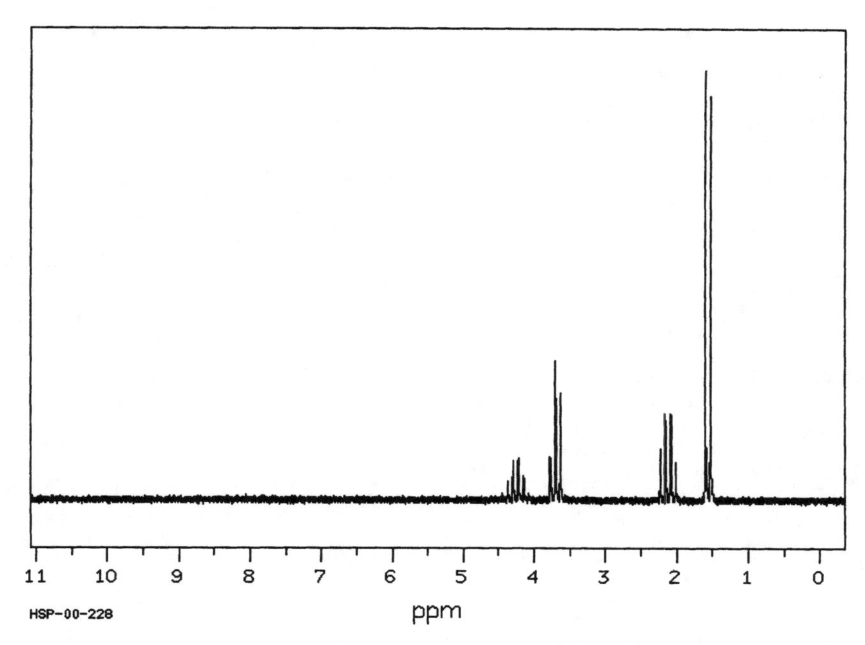

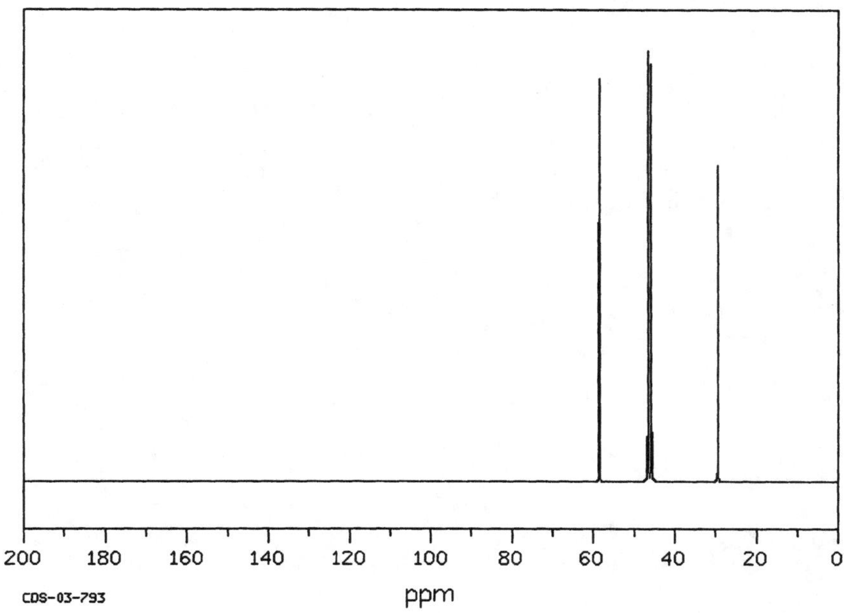

Spectra obtained from: SDBSWeb: http://www.aist.go.jp/RIODB/SDBS/

Answer: B.

Chapter 14 - Conjugated Dienes and Ultraviolet Spectroscopy

Draw structures corresponding to each name below.

1. 2-methyl-1,3-butadiene

Answer:

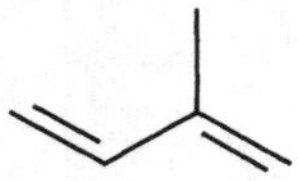

2. (2Z,4Z)-hexadiene

Answer:

Give IUPAC names for the following alkenes:

3.

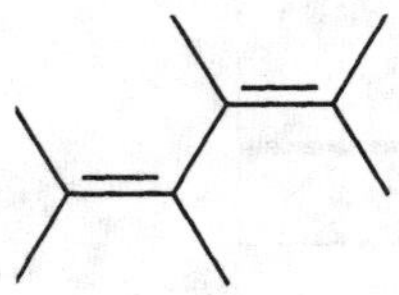

Answer: 2,3,4,5-tetramethyl-2,4-hexadiene

4.

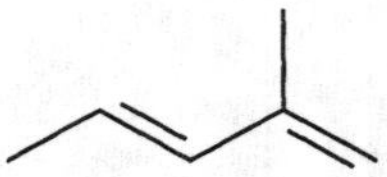

Answer: (3*E*)-2-methyl-1,3-pentadiene

Circle any conjugated portions in the molecules below.

5. O OCH$_3$

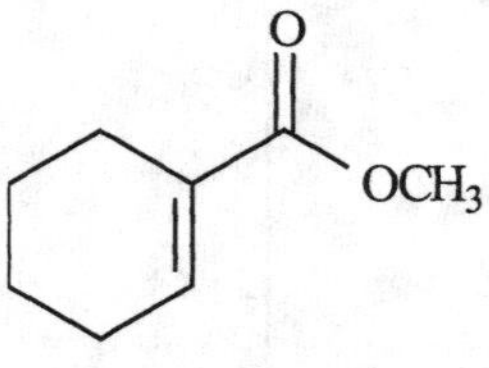

Answer:

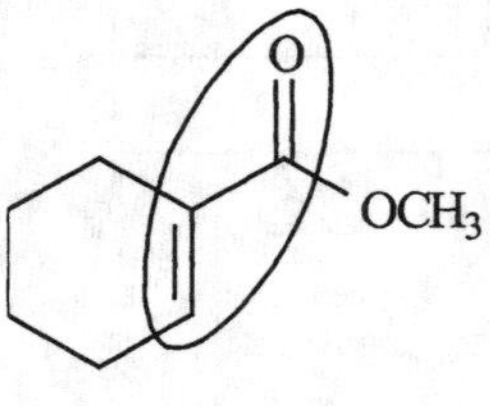

O OCH$_3$

6. O O

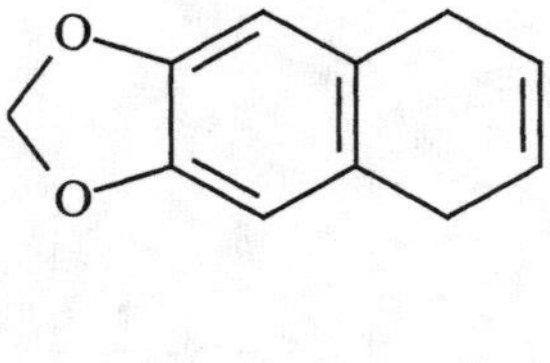

Answer:

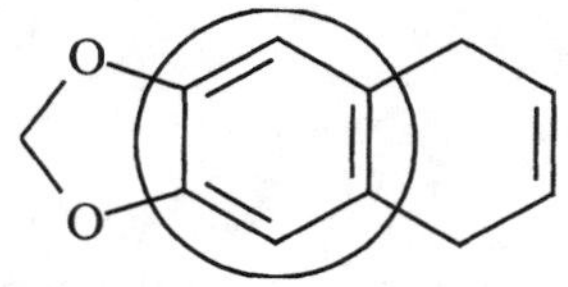

7. $H_2C{=}CH{-}C{\equiv}N$

Answer:

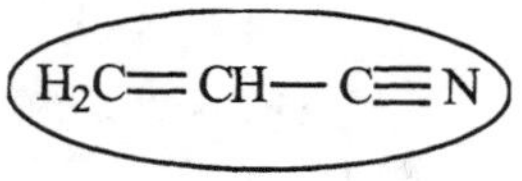

$H_2C{=}CH{-}C{\equiv}N$

8.

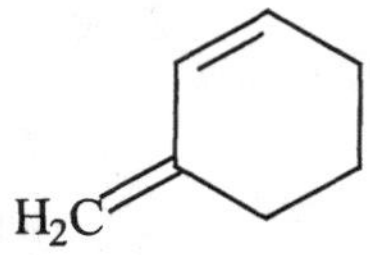

H_2C

Answer:

H_2C

CH_3

C

CH_2

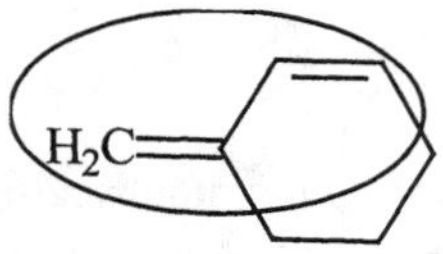

9.

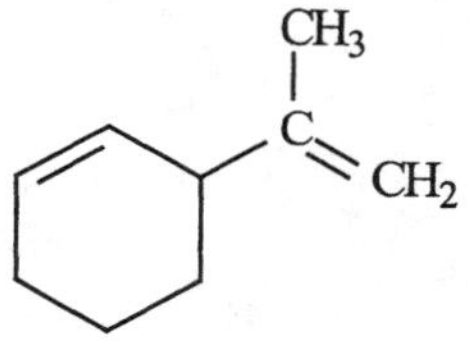

Answer: not conjugated

Consider the reaction below to answer the following questions:

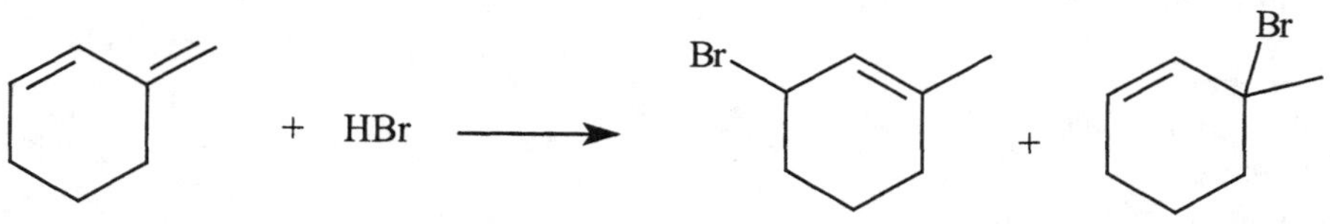

A	+ HBr ⟶ B	Br C	+ Br D

10. The nucleophile in this reaction is ____:

Answer: A

11. The electrophile in this reaction is ____:

Answer: B

12. The kinetically controlled product in this reaction is _____ .

Answer: D

13. The product that results from 1,4-addition is _____ .

Answer: C

14. Write a stepwise mechanism that accounts for both of the products shown. Show all intermediate structures and all electron flow with arrows.

Answer:

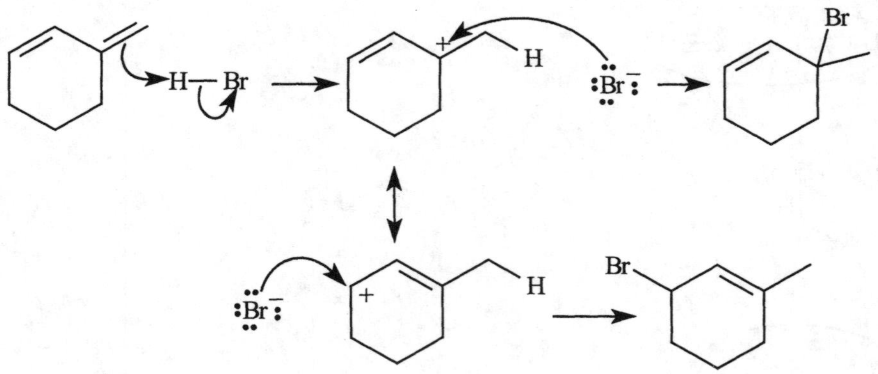

15. This reaction shows the prefered electrophilic addition of HBr to this unsymmetrical alkene. Draw the products of electrophilic addition to the opposite end of the conjugated diene.

Answer:

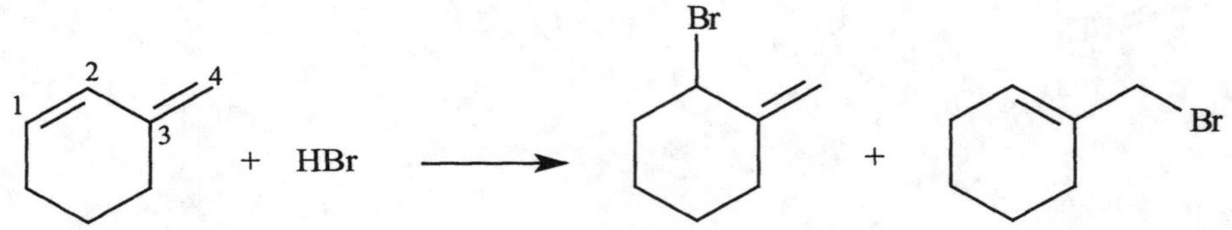

16. Electrophilic addition reaction of conjugated dienes that occur at high temperature and/or long reaction times (reversible conditions) are said to be under:

a. 1,2- control
b. kinetic control
c. 1,4-control
d. thermodynamic control

Answer: d

Consider the data given below to answer the following questions.

Cyclobutadiene is an extremely unstable compound whose isolation is impossible even at the lowest temperatures routinely accessible in the organic laboratory. However, free cyclobutadienes almost surely occur in some reactions as intermediates. We might expect cyclobutadienes to undergo Diels-Alder cycloaddition reactions with itself (dimerization) or with reactive dienophiles. In fact, these extremely facile Diels-Alder reactions have been used to recognize intermediate cyclobutadiene. Write the structures of the Diels-Alder products you would expect to isolate from each of the following reactions.

17.

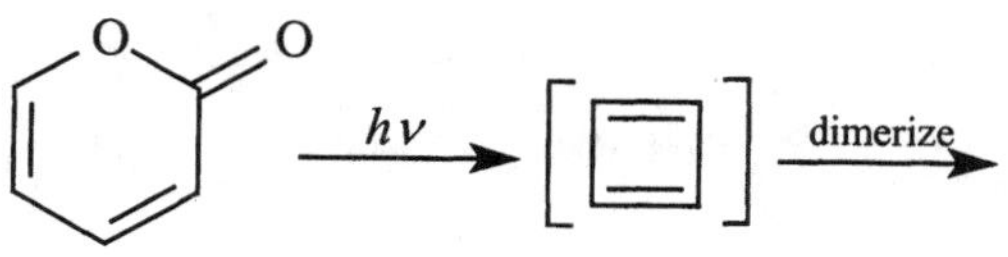

hν → [ ] → dimerize →

Answer:

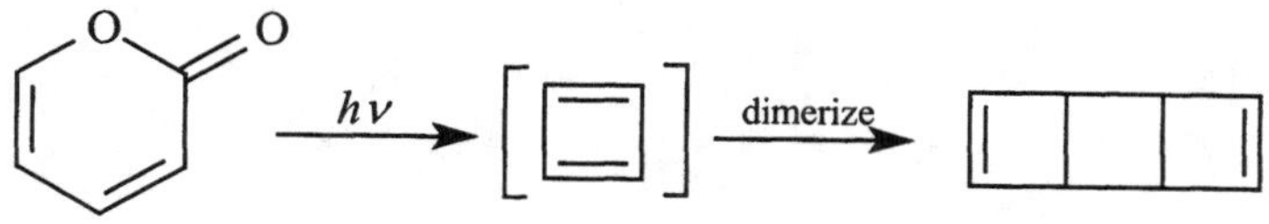

hν → [ ] → dimerize →

18.

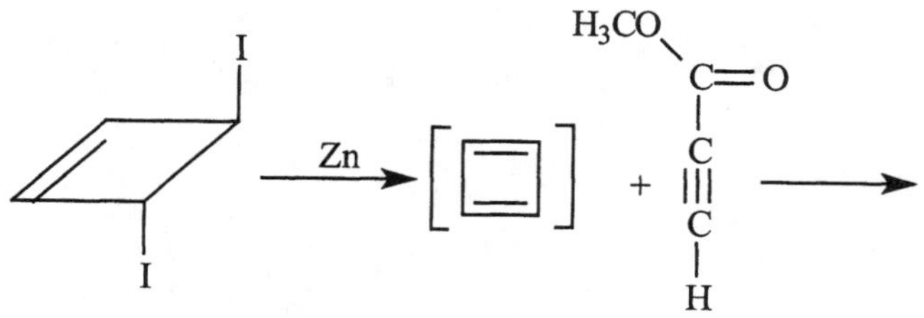

Zn → [ ] + H_3CO–C(=O)–C≡C–H →

Answer:

Zn → [ ] + H_3CO–C(=O)–C≡C–H → C(=O)–OCH_3

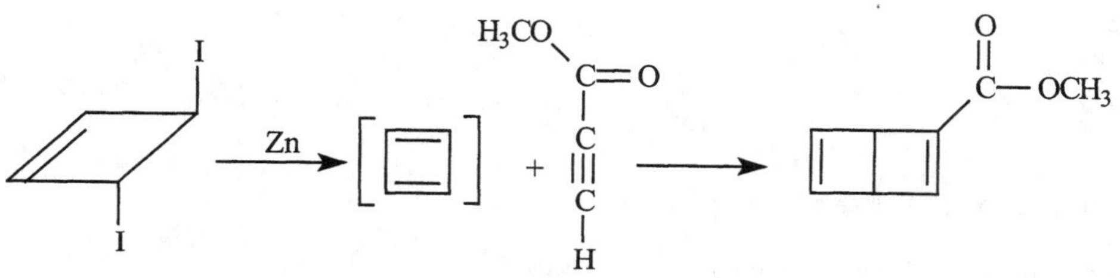

The following molecules may be prepared using the Diels-Alder reactions. Write the structures of the starting diene and dienophile necessary to prepare each molecule and label them.

19.

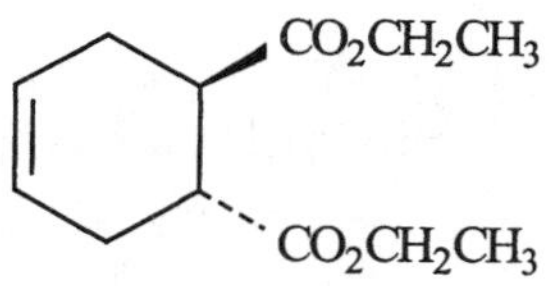

$CO_2CH_2CH_3$

$CO_2CH_2CH_3$

Answer:

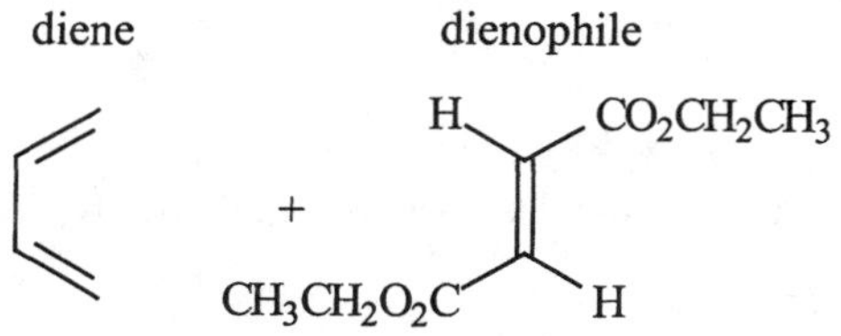

diene dienophile

H $CO_2CH_2CH_3$

\+

$CH_3CH_2O_2C$ H

20.

H_3C O C CH_3

H_3C

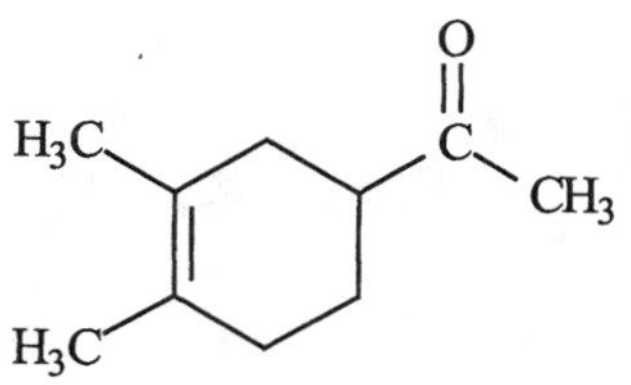

Answer:

diene dienophile

21.

Answer:

diene dienophile

22. For a diene to undergo a Diels-Alder reaction it must:

a. be substituted with electron-withdrawing groups
b. be able to adopt and s-trans conformation
c. be substituted with electron-donating groups
d. be able to adopt an s-cis conformation

Answer: d

23. For Diels-Alder cycloaddition reactions to take place most rapidly and in highest yield the dienophile must:

a. be substituted with electron-withdrawing groups
b. be able to adopt and s-trans conformation
c. be substituted with electron-donating groups
d. be able to adopt an s-cis conformation

Answer: a

24. Which of the following compounds will react as a diene in a Diels-Alder reaction?

a. 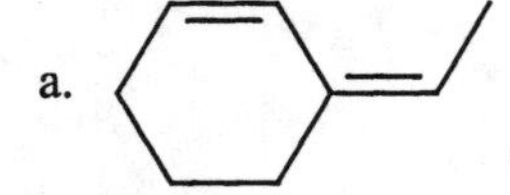

b. 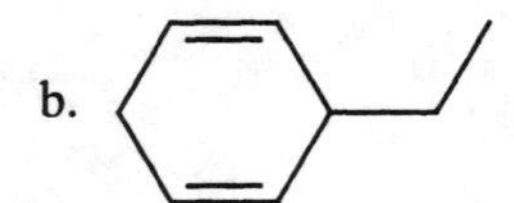

c. 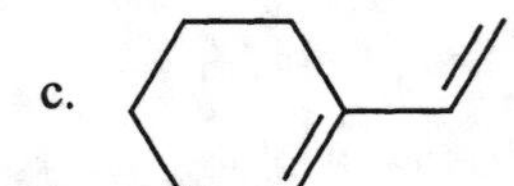

d. 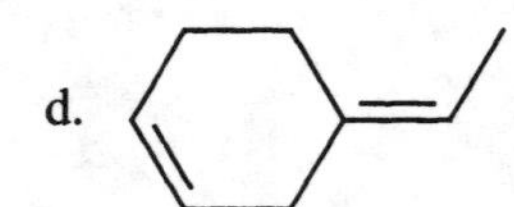

Answer: c

Write the structure(s) of the product(s) for each of the reactions below. Be sure to indicate any relevant stereochemistry.

25. 1. NBS, CCl_4; 2. $KOC(CH_3)_3$, $HOC(CH_3)_3$

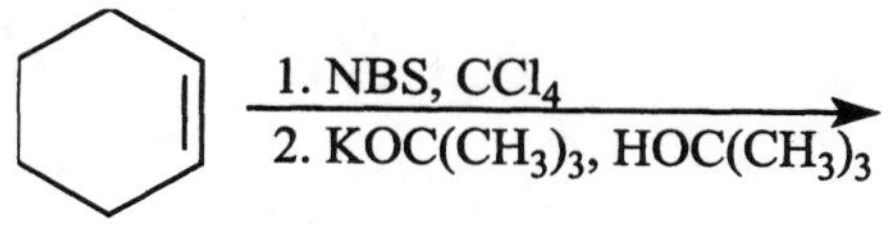

Answer:

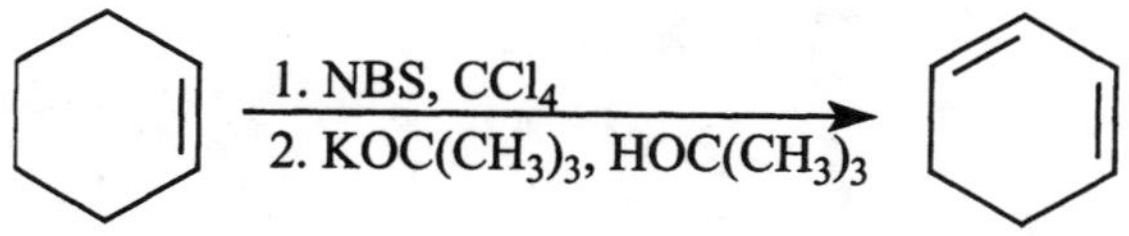

1. NBS, CCl_4; 2. $KOC(CH_3)_3$, $HOC(CH_3)_3$

26. HBr, ether

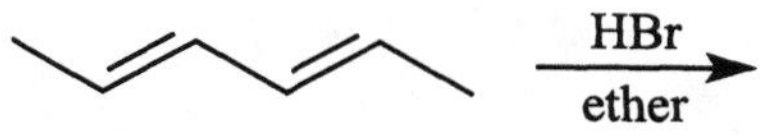

Answer:

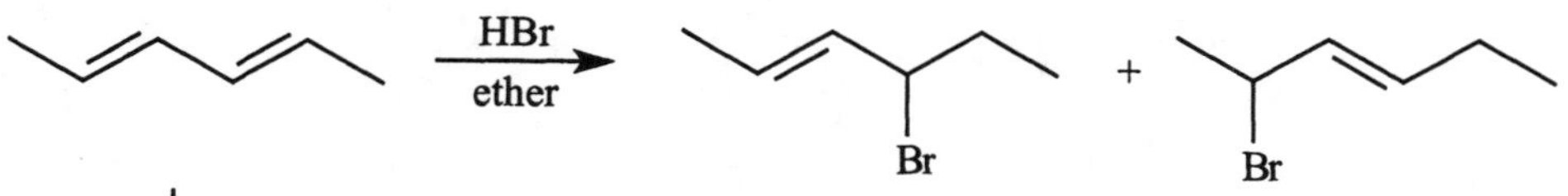

HBr, ether

Br + Br

27. H_2O, H_2SO_4

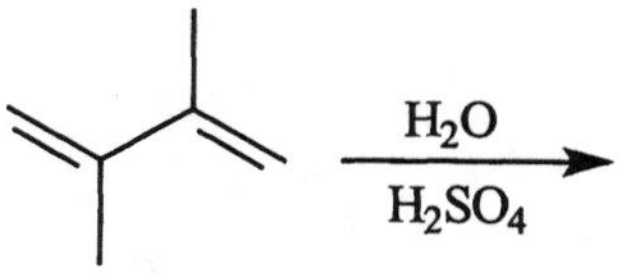

Answer:

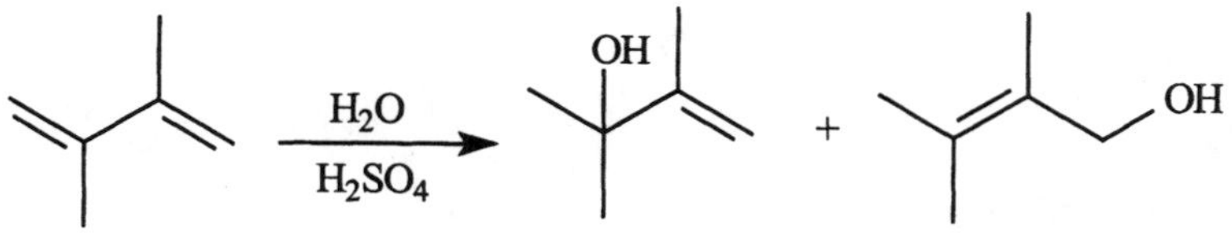

H_2O, H_2SO_4

OH + OH

28. DCl, ether

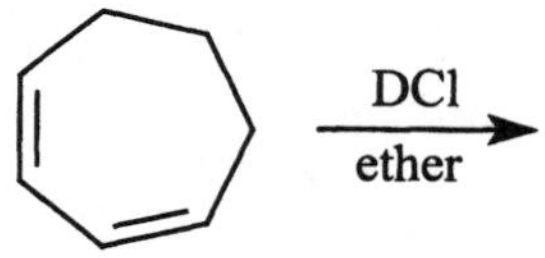

Answer:

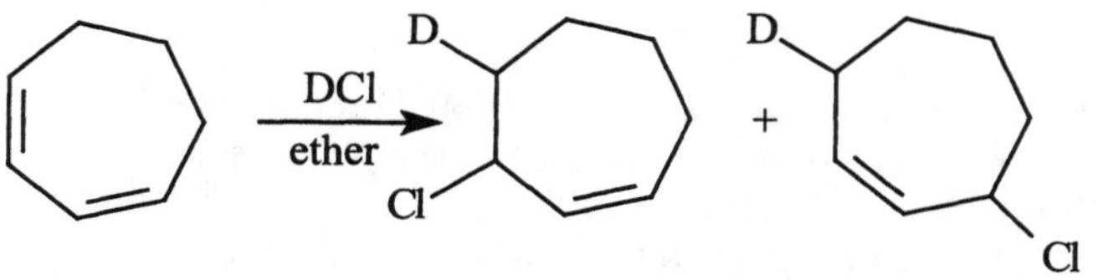

DCl, ether

D, Cl + D, Cl

29.

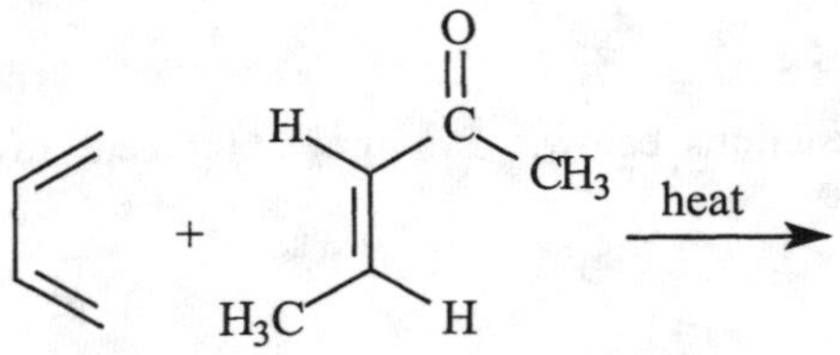

O C CH$_3$ H + H$_3$C H heat

Answer:

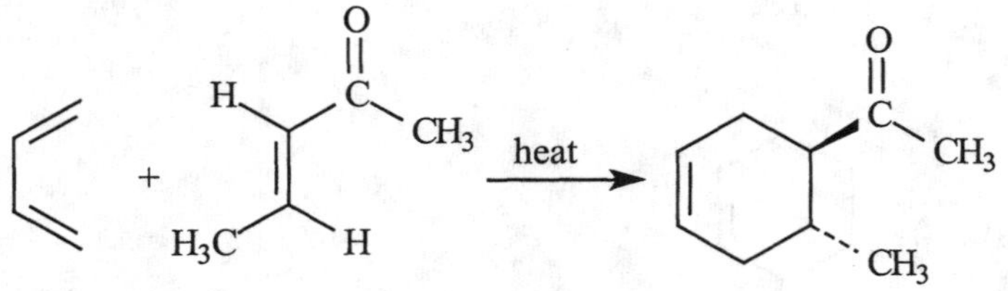

O C CH$_3$ H + H$_3$C H heat O C CH$_3$ CH$_3$

30. 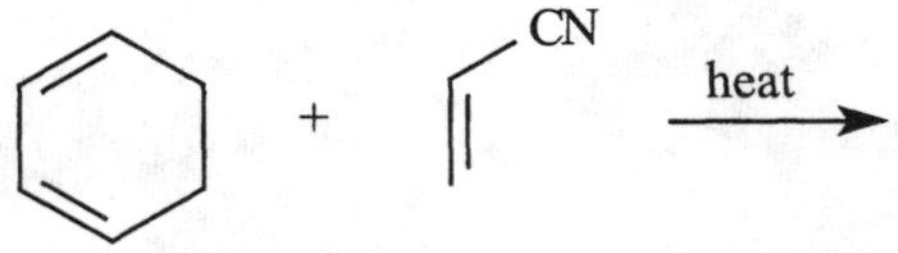 + CN heat

Answer:

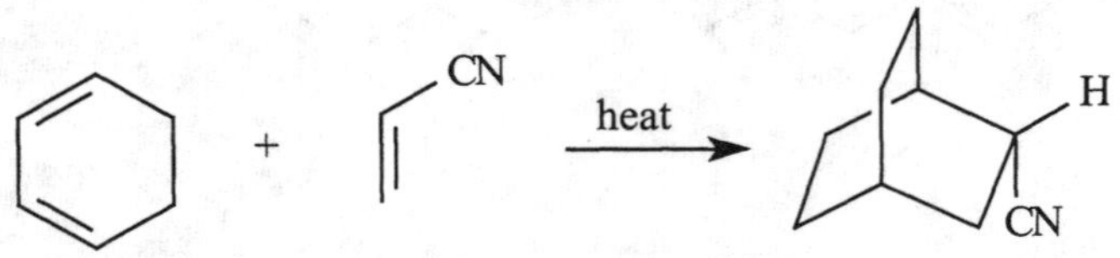

+ CN heat H CN

31. 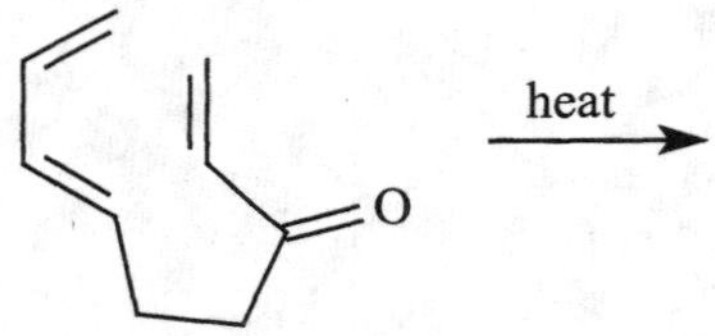 O heat

Answer:

O heat O

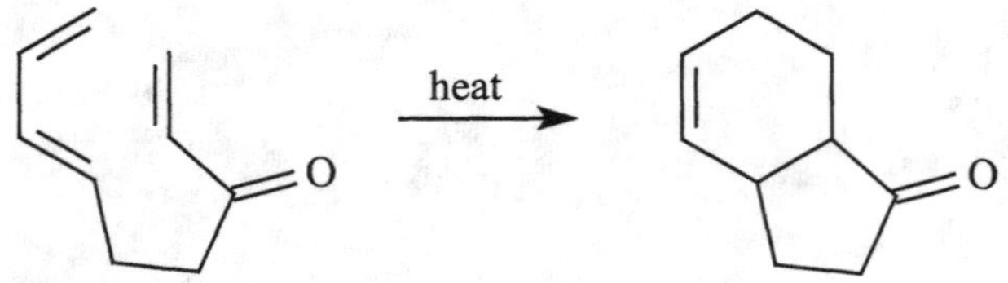

32. When an organic molecule is irradiated with ultraviolet radiation, the energy absorbed by the molecule corresponds to:

a. the amount necessary to increase molecular motions in functional groups
b. the amount necessary to excite electrons from one molecular orbital to another
c. the amount necessary to "flip" the spin of atomic nuclei
d. the amount necessary to strip a molecule of one electron to generate a radical cation

Answer: b

33. A physical constant that is the quantitative measure of the amount of UV light abosrbed by a compound.

a. absorbance
b. molar absorptivity
c. λ_{max}
d. π^*

Answer: b

34. The amount of energy in electromagnetic raditation is related to the frequency and wavelength of the radiation. High energy radiation like gamma rays is of:

a. low frequency and short wavelength
b. low frequency and long wavelength
c. high frequency and short wavelength
d. high frequency and long wavelength

Answer: c

35. Which of the following compounds would show the longest wavelength λ_{max} in its UV spectrum?

a.

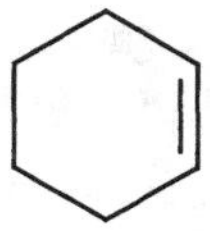

b.

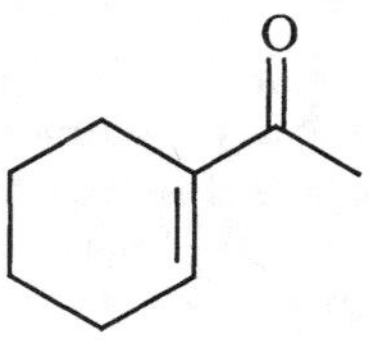

c.

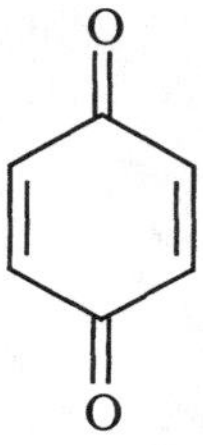

d.

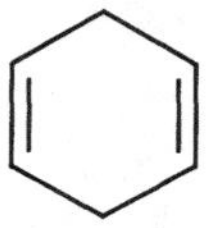

Answer: c

Indicate which spectral technique, NMR, IR, UV or MS, would most readily allow differentiation between compounds in each pair of compounds below. Explain your answer in each case.

36. 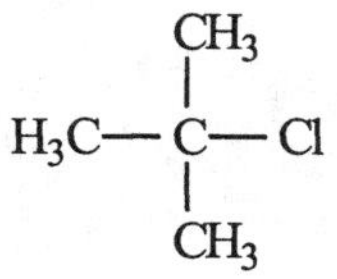 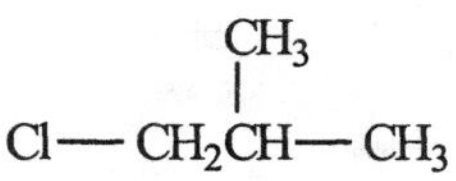 $H_3C-C(CH_3)_2-Cl$ $\qquad$ $Cl-CH_2CH(CH_3)-CH_3$

Answer: NMR; these isomers have the same molecular weight and will show no strong IR and no UV absorptions. The compound on the left will have a single peak in its ^1H NMR spectrum while the compound on the right will have three multiplets.

37. 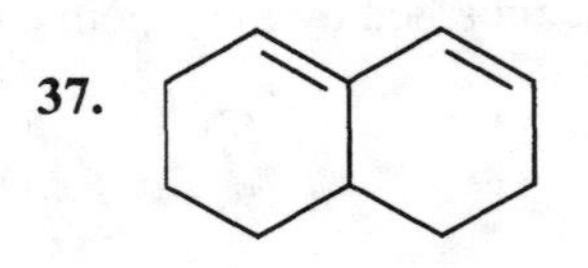 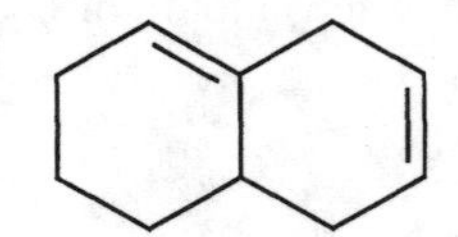

Answer: UV; these compounds will have similar NMR, IR and mass spectra. The UV spectra will be significantly different since the compound on the left is conjugated.

38. 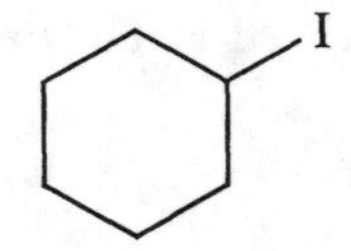

Answer: MS; these compounds have different molecular weights but similar NMR, IR and UV spectra.

39. 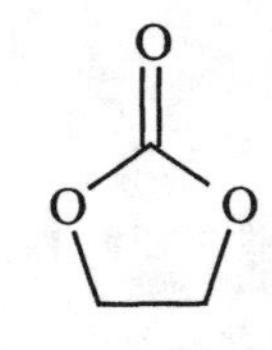

Answer: IR; these compounds have same MW, similar NMR (one singlet) and no strong UV. The compound on the right will have a strong carbonyl absorption in its IR spectrum which the other compound will not.

40. In 1839 Charles Goodyear discovered a process by which both natural and synthetic rubbers are hardened. This process is called:

a. diazotization
b. vulcanization
c. polymerization
d. condensation

Answer: b

41. 2-Chloro-1,3-butadiene is polymerized to yield an excellent, expensive synthetic rubber with good weather resistance called:

a. chloroprene
b. isoprene
c. styrene
d. neoprene

Answer: d

Consider the reaction below to answer the following questions.

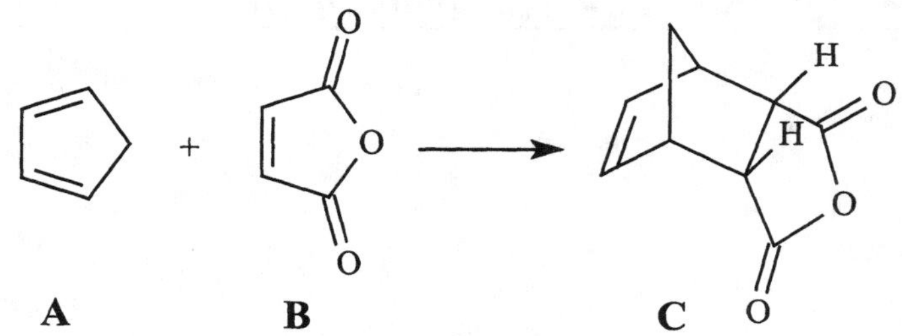

A B C

42. This is an example of a ____________ reaction.

a. Woodward-Hoffman
b. conjugate addition
c. Diels-Alder
d. electrophilic addition

Answer: c

43. The dienophile in the reaction is ____ .

Answer: B

44. The diene in the reaction is ____.

Answer: A

Chapter 15 – Benzene and Aromaticity

1. *m*-fluoronitrobenzene

Answer:

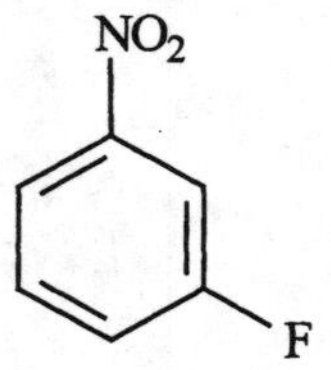

2. *p*-bromoaniline

Answer:

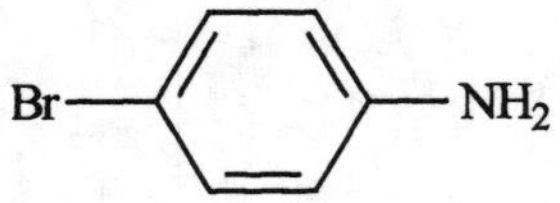

3. *o*-chlorophenol

Answer:

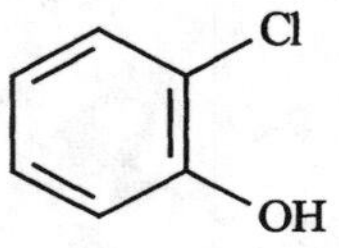

4. 3,5-dimethylbenzoic acid

Answer:

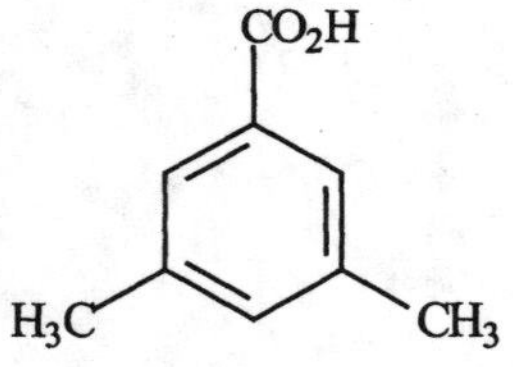

5. *p*-chlorobenzaldehyde

Answer:

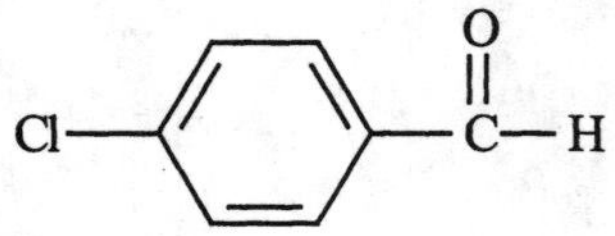

6. 1-phenyl-3-methylpentane

Answer:

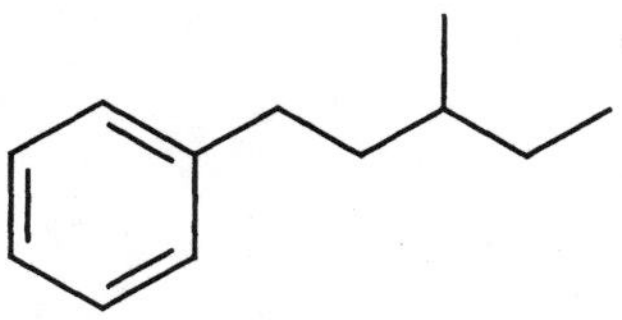

Provide correct IUPAC names for each of the following compounds.

NO_2

7.

CH_3

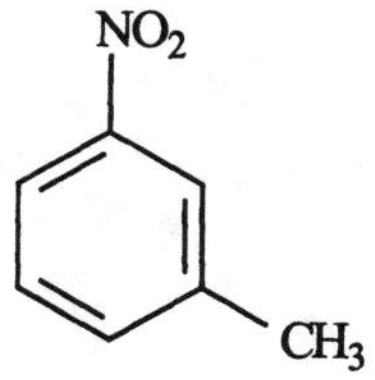

Answer: *m*-nitrotoluene or 1-methyl-3-nitrobenzene

8.

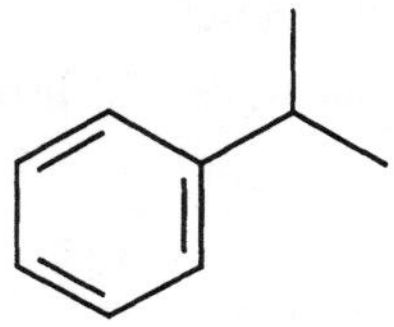

Answer: (1-methylethyl) benzene or isopropylbenzene or cumene

CH_3

9.

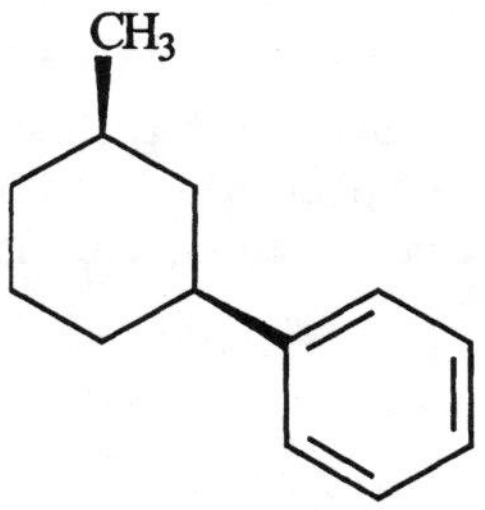

Answer: *cis*-1-methyl-3-phenylcyclohexane

NH_2

10. H_2N— —CH_3

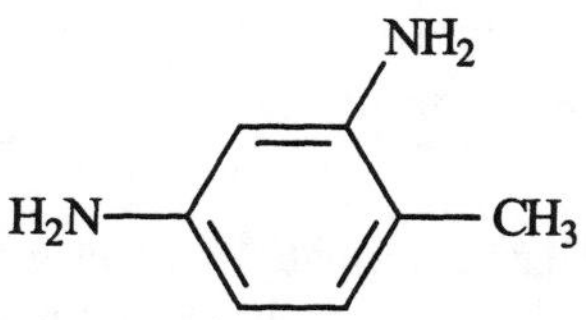

Answer: 1-methyl-2,4-benzenediamine or 2,4-diaminotoluene

11. 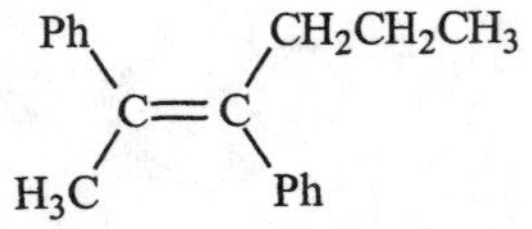 (structure: Ph and H_3C on one carbon, $CH_2CH_2CH_3$ and Ph on the other, C=C)

Answer: (*E*)-2,3-diphenyl-2-hexene

For each molecule below, predict whether the molecule would be expected to show aromatic character or not. Explain your answer in each case.

12.

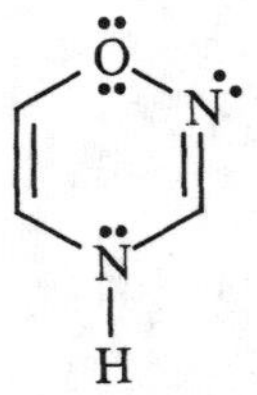

Answer: To meet the criterion of a cyclic, planar, conjugated molecule, the oxygen and the nitrogen bearing the hydrogen must both be sp^2-hybridized. If this occurs, both heteroatoms contribute two electrons each to the pi system. This results in a total of eight pi electrons, which is not aromatic according to the Hückel $(4n+2)$ Rule.

13.

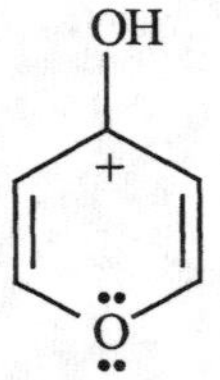

Answer: The carbocation is sp^2-hybridized, so if the oxygen is also sp^2-hybridized then each atom in the cycle has a conjugated *p*-orbital. Each double bond contributes two pi electrons and the oxygen contributes two pi electrons, for a total of six pi electrons in the conjugated system. Therefore, this species is predicted to show aromatic character.

14.

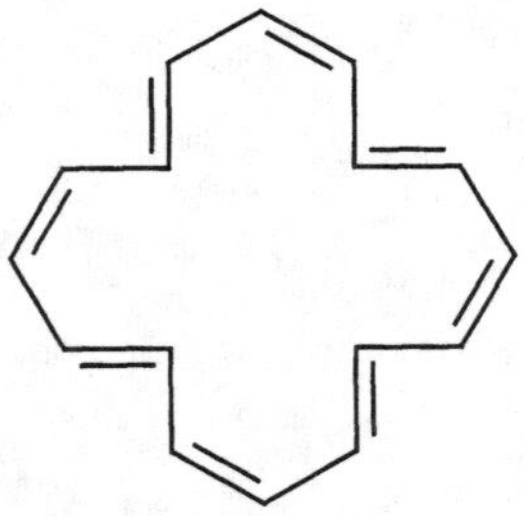

Answer: This compound, [16]annulene, appears to be a cyclic, planar, conjugated molecule with 16 pi electrons. However, 16 is not a Hückel number, so the compound is probably not planar, and is not aromatic.

15.

Answer: This compound has a pyridine-type nitrogen, which is sp^2- hybridized and has its lone pair of electrons in the plane of the ring. If oxygen is also sp^2- hybridized, then it contribute two pi electrons to the cyclic, conjugated pi system for a total of six pi electrons. Therefore, this molecule is predicted to show aromatic character.

Answer the following questions concerning sulfathiazole, below.

sulfathiazole

16. What is the hybridization of the nitrogen atom is sulfathiazole?

Answer: The hybridization of the nitrogen atom is sp^2 in sulfathiazole.

17. Assuming that the sulfur atom is sp^2-hybridized, how many π-electrons are there in the sulfathiazole ring?

Answer: There are six π-electrons in the sulfathiazole ring.

18. What reactivity do you predict for sulfathiazole?

Answer: Sulfathiazole is predicted to have aromatic reactivity since it is cyclic, planar, conjugated and has six π-electrons.

Refer to the data below to answer the following questions.

The ^1H NMR spectrum of [14]annulene at –60°C shows two signals, one at 0 ppm and one at 7.6 ppm, with an area ratio of 5:2.

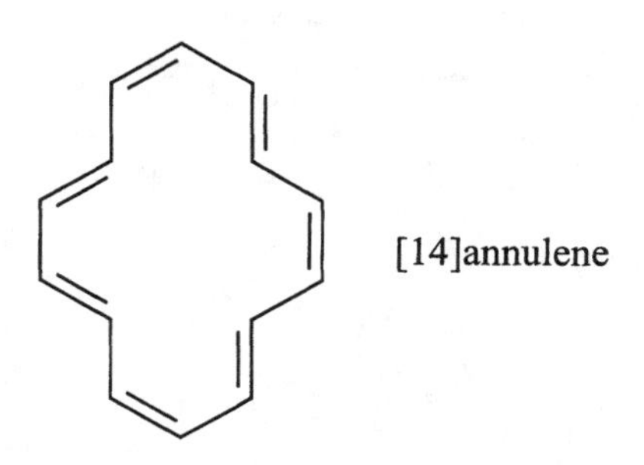

[14]annulene

19. Is [14]annulene aromatic?

Answer: [14]annulene contains a cyclic, conjugated pi system with 14 pi electrons ($14 = 4n + 2$; $n = 3$). It is difficult to predict, however, if the molecule is planar without making a model. The ^1H NMR signal at 7.6 ppm is consistent with the presence of a ring current, which is characteristic of aromatic molecules. Thus, [14]annulene is aromatic.

20. Draw in the protons on the [14]annulene skeleton provided below which are responsible for the ^{1}H NMR signal at 0 ppm.

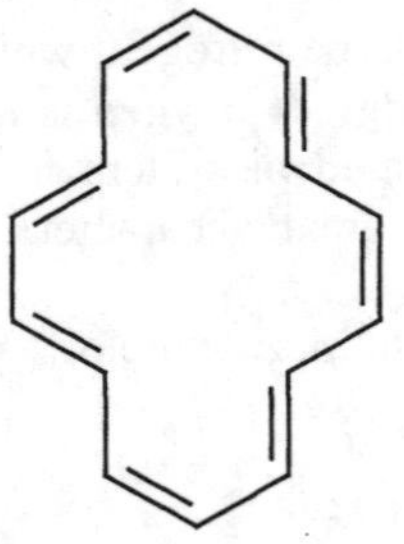

Answer:

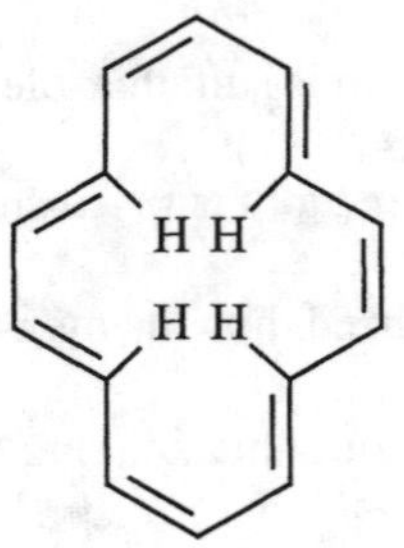

H H
H H

21. Explain why these protons have such absorb at such high field.

Answer: When an aromatic ring is oriented perpendicularly to a strong magnetic field the induced ring current deshields protons outside the ring and shields protons inside the ring. Thus, the protons inside the ring absorb at a field higher than normal (0 ppm versus 4.5–6.5 ppm).

Consider the data below to answer the following questions.

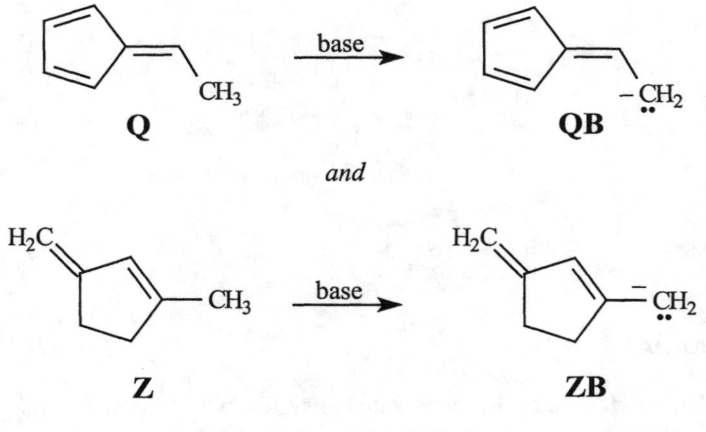

Q (CH_3) —base→ **QB** ($^{-}\ddot{C}H_2$)

and

Z (H_2C, CH_3) —base→ **ZB** (H_2C, $^{-}\ddot{C}H_2$)

22. Conjugate bases **QB** and **ZB** are both resonance stabilized. Draw the indicated number of resonance forms for **QB** and **ZB**.

$-\ddot{C}H_2$ ↔ ↔ ↔

QB

H_2C $\ddot{C}H_2^-$ ⟷ ⟷

ZB

Answer:

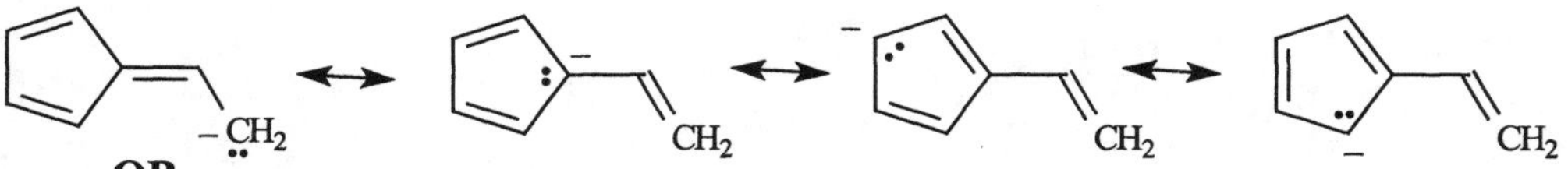

$-\ddot{C}H_2$ ↔ CH_2 ↔ CH_2 ↔ CH_2

QB

H_2C $\ddot{C}H_2^-$ ⟷ H_2C CH_2 ⟷ $H_2\ddot{C}^-$ CH_2

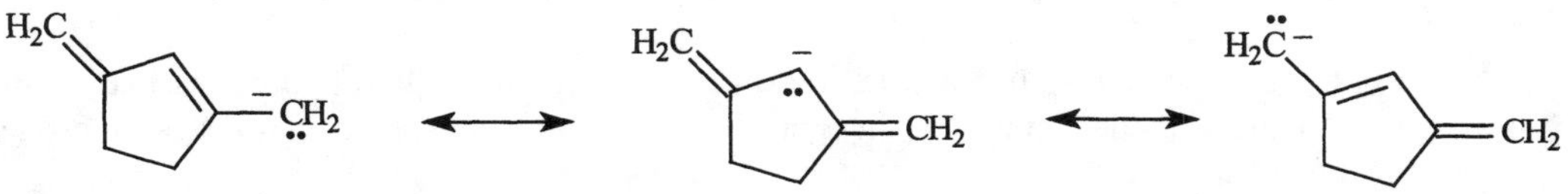

ZB

23. Which of the compounds above, **Q** or **Z**, would you predict to be *most acidic*? Explain your answer.

Answer: The conjugate bases of Compounds **Q** and **Z** are both resonance stabilized. Let's examine all resonance structures for both conjugate bases:

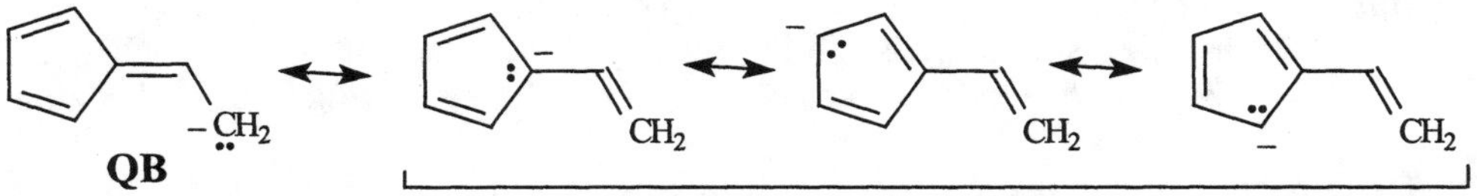

$-\ddot{C}H_2$ ↔ CH_2 ↔ CH_2 ↔ CH_2

QB

aromatic ions

H_2C $\ddot{C}H_2^-$ ⟷ H_2C CH_2 ⟷ $H_2\ddot{C}^-$ CH_2

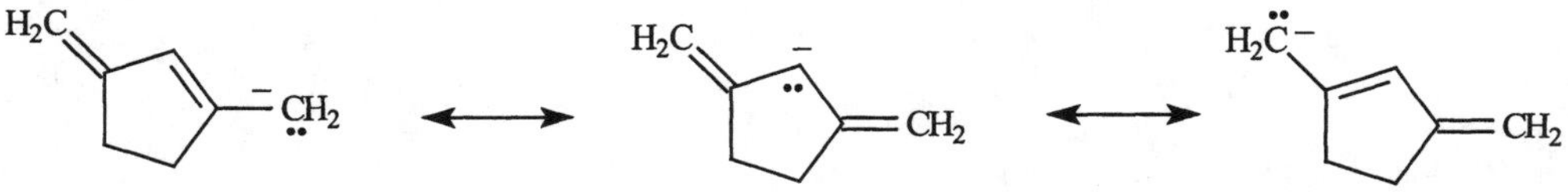

ZB

For the conjugate base **QB** the negative charge is delocalized into the ring. This generates a cyclopentadienyl anion which is aromatic. For the conjugate base **ZB**, the negative charge is delocalized by resonance but no aromatic ions result. Therefore, Compound **Q** should be the most acidic, since its anion is the most stable.

24. Most alkyl halides are nonpolar covalent compounds and, therefore, are soluble in nonpolar solvents and insoluble in water. Cycloheptatrienyl bromide is an unusual alkyl halide in that it is insoluble in nonpolar solvents, but is readily soluble in water! This behavior is consistent with cycloheptatrienyl bromide being an ionic compound. Why does cycloheptatrienyl bromide exist as an ionic compound? Explain by comparing the covalent structure to the ionic structure.

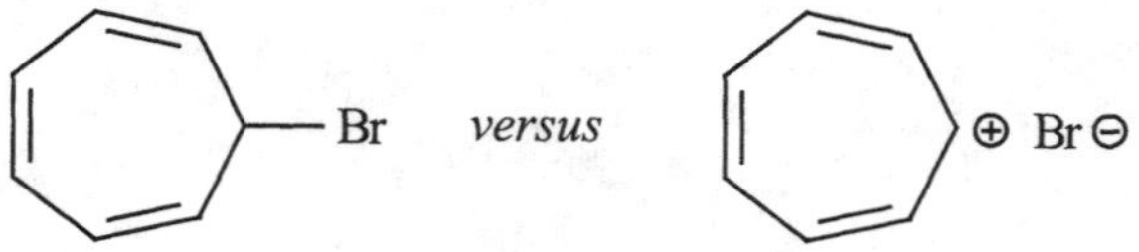

Br *versus* ⊕ Br⊖

Answer: In the covalent structure, the carbon bonded to the bromine is sp^3-hybridized, so the ring cannot be aromatic. In the ionic structure, the carbocation is sp^2-hybridized, so the structure is a cyclic, conjugated, six pi electron system and aromatic

Consider the data below to answer the following questions.

C_9H_{12} ; ^1H NMR: 7.18 δ (broad singlet, 5H),
2.55 δ (triplet, 2H),
1.70 δ (sextet, 2H)
0.9 δ (triplet, 3H)

25. Describe the signal at 7.18 δ in terms of its splitting, integration and chemical shift.

Answer: The integration of the signal at 7.18 δ indicates that there are five hydrogens that are more or less equivalent (broad singlet); the chemical shift indicates that these five hydrogens are aromatic. This is typical for a monosubstituted benzene.

26. Describe the signal at 2.55 δ in terms of its splitting, integration, and chemical shift.

Answer: The integration of the signal at 2.55 δ indicates that it is two hydrogens that are split (triplet) by two adjacent hydrogens, or a -CH_2- next to a -CH_2-. The chemical shift indicates that this -CH_2- could be next to an aromatic ring.

27. Describe the signal at 1.70 δ in terms of its splitting, integration and chemical shift.

Answer: The integration of the signal at 1.70 δ indicates that it is two hydrogens split by five adjacent hydrogens (sextet); most probably a -CH_2- between a -CH_2- and a -CH_3. Its chemical shift indicates that there is some electronegative group causing some deshielding to occur.

28. Describe the signal at 0.9 δ in terms of its splitting, integration and chemical shift.

Answer: The integration of the signal at 0.9 δ indicates that it is three hydrogens split by two adjacent hydrogens (triplet) or a -CH_3 next to a -CH_2-. Its chemical shift is in the normal range for a methyl group.

29. Propose a structure for this compound.

Answer:

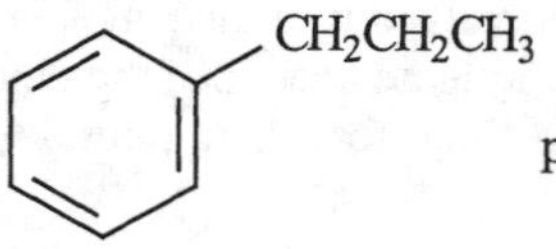

$CH_2CH_2CH_3$

propylbenzene

Consider the data below to answer the following questions.

C_9H_{12}; ^{1}H NMR: 6.65 δ (singlet, 3H),
2.25 δ (singlet, 9H)

30. Describe the signal at 6.65 δ in terms of its splitting, integration and chemical shift.

Answer: The signal at 6.65 δ indicates that it is 3 equivalent hydrogens in the aromatic region of the spectrum. This could be a 1,3,5-trisubstituted compound.

31. Describe the signal at 2.25 δ in terms of its splitting, integration and chemical shift.

Answer: The signal at 2.25 δ indicates that it is nine equivalent hydrogens attached to an aromatic ring; probably three -CH_3 groups.

32. Propose a structure for this compound.

Answer:

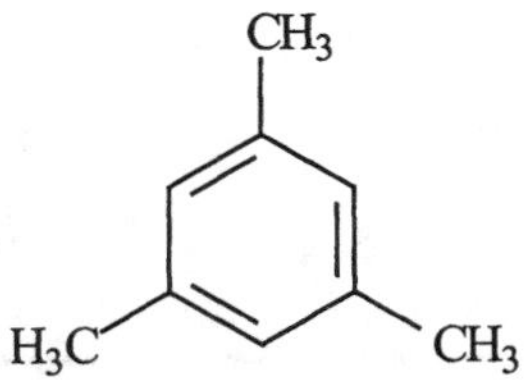

CH_3

H_3C CH_3

33. What is the structure of a hydrocarbon that shows a molecular ion at $m/z = 182$ in the mass spectrum and has the following ^{1}H NMR spectrum?

7.2 δ,singlet, 5H
2.9 δ,singlet, 2H

Answer: The molecular weight of the hydrocarbon corresponds to the formula $C_{14}H_{14}$, which indicates eight double bonds and/or rings. Since the ratio of protons in the ^{1}H NMR is 5:2, there must be 10 aromatic and 4 aliphatic protons. There must be two equivalently substituted phenyl rings, which accounts for 12 carbons. Since all aliphatic protons are equivalent, and we need two more carbons to complete the structure, the compound must be 1,2-dIphenylethane.

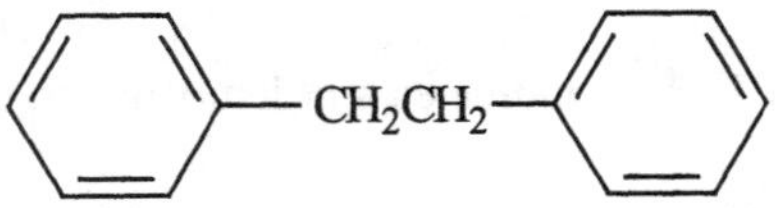

CH_2CH_2

Consider the data below to answer the following questions.

C_7H_7ClO ; IR: 810 cm^{-1}

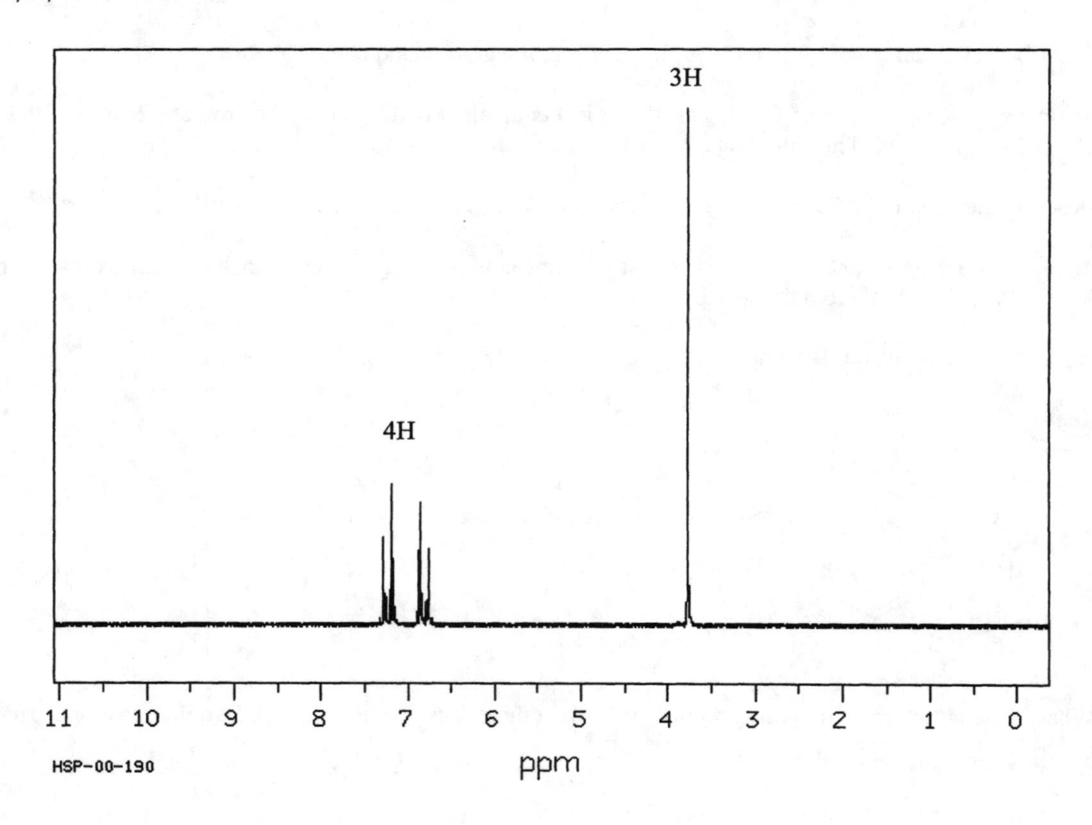

Spectrum obtained from: SDBSWeb: http://www.aist.go.jp/RIODB/SDBS/

34. Calculate the degrees of unsaturation for this compound.

> ***Answer:*** The formula C_7H_7ClO corresponds to a base formula of C_7H_8. A saturated formula is C_7H_{16} so there are $(16 - 8) \div 2 = 4$ degrees of unsaturation.

35. What is the significance of an IR absorption at 810 cm^{-1}?

> ***Answer:*** An IR absorption at 810 cm^{-1} indicates a *p*-disubstituted aromatic ring.

36. Describe the signal at 3.7 δ in terms of its splitting, integration and chemical shift.

> ***Answer:*** The signal at 3.7 δ indicates that there are three hydrogens next to zero hydrogens (singlet) shifted by attachment to an electronegative atom like oxygen; probably an $-OCH_3$.

37. Propose a structure for this compound.

> ***Answer:*** Cl–C_6H_4–OCH_3

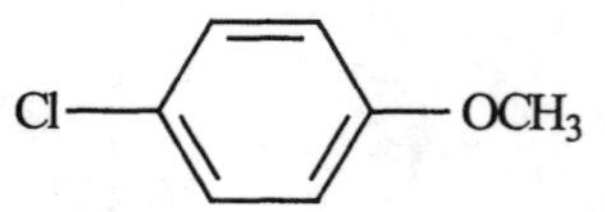

Chapter 16 – Chemistry of Benzene: Electrophilic Aromatic Substitution

MATCH a structure or term from the following list with each description below. Place the letter of the structure or term in the blank to the left of the description.

a. benzyne
b. $^{+}NO_2$
c. R_3C^+
d. electron-donating
e. ^{+}NO
f. Meisenheimer complex
g. $R-C\equiv O^+$
h. electron-withdrawing

1. ______ The reactive electrophile in Friedel-Crafts acylation reactions.

Answer: g

2. ______ The electrophile in aromatic nitration.

Answer: b

3. ______ Groups which activate aromatic rings towards electrophilic substitution.

Answer: d

4. ______ Groups which activate aromatic rings towards nucleophilic substitution.

Answer: h

5. ______ Intermediate in the elimination-addition mechanism of nucleophilic aromatic substitution.

Answer: a

Consider the Friedel-Crafts alkylation reaction below to answer the following questions:

$$\text{benzene} \xrightarrow[AlCl_3]{CH_3CH_2Cl} C_6H_5CH_2CH_3 + HCl$$

6. Draw the structure of the electrophile in this reaction.

Answer: $CH_3\overset{+}{C}H_2$

7. What is the role of the $AlCl_3$ in the reaction?

Answer: The $AlCl_3$ is a Lewis acid catalyst that assists in the ionization of the alkyl halide to give the carbocation electrophile.

8. Write the complete stepwise mechanism for this reaction. Show all electron flow with arrows and include all intermediate structures.

Answer:

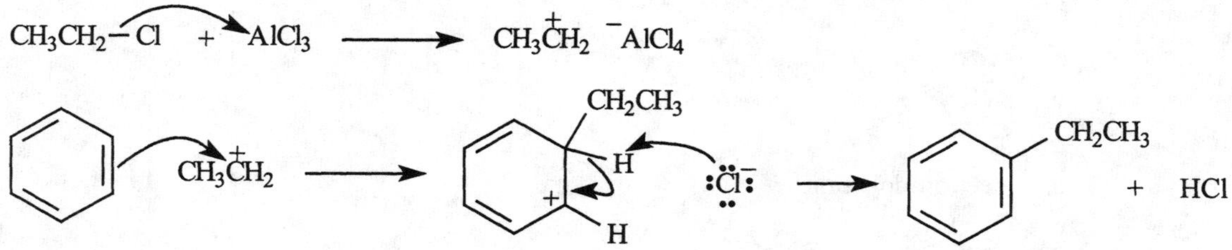

$CH_3CH_2{-}Cl + AlCl_3 \longrightarrow CH_3\overset{+}{C}H_2 \; {}^{-}AlCl_4$

$CH_3\overset{+}{C}H_2$ $\longrightarrow$ CH_2CH_3 H + H $:\ddot{Cl}:^{-}$ $\longrightarrow$ CH_2CH_3 + HCl

9. Aniline reacts with nitrous acid, HNO_2, to yield a stable diazonium salt. This diazonium salt undergoes electrophilic aromatic substitution on activated aromatic rings to yield brightly colored azo compounds that are widely used as dyes. The intermediate structures for the mechanism of this reaction are given below. Show all electron flow with arrows for this mechanism on the structures provided.

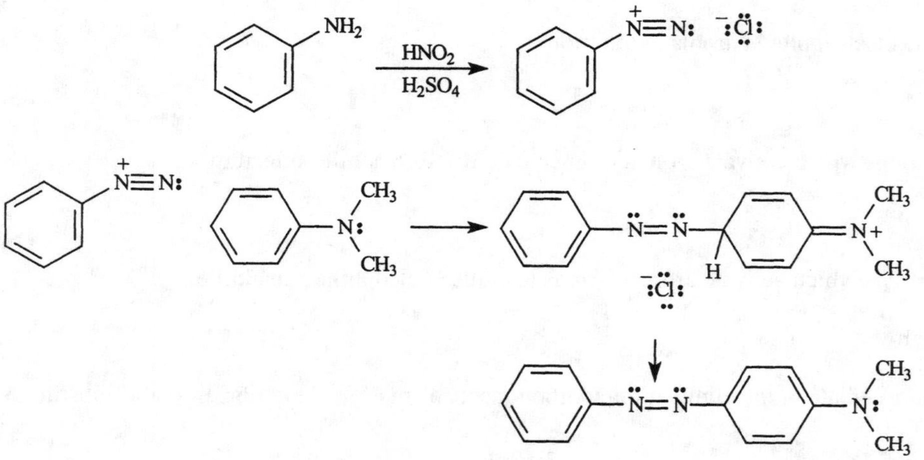

NH_2 $\xrightarrow[H_2SO_4]{HNO_2}$ $\overset{+}{N}{\equiv}N: \; {}^{-}:\ddot{Cl}:$

$\overset{+}{N}{\equiv}N:$ CH_3 N: CH_3 $\longrightarrow$ $\ddot{N}{=}\ddot{N}$ H $=N+$ CH_3 CH_3 $^{-}:\ddot{Cl}:$

$\downarrow$

$\ddot{N}{=}\ddot{N}$ CH_3 N: CH_3

Answer:

NH_2 $\xrightarrow[H_2SO_4]{HNO_2}$ $\overset{+}{N}{\equiv}N: \; {}^{-}:\ddot{Cl}:$

$\overset{+}{N}{\equiv}N:$ CH_3 N: CH_3 $\longrightarrow$ $\ddot{N}{=}\ddot{N}$ H $=N+$ CH_3 CH_3 $^{-}:\ddot{Cl}:$

$\downarrow$

$\ddot{N}{=}\ddot{N}$ CH_3 N: CH_3

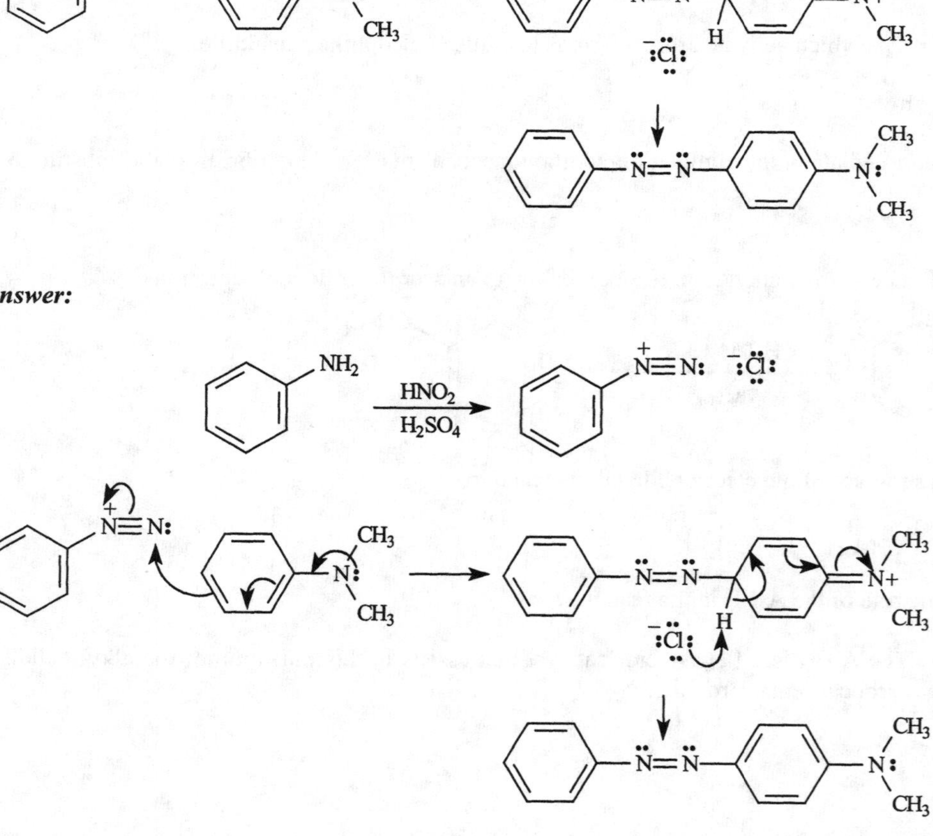

Consider the data below to answer the following questions.

The -NH_2 group is listed in our textbook as the strongest *o,p*-directing activator in electrophilic aromatic substitution reactions. However, when aniline is subjected to standard nitration conditions poor yields of *m*-nitroaniline result.

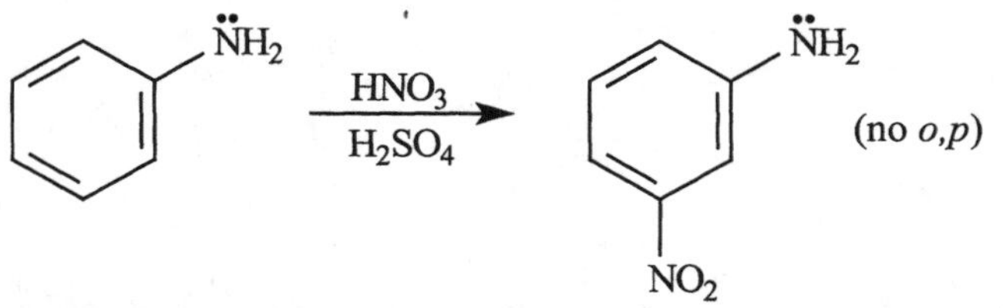

NH_2 $\xrightarrow[H_2SO_4]{HNO_3}$ NH_2 (no *o,p*)

NO_2

10. Draw all the resonance forms of aniline showing the electron-donating effect of the -NH_2 substituent.

Answer:

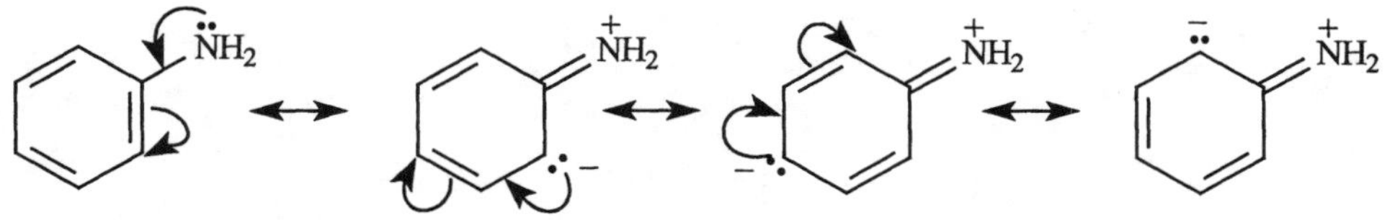

NH_2 ⟷ $\overset{+}{N}H_2$ ⟷ $\overset{+}{N}H_2$ ⟷ $\overset{+}{N}H_2$

11. Clearly, the reaction conditions are influencing the directing effect of the -NH_2 group. Explain why this occurs, using both words and structures.

Answer:

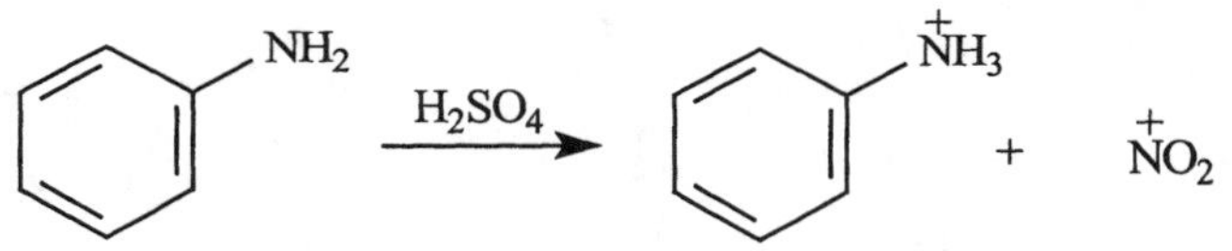

NH_2 $\xrightarrow{H_2SO_4}$ $\overset{+}{N}H_3$ + $\overset{+}{N}O_2$

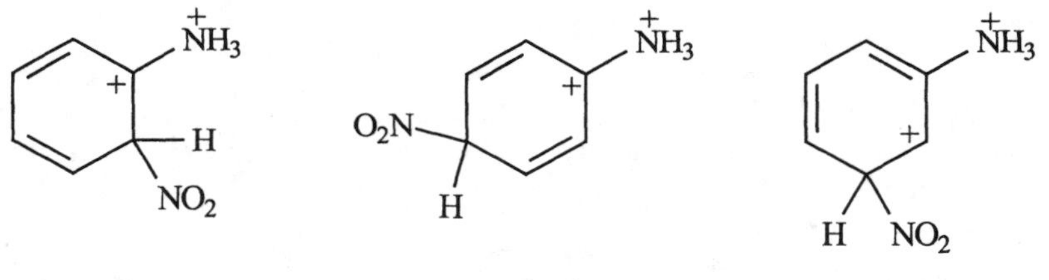

$\overset{+}{N}H_3$ H NO_2 — *ortho* attack

$\overset{+}{N}H_3$ O_2N H — *para* attack

$\overset{+}{N}H_3$ H NO_2 — *meta* attack

When aniline is placed in strong acid the nitrogen atom is protonated. Electrophilic aromatic substitution on the anilinium ion—whose aromatic ring is now deactivated by a positively charged substituent—occurs primarily at the *meta* position since this keeps the positive charge of the intermediate carbocation away from the positively charged nitrogen. The intermediates shown above for *ortho* and *para* substitution are destabilized more than the intermediate for *meta* substitution, so *m*-nitroaniline is the major product.

Consider the reaction below to answer the following questions.

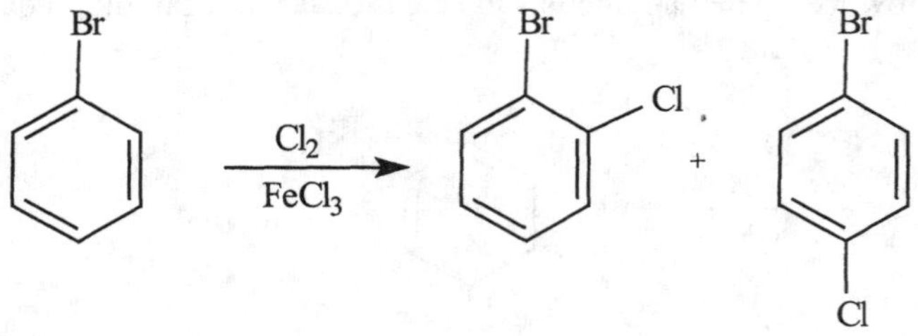

Br / Cl_2, $FeCl_3$ / Br, Cl + Br, Cl

12. Write the complete stepwise mechanism for the formation of the *ortho* product. Show all intermediate structures and show all electron flow with arrows.

Answer:

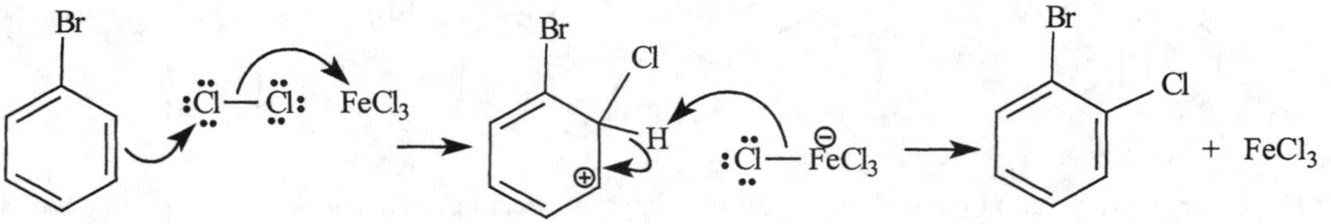

Br :Cl—Cl: $FeCl_3$ → Br, Cl, H, ⊕ :Cl—$FeCl_3$ ⊖ → Br, Cl + $FeCl_3$

13. Draw resonance structures for the intermediate carbocation that explain the directing effect of the -Br.

Answer:

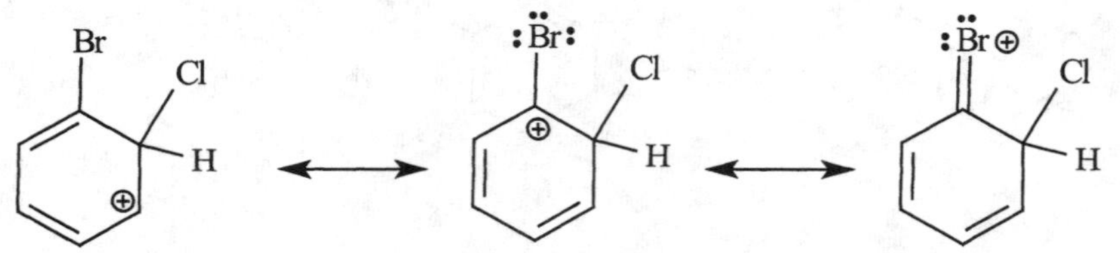

Br, Cl, H, ⊕ ⟷ :Br:, ⊕, Cl, H ⟷ :Br⊕, Cl, H

Rank the compounds in each group below according to their reactivity toward electrophilic aromatic substitution (most reactive $=1$; least reactive $=3$). Place the number corresponding to the compounds' relative reactivity in the blank below the compound.

14.

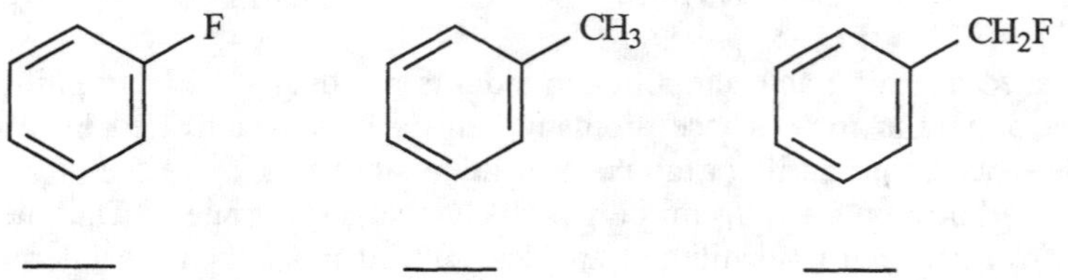

F CH_3 CH_2F

___ ___ ___

Answer:

F CH_3 CH_2F

3 1 2

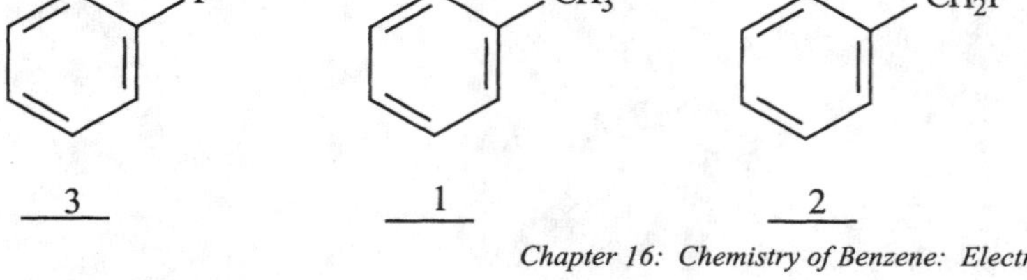

15.

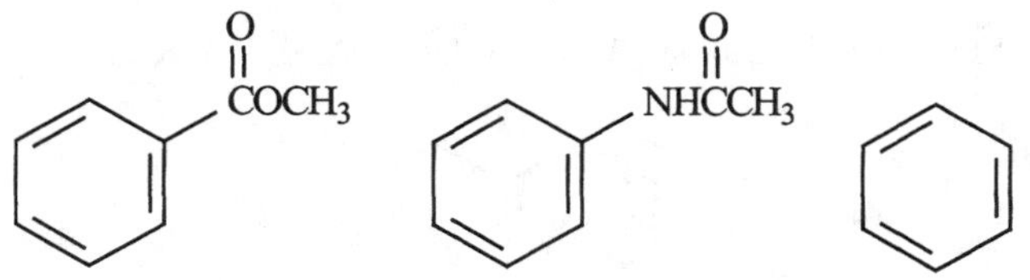

O ‖ $COCH_3$ O ‖ $NHCCH_3$

____ ____ ____

Answer:

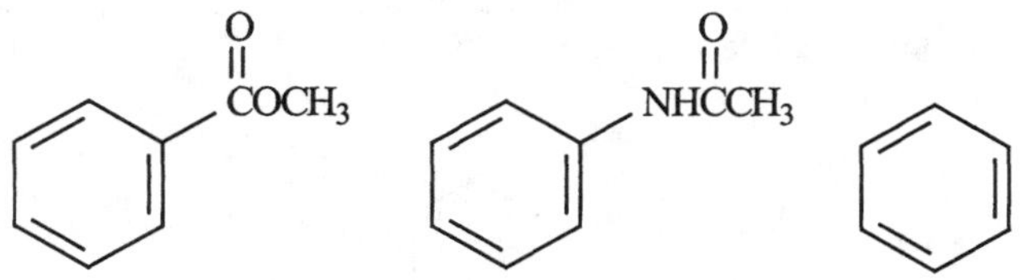

O ‖ $COCH_3$ O ‖ $NHCCH_3$

3 1 2

16. At what position, and on what ring, is bromination of phenyl benzoate expected to occur? Explain your answer by drawing resonance structures of the intermediates.

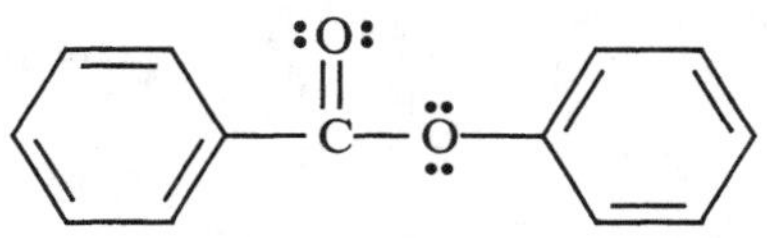

:O: ‖ C—Ö—

phenyl benzoate

Answer:

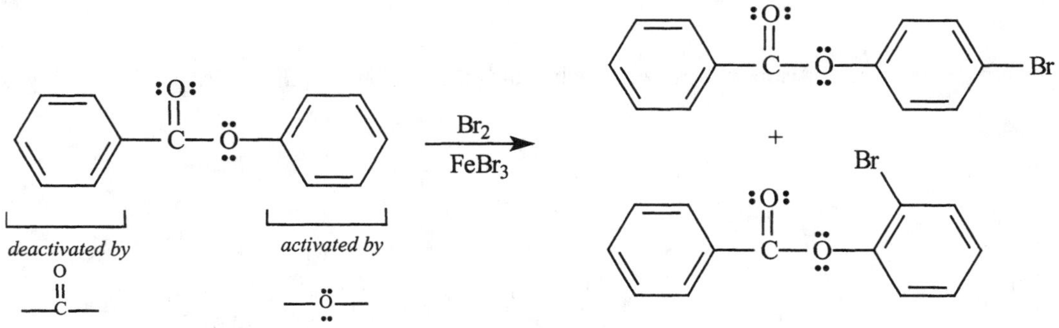

:O: ‖ C—Ö—

$\xrightarrow[FeBr_3]{Br_2}$

:O: ‖ C—Ö— Br

\+

Br

:O: ‖ C—Ö—

deactivated by

O ‖ —C—

activated by

—Ö—

Attack occurs in the activated ring and yields *ortho* and *para* bromination

To answer the following questions, refer to the data below:

Isobutylbenzene is the starting material for the industrial synthesis of the NSAID, ibuprofen.

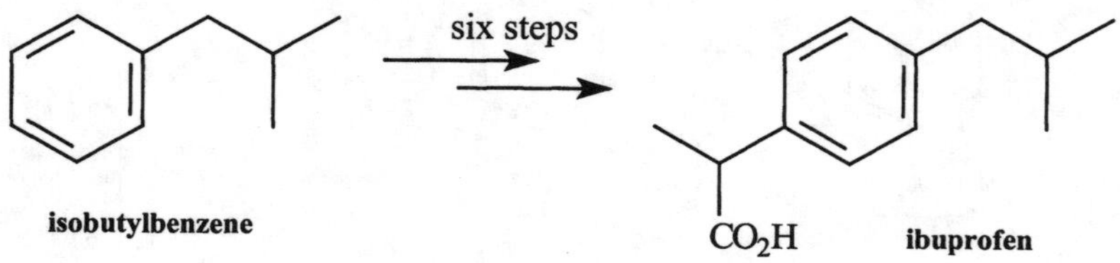

six steps

isobutylbenzene CO_2H **ibuprofen**

17. Attempts to prepare isobutylbenzene by direct Friedel-Crafts alkylation of benzene result in *tert*-butylbenzene as the major product. Write the complete stepwise mechanism for this reaction, showing all electron flow with arrows and showing all intermediate structures.

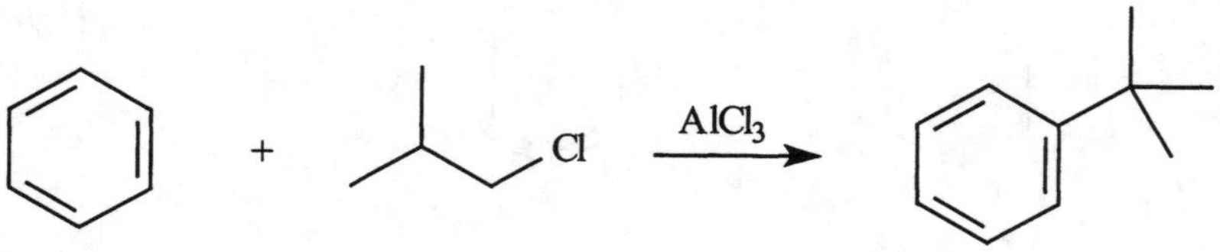

+ Cl $AlCl_3$

Answer:

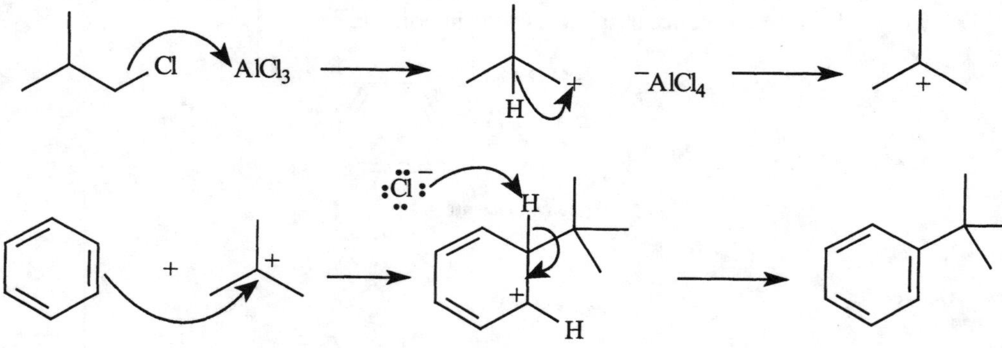

Cl $AlCl_3$ H + $^{-}AlCl_4$ +

$:\ddot{Cl}:^{-}$ H

+ + + H

18. Propose a synthesis for isobutylbenzene which avoids the problems of direct Friedel-Crafts alkylation.

Answer:

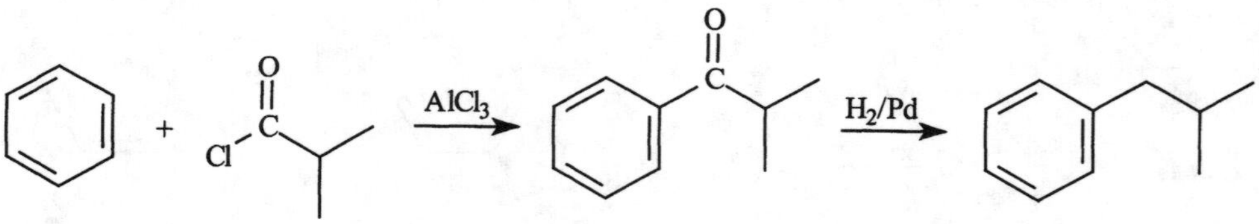

+ Cl C O $AlCl_3$ C O H_2/Pd

19. Would you expect (nitromethyl)benzene to be more reactive or less reactive than toluene? Explain.

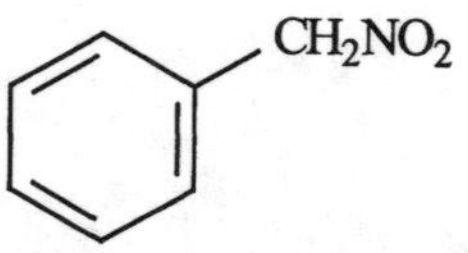

CH_2NO_2

Answer: (Nitromethyl)benzene should be less reactive than toluene owing to the strong inductive electron withdrawing effect of the nitro group.

Consider the reaction below to answer the following questions.

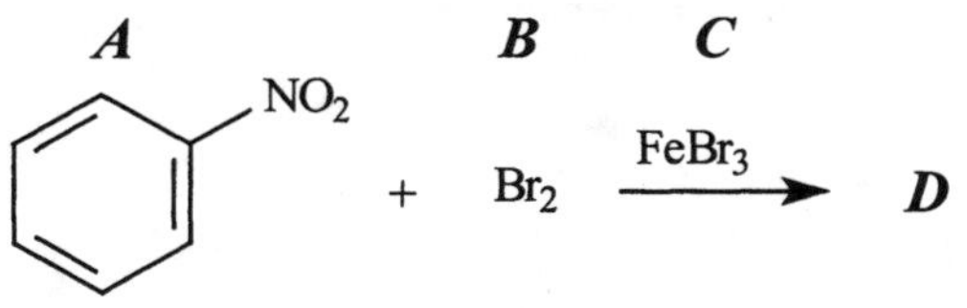

$$\underset{A}{C_6H_5NO_2} + \underset{B}{Br_2} \xrightarrow{\underset{C}{FeBr_3}} D$$

20. The nucleophile in the reaction is:

Answer: A

21. The Lewis acid catalyst in the reaction is:

Answer: C

22. This reaction proceeds ____________(faster or slower) than benzene.

Answer: slower

23. Draw the structure of product ***D***.

Answer:

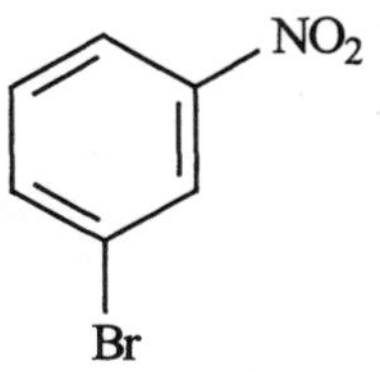

NO_2

Br

24. The following reaction proceeds by an intramolecular nucleophilic aromatic substitution mechanism. Write the complete stepwise mechanism, showing all intermediate structures and all electron flow with arrows.

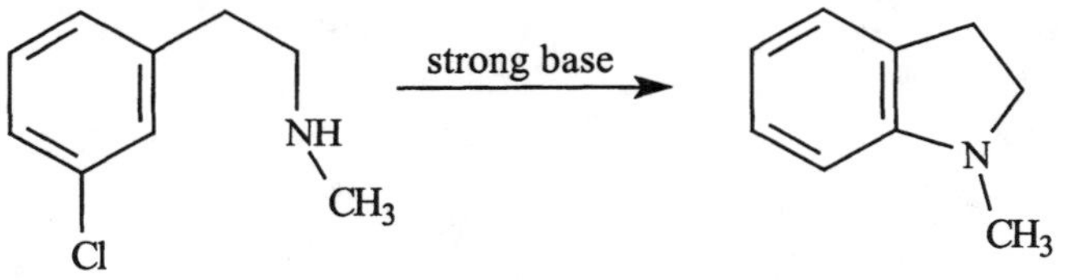

strong base

NH

CH_3

Cl

N

CH_3

Answer:

:NH

H

CH_3

Cl

:B

:NH

CH_3

B—H

N

H

CH_3

:B

N

CH_3

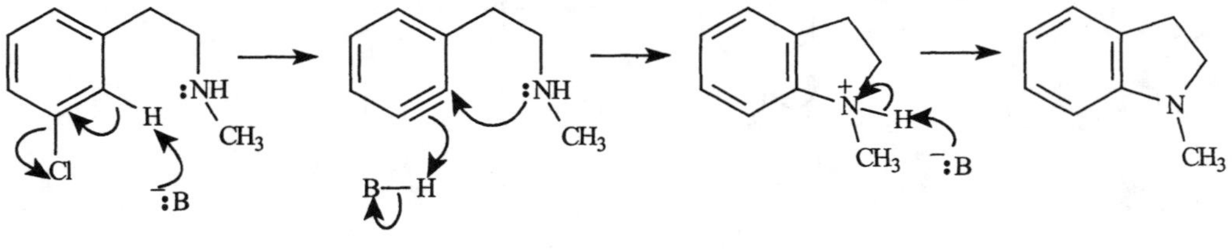

25. Tetracyclone is often used to trap benzynes as Diels-Alder adducts. What is the structure of the Diels-Alder adduct that results when benzyne is trapped by tetracyclone?

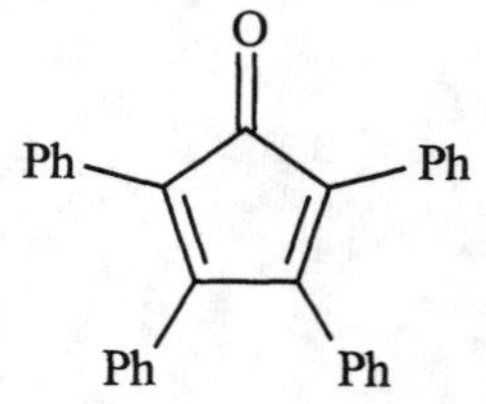

O
Ph Ph
tetracyclone
Ph Ph

Answer:

O
Ph
Ph
Ph Ph

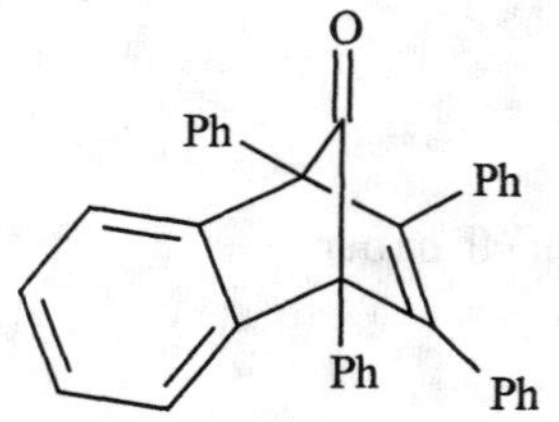

26. On the structural intermediates below, show all electron flow with arrows for the nucleophilic aromatic subsitution reaction of *p*-nitrochlorobenzene with KOH.

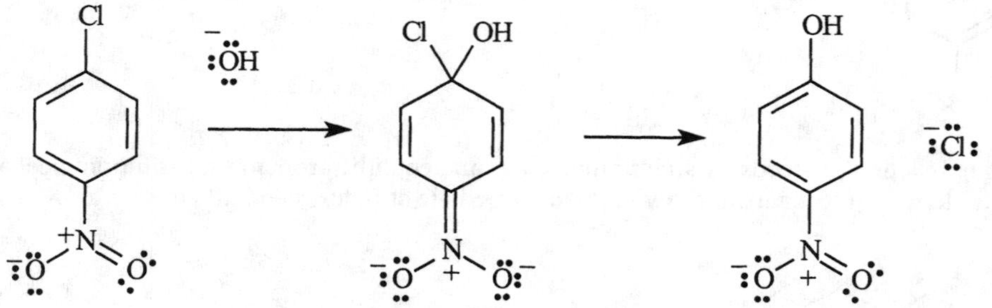

Cl $:\ddot{O}H^-$ Cl OH OH $:\ddot{Cl}:$

Answer:

Cl $:\ddot{O}H^-$ Cl OH OH $:\ddot{Cl}:^-$

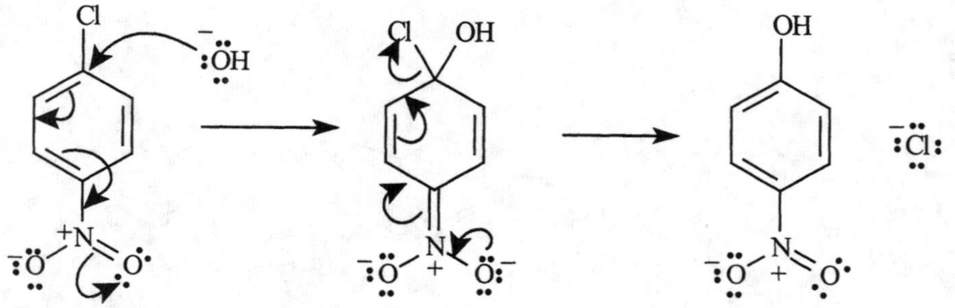

Given the major organic product(s) of each of the following reactions. If no is predicted, write "N.R."

27. Benzene $\xrightarrow[AlCl_3]{CH_3CH_2CH_2Cl}$

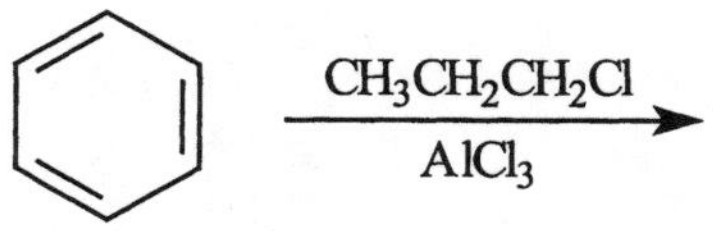

Answer:

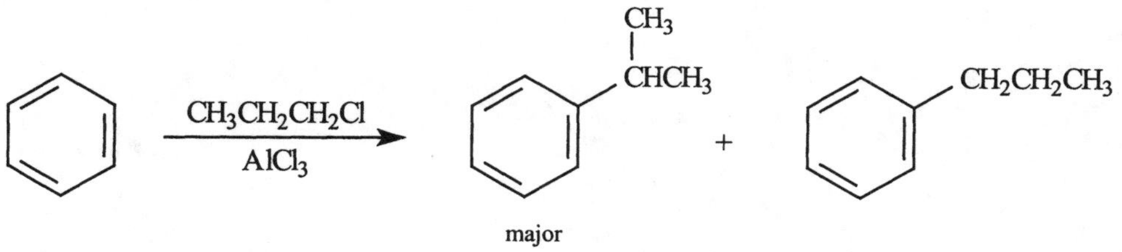

Benzene $\xrightarrow[AlCl_3]{CH_3CH_2CH_2Cl}$ $C_6H_5CH(CH_3)CH_3$ (major) + $C_6H_5CH_2CH_2CH_3$

28. $H_3C-C_6H_4-SO_3H$ $\xrightarrow[2.\ H_3O^+]{1.\ NaOH,\ 300°C}$

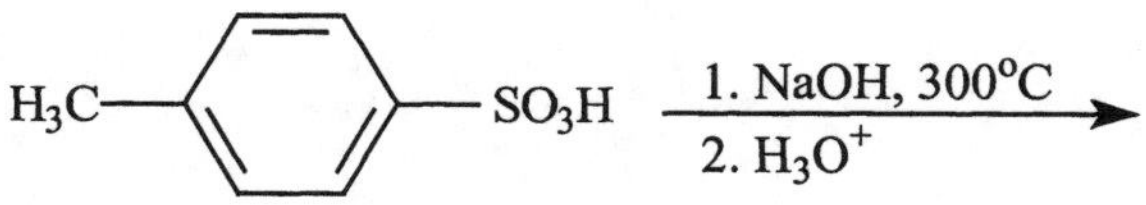

Answer:

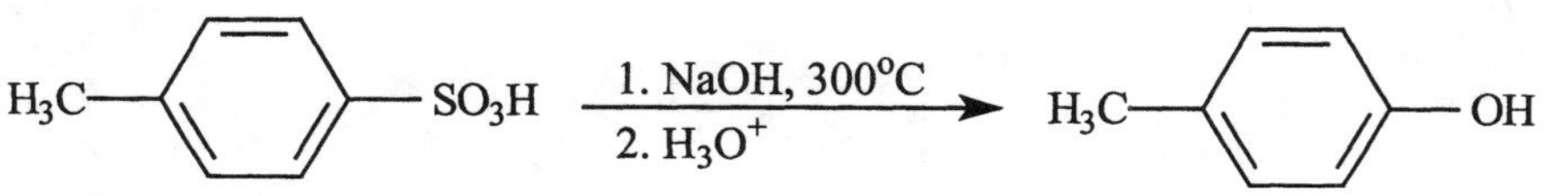

$H_3C-C_6H_4-SO_3H$ $\xrightarrow[2.\ H_3O^+]{1.\ NaOH,\ 300°C}$ $H_3C-C_6H_4-OH$

29. m-$C_6H_4(NO_2)_2$ $\xrightarrow[2.\ NaOH]{1.\ SnCl_2,\ H_3O^+}$

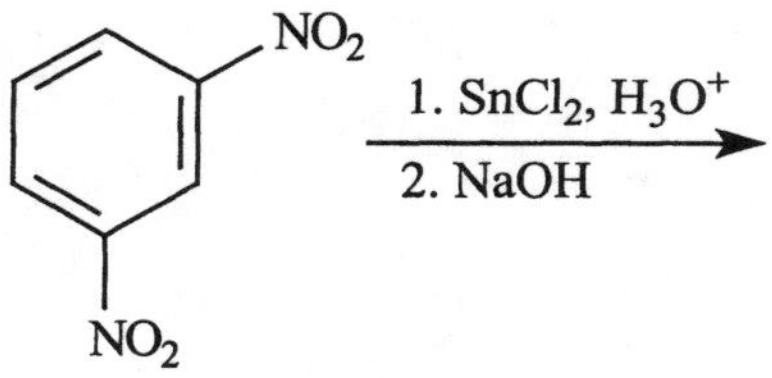

Answer:

m-$C_6H_4(NO_2)_2$ $\xrightarrow[2.\ NaOH]{1.\ SnCl_2,\ H_3O^+}$ m-$C_6H_4(NH_2)_2$

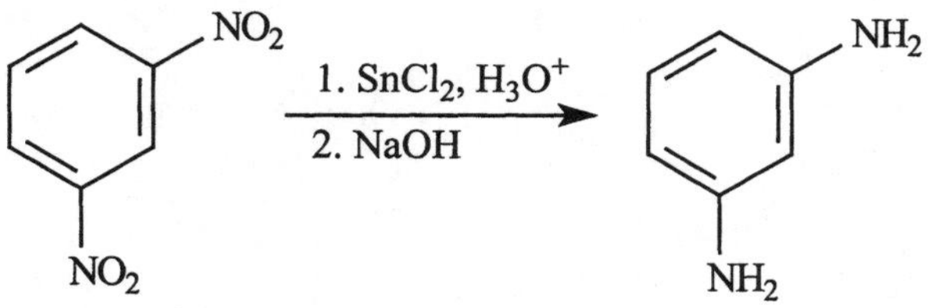

30. (4-bromotoluene: Br and CH_3 para on benzene ring) $\xrightarrow[NH_3]{KNH_2}$

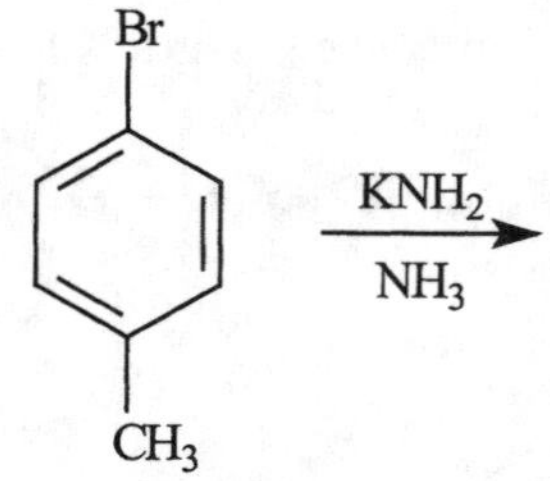

Answer:

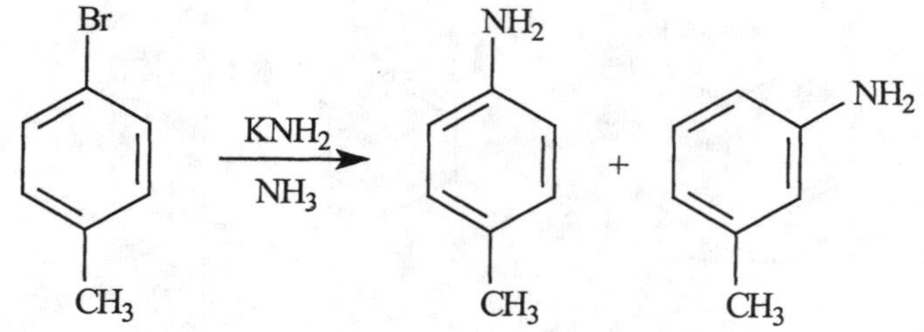

(Br, CH_3 para-substituted benzene) $\xrightarrow[NH_3]{KNH_2}$ (NH_2, CH_3 para-substituted benzene) + (NH_2, CH_3 meta-substituted benzene)

31. ($C(CH_3)_3$, CH_3 para-substituted benzene) $\xrightarrow[H_3O^+]{KMnO_4}$

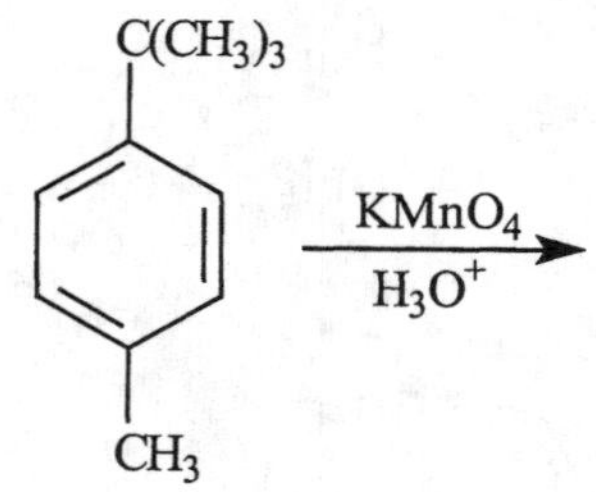

Answer:

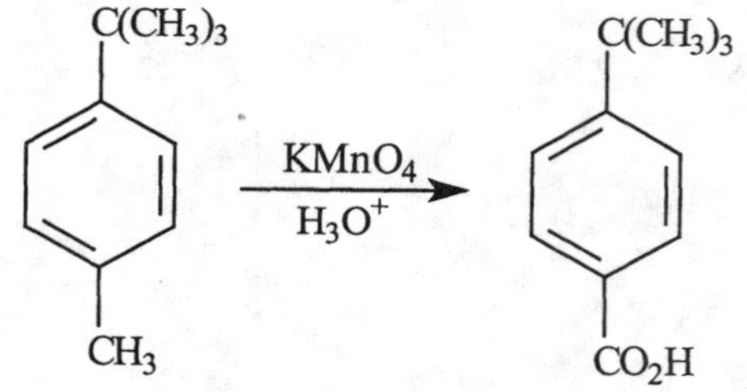

($C(CH_3)_3$, CH_3 para-substituted benzene) $\xrightarrow[H_3O^+]{KMnO_4}$ ($C(CH_3)_3$, CO_2H para-substituted benzene)

32. (OCH_3, NO_2 meta-substituted benzene) $\xrightarrow[FeBr_3]{Br_2}$

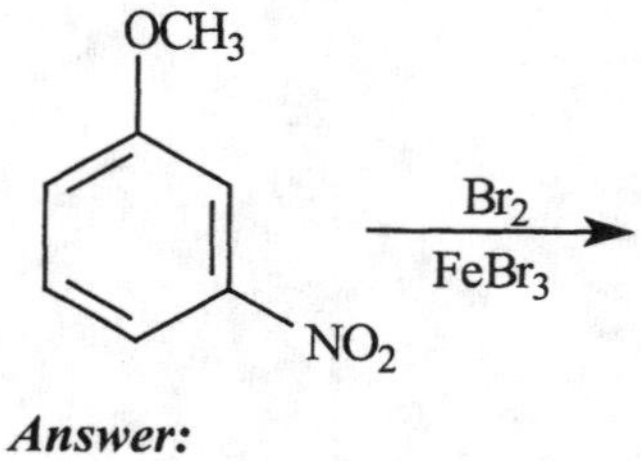

Answer:

(OCH_3, NO_2 meta-substituted benzene) $\xrightarrow[FeBr_3]{Br_2}$ (OCH_3, NO_2, Br; Br para to OCH_3) + (OCH_3, NO_2, Br; Br ortho to OCH_3)

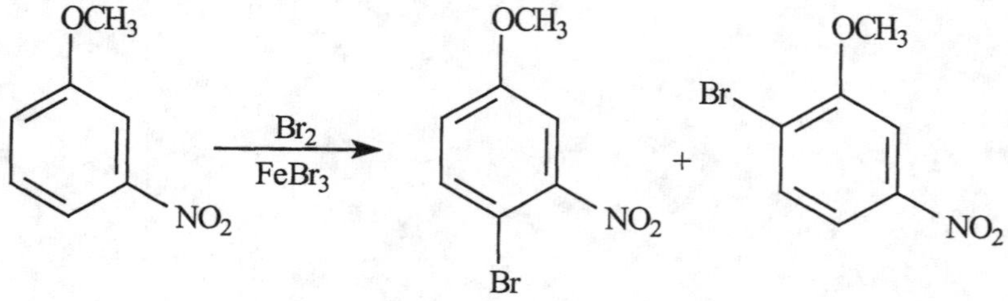

33. H_3C–C$_6H_4$–$NHCCH_3$ (C=O) $\xrightarrow[FeCl_3]{Cl_2}$

Answer:

H_3C–C$_6H_4$–$NHCCH_3$ (C=O) $\xrightarrow[FeCl_3]{Cl_2}$ H_3C–C$_6H_3$(Cl)–$NHCCH_3$ (C=O)

34. C$_6H_5$–CH_3 $\xrightarrow[H_2SO_4]{SO_3}$

Answer:

C$_6H_5$–CH_3 $\xrightarrow[H_2SO_4]{SO_3}$ HO_3S–C$_6H_4$–CH_3 + C$_6H_4$(CH_3)(SO_3H)

35. C$_6H_5$–Br $\xrightarrow[CuCl_2]{I_2}$

Answer:

C$_6H_5$–Br $\xrightarrow[CuCl_2]{I_2}$ C$_6H_4$(I)–Br + I–C$_6H_4$–Br

36. C$_6H_5$–C(=O)–CH_3 $\xrightarrow[2. H_2/Pd]{1. HNO_3, H_2SO_4}$

Answer:

C$_6H_5$–C(=O)–CH_3 $\xrightarrow[2. H_2/Pd]{1. HNO_3, H_2SO_4}$ C$_6H_4$(CH_2CH_3)(NH_2)

37. 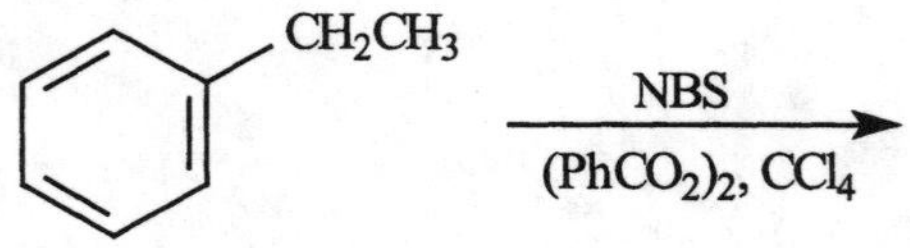 CH_2CH_3 $\xrightarrow[(PhCO_2)_2,\ CCl_4]{NBS}$

Answer:

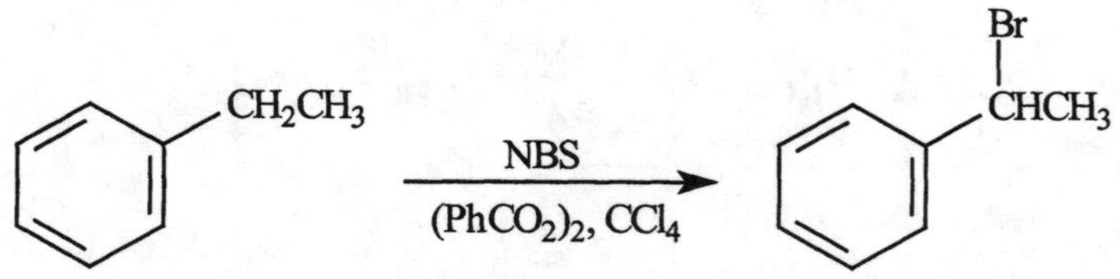

CH_2CH_3 $\xrightarrow[(PhCO_2)_2,\ CCl_4]{NBS}$ Br, $CHCH_3$

38. 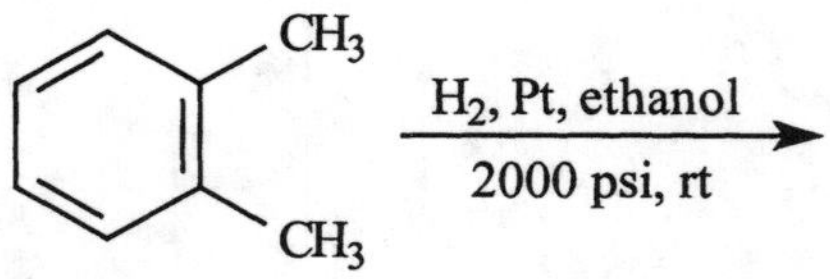 CH_3, CH_3 $\xrightarrow[2000\ psi,\ rt]{H_2,\ Pt,\ ethanol}$

Answer:

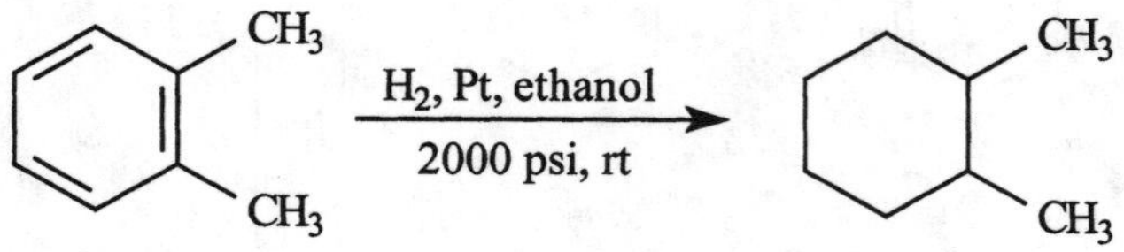

CH_3, CH_3 $\xrightarrow[2000\ psi,\ rt]{H_2,\ Pt,\ ethanol}$ CH_3, CH_3

39. 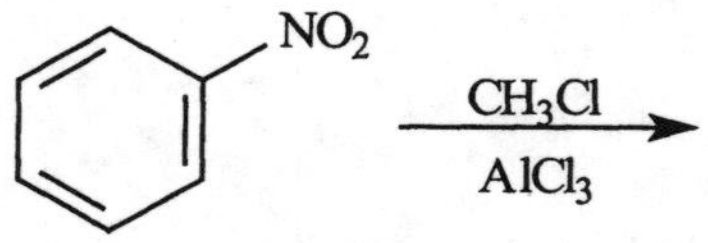 NO_2 $\xrightarrow[AlCl_3]{CH_3Cl}$

Answer:

NO_2 $\xrightarrow[AlCl_3]{CH_3Cl}$ N.R.

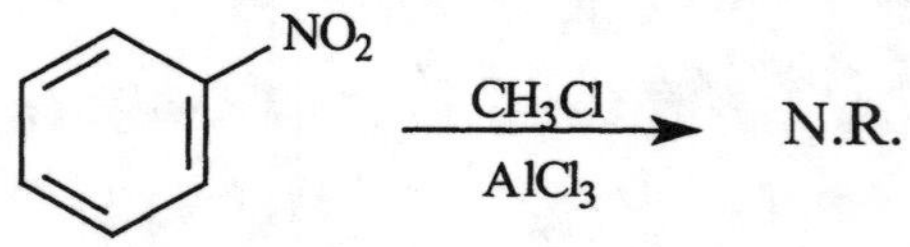

(Friedel-Crafts reactions do not proceed in the presence of a m-director)

40. 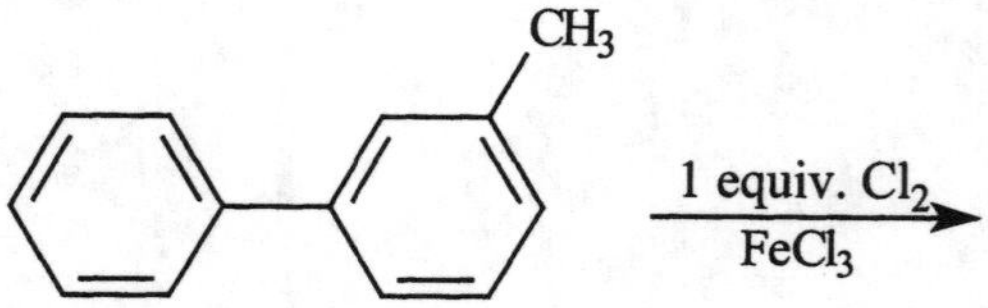 CH_3 $\xrightarrow[FeCl_3]{1\ equiv.\ Cl_2}$

Answer:

$$\text{3-methylbiphenyl} \xrightarrow[\text{FeCl}_3]{\text{1 equiv. Cl}_2} \text{4-chloro-3-methylbiphenyl} + \text{2-chloro-5-methylbiphenyl}$$

41. $CH_3O-C_6H_5 \xrightarrow[AlCl_3]{CH_3\overset{O}{\overset{\|}{C}}Cl}$

Answer:

$$CH_3O-C_6H_5 \xrightarrow[AlCl_3]{CH_3\overset{O}{\overset{\|}{C}}Cl} o\text{-}CH_3O-C_6H_4-\overset{O}{\overset{\|}{C}}CH_3 + p\text{-}CH_3O-C_6H_4-\overset{O}{\overset{\|}{C}}CH_3$$

42. $C_6H_5CH_3 \xrightarrow[H_3O^+]{KMnO_4} \xrightarrow[FeBr_3]{Br_2}$

Answer:

$$C_6H_5CH_3 \xrightarrow[H_3O^+]{KMnO_4} \xrightarrow[FeBr_3]{Br_2} m\text{-}Br-C_6H_4-COOH$$

Choose the *best* reagent(s) from the list provided below for carrying out the following conversions. Place the letter of the reagent in the box beside the reaction number over the arrow. There is only one answer for each reaction.

a. $KMnO_4$, H_3O^+
b. Br_2, $FeBr_3$
c. Cl_2, $FeCl_3$
d. CH_3Cl, $AlCl_3$
e. HNO_3, H_2SO_4
f. $ClCO(CH_2)_2CH_3$, $AlCl_3$
g. $CH_3CH_2CH_2CH_2Cl$, $AlCl_3$
h. H_2/Pd
i. NBS, peroxides

43.

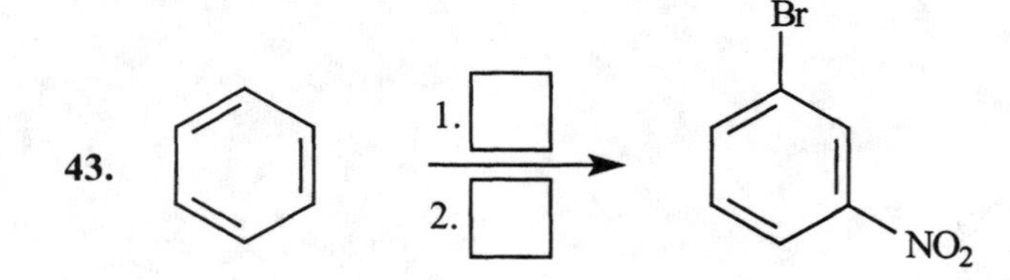

Answer:

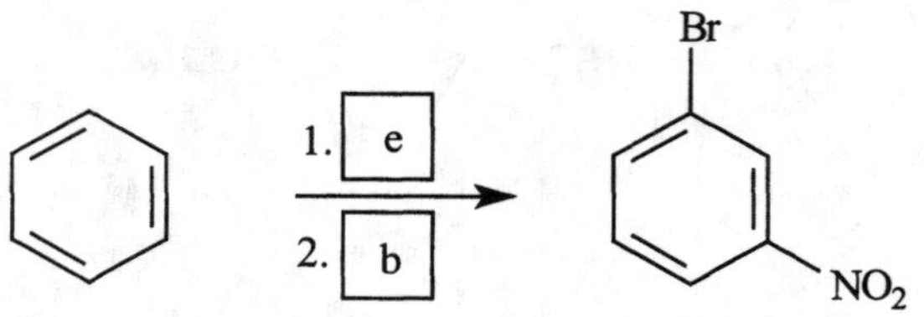

1. e
2. b

Br
NO2

44.

1.
2.

O
NO2

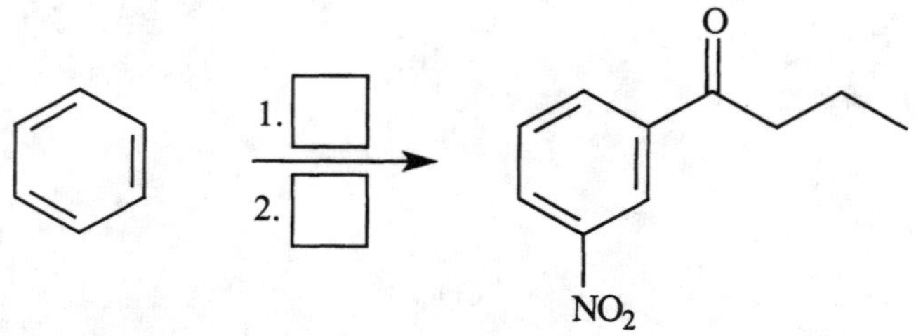

Answer:

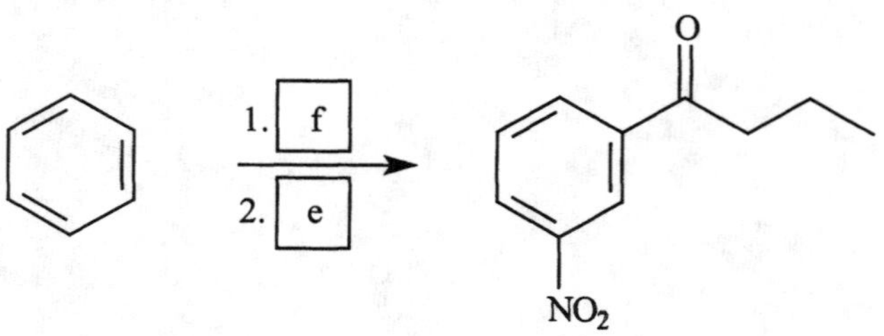

1. f
2. e

O
NO2

45.

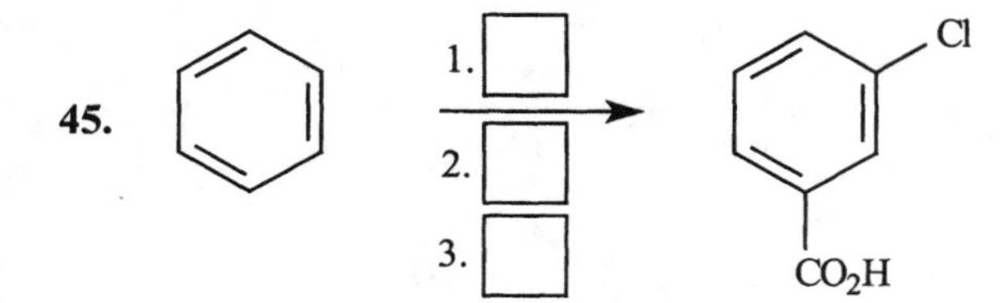

Answer:

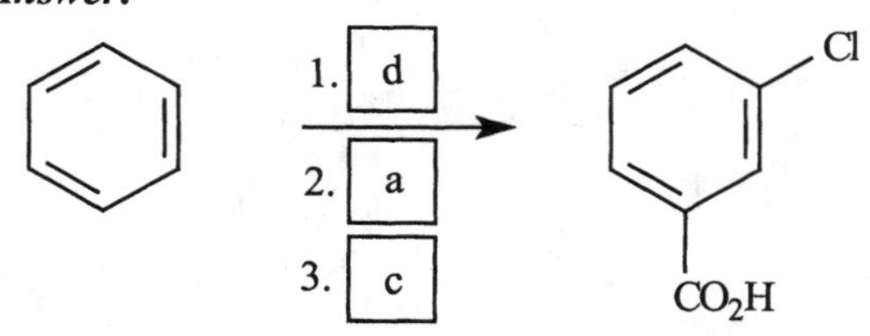

46.

Br

$CHCH_2CH_2CH_3$

1. ☐
2. ☐
3. ☐

Answer:

Br

$CHCH_2CH_2CH_3$

1. f
2. h
3. i

Propose syntheses to carry out each of the following conversions. Assume *ortho* and *para* isomers can be separated.

47.

Br

Answer:

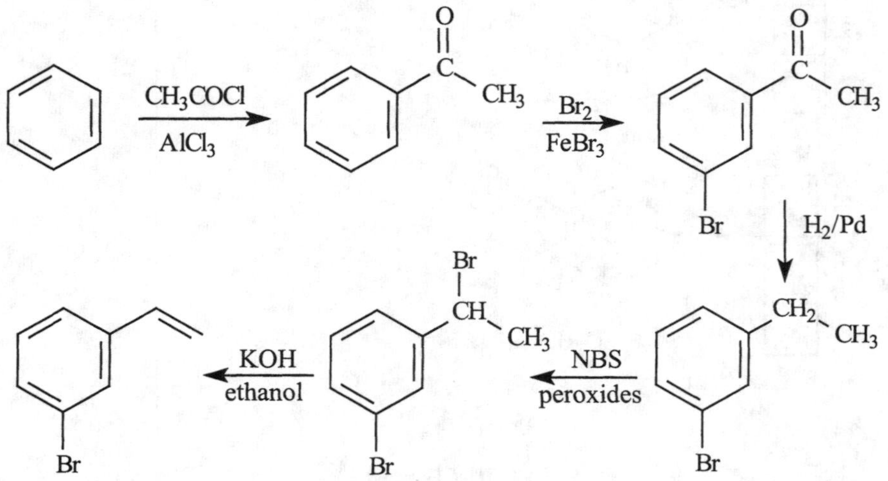

Benzene $\xrightarrow[AlCl_3]{CH_3COCl}$ $C_6H_5COCH_3$ $\xrightarrow[FeBr_3]{Br_2}$ m-$BrC_6H_4COCH_3$ $\xrightarrow{H_2/Pd}$ m-$BrC_6H_4CH_2CH_3$ $\xrightarrow[peroxides]{NBS}$ m-$BrC_6H_4CHBrCH_3$ $\xrightarrow[ethanol]{KOH}$ m-$BrC_6H_4CH=CH_2$

48. $C_6H_5CH_3$ ⟶ 2,6-di-$C(CH_3)_3$-4-CH_3-phenol

BHT
(a food preservative)

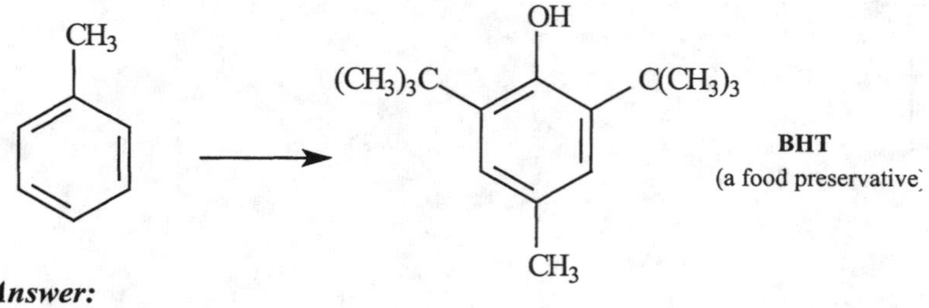

Answer:

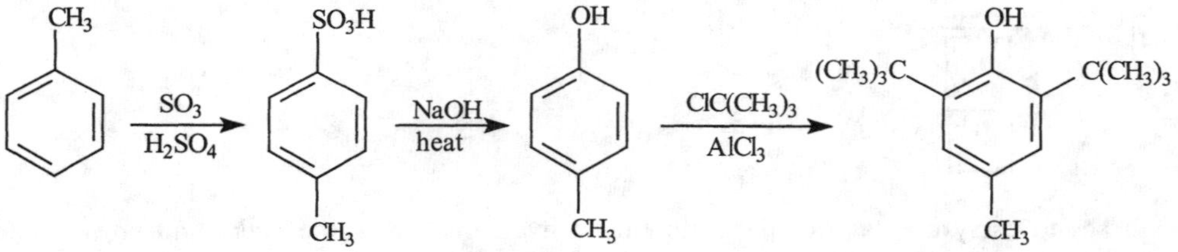

$C_6H_5CH_3$ $\xrightarrow[H_2SO_4]{SO_3}$ p-$CH_3C_6H_4SO_3H$ $\xrightarrow[heat]{NaOH}$ p-$CH_3C_6H_4OH$ $\xrightarrow[AlCl_3]{ClC(CH_3)_3}$ 2,6-di-$(CH_3)_3C$-4-CH_3-phenol

49. Benzene ⟶ $C_6H_5CH_2C{\equiv}N$

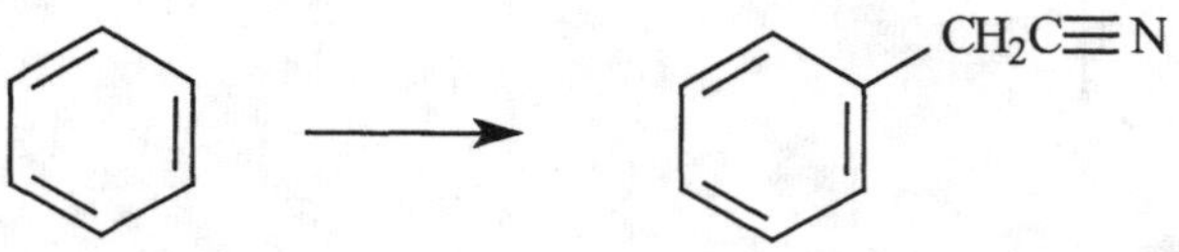

Answer:

Benzene $\xrightarrow[AlCl_3]{CH_3Cl}$ $C_6H_5CH_3$ $\xrightarrow[peroxides]{NBS}$ $C_6H_5CH_2Br$ $\xrightarrow[acetone]{KCN}$ $C_6H_5CH_2C{\equiv}N$

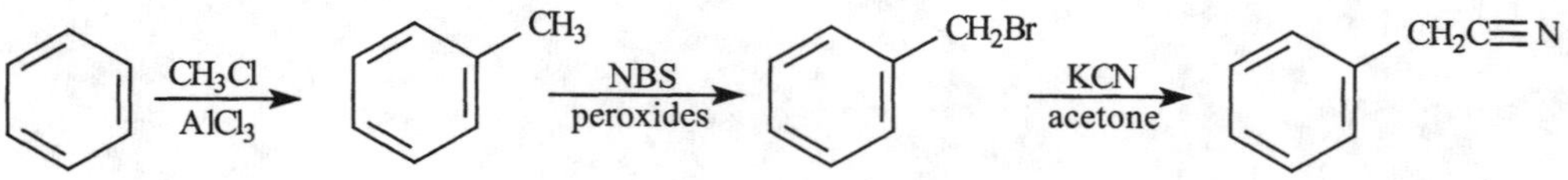

50. → (2,4-dichlorophenol: OH, Cl, Cl)

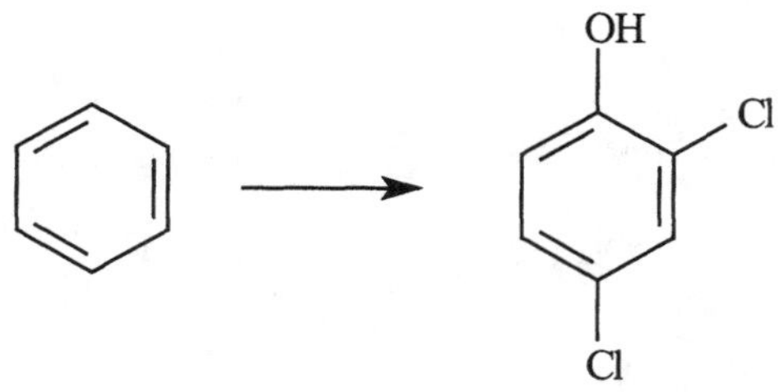

Answer:

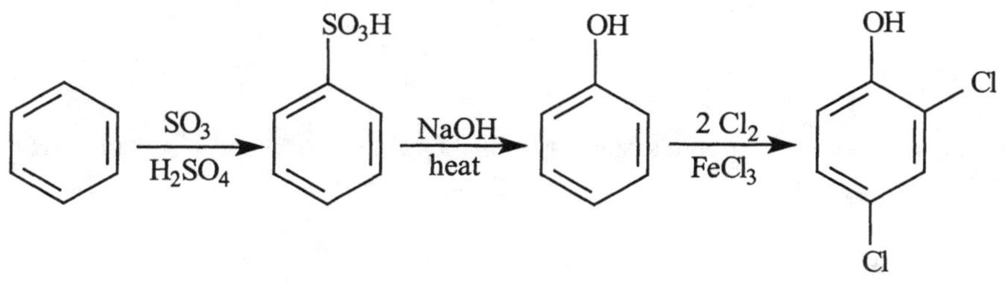

SO$_3$ / H$_2$SO$_4$ → SO$_3$H → NaOH, heat → OH → 2 Cl$_2$ / FeCl$_3$ → OH, Cl, Cl

51. → D

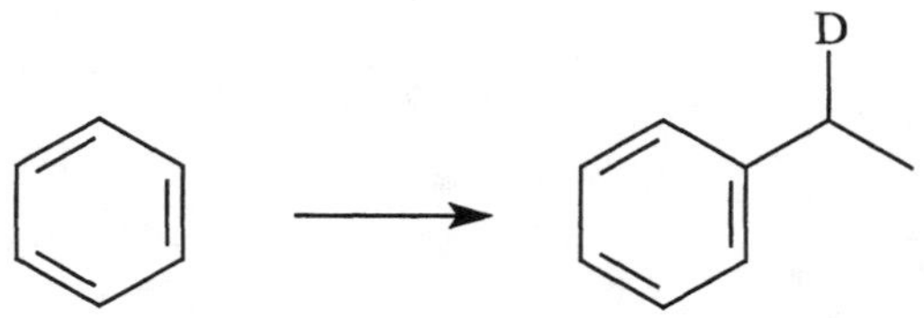

Answer:

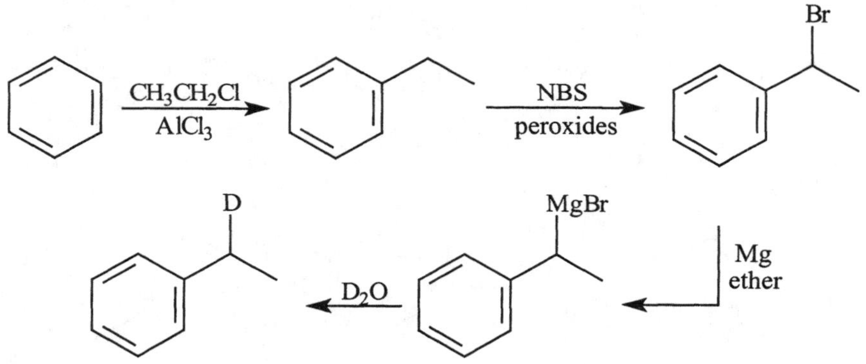

CH$_3$CH$_2$Cl / AlCl$_3$ → NBS / peroxides → Br

Mg / ether → MgBr → D$_2$O → D

52. CH$_3$ → COOH, NH$_2$

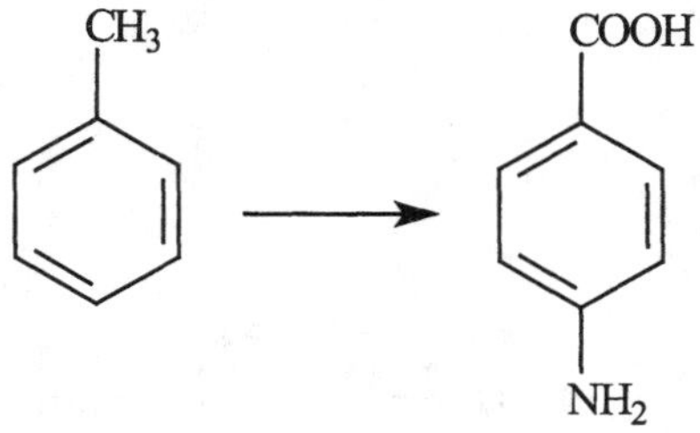

PABA
(active ingredient in some sunscreens)

Answer:

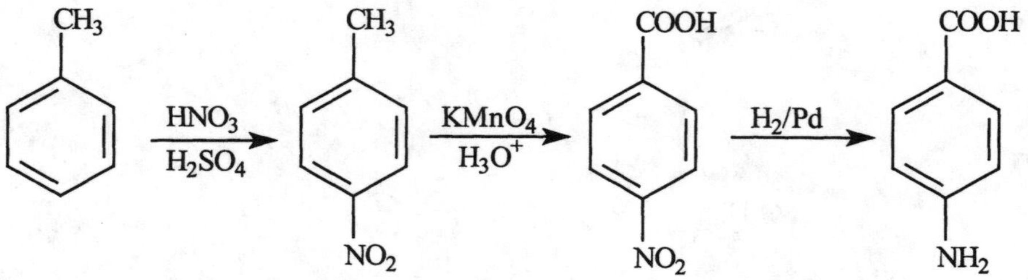

CH_3 → (HNO_3, H_2SO_4) → CH_3 / NO_2 → ($KMnO_4$, H_3O^+) → COOH / NO_2 → (H_2/Pd) → COOH / NH_2

Propose syntheses of the following compounds starting with benzene or toluene. Assume ortho and para isomers can be separated.

53.

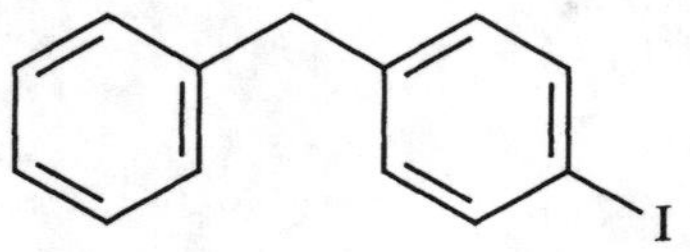

I

Answer:

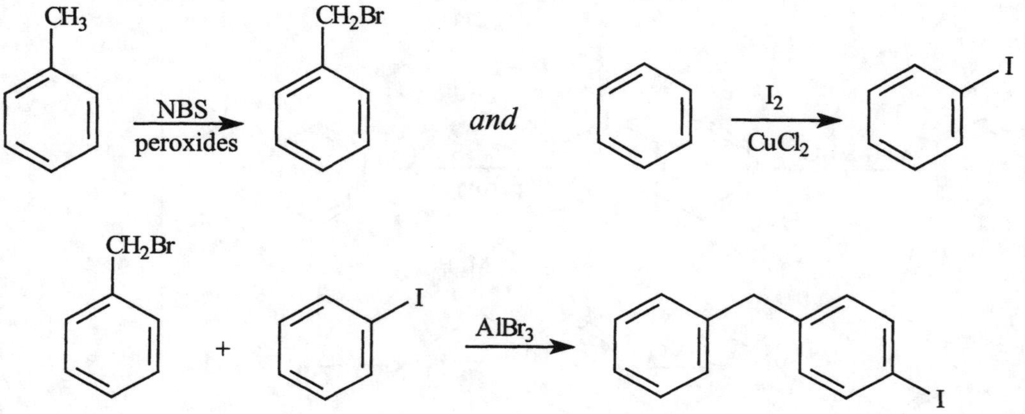

CH_3 → (NBS, peroxides) → CH_2Br *and* → (I_2, $CuCl_2$) → I

CH_2Br + I → ($AlBr_3$) → I

54. 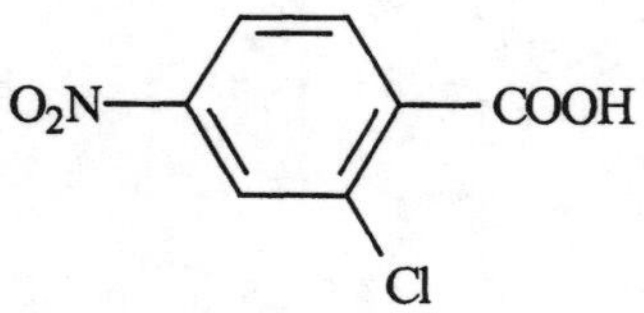 O_2N— —COOH

Cl

Answer:

—CH_3 → (HNO_3, H_2SO_4) → O_2N— —CH_3 → (Cl_2, $FeCl_3$) → O_2N— —CH_3 / Cl

($KMnO_4$, H_3O^+)

O_2N— —COOH

Cl

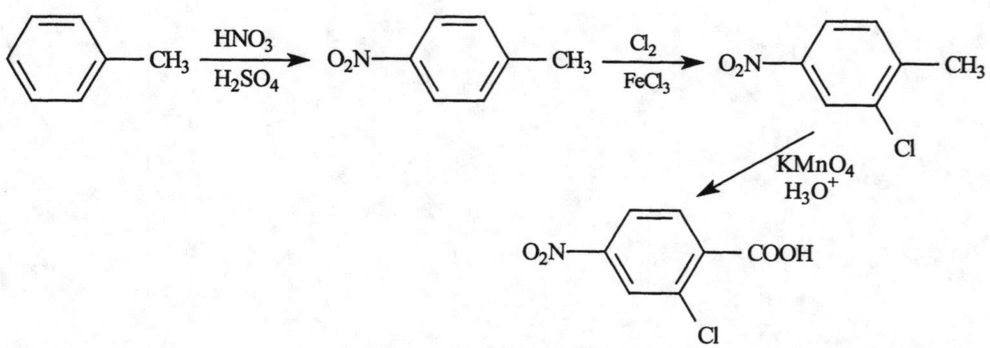

Chapter 17 - Alcohols and Phenols

Draw structures corresponding to the following IUPAC names:

1. *cis*-4-*tert*-butylcyclohexanol

Answer:

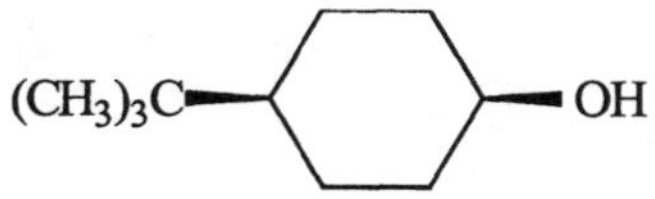

$(CH_3)_3C$ OH

2. 3-methyl-2-buten-1-ol

Answer:

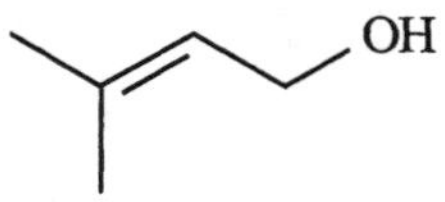

OH

3. 2-phenyl-2-propanol

Answer:

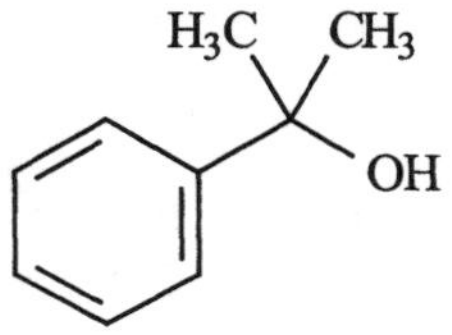

H_3C CH_3 OH

4. glycerol

Answer:

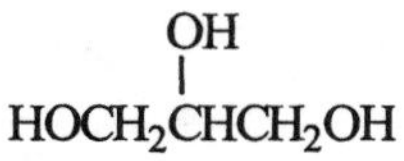

$HOCH_2CH(OH)CH_2OH$

5. 2, 4, 6-trinitrophenol

Answer:

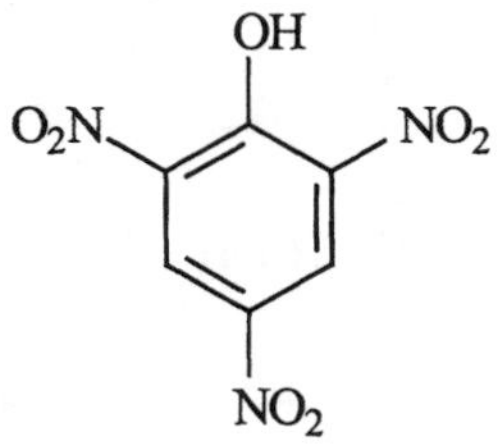

OH O_2N NO_2 NO_2

Give acceptable names for each of the following substances.

6. [structure: $CH_3CH=C(CH_2CH_3)CH_2OH$] OH

Answer: 2-ethyl-2-buten-1-ol

7. $HOCH_2CH_2OH$

Answer: 1, 2-ethanediol or ethylene glycol

8. [structure: $CH_2=CHCH_2OH$] OH

Answer: allyl alcohol or 2-propen-1-ol

9. HO—[benzene ring]—OH

Answer: hydroquinone or *p*-dihydroxybenzene or 1,4-benzenediol

Rank the following groups of compounds from most acidic (1) to least acidic (4). Place the number corresponding to the compound's relative rank in the blank below the structure.

10.

$CH_2(NO_2)CH_2CH_2CH_2OH$	$CH_3CH_3CH_2CH(NO_2)OH$	$CH_3CH_2CH_2CH_2OH$	$CH_3CH(NO_2)CH_2CH_2OH$
____	____	____	____

Answer:

$CH_2(NO_2)CH_2CH_2CH_2OH$	$CH_3CH_3CH_2CH(NO_2)OH$	$CH_3CH_2CH_2CH_2OH$	$CH_3CH(NO_2)CH_2CH_2OH$
3	1	4	2

11.

$(CF_3)_2CHOH$	$CH_3C\equiv C-H$	$(CH_3)_3COH$	CH_3CH_2OH
____	____	____	____

Answer:

$(CF_3)_2CHOH$	$CH_3C\equiv C-H$	$(CH_3)_3COH$	CH_3CH_2OH
1	4	3	2

12.

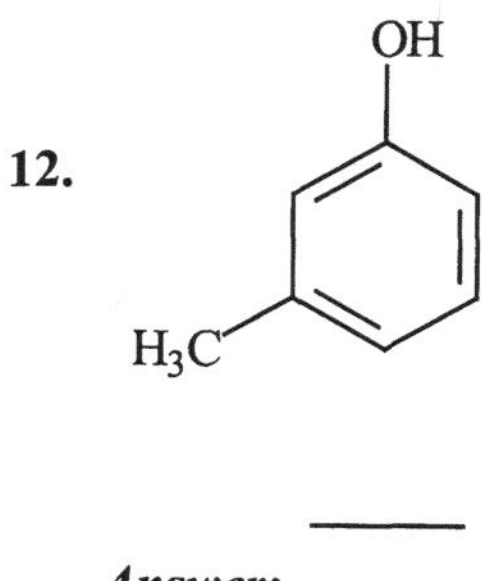

H_3C, OH (meta)	OH / CN (para)	CH_2OH / CN (para)	CO_2H / CN (para)
____	____	____	____

Answer:

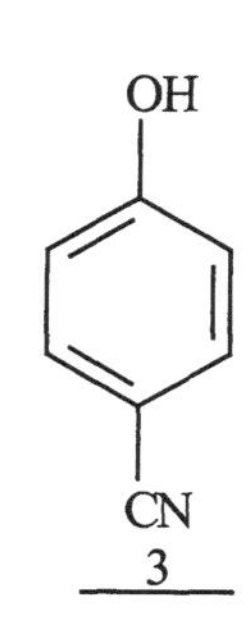

H_3C, OH (meta)	OH / CN (para)	CH_2OH / CN (para)	CO_2H / CN (para)
2	3	1	4

13. Explain why nonafluoro-2-methyl-2-propoxide is a much weaker base than *tert*-butoxide.

$$(CF_3)_3C\text{—}\ddot{\underset{\cdot\cdot}{O}}:^- \quad \text{versus} \quad (CH_3)_3C\text{—}\ddot{\underset{\cdot\cdot}{O}}:^-$$

Answer: Nonafluoro-2-methyl-2-propoxide anion is more stable than *tert*-butoxide anion because the electron-withdrawing fluoride atoms inductively delocalize the negative charge. Since nonafluoro-2-methyl-2-propoxide is more stable than *tert*-butoxide, it is a weaker base.

Refer to the data below to answer the following questions.

pK_as of Some Phenols (Y-substituted phenol, $Y\text{-}C_6H_4\text{-}OH$)

Y	pK_a
-H	9.89
m-NO_2	8.28
p-NO_2	7.17
m-OCH_3	9.65
p-OCH_3	10.21

14. The *weakest* acid in the table is:

Answer: *p*-methoxyphenol

15. Which of the acids in the Table has the weakest conjugate base?

Answer: *p*-nitrophenol

16. How do you account for the difference in acidity between *meta* and *para*-nitrophenol?

Answer: In *m*-nitrophenol, the *inductive effect* of the electron-withdrawing nitro group helps to stabilize the negative charge on oxygen. However, when the nitro group is *para* to the oxygen, direct conjugation of the negative charge on oxygen with the nitro group can occur. *p*-Nitrophenolate ion is, thus, more stable than *m*-nitrophenolate ion, and, as a result, forms more readily.

versus

To answer the following questions, consider the reaction below:

17. The best reagents for accomplishing the above transformation are:

a. 1. OsO_4, pyridine
   2. $NaHSO_3$, H_2O

b. 1. $Hg(OAc)_2$, H_2O
   2. $NaBH_4$

c. 1. RCO_3H, CH_2Cl_2
   2. H_3O^+

d. 1. BH_3, THF
   2. H_2O_2, ^-OH

Answer: d

18. The alcohol product is classified as a:

a. 1° alcohol
b. 2° alcohol
c. 3° alcohol
d. 4° alcohol

Answer: b

19. On the templates provided below, draw both conformations of the the alcohol product. *Circle* the *least stable*conformation.

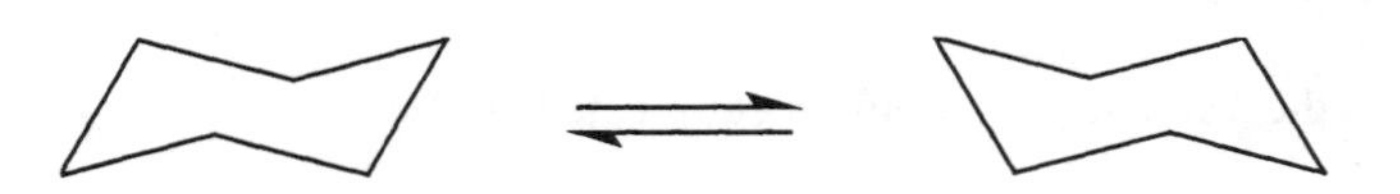

Answer:

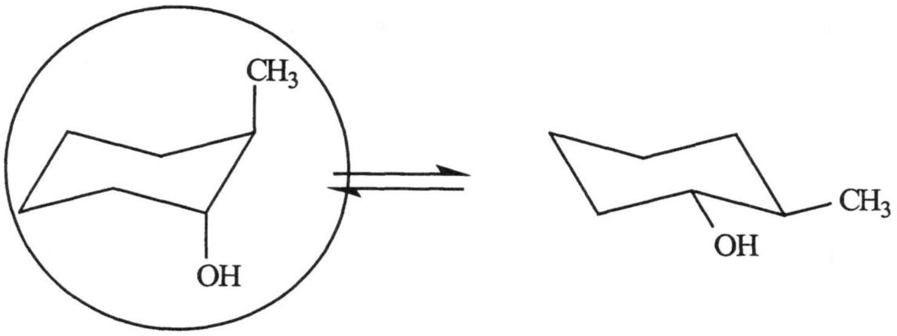

(chemical structure diagram — chair conformations of 2-methylcyclohexanol in equilibrium; labels: CH3, OH, CH3, OH)

20. Provide the IUPAC name for the product alcohol.

Answer: *trans*-2-methylcyclohexanol

To answer the following questions, consider the reaction below:

(reaction scheme: 2-methylcyclohexanol with OH, CH3 → $POCl_3$ / pyridine → 3-methylcyclohexene, CH3)

21. On the structures provided below, draw arrows which account for the complete stepwise mechanism for this reaction.

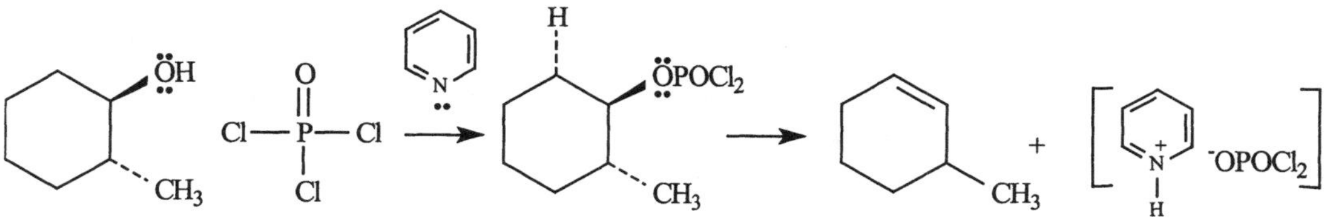

(mechanism structures: ÖH, CH3, Cl—P(=O)(Cl)—Cl, pyridine N, H, $\ddot{O}POCl_2$, CH3, → alkene CH3 + [pyridinium N–H $^{-}OPOCl_2$])

Answer:

(mechanism with curved arrows: ÖH, CH3, Cl—P(=O)(Cl)—Cl, pyridine N, H, $\ddot{O}POCl_2$, CH3, → alkene CH3 + [pyridinium N–H $^{-}OPOCl_2$])

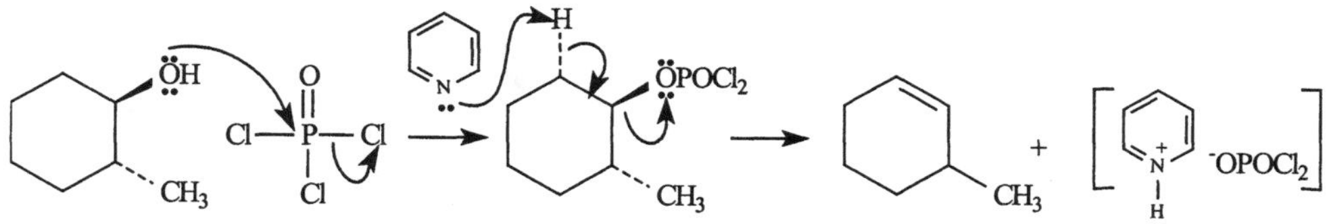

22. The dehydration of secondary and tertiary alcohols by reaction with $POCl_3$ in pyridine is an example of:

a. an E1 process
b. an S_N1 process
c. an E2 process
d. an S_N2 process

Answer: c

23. Why is 3-methylcyclohexene the major product of this reaction instead of 1-methycyclohexene?

Answer: In E2 elimination, dehydration proceeds most readily when the two groups to be eliminated have a trans-diaxial relationship. In this compound, the only hydrogen with the proper geometric relationship to the –OH group is at C_6 so the major product of this reaction is 3-methylcyclohexene.

24. Acid-catalyzed dehydration of 2,2-dimethylcyclohexanol yields 1,2-dimethylcyclohexene as one of the major products. Write the complete stepwise mechanism for this reaction. Show all electron flow with arrows and show all intermediate structures.

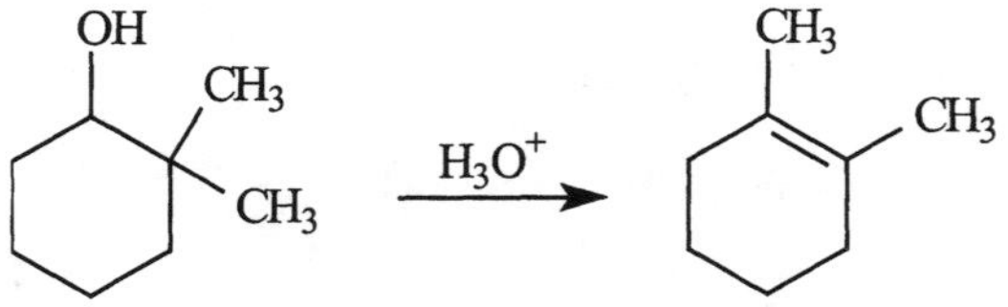

OH, CH_3, CH_3 $\xrightarrow{H_3O^+}$ CH_3, CH_3

Answer:

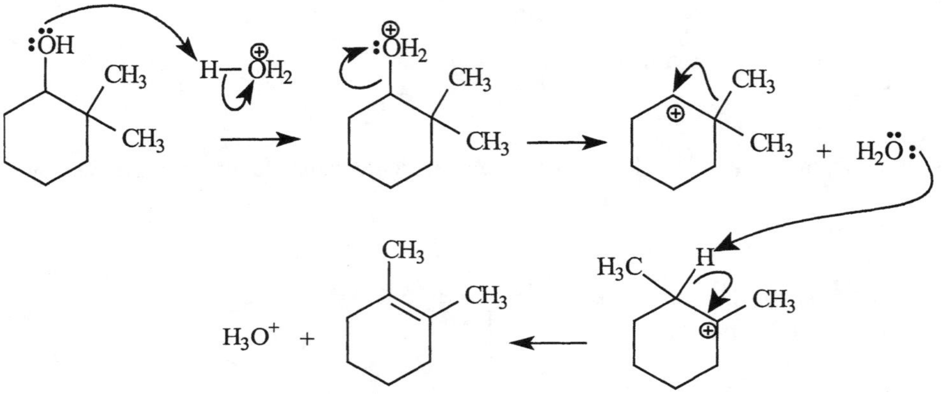

:ÖH, CH_3, CH_3 + H–$\overset{\oplus}{O}H_2$ ⟶ :$\overset{\oplus}{O}H_2$, CH_3, CH_3 ⟶ ⊕, CH_3, CH_3 + $H_2\ddot{O}$:

H_3O^+ + CH_3, CH_3 ⟵ H_3C, H, ⊕, CH_3

To answer the following questions, consider the reaction below:

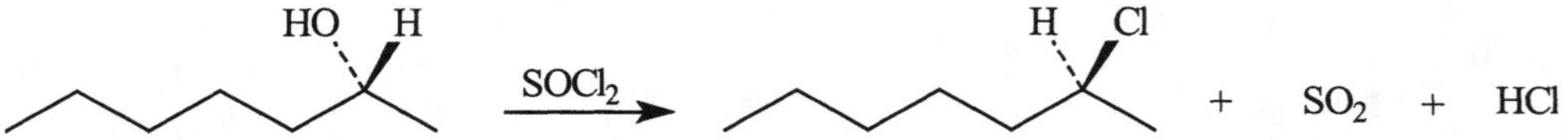

HO H $\xrightarrow{SOCl_2}$ H Cl + SO_2 + HCl

25. Provide the complete IUPAC name for the starting material in this reaction.

Answer: (*R*)-2-heptanol

26. The starting material can be classified as a:

a. 1° alcohol
b. 2° alcohol
c. 3° alcohol
d. 4° alcohol

Answer: b

27. Write the complete stepwise mechanism for the reaction. Show all intermediates and all electron flow with arrows.

Answer:

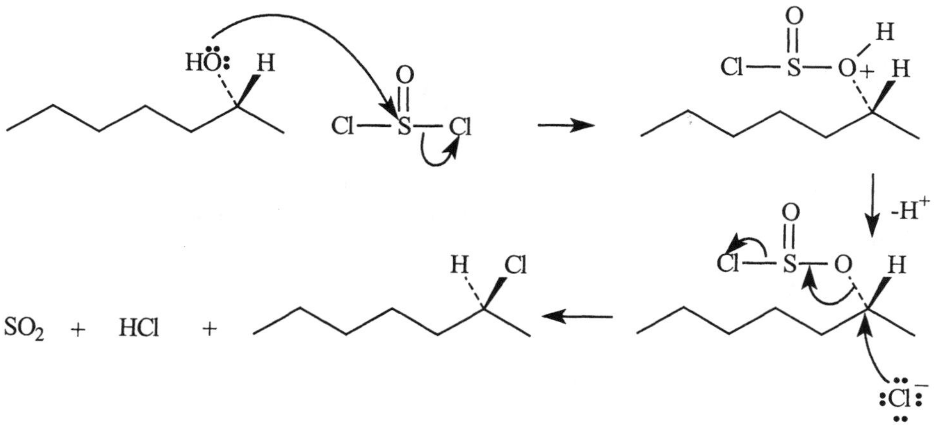

HÖ: H

O

Cl—S—Cl

O

H

Cl—S—O+ H

-H⁺

O

H Cl

Cl—S—O H

SO_2 + HCl +

:Cl:⁻

28. The conversion of an alcohol into an alkyl chloride by reaction with $SOCl_2$ is an example of:

a. an E1 process
b. an S_N1 process
c. an E2 process
d. an S_N2 process

Answer: d

Consider the Grignard reaction below to answer the following questions.

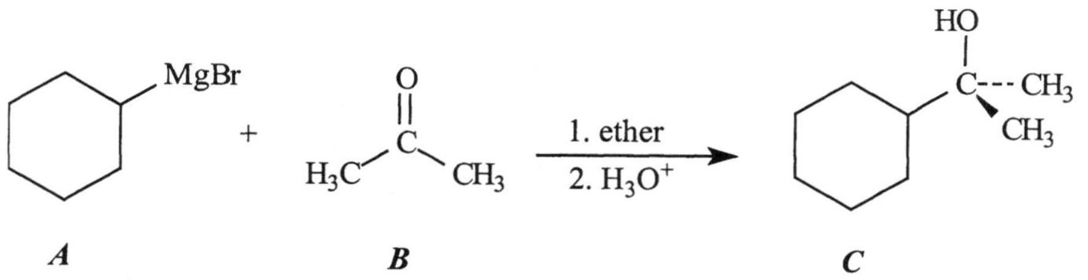

MgBr

+

O

H_3C C CH_3

1. ether

2. H_3O^+

HO

C--- CH_3

CH_3

A *B* *C*

29. The electrophile in this reaction is:

Answer: B

30. The nucleophile in this reaction is:

Answer: A

31. The alcohol product can be classified as a:

a. 1° alcohol
b. 2° alcohol
c. 3° alcohol
d. 4° alcohol

Answer: c

A highly useful and general method for the synthesis of alcohols is the addition of Grignard reagents to carbonyl compounds. Show what Grignard reagent and what carbonyl compound you would start with to prepare each alcohol below. List all possibilities.

32. $C_6H_5\text{–}C(OH)(CH_3)\text{–}CH_2CH_3$

Answer:

$C_6H_5\text{–}C(=O)\text{–}CH_2CH_3 + BrMg\text{—}CH_3$

or

$C_6H_5\text{–}C(=O)\text{–}CH_3 + BrMg\text{—}CH_2CH_3 \longrightarrow C_6H_5\text{–}C(OH)(CH_3)\text{–}CH_2CH_3$

or

$CH_3CH_2\text{—}C(=O)\text{—}CH_3 + BrMg\text{—}C_6H_5$

33. $PhCH_2\text{—}C(OH)(CH_3)\text{—}CH_3$

Answer:

$PhCH_2\text{—}C(=O)\text{—}CH_3 + BrMg\text{—}CH_3$

or

$PhCH_2\text{—}C(=O)\text{—}OCH_3 + 2\ BrMg\text{—}CH_3 \longrightarrow PhCH_2\text{—}C(OH)(CH_3)\text{—}CH_3$

or

$CH_3\text{—}C(=O)\text{—}CH_3 + BrMg\text{—}CH_2Ph$

34. $CH_3CH_2CHCH_2OH$ (with CH_2CH_3 on the CH)

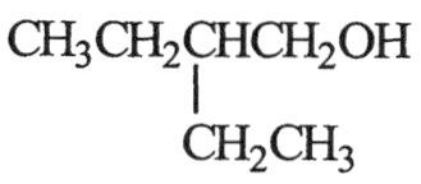

Answer:

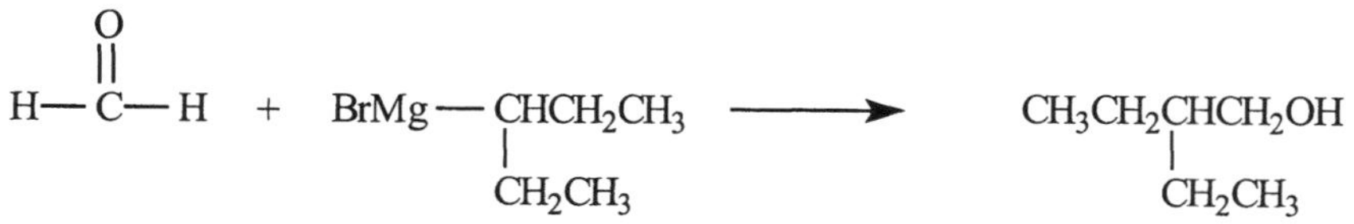

$$H-\overset{O}{\overset{\|}{C}}-H \;+\; BrMg-\underset{CH_2CH_3}{CHCH_2CH_3} \longrightarrow \underset{CH_2CH_3}{CH_3CH_2CHCH_2OH}$$

35. OH

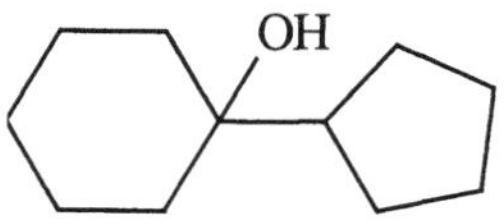

Answer:

O + BrMg ⟶ OH

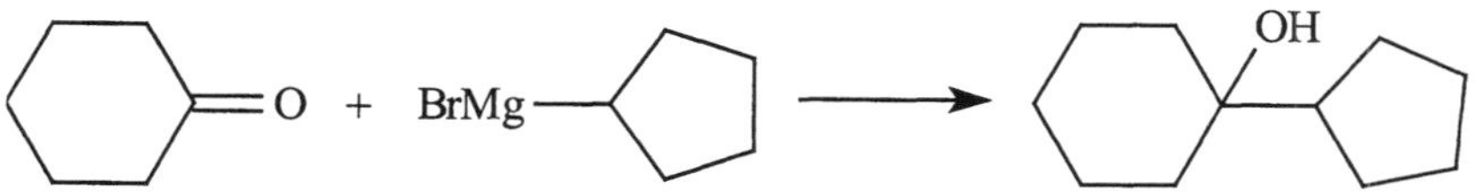

Give the major organic product(s) of the following reactions or sequences of reactions. Show all relevant stereochemistry.

36. OH OH $\xrightarrow[H_2O,\ acetone]{CrO_3,\ H_2SO_4}$

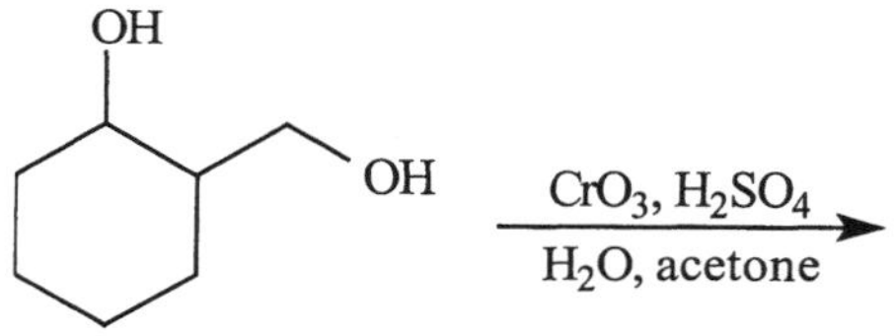

Answer:

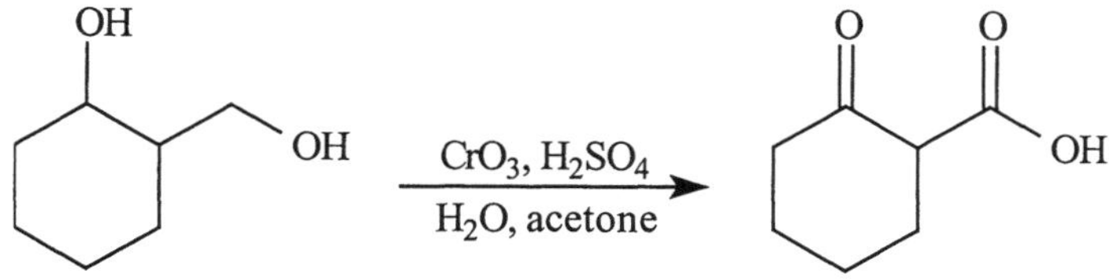

OH OH $\xrightarrow[H_2O,\ acetone]{CrO_3,\ H_2SO_4}$ O O OH

37. O H + MgBr $\xrightarrow[2.\ H_3O^+]{1.\ ether}$

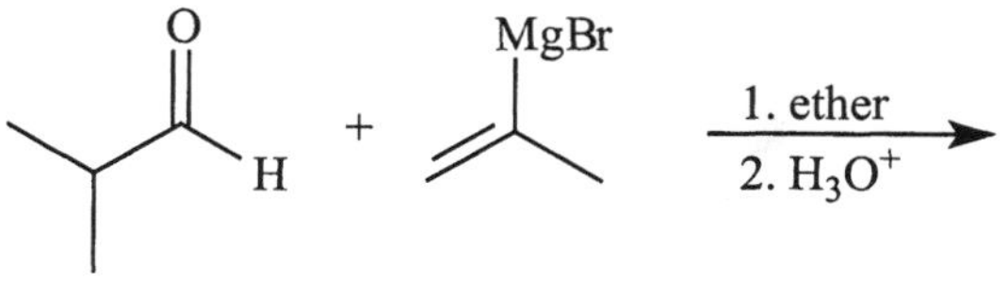

Answer:

O H + MgBr $\xrightarrow[2.\ H_3O^+]{1.\ ether}$ OH

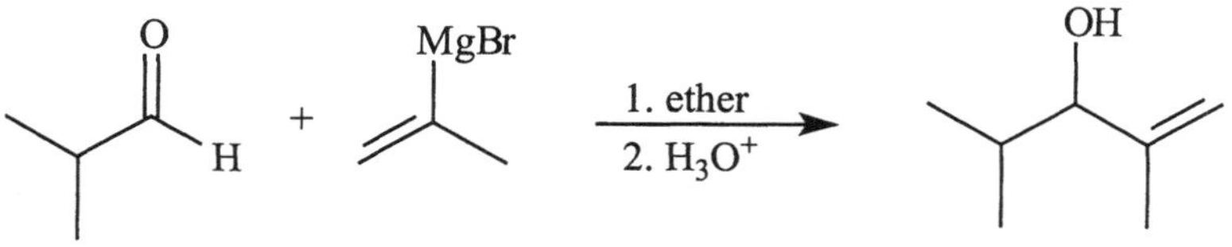

38.

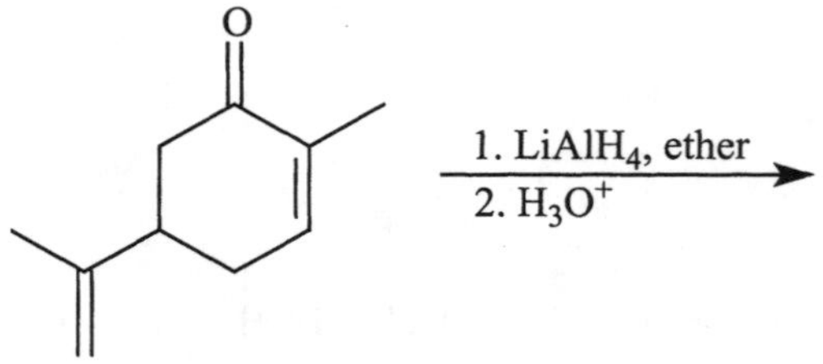

O

1. $LiAlH_4$, ether
2. H_3O^+

Answer:

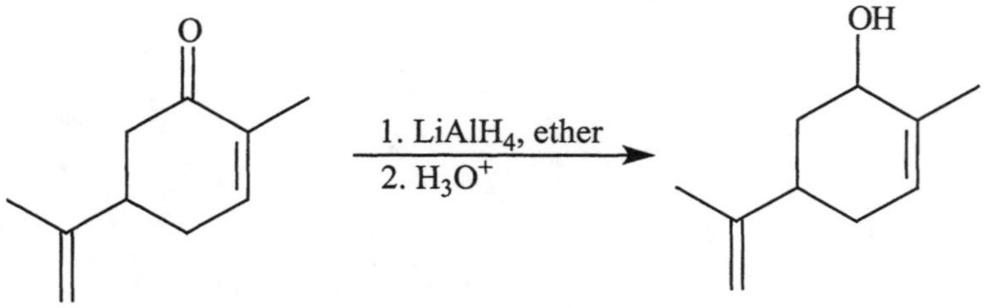

O

1. $LiAlH_4$, ether
2. H_3O^+

OH

39.

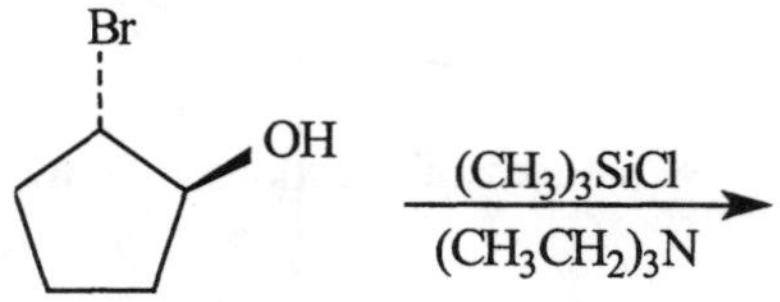

Br

OH

$(CH_3)_3SiCl$
$(CH_3CH_2)_3N$

Answer:

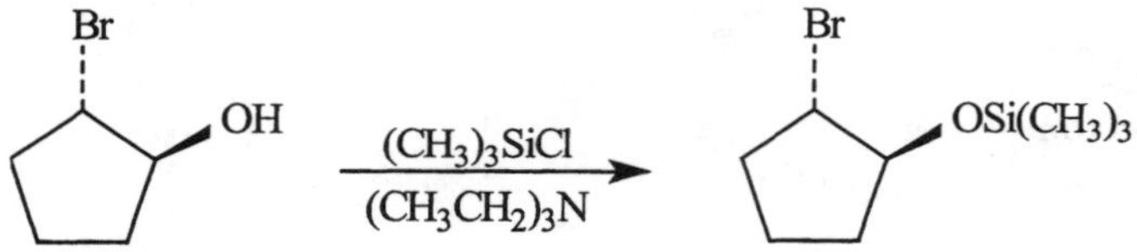

Br

OH

$(CH_3)_3SiCl$
$(CH_3CH_2)_3N$

Br

$OSi(CH_3)_3$

40. $CH_3-C(CH_3)_2-CH_2-OH \xrightarrow{H_3O^+}$

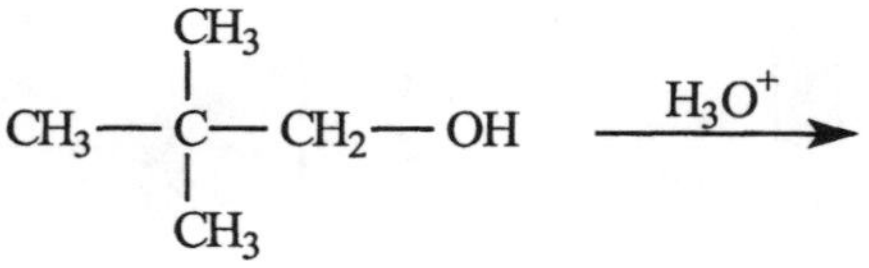

Answer:

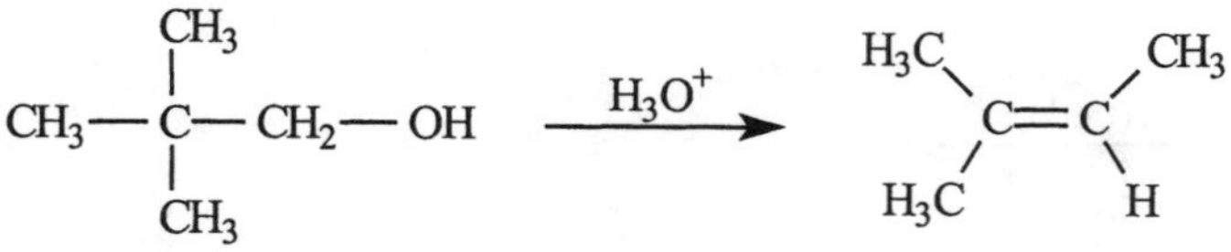

$CH_3-C(CH_3)_2-CH_2-OH \xrightarrow{H_3O^+} (H_3C)_2C{=}C(CH_3)H$

41. $C_6H_5-C(=O)-OCH_3$ + 2 C_6H_5MgBr $\xrightarrow[2.\ H_3O^+]{1.\ ether}$

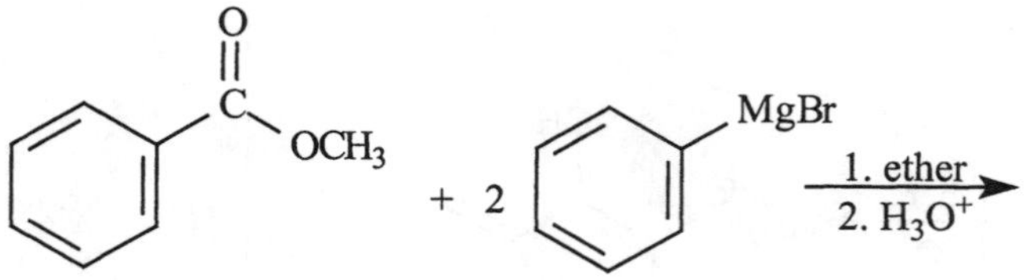

Answer:

Methyl benzoate ($C_6H_5COOCH_3$) + 2 C_6H_5MgBr $\xrightarrow[\text{2. } H_3O^+]{\text{1. ether}}$ $(C_6H_5)_3C{-}OH$

42. C_6H_5COOH $\xrightarrow[\text{2. } H_3O^+]{\text{1. LiAlH}_4\text{, ether}}$

Answer:

C_6H_5COOH $\xrightarrow[\text{2. } H_3O^+]{\text{1. LiAlH}_4\text{, ether}}$ $C_6H_5CH_2OH$

43. $(CH_3)_2CHCH_2CHO$ $\xrightarrow[\text{2. } H_3O^+]{\text{1. NaBH}_4\text{, ethanol}}$

Answer:

$(CH_3)_2CHCH_2CHO$ $\xrightarrow[\text{2. } H_3O^+]{\text{1. NaBH}_4\text{, ethanol}}$ $(CH_3)_2CHCH_2CH_2OH$

44. $H_3C{-}C(CH_3)_2{-}OH$ + NaH $\longrightarrow$

Answer:

$H_3C{-}C(CH_3)_2{-}OH$ + NaH $\longrightarrow$ $H_3C{-}C(CH_3)_2{-}O^-Na^+$ + H_2

45. Cyclopentanol (cyclopentyl–OH) $\xrightarrow[\text{pyridine}]{POCl_3}$

Answer:

Cyclopentyl–OH $\xrightarrow[\text{pyridine}]{POCl_3}$ cyclopentene

46. 1-Cyclohexylethanol (H, OH) $\xrightarrow[\text{2. NaOCH}_3\text{, CH}_3\text{OH}]{\text{1. }p\text{-TosCl, pyridine}}$

Answer:

1-Cyclohexylethanol (H, OH) $\xrightarrow[\text{2. NaOCH}_3\text{, CH}_3\text{OH}]{\text{1. }p\text{-TosCl, pyridine}}$ 1-cyclohexyl-1-methoxyethane (H_3CO, H) + ethylidenecyclohexane

47. 2-Methylphenol (OH, CH_3) $\xrightarrow[H_2O]{(KSO_3)_2NO}$

Answer:

2-Methylphenol (OH, CH_3) $\xrightarrow[H_2O]{(KSO_3)_2NO}$ 2-methyl-1,4-benzoquinone (O, O, CH_3)

48. 4-Methylphenol (OH, CH_3) + $(CH_3)_2C{=}CH_2$ $\xrightarrow{H_2SO_4}$

Answer:

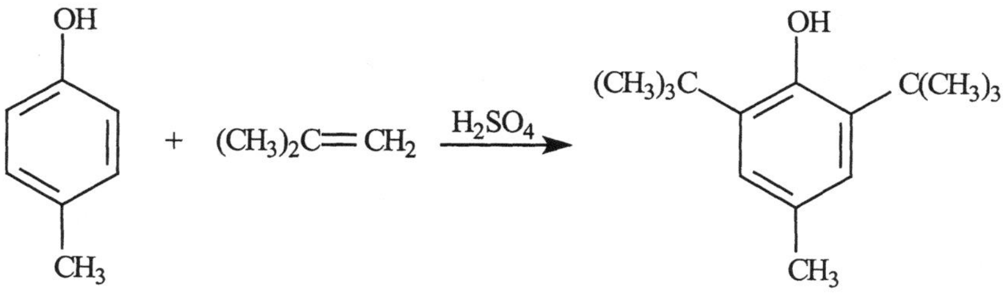

$$\text{4-methylphenol} + (CH_3)_2C{=}CH_2 \xrightarrow{H_2SO_4} \text{2,6-di-}tert\text{-butyl-4-methylphenol (OH, }(CH_3)_3C\text{, }C(CH_3)_3\text{, }CH_3)$$

49. p-benzoquinone $\xrightarrow[\text{alcohol}]{NaBH_4}$

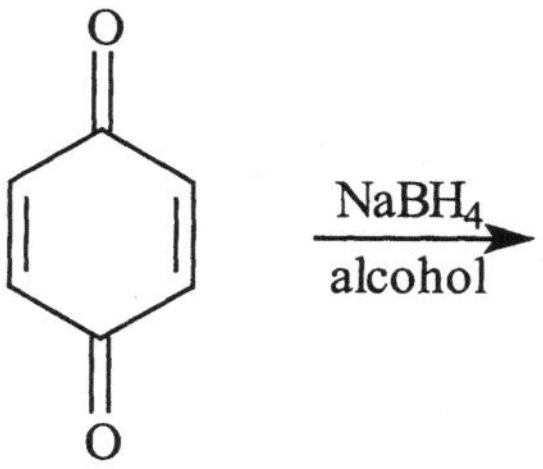

Answer:

$$\text{p-benzoquinone} \xrightarrow[\text{alcohol}]{NaBH_4} \text{hydroquinone (OH, OH)}$$

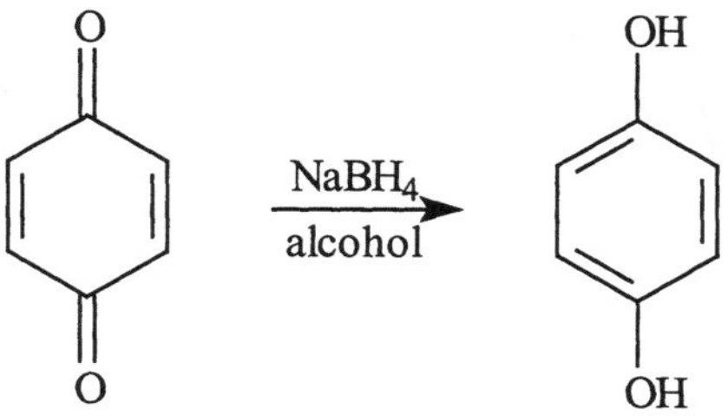

Choose the *best* reagent(s) for carrying out the following conversions from the list provided below. Place the letter of the best choice in the blank to the left of the conversion. Reagents may be used more than once.

a. 1. CH_3MgBr, ether
   2. H_3O^+

b. 1. PBr_3
   2. NaOH

c. 1. $(CH_3)_3SiCl$, $(CH_3CH_2)_3N$
   2. CH_3MgBr, ether
   3. H_3O^+

d. 1. $LiAlH_4$, ether
   2. H_3O^+

e. 1. *p*-TosCl, pyridine
   2. NaOH

f. CrO_3, H_2SO_4, H_2O

g. 1. $NaBH_4$, ethanol
   2. H_3O^+

h. PCC, CH_2Cl_2

50. 3-methylpent-3-en-1-ol (OH) ⟶ 3-methylpent-3-enoic acid (O, OH)

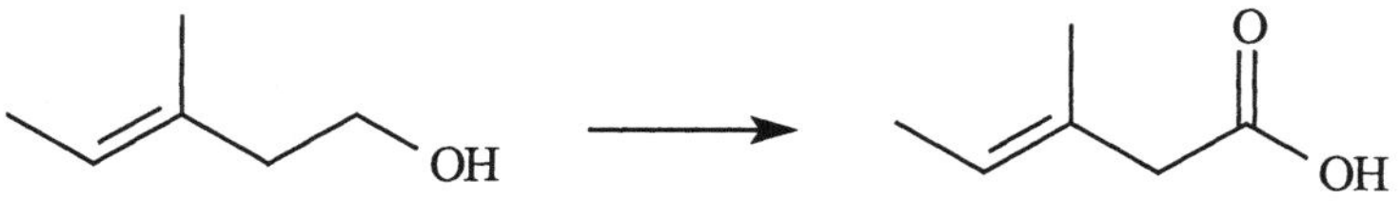

Answer: f

51.

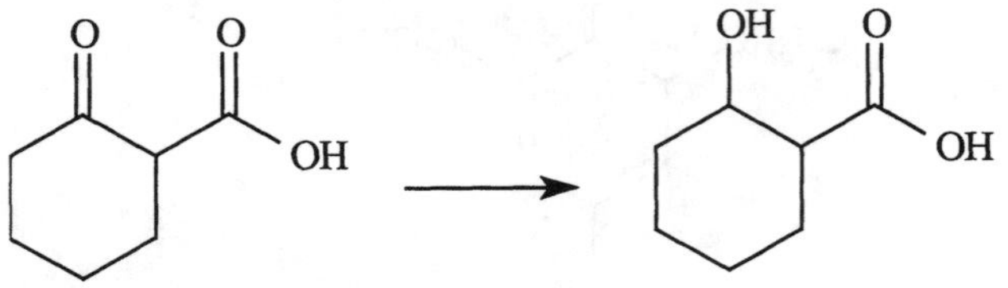

O O OH → OH O OH

Answer: g

52.

OH → H O

Answer: h

53.

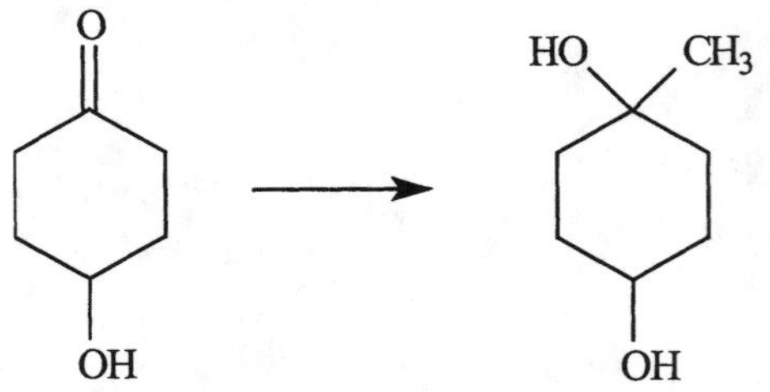

O OH → HO CH$_3$ OH

Answer: c

54.

HO H → H OH

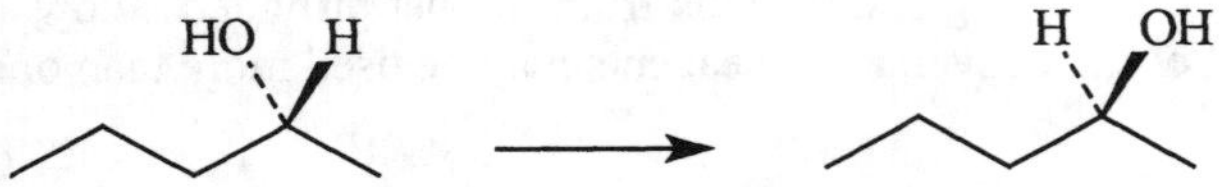

Answer: e

55. Propose a synthesis of Dimestrol starting from *p*-methoxypropiophenone as the only source of carbon.

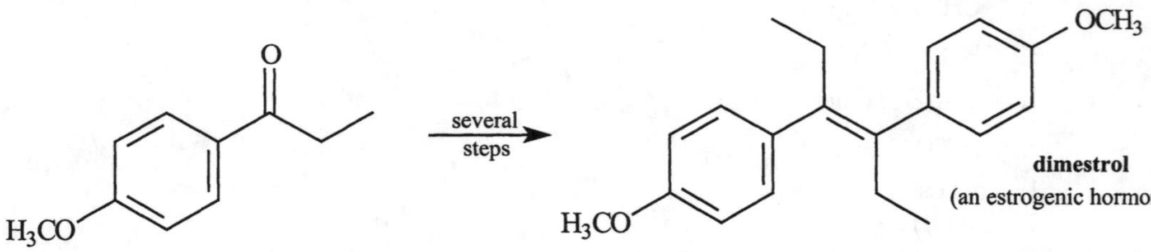

O H$_3$CO —several steps→ OCH$_3$ H$_3$CO

dimestrol
(an estrogenic hormone)

Answer:

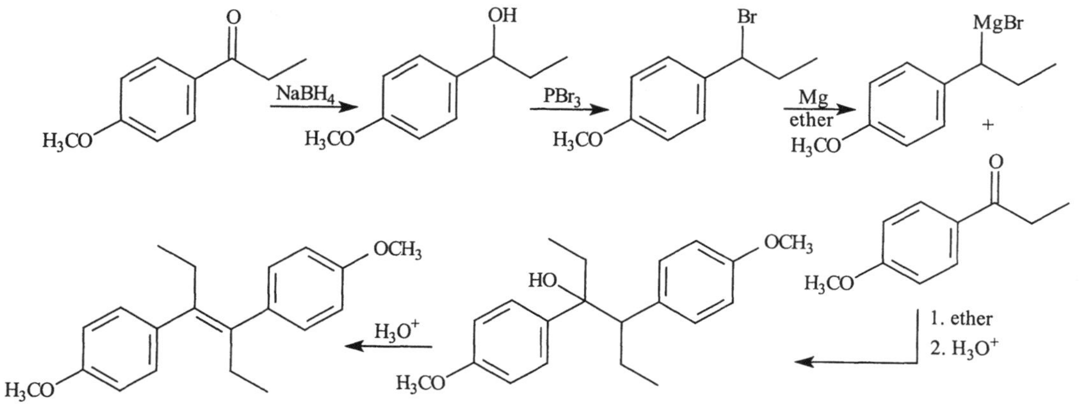

H_3CO (O) → NaBH$_4$ → H_3CO (OH) → PBr$_3$ → H_3CO (Br) → Mg, ether → H_3CO (MgBr) + H_3CO (O) → 1. ether 2. H_3O^+ → H_3CO (HO) (OCH_3) → H_3O^+ → H_3CO (OCH_3)

56. Outline the synthetic steps necessary to carry out the conversion below. You may use any organic or inorganic reagents you need. Show the structures of all intermediate compounds that would probably be isolated during the course of your synthesis, and show all necessary reagents.

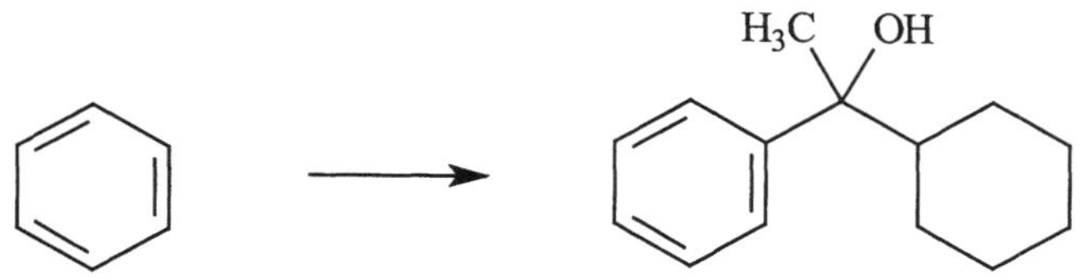

H_3C OH

Answer:

Br_2, $FeBr_3$ → Br → Mg, ether → MgBr + H_3C (O) → 1. ether 2. H_3O^+ → H_3C OH

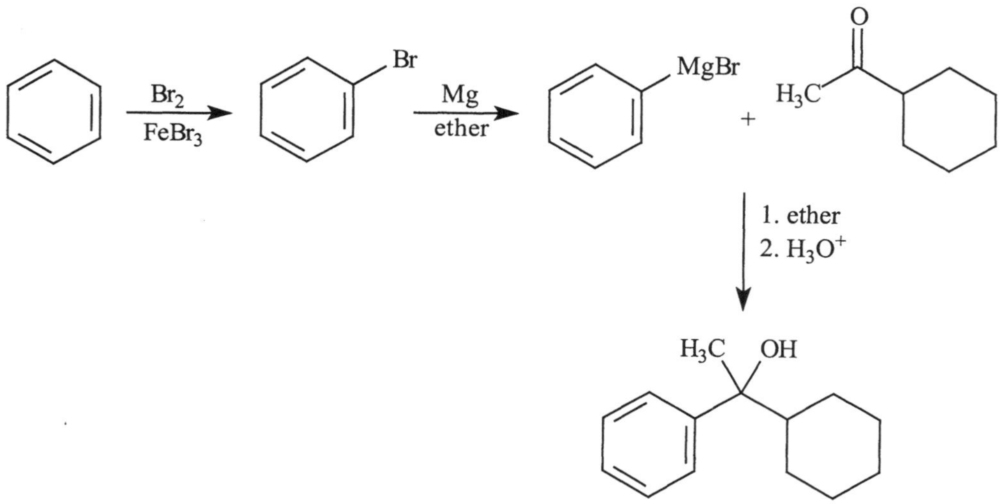

57. Synthesize the following alcohol starting with cyclohexene and bromocylopentane as the only organic starting materials. Show all reagents and all intermediates in your synthesis.

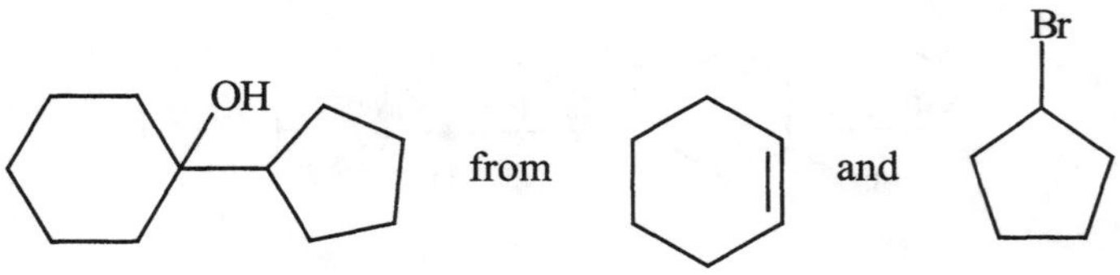

from and

Br

OH

Answer:

1. $Hg(OAc)_2$, H_2O, THF
2. $NaBH_4$

OH

PCC

CH_2Cl_2

O

+

Br

MgBr

Mg

ether

1. ether
2. H_3O^+

OH

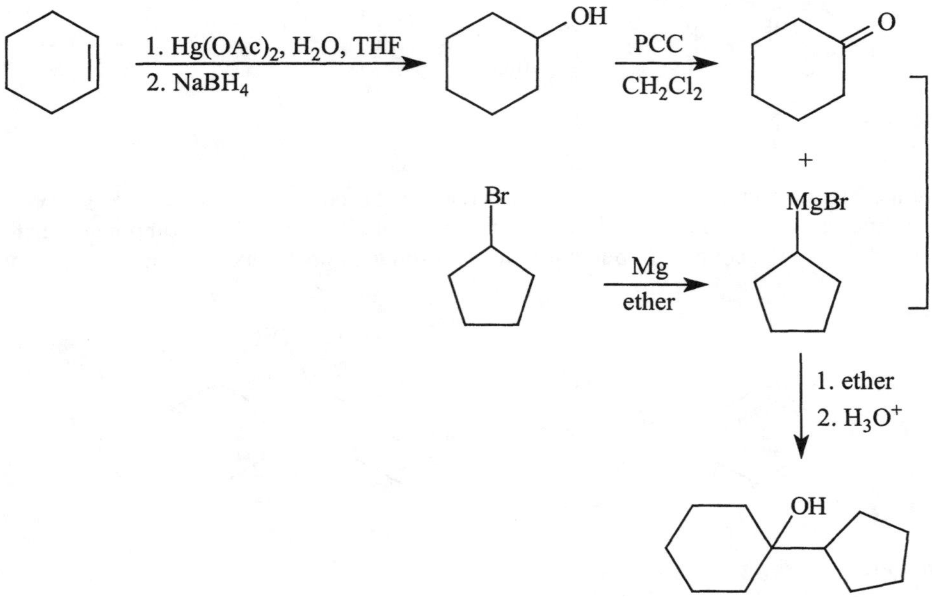

Propose structures for alcohols that have the following ^1H NMR spectra.

58. C_3H_8O

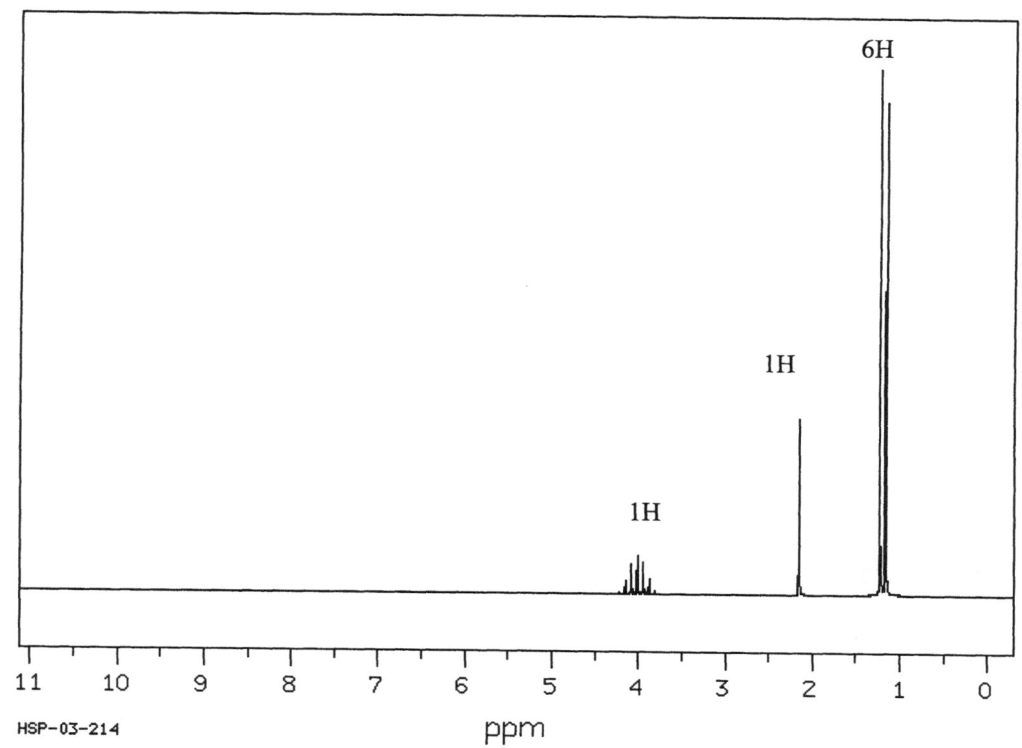

Spectrum obtained from: SBDSWeb: http://www.aist.go.jp/RIODB/SDBS/

Answer: isopropyl alcohol (2-propanol), $(CH_3)_2CHOH$

59. C_7H_8O (neat solution; no solvent)

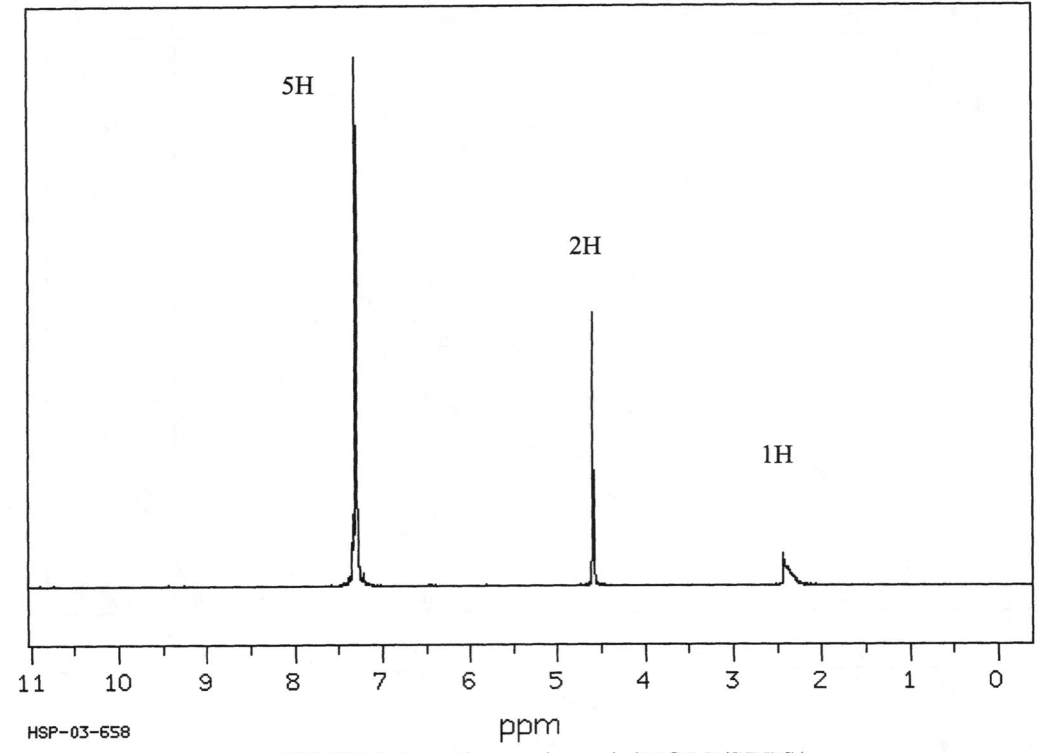

Spectrum obtained from: SBDSWeb: http://www.aist.go.jp/RIODB/SDBS/

Answer: benzyl alcohol, $PhCH_2OH$

Chapter 18 - Ethers and Epoxides; Thiols and Sulfides

Draw structures corresponding to each of the following IUPAC names.

1. tetrahydrofuran

Answer:

2. 12-crown-4

Answer:

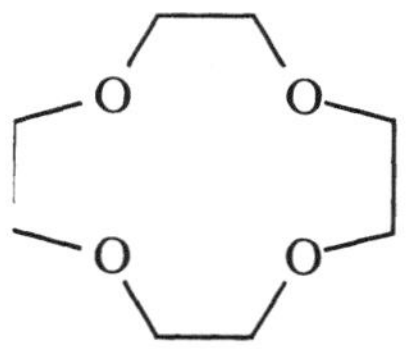

3. 1-isopropoxycyclopentene

Answer:

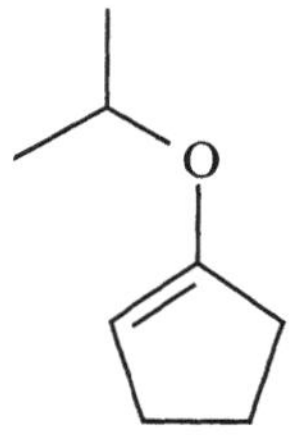

4. allyl benzyl ether

Answer:

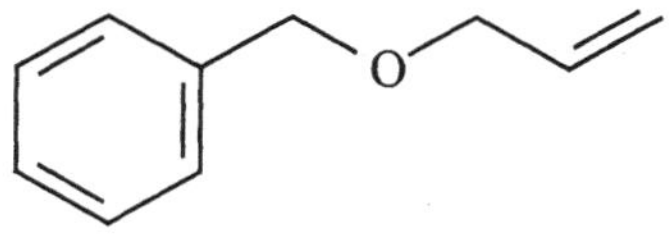

5. diethyl ether

Answer:

$$CH_3CH_2—O—CH_2CH_3$$

6. 3-methyl-1-butanethiol

Answer:

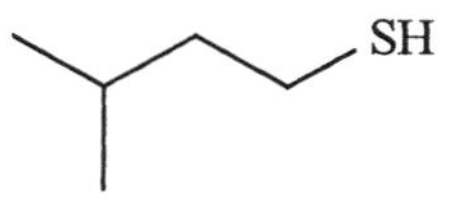

SH

7. cyclopropyl ethyl sulfide

Answer:

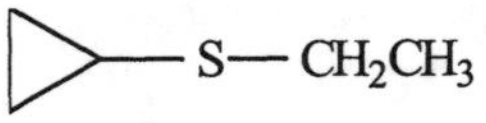

▷—S— CH_2CH_3

Provide correct IUPAC names for each of the structures below.

8.

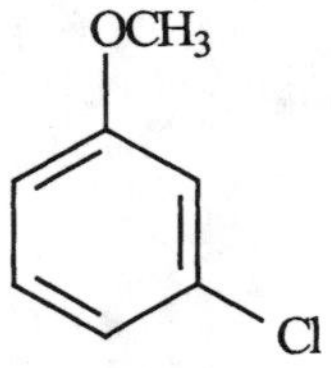

OCH_3 on benzene ring, Cl at meta position

Answer: *m*-chloroanisole or *m*-chloromethoxybenzene of (*m*-chlorophenyl) methyl ether

9. $H_3C—C(CH_3)_2—CH_2—O—CH_2CH_3$

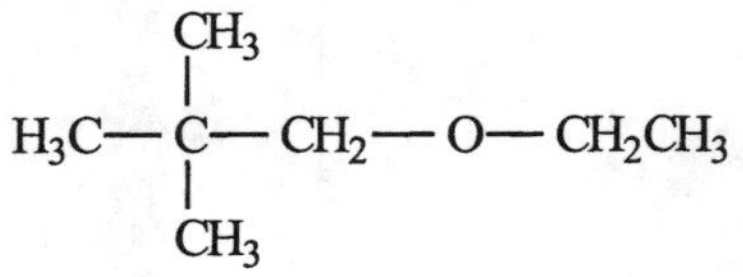

Answer: 1-ethoxy-2,2-dimethylpropane or ethyl neopentyl ether

10. cyclohexyl—S—cyclohexyl

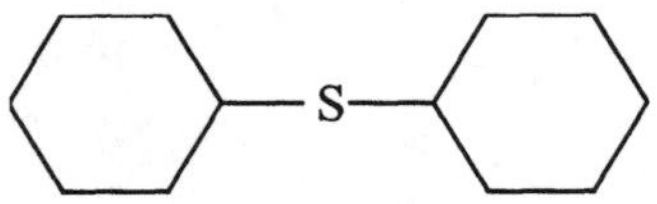

Answer: dicyclohexyl sulfide

Consider the reaction below to answer the following questions.

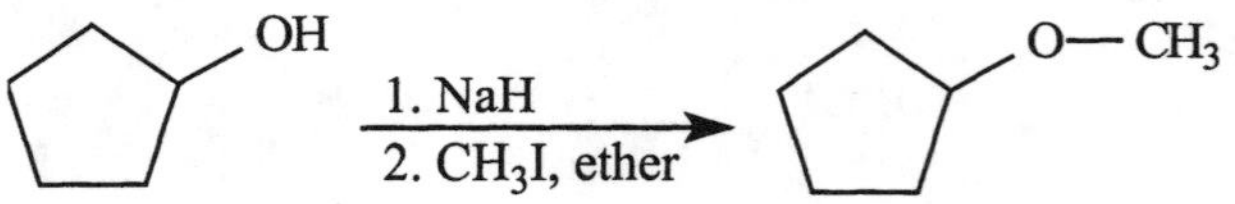

cyclopentyl—OH $\xrightarrow[\text{2. } CH_3I\text{, ether}]{\text{1. NaH}}$ cyclopentyl—O— CH_3

11. Write the complete stepwise mechanism for the reaction. Show all intermediate structures and all electron flow with arrows.

Answer:

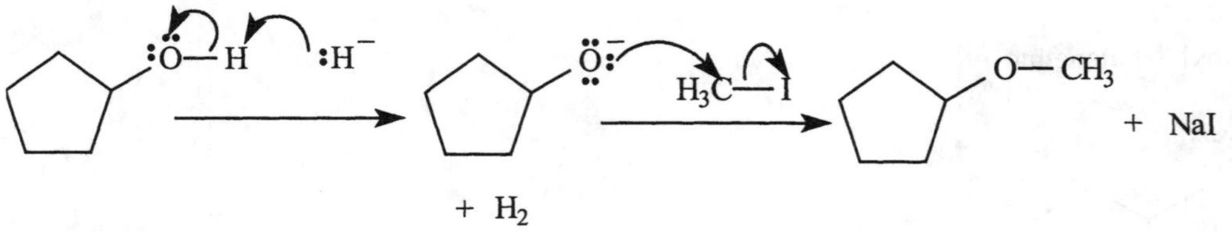

cyclopentyl—:Ö—H :H^- ⟶ cyclopentyl—$\ddot{O}:^-$ + H_2 ; $H_3C—I$ ⟶ cyclopentyl—O— CH_3 + NaI

12. Mechanistically, the Williamson ether synthesis outlined above is:

a. an E1 process
b. an S_N1 process
c. an E2 process
d. an S_N2 process

Answer: d

13. Alternatively, cyclopentyl methyl ether may be synthesized from cyclopentene. Outline a synthesis of cyclopentyl methyl ether from cyclopentene.

Answer:

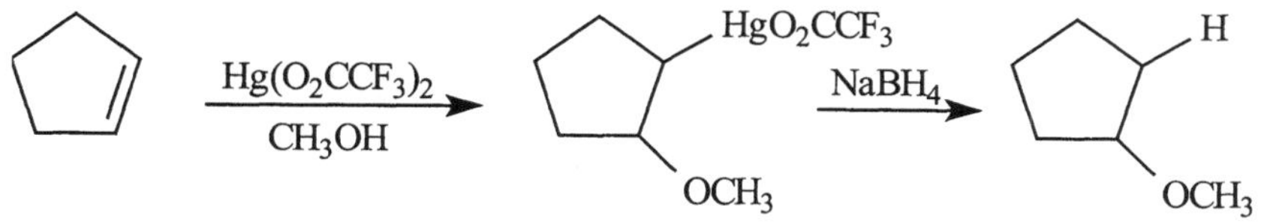

$Hg(O_2CCF_3)_2$ / CH_3OH → HgO_2CCF_3, OCH_3 → $NaBH_4$ → H, OCH_3

14. Diphenyl ether is inert to cleavage by HI or HBr. Explain.

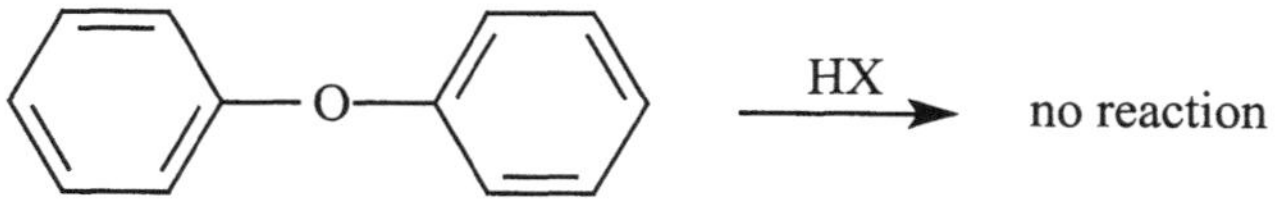

O — HX → no reaction

Answer: Acidic ether cleavages are typical nucleophilic substitution reactions that take place by either an S_N1 or S_N2 pathway. Diaryl ethers like diphenyl ether are inert under ordinary acidic conditions because the generation of an aryl cation is an S_N1 process that is energetically unfavorable, and "back-side" attack at the ring carbon bound to oxygen is sterically unfavorable.

15. Write the complete stepwise mechanism for the reaction below. Show all electron flow with arrows and draw all intermediate structures.

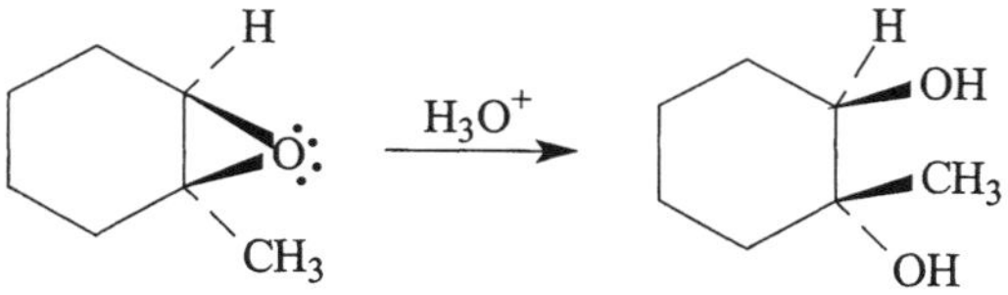

H, O:, CH_3 — H_3O^+ → H, OH, CH_3, OH

Answer:

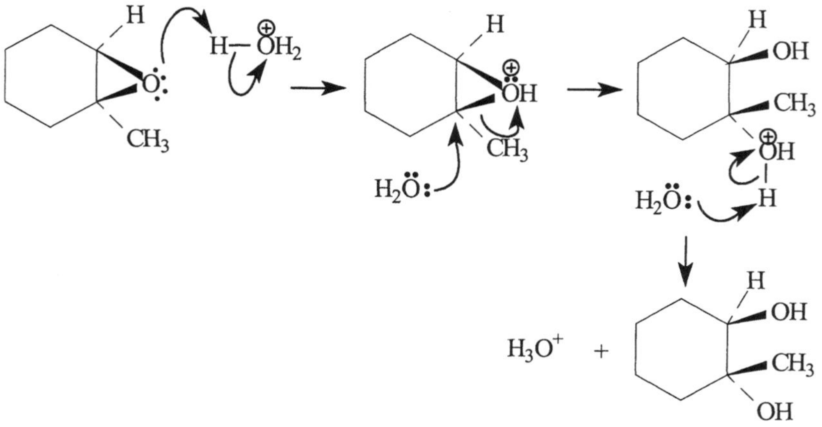

H, O:, CH_3 + $H-\overset{\oplus}{O}H_2$ → H, $\overset{\oplus}{O}H$, CH_3, $H_2\ddot{O}:$ → H, OH, CH_3, $\overset{\oplus}{O}H$–H, $H_2\ddot{O}:$ → H_3O^+ + H, OH, CH_3, OH

Consider the data below to answer the following questions.

Acetals are a special class of ethers which have two ether linkages at a single carbon. Tetrahydropyranyl ethers are acetals that are easily cleaved with mild aqueous acids at room temperature to yield alcohols.

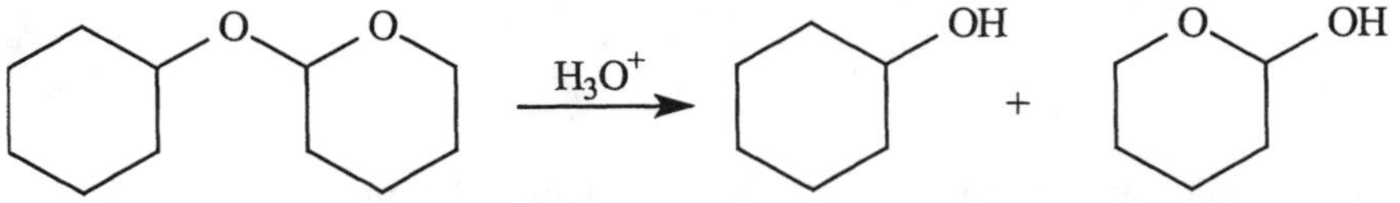

H_3O^+

16. Draw arrows showing the electron flow for this reaction on the structures provided below.

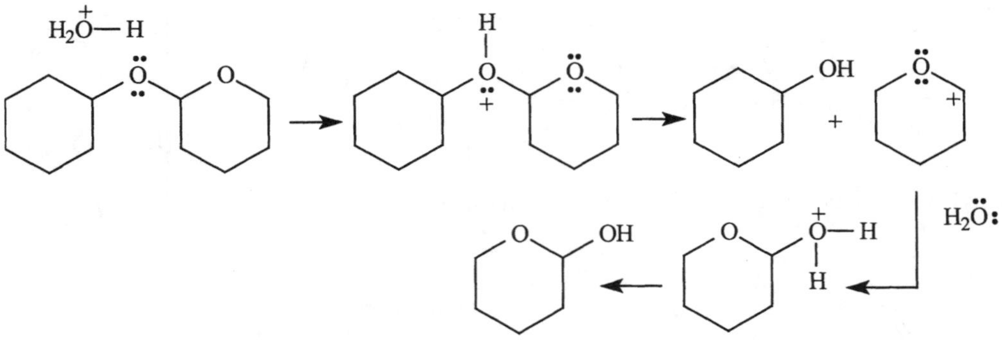

Answer:

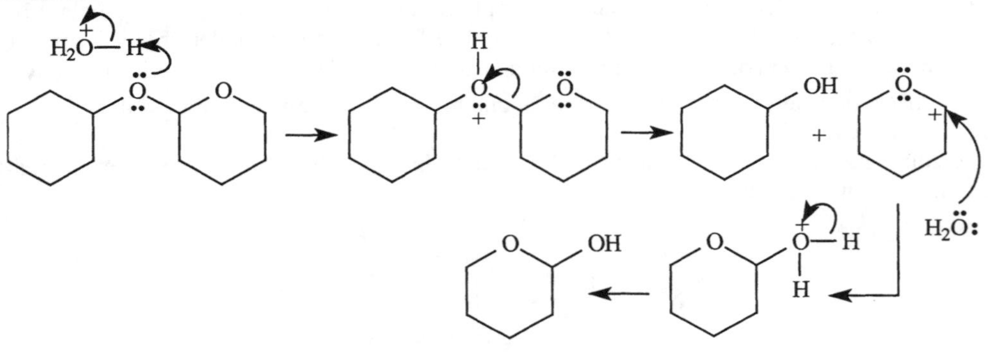

17. This ether cleavage occurs so easily under such mild conditions because the carbocation intermediate in step two is very stable. Explain why this carbocation is stabilized.

Answer: The carbocation generated in the first step of the S_N1 process is resonance-stabilized., so it forms easily.

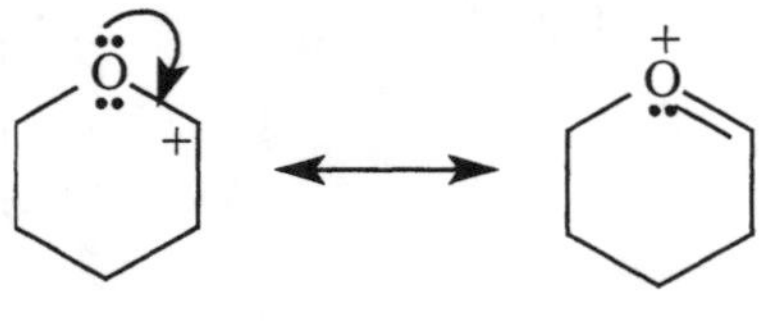

18. When 1,2-epoxypropane is treated with sodium ethoxide in ethanol 1-epoxy-2-propanol is the major product while only a trace amount of 2-ethoxy-1-propanol is produced. Explain these results based on the reaction mechanism.

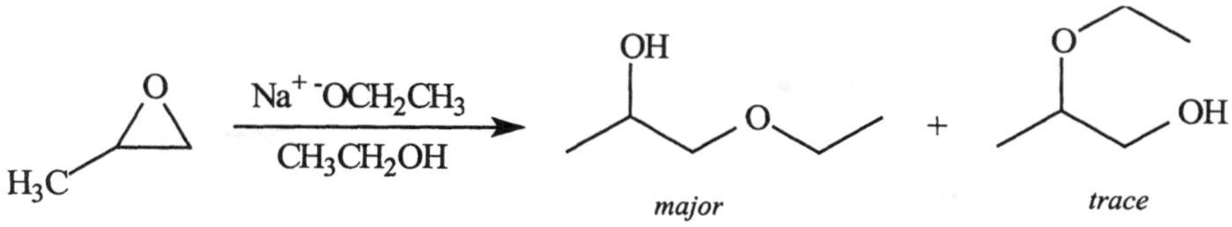

$Na^+ \ ^-OCH_2CH_3$, CH_3CH_2OH

major + *trace*

Answer: Basic nucleophiles like ethoxide react with epoxides in a typical S_N2-type process, so attack takes place at the less hindered epoxide carbon.

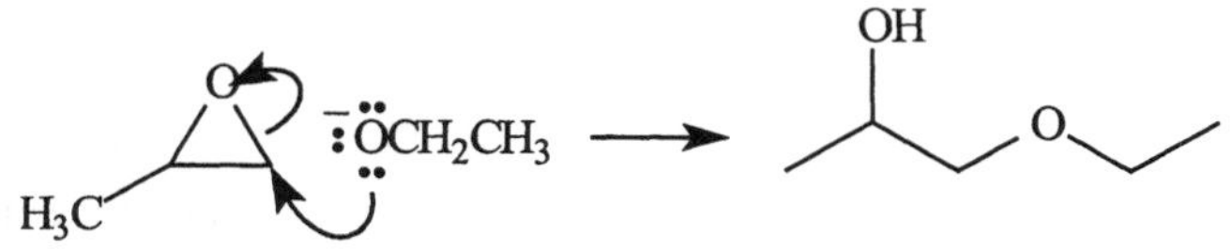

Consider the data below to answer the following questions.

Epoxides are synthesized industrially in one step by silver oxide air oxidation of ethylene and on a laboratory scale in one step by treating an alkene with *m*-chloroperoxybenzoic acid. An alternative two step process converts alkenes to halohydrins, which are converted by treatment with base to epoxides.

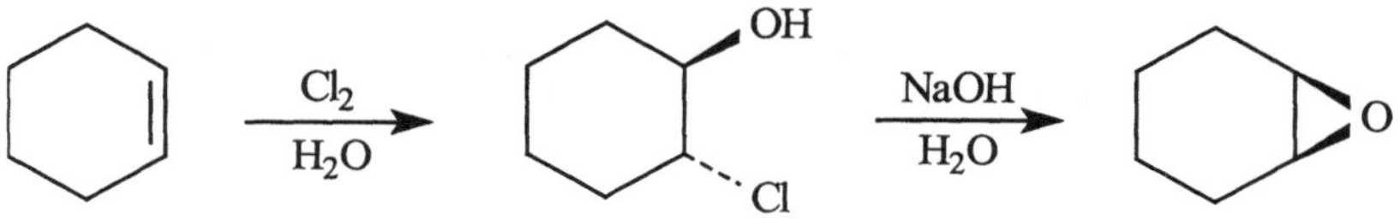

Cl_2, H_2O → NaOH, H_2O →

19. Show electron flow with arrows on the structures provided below for each step in the above transformation.

Step One

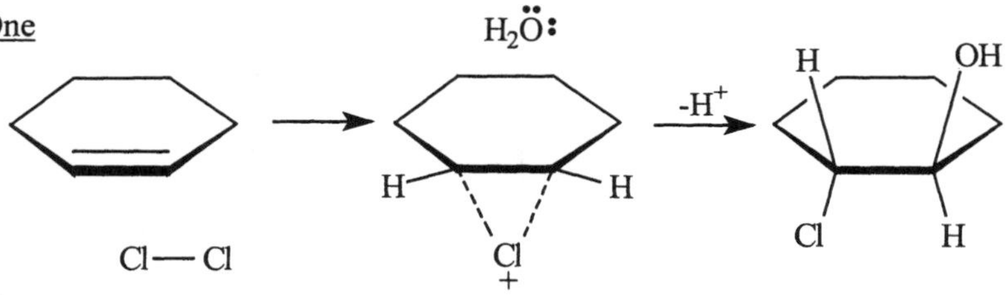

Step Two

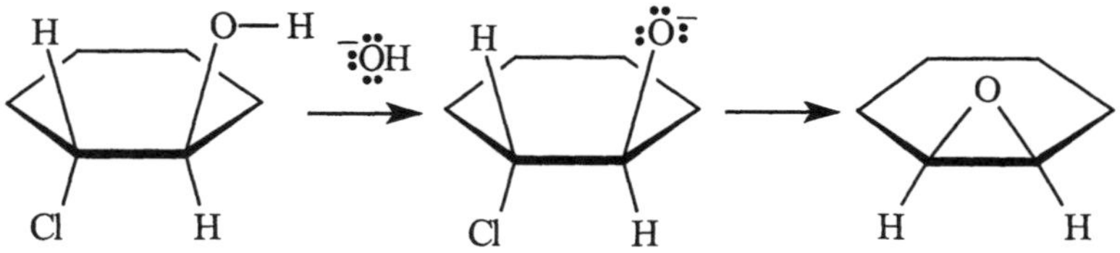

Answer:

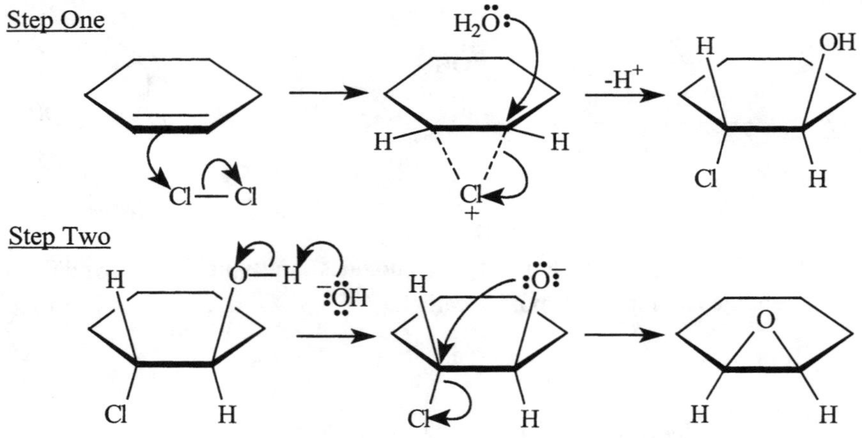

Step One

Step Two

20. The synthesis of epoxides by base treatment of halohydrins is an example of an intramolecular:

a. S_N1 reaction
b. hydrolysis reaction
c. dehydration reaction
d. Williamson ether synthesis

Answer: d

Propose structure(s) for the starting material(s), reagent(s), or major organic product(s) of the following reactions or sequences of reactions. Show all relevant stereochemistry.

21. 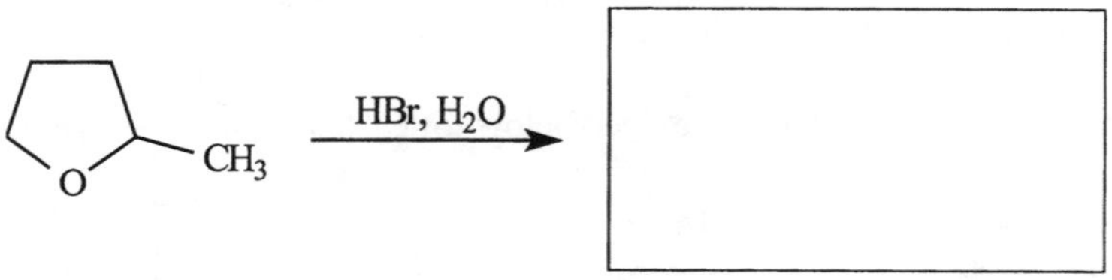 CH_3 — HBr, H_2O →

Answer:

CH_3 — HBr, H_2O → Br, CH_3, OH

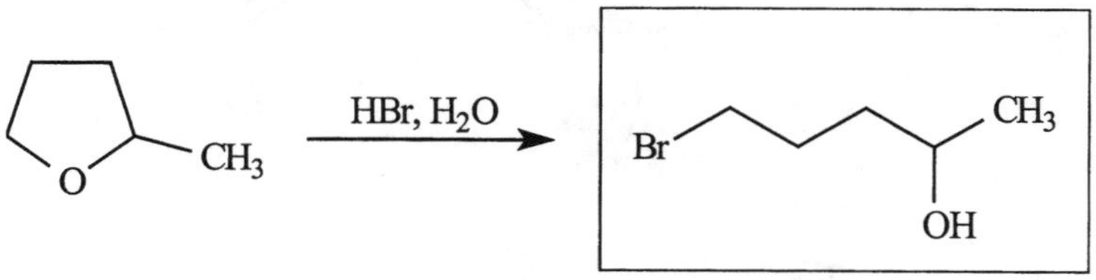

22. Cyclohexane with =CH_2 $\xrightarrow[\text{2. NaBH}_4]{\text{1. Hg(O}_2\text{CCF}_3)_2\text{, (CH}_3)_3\text{COH}}$ [ ]

Answer:

Cyclohexane with =CH_2 $\xrightarrow[\text{2. NaBH}_4]{\text{1. Hg(O}_2\text{CCF}_3)_2\text{, (CH}_3)_3\text{COH}}$ cyclohexane carbon bearing $OC(CH_3)_3$ and CH_3

23. [ ] $\xrightarrow[\text{CH}_2\text{Cl}_2\text{, rt}]{m\text{-chloroperoxybenzoic acid}}$ epoxide: H_3CH_2C, H_3C on one C; H, CH_3 on the other C

Answer:

H_3CH_2C / H_3C C=C H / CH_3 $\xrightarrow[\text{CH}_2\text{Cl}_2\text{, rt}]{m\text{-chloroperoxybenzoic acid}}$ epoxide: H_3CH_2C, H_3C on one C; H, CH_3 on the other C

24. H_3C / H C=C CH_3 / H $\xrightarrow[\text{H}_2\text{O}]{\text{Cl}_2}$ [ ] $\xrightarrow[\text{H}_2\text{O}]{\text{NaOH}}$ [ ]

Answer:

H_3C / H C=C CH_3 / H $\xrightarrow[\text{H}_2\text{O}]{\text{Cl}_2}$ HO, H_3C, H on C — C with CH_3, H, Cl $\xrightarrow[\text{H}_2\text{O}]{\text{NaOH}}$ epoxide (O): H_3C, H on one C; CH_3, H on the other C

25. 1-methylcyclopentene oxide (CH_3, O) $\xrightarrow[\text{NH}_3]{\text{NaNH}_2}$ $\xrightarrow{\text{H}_2\text{O}}$ [ ]

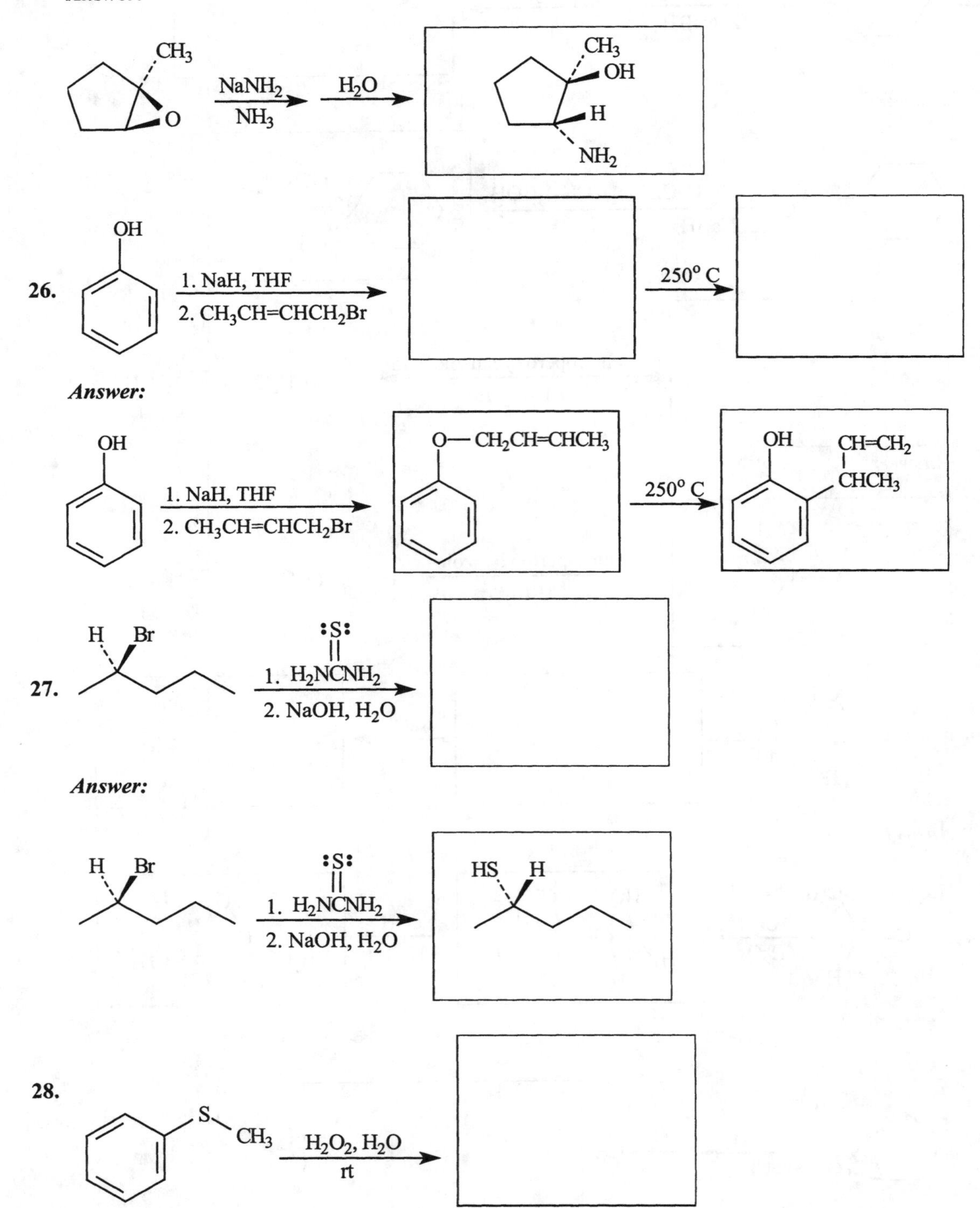

Answer:
CH3
O
NaNH2
NH3
H2O
CH3
OH
H
NH2
OH
26.
1. NaH, THF
2. CH3CH=CHCH2Br
250° C
Answer:
OH
1. NaH, THF
2. CH3CH=CHCH2Br
O— CH2CH=CHCH3
250° C
OH
CH=CH2
CHCH3
H
Br
27.
:S:
1. H2NCNH2
2. NaOH, H2O
Answer:
H
Br
:S:
1. H2NCNH2
2. NaOH, H2O
HS
H
28.
S
CH3
H2O2, H2O
rt

Answer:

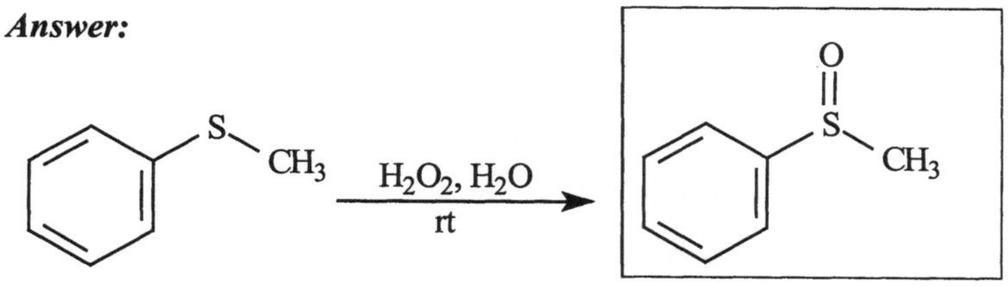

S-CH$_3$ (phenyl) $\xrightarrow[rt]{H_2O_2, H_2O}$ [phenyl–S(=O)–CH$_3$]

29. (cyclohexene oxide) $\xrightarrow[ether]{\boxed{\quad}}$ OH / I (trans-2-iodocyclohexanol)

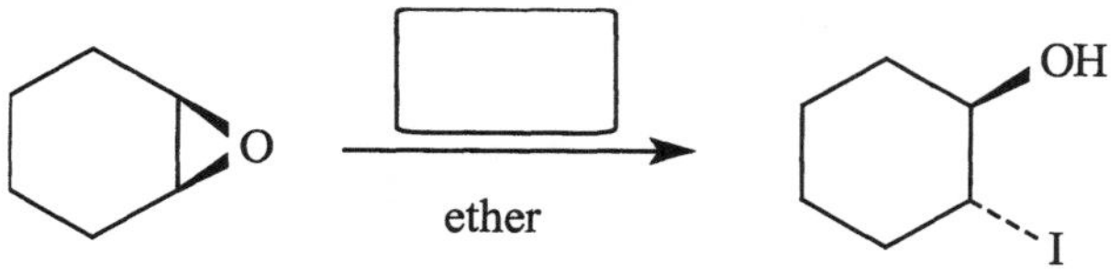

Answer:

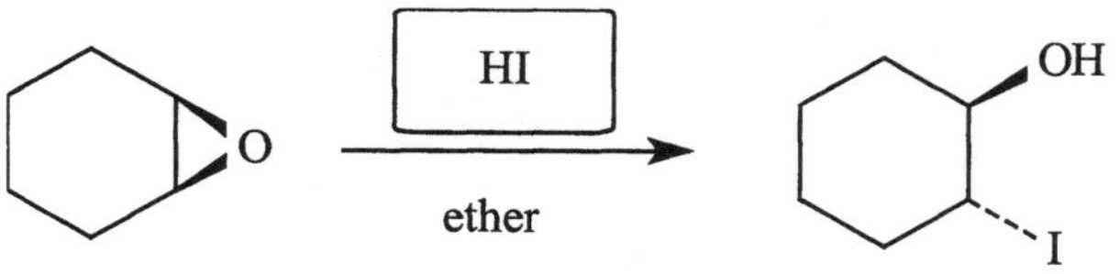

(cyclohexene oxide) $\xrightarrow[ether]{\boxed{HI}}$ OH / I

30. (phenyl)–$CH_2O^- Na^+$ $\xrightarrow{CH_3I}$ [ ]

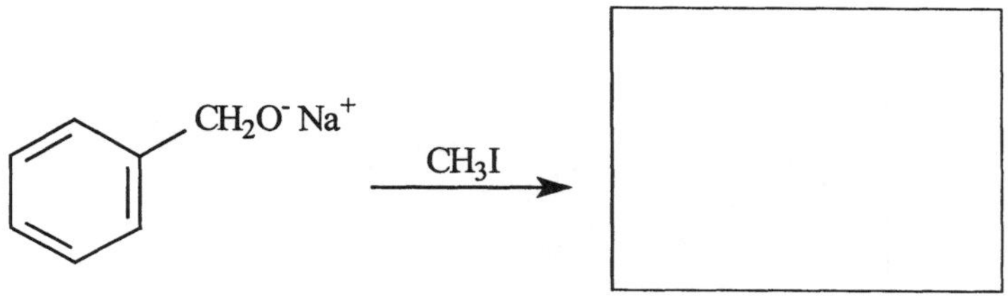

Answer:

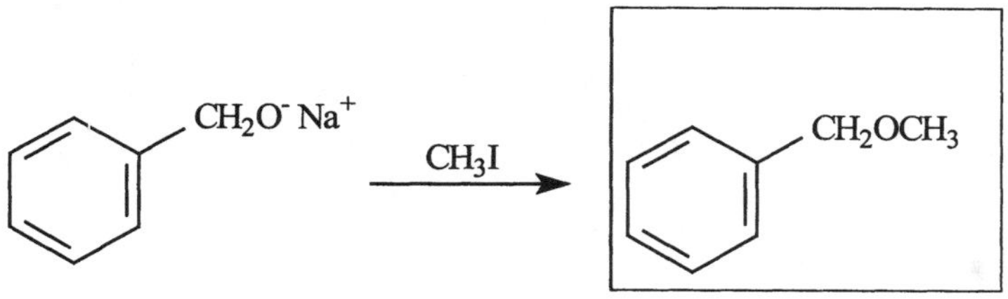

(phenyl)–$CH_2O^- Na^+$ $\xrightarrow{CH_3I}$ [(phenyl)–CH_2OCH_3]

31. [ ] $\xrightarrow[heat]{HI, H_2O}$ $CH_3CH(OH)CH_3$ + ICH_2CH_3

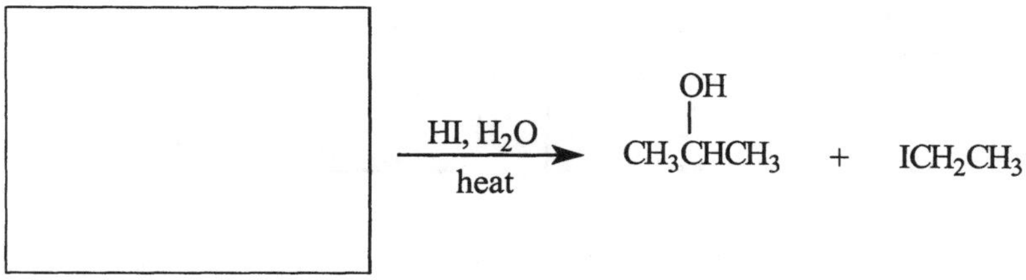

Answer:

$$(CH_3)_2CH{-}O{-}CH_2CH_3 \xrightarrow[\text{heat}]{HI,\ H_2O} CH_3CH(OH)CH_3 + ICH_2CH_3$$

32. $H_3C{-}CH{-}C(CH_3)(CH_2CH_3)$ (epoxide, O bridging C2–C3) $\xrightarrow{\square}$ $H_3C{-}CH(OH){-}C(CH_3)(OH)CH_2CH_3$

Answer:

$H_3C{-}CH{-}C(CH_3)(CH_2CH_3)$ (epoxide) $\xrightarrow{H_3O^+}$ $H_3C{-}CH(OH){-}C(CH_3)(OH)CH_2CH_3$

33. $(CH_3)_3COH \xrightarrow[2.\ \square]{1.\ NaH} (CH_3)_3COCH(CH_3)CH_2CH_3$

Answer:

$(CH_3)_3COH \xrightarrow[2.\ I{-}CH(CH_3)CH_2CH_3]{1.\ NaH} (CH_3)_3COCH(CH_3)CH_2CH_3$

34. Cyclohexyl–$OC(CH_3)_3$ $\xrightarrow{CF_3CO_2H}$ $\square$ + $\square$

Answer:

Cyclohexyl–$OC(CH_3)_3$ $\xrightarrow{CF_3CO_2H}$ Cyclohexyl–OH + $(CH_3)_2C{=}CH_2$

35. Propose a synthesis of 1,4-dioxane, starting from 1,2-dibromoethane as the only source of carbon.

$BrCH_2CH_2Br \longrightarrow$ [1,4-dioxane structure]

Answer:

$BrCH_2CH_2Br \xrightarrow{2\ NaOH} HOCH_2CH_2OH \xrightarrow[2.\ BrCH_2CH_2Br]{1.\ 2\ NaH}$ [1,4-dioxane structure]

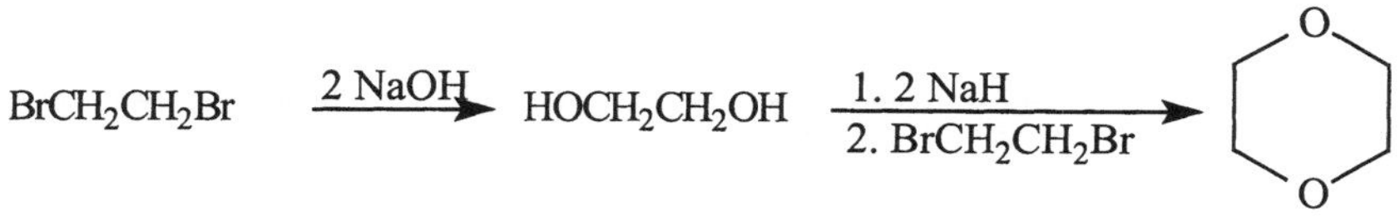

36. Choose the *best* reagent for carrying out the following reactions from the list below. Place the letter of the reagent(s) in the box over the reaction arrow. Only one letter per box.

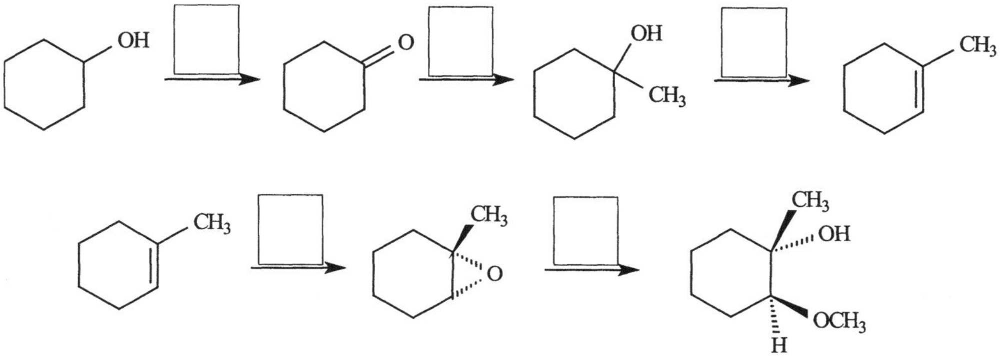

Cyclohexylmethanol (OH) → [ ] → cyclohexanecarbaldehyde (O) → [ ] → 1-cyclohexylethanol (OH, CH_3) → [ ] → 1-ethylidene... (cyclohexene with CH_3)

Cyclohexenyl-CH_3 → [ ] → epoxide (CH_3, O) → [ ] → product (CH_3, OH, OCH_3, H)

A.	NaH, then CH_3I	B.	$NaOCH_3$, CH_3OH
C.	*m*-$ClC_6H_4CO_3H$	D.	CH_3MgBr in ether, then H_3O^+
E.	warm H_2SO_4/H_2O	F.	$Hg(O_2CCF_3)_2$, CH_3OH
G.	H_2/Pd	H.	PCC, CH_2Cl_2
I.	Cl_2, H_2O	J.	$LiAlH_4$ in ether, then H_3O^+

Answer:

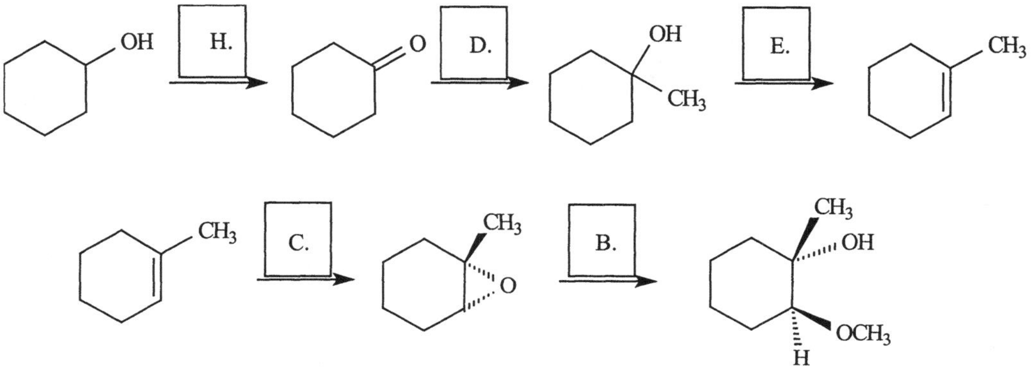

Cyclohexylmethanol (OH) → [H.] → aldehyde (O) → [D.] → alcohol (OH, CH_3) → [E.] → alkene (CH_3)

Alkene (CH_3) → [C.] → epoxide (CH_3, O) → [B.] → product (CH_3, OH, OCH_3, H)

37. Complete the synthetic sequence below by drawing the structures of the reaction in the boxes provided.

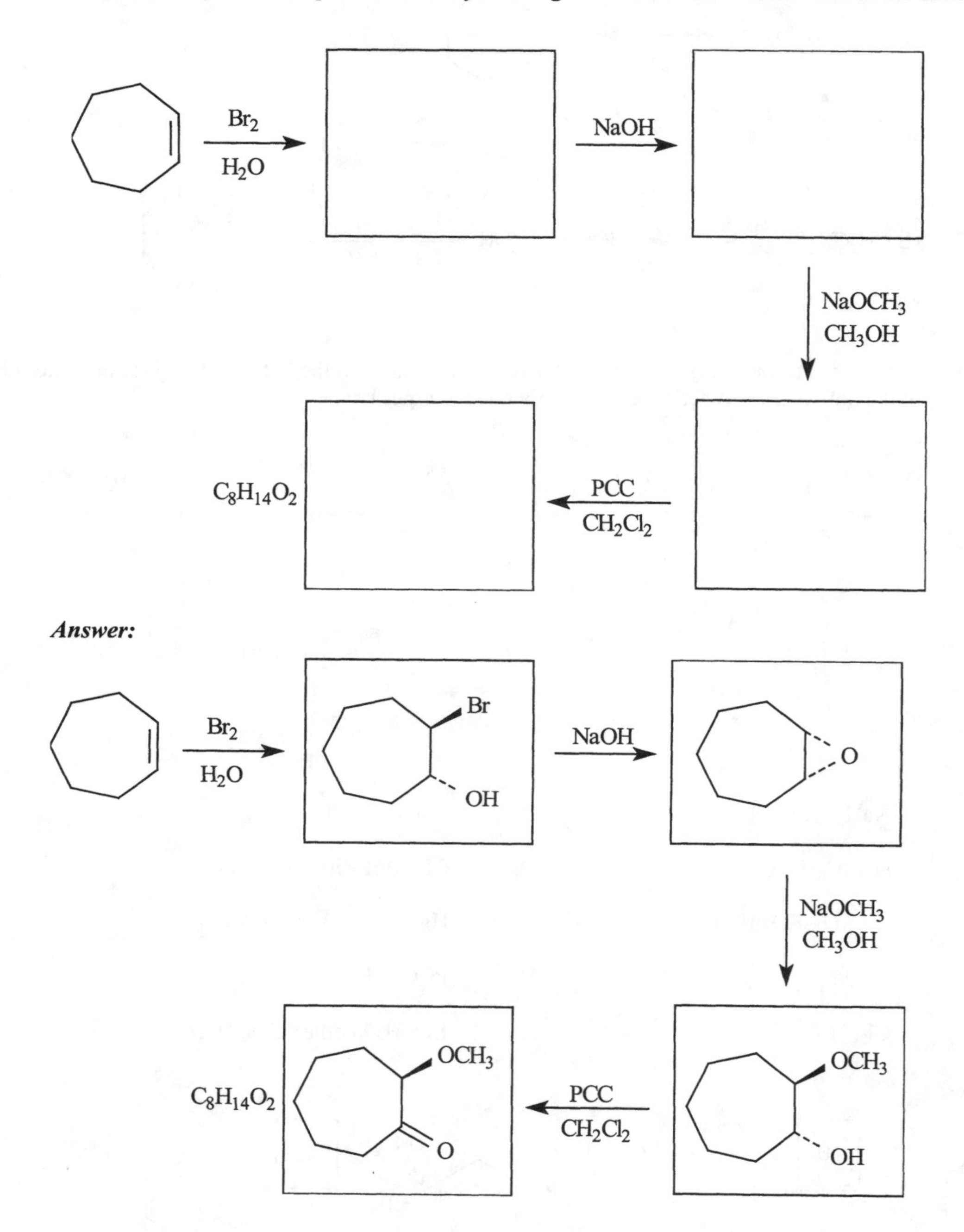

38. Show how the ether below could be prepared from toluene and any other necessary reagents. Show all reagents and all intermediate structures.

H_3C– (toluene) ⟶ H_3C–(ring, Cl)–OCH_2CH_3

Answer:

H_3C– $\xrightarrow[H_2SO_4]{SO_3}$ H_3C–(ring)–SO_3H $\xrightarrow[heat]{NaOH}$ H_3C–(ring)–OH

1. NaH
2. CH_3CH_2Br

H_3C–(ring)–OCH_2CH_3 $\xrightarrow[FeCl_3]{Cl_2}$ H_3C–(ring, Cl)–OCH_2CH_3

39. Propose a synthesis for the following compound using benzene or toluene and any other reagents necessary. Show all major intermediate compounds that would probably be isolated during the course of your synthesis.

O, H

Answer:

CH_3 $\xrightarrow{NBS}$ CH_2Br

1. Mg, ether
2. (ethylene oxide) O
3. H_3O^+

OH

PCC
CH_2Cl_2

O, H

Chapter 19 - Aldehydes and Ketones: Nucleophilic Addition Reactions

Draw structures corresponding to each of the following names:

1. 2,2,2-trichloroethanal (chloral)

Answer: Cl_3CCHO

2. benzophenone

Answer:

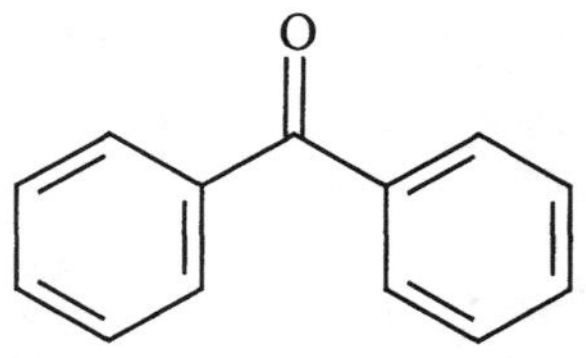

3. *trans*-3-isopropylcyclohexanecarbaldehyde

Answer:

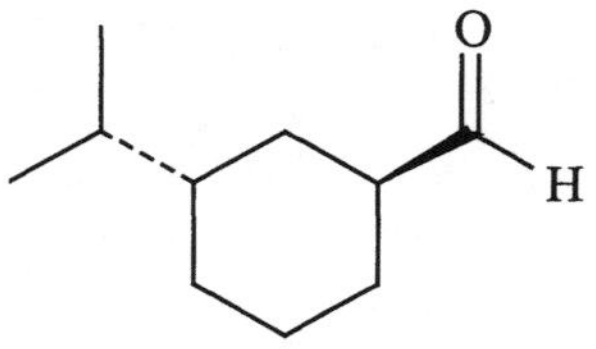

O

H

4. 5,5-dimethyl-1,3-cyclohexanedione (dimedone)

Answer:

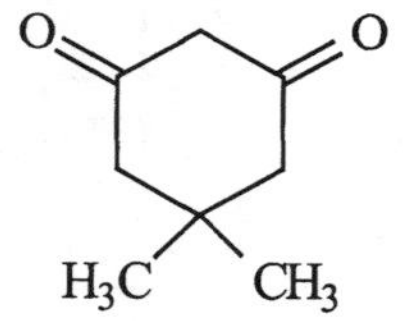

O O

H_3C CH_3

5. 2-cyclohexenone

Answer:

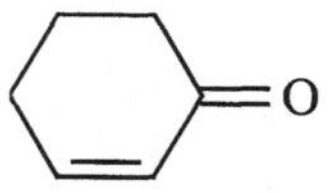

O

6. What is the correct structure for 2-hydroxyacetophenone? Circle the letter of your response.

a.

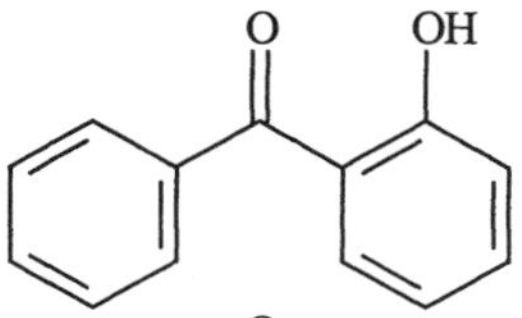

b.

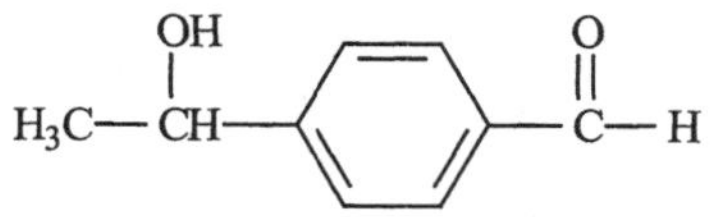

c.

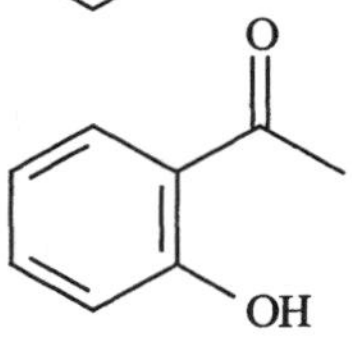

d.

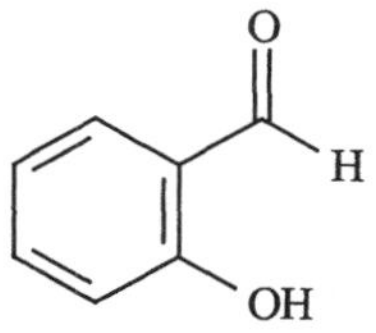

Answer: c

Provide IUPAC names for each structure below.

7.

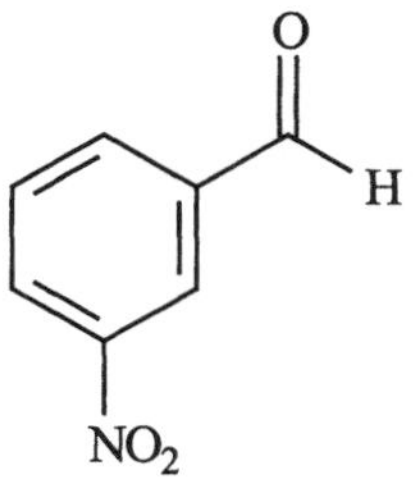

Answer: *m*-nitrobenzaldehyde

8.

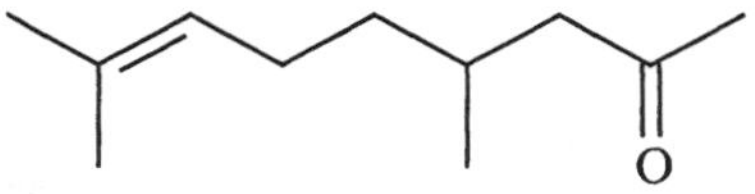

Answer: 4,8-dimethyl-7-nonen-2-one

9.

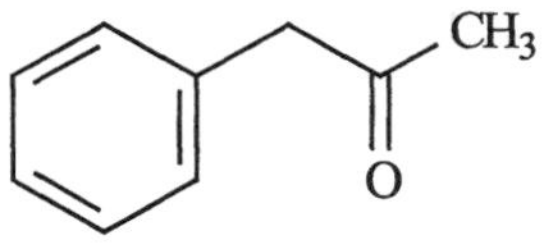

Answer: phenylacetone or 1-phenyl-2-propanone

10.

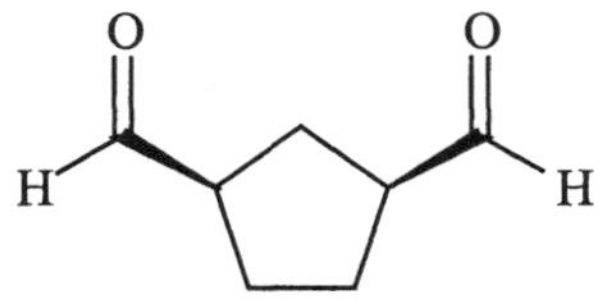

Answer: *cis*-1,3-cyclopentanedicarbaldehyde

11.

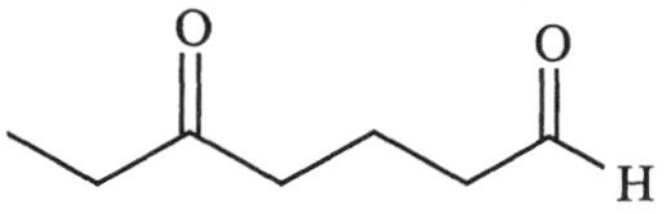

Answer: 5-oxoheptanal

Consider the reaction below to answer the following questions:

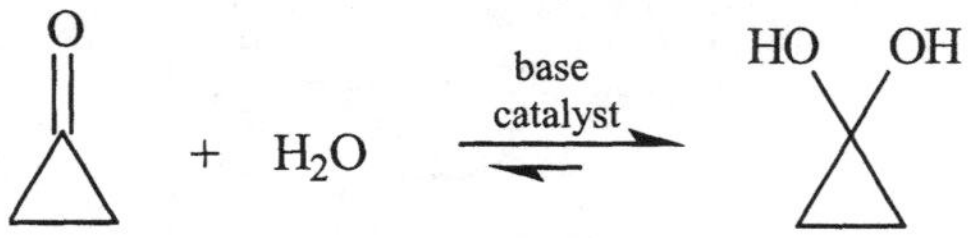

O + H_2O base catalyst HO OH

12. Write the complete stepwise mechanism for the reaction shown above. Show all intermediate structures and all electron flow with arrows.

Answer:

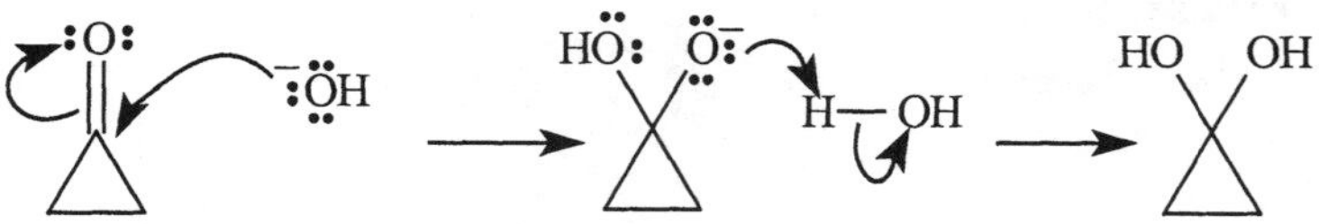

:O: :ÖH → HÖ: Ö: H—OH → HO OH

13. The substance formed on addition of water to an aldehyde or ketone is called a hydrate or a:

a. vicinal diol
b. geminal diol
c. acetal
d. ketal

Answer: b

14. The exact position of the equilibrium between ketone/aldehydes and their hydrates depends on the structure of the carbonyl compound. Although the equilibrium favors the carbonyl compound in most cases, cyclopropanone forms a stable hydrate. Explain this phenomenon based on the structures of cyclopropanone and its hydrate.

Answer: The carbonyl carbon in cyclopropane is highly strained because the preferred bond angle for an sp^2 -hybridized carbon is 120° but the real angle is 60°. This angle strain is somewhat relieved when cyclopropanone is hydrated—the preferred bond angle for an sp^3 -hybridized carbon is about 109.5°. Going from sp^2 - to sp^3 hybridization relieves angle strain by about 10°. Thus, the hydrate of cyclopropane is more stable than the carbonyl form, and the equilibrium lies to the right in this reaction.

15. Many nucleophilic addition reactions of aldehydes and ketones are catalyzed by acid or base. Bases catalyze hydration by:

a. making the carbonyl group more electrophilic
b. shifting the equilibrium of the reaction
c. making the carbonyl group less electrophilic
d. converting the water to hydroxide ion, a much better nucleophile

Answer: d

17. Enamines formed from the cyclic secondary amine pyrrolidine are important intermediates in the synthesis of 1,5-diketones.

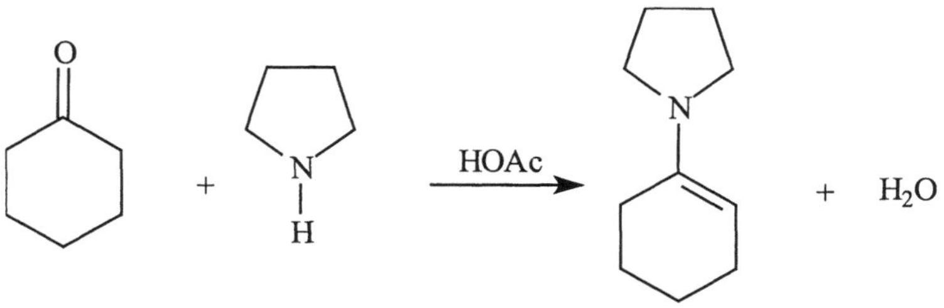
O
N
H
HOAc
N
+ H2O

On the structures provided below, draw arrows showing electron flow for the reaction mechanism for the acetic acid-catalyzed formation of an enamine from cyclohexanone and pyrrolidine.

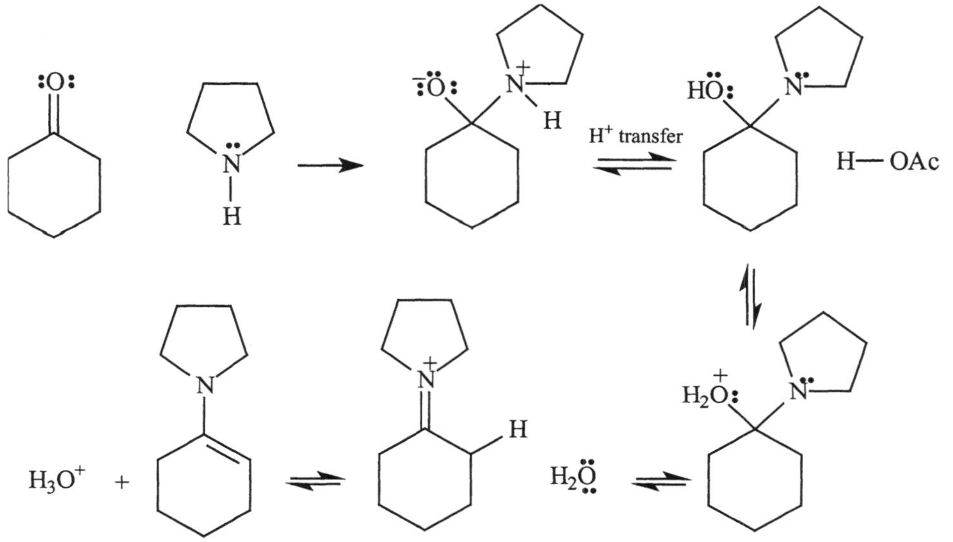
:O:
N
H
O
N
H
H+ transfer
HO
N
H— OAc
H2O
N
H
H2O
N
N
H3O+ +

Answer:

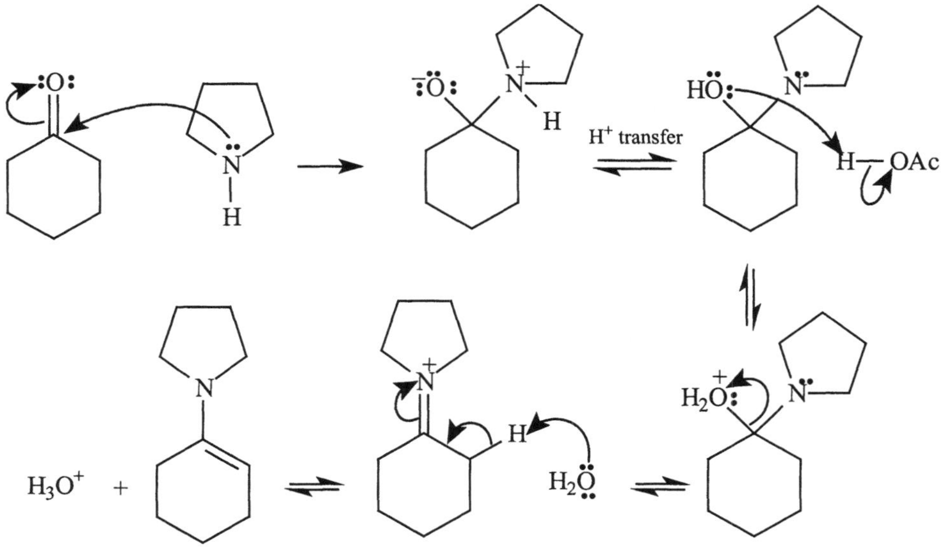
:O:
N
H
O
N
H
H+ transfer
HO
N
H—OAc
H2O
N
H
H2O
N
N
H3O+ +

Consider the data below to answer the following questions.

Cyanohydrins are important intermediates in the synthesis of α-hydroxycarboxylic acids from ketones and aldehydes. The nitrile functional group can be hydrolyzed by aqueous acid to yield a carboxylic acid. Nitriles can also be hydrolyzed to carboxylic acids using aqueous base. Unfortunately, when a cyanohydrin is treated with aqueous base the original carbonyl compound is isolated.

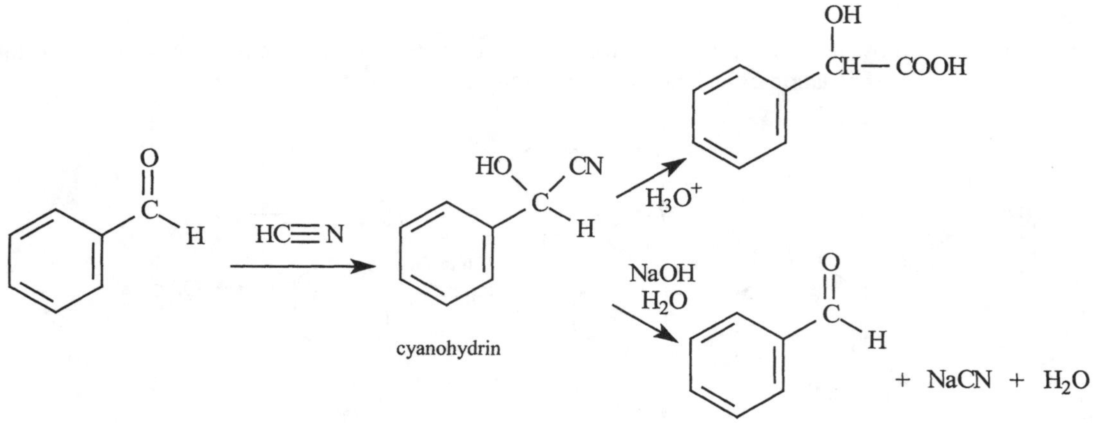

HC≡N

cyanohydrin

H_3O^+

NaOH
H_2O

+ NaCN + H_2O

18. The reaction of an aldehyde with hydrogen cyanide is an example of ________ reaction.

a. a nucleophilic substitution
b. an electrophilic addition
c. an electrophilic substitution
d. a nucleophilic addition

Answer: d

19. Identify the electrophile in the reaction of benzaldehyde with hydrogen cyanide.

Answer: The benzaldehyde is the electrophile in this reaction.

20. The reaction of benzaldehyde with hydrogen cyanide is catalyzed by the addtion of a small amount of KCN. Write the complete reaction mechanism for the KCN-catalyzed reaction. Show all electron flow with arrows and show all intermediate structures.

Answer:

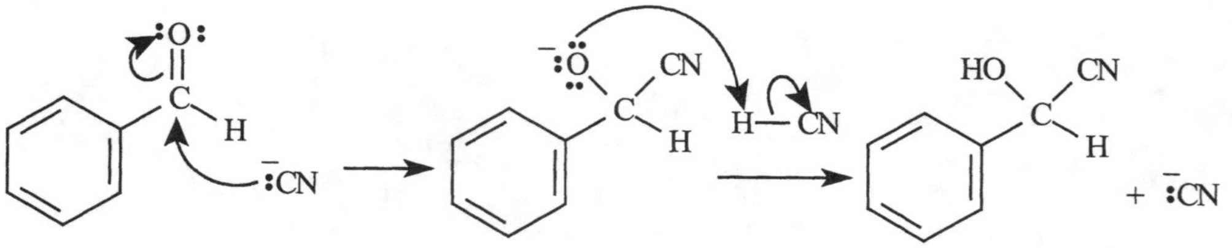

H—CN

+ $^{-}$:CN

21. Formulate a reasonable mechanism for the reaction of the cyanohydrin of benzaldeyhe, shown above, with aqueous NaOH. Show all intermediate structures and all electron flow with arrows.

Answer:

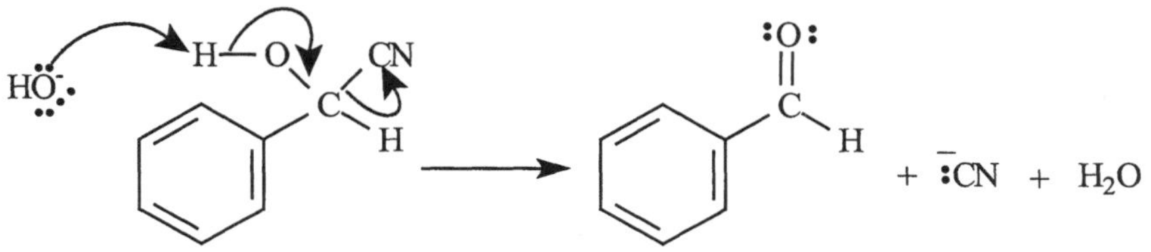

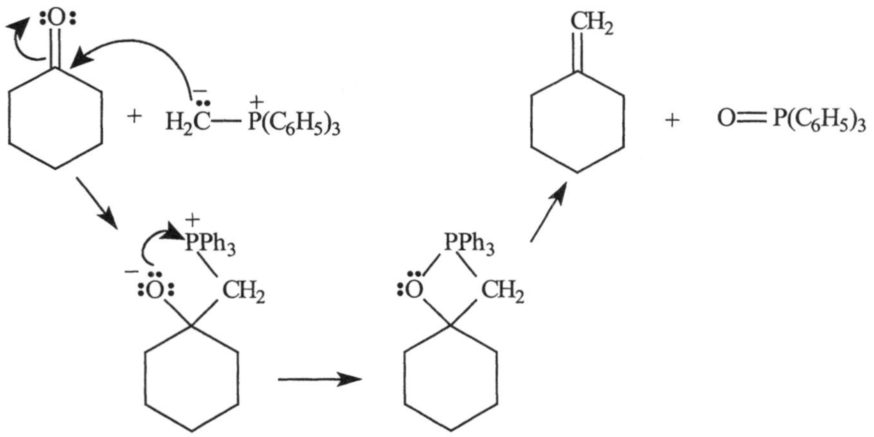

HO: H—O CN C H → C H + :CN + H_2O

22. In the Wittig reaction, a phosphorus ylide adds to a ketone or aldehyde to yield an alkene. Write the complete stepwise mechanism for the Wittig reaction shown below. Show all intermediate structures and all electron flow with arrows.

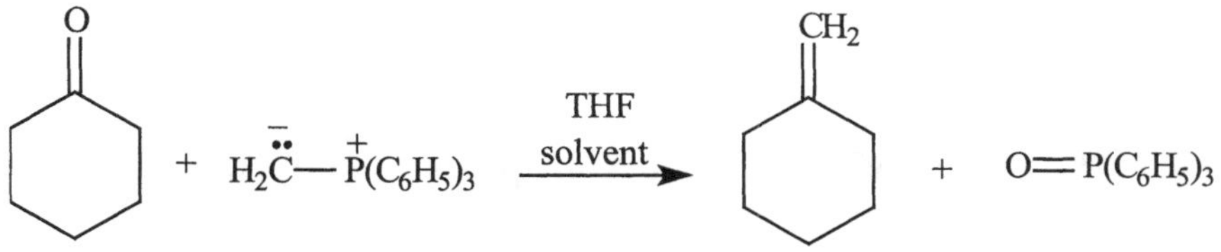

O + $H_2\bar{C}—\overset{+}{P}(C_6H_5)_3$ —THF solvent→ CH_2 + $O=P(C_6H_5)_3$

Answer:

:O: + $H_2\bar{C}—\overset{+}{P}(C_6H_5)_3$ → CH_2 + $O=P(C_6H_5)_3$

$\overset{+}{P}Ph_3$ $:\bar{O}:$ CH_2 → PPh_3 :O CH_2

Consider the reaction below to answer the following questions.

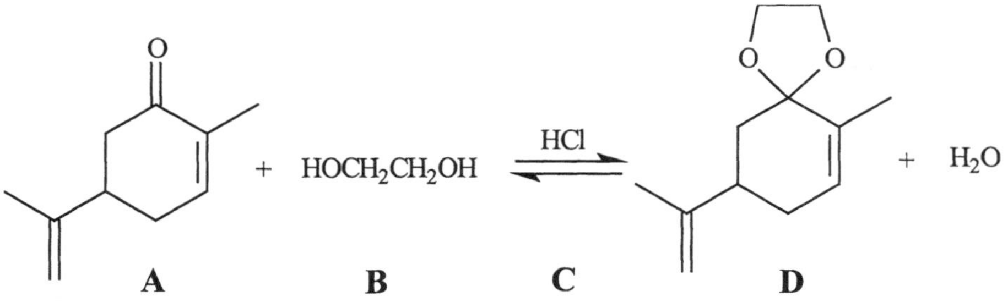

A + $HOCH_2CH_2OH$ (B) ⇌ HCl (C) D + H_2O

23. The nucleophile in this reaction is:

Answer: B

24. The catalyst in this reaction is:

Answer: C

25. The product of this reaction is called:

a. an ylide
b. an acetal
c. a *gem* diol
d. a hydrate

Answer: b

26. Write the complete stepwise mechanism for this reaction. Show all electron flow with arrows and show all intermediate structures.

Answer:

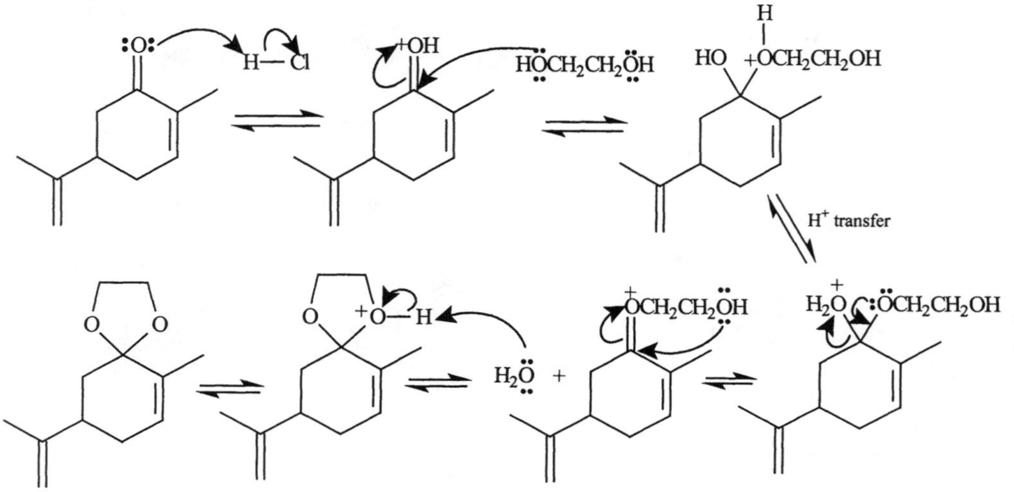

H—Cl $HOCH_2CH_2OH$ HO +OCH_2CH_2OH H

H^+ transfer

+OCH_2CH_2OH H_2O + H_2O :OCH_2CH_2OH O O +O—H

α,β-Unsaturated aldehydes and ketones can undergo reaction with nucleophiles at the β carbon, as shown below.

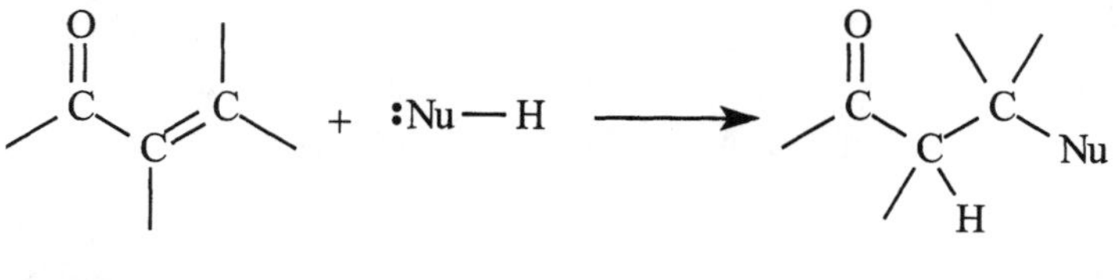

:Nu—H Nu H

27. Draw a resonance form for the unsaturated carbonyl that accounts for this reactivity.

Answer:

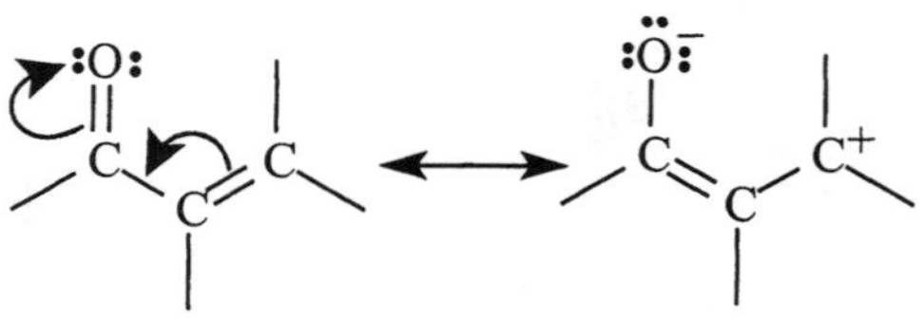

28. This reaction is called a ________ reaction.

a. conjugate addition.
b. electrophilic addition.
c. direct addition
d. 1,2-addition.

Answer: a

Give the major organic product(s) for each of the following reactions or sequences of reactions. Show all relevant stereochemistry.

29.

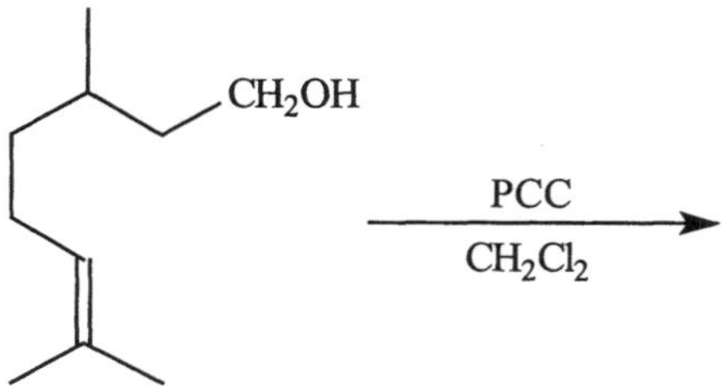

CH_2OH

PCC

CH_2Cl_2

Answer:

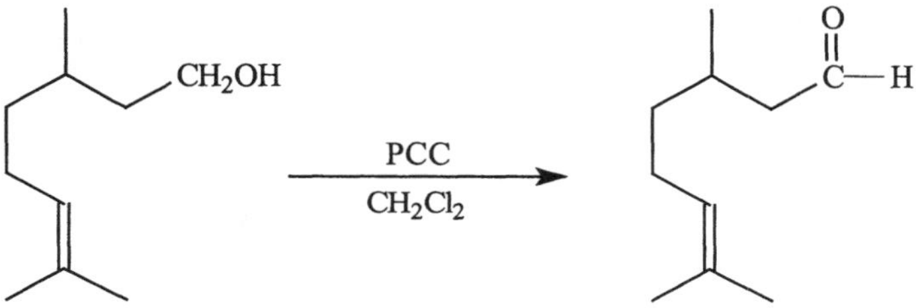

CH_2OH

PCC

CH_2Cl_2

O

C—H

30.

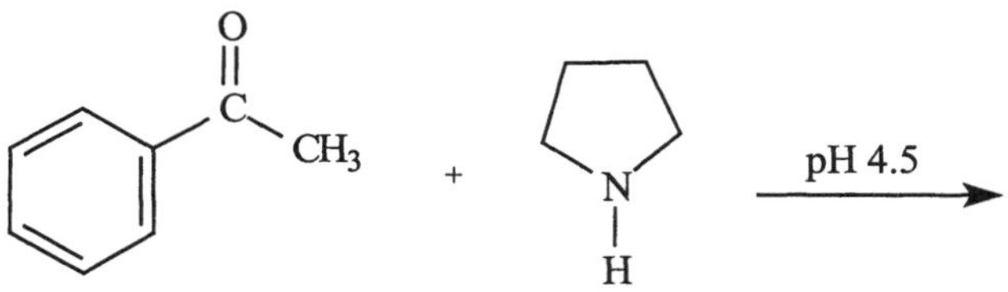

O

C

CH_3

+

N

H

pH 4.5

Answer:

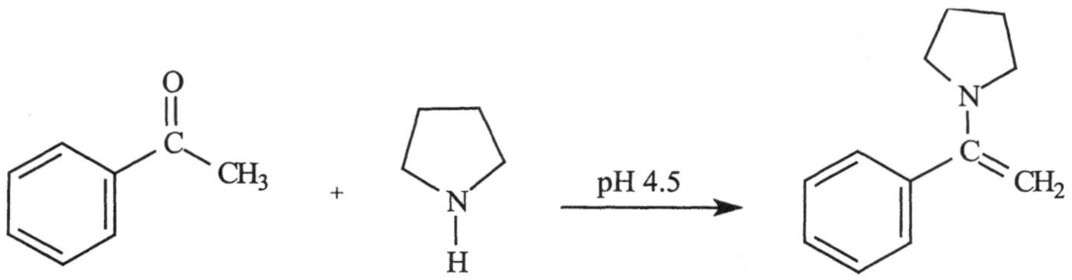

O

C

CH_3

+

N

H

pH 4.5

N

C

CH_2

31.

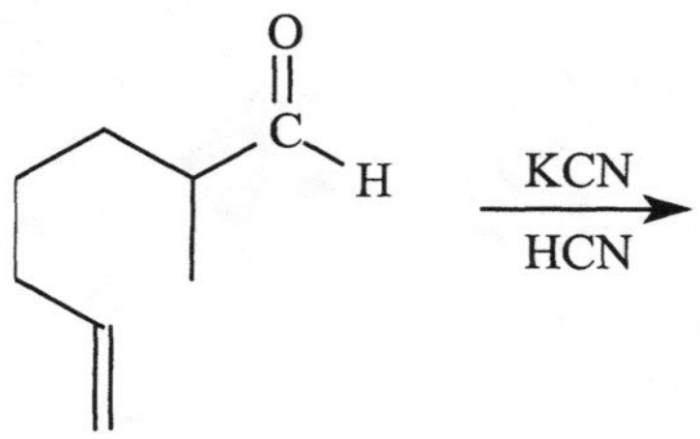

O
C
H

$\xrightarrow[HCN]{KCN}$

Answer:

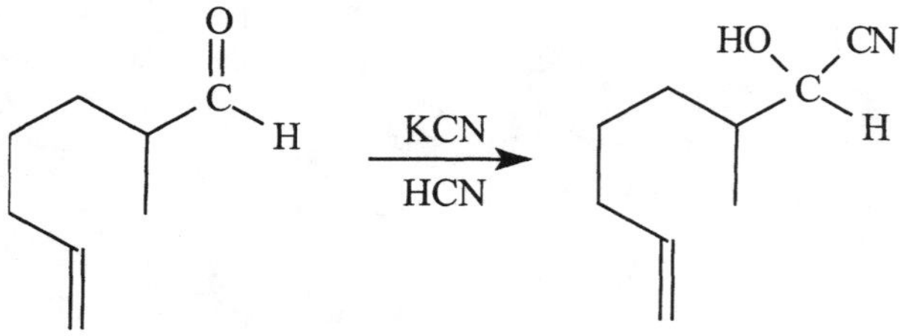

$\xrightarrow[HCN]{KCN}$

HO CN
C
H

32.

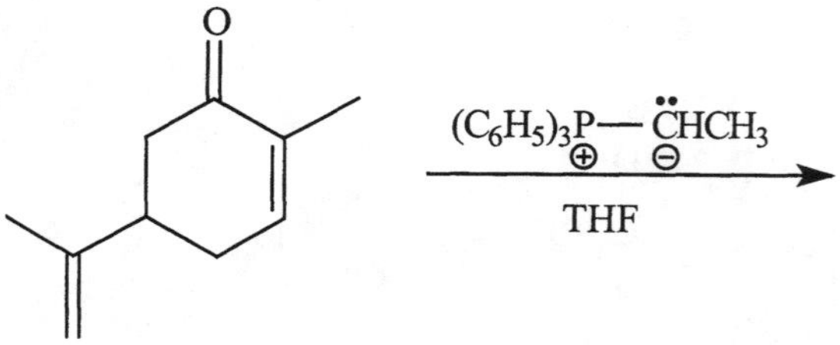

O

$\xrightarrow[THF]{(C_6H_5)_3\overset{\oplus}{P}—\ddot{C}\overset{\ominus}{H}CH_3}$

Answer:

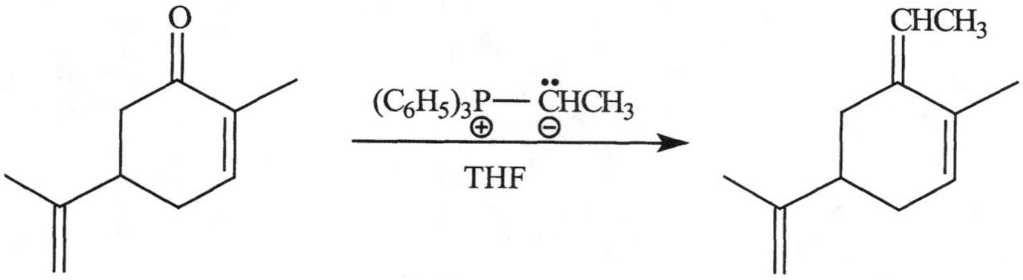

O

$\xrightarrow[THF]{(C_6H_5)_3\overset{\oplus}{P}—\ddot{C}\overset{\ominus}{H}CH_3}$

CHCH$_3$

33.

OH
H
O

$\xrightarrow[NH_4OH]{Ag_2O, H_2O}$

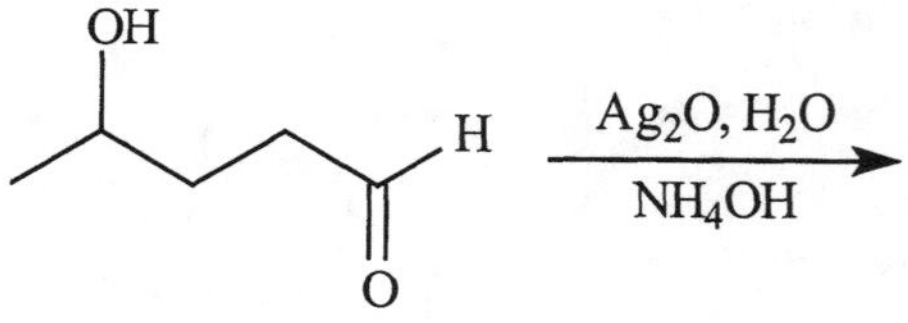

Answer:

OH
H
O

$\xrightarrow[NH_4OH]{Ag_2O, H_2O}$

OH
OH
O

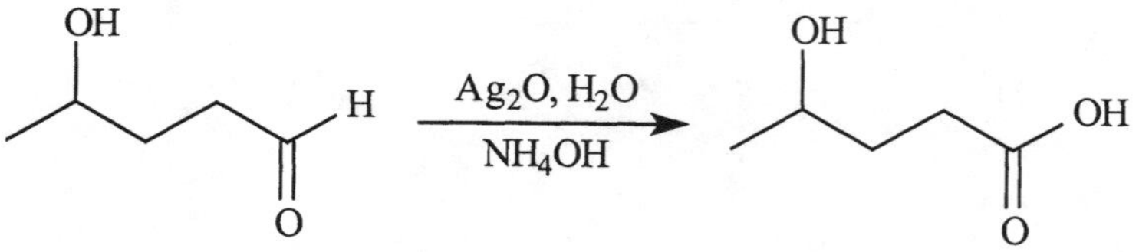

34.

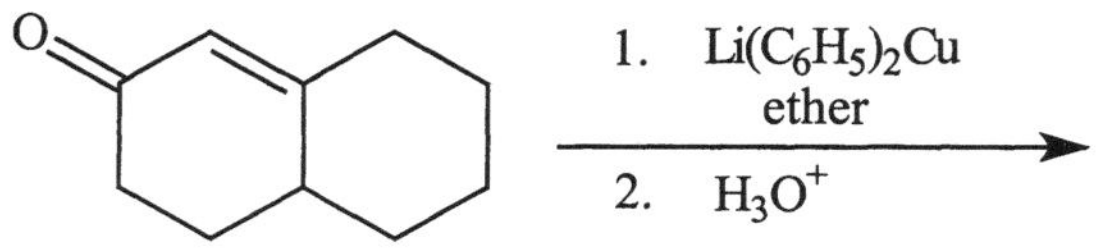

1. $Li(C_6H_5)_2Cu$ ether
2. H_3O^+

Answer:

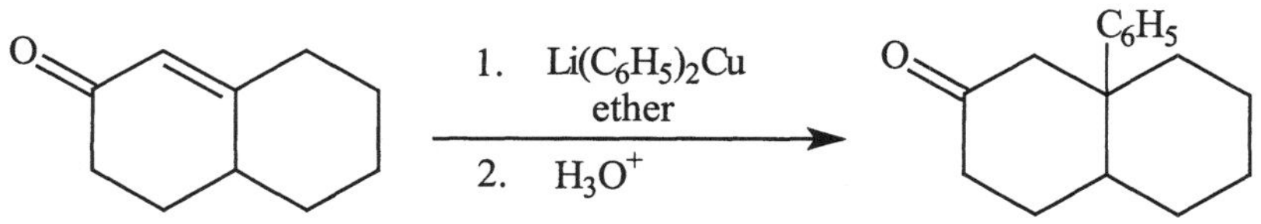

1. $Li(C_6H_5)_2Cu$ ether
2. H_3O^+

C_6H_5

35.

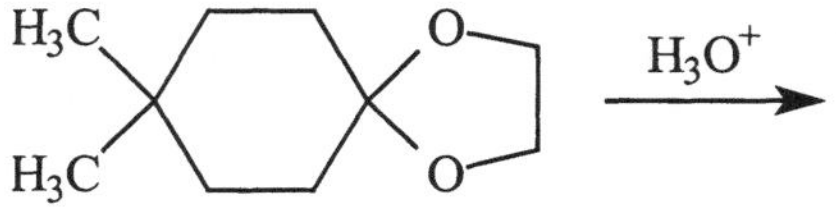

H_3C H_3C O O $\xrightarrow{H_3O^+}$

Answer:

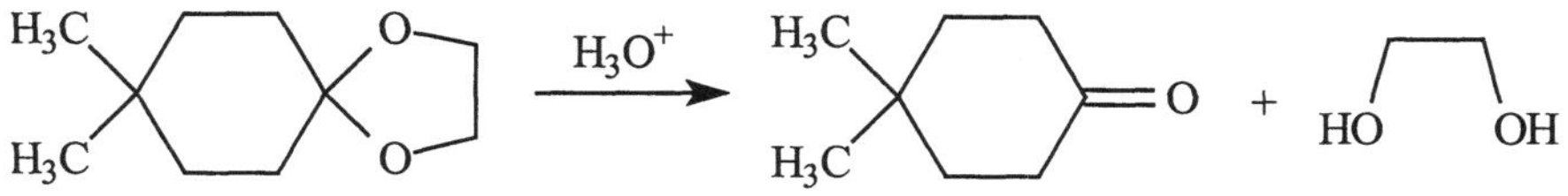

H_3C H_3C O O $\xrightarrow{H_3O^+}$ H_3C H_3C O + HO OH

36.

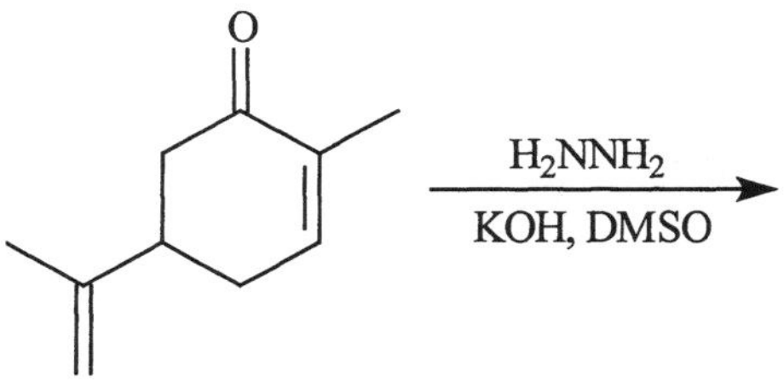

O $\xrightarrow[\text{KOH, DMSO}]{H_2NNH_2}$

Answer:

O $\xrightarrow[\text{KOH, DMSO}]{H_2NNH_2}$

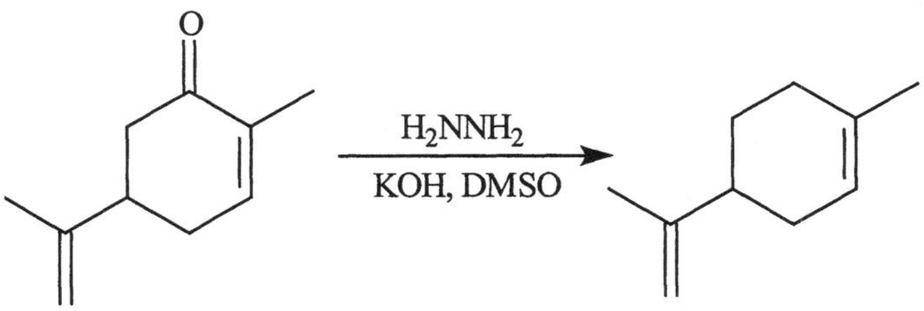

37.

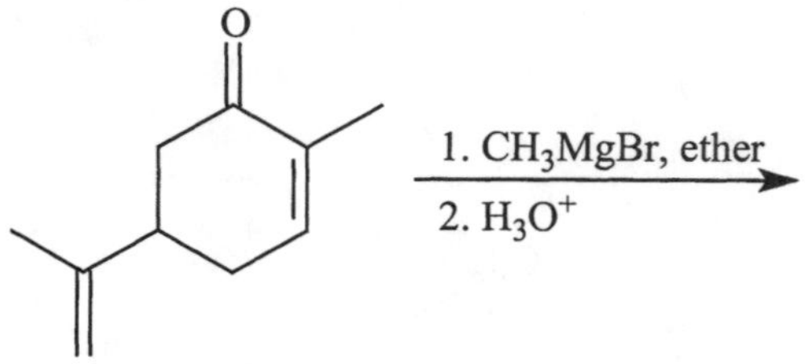

1. CH_3MgBr, ether
2. H_3O^+

Answer:

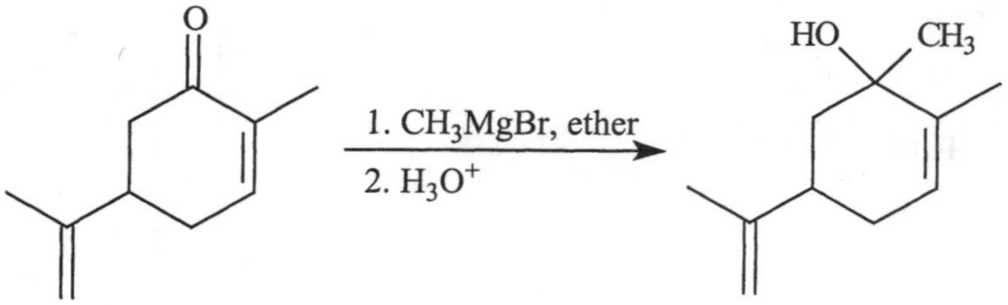

1. CH_3MgBr, ether
2. H_3O^+

HO CH₃

38. $CH_3(CH_2)_{10}COCH_3$ (with C=O) $\xrightarrow[2.\ H_3O^+]{1.\ \text{DIBAH, toluene}}$

Answer:

$CH_3(CH_2)_{10}COCH_3$ (with C=O) $\xrightarrow[2.\ H_3O^+]{1.\ \text{DIBAH, toluene}}$ $CH_3(CH_2)_{10}CH$ (with C=O)

39.

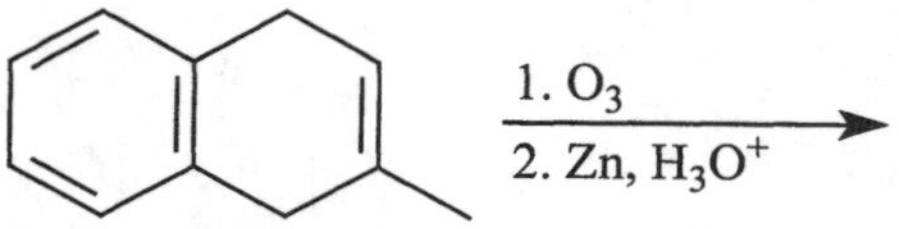

1. O_3
2. Zn, H_3O^+

Answer:

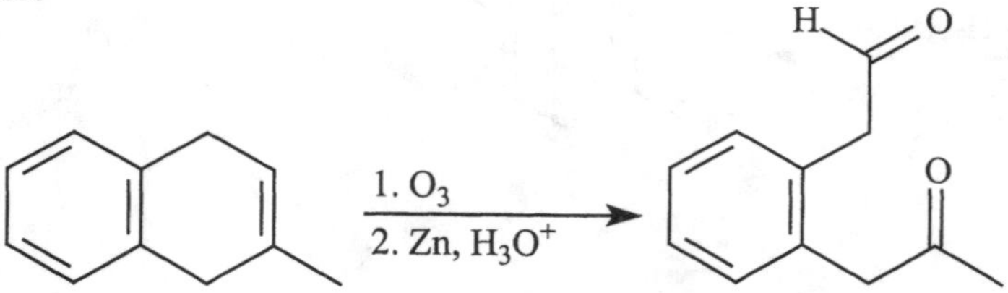

1. O_3
2. Zn, H_3O^+

H O

O

40. $H_3C-C(=O)-CH=CH_2$ + $HN(CH_2CH_3)_2$ $\xrightarrow{\text{ethanol}}$

Answer:

$H_3C-C(=O)-CH=CH_2$ + $HN(CH_2CH_3)_2$ $\xrightarrow{\text{ethanol}}$ $H_3CC(=O)CH_2CH_2N(CH_2CH_3)_2$

41. 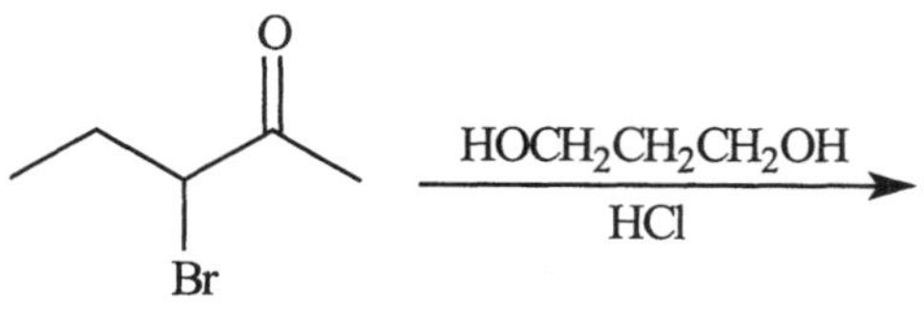 [structure: 3-bromo-2-pentanone] $\xrightarrow[HCl]{HOCH_2CH_2CH_2OH}$

Answer:

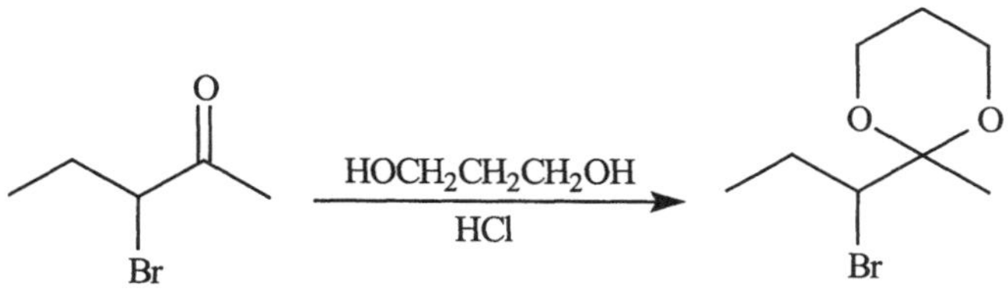

[structure: 3-bromo-2-pentanone] $\xrightarrow[HCl]{HOCH_2CH_2CH_2OH}$ [structure: 1,3-dioxane ketal with Br]

42. 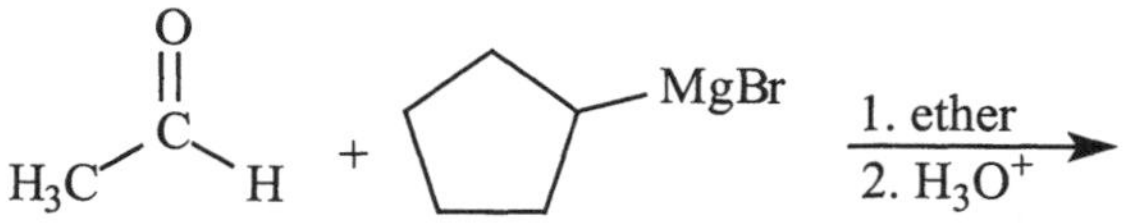 $H_3C-C(=O)-H$ + [cyclopentyl]–MgBr $\xrightarrow[2.\ H_3O^+]{1.\ ether}$

Answer:

$H_3C-C(=O)-H$ + [cyclopentyl]–MgBr $\xrightarrow[2.\ H_3O^+]{1.\ ether}$ [cyclopentyl]–CH(OH)–CH_3

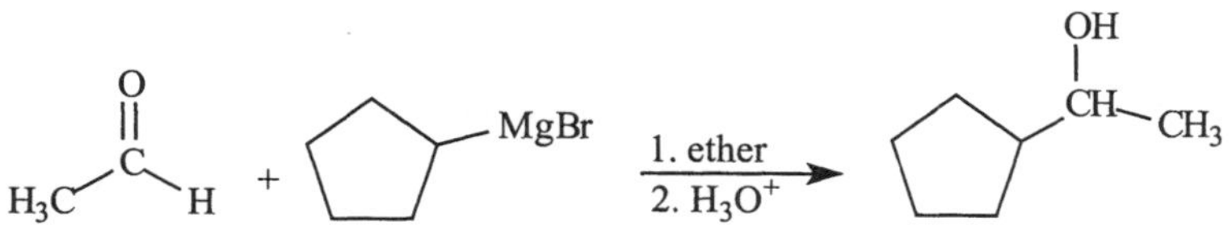

Choose the ***BEST*** reagent for carrying out each of the following conversions.

43. 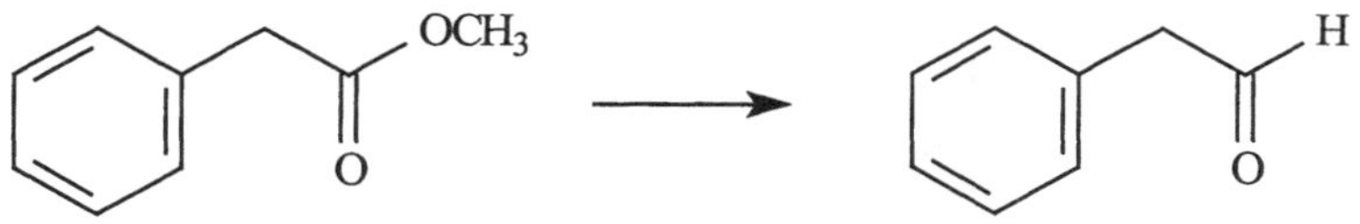 [structure: $PhCH_2CO_2CH_3$] ⟶ [structure: $PhCH_2CHO$]

A. $LiAlH_4$, THF
B. $NaBH_4$, ethanol
C. 1. DIBAH, toluene
2. H_3O^+
D. All of the above work well

Answer: C

44. 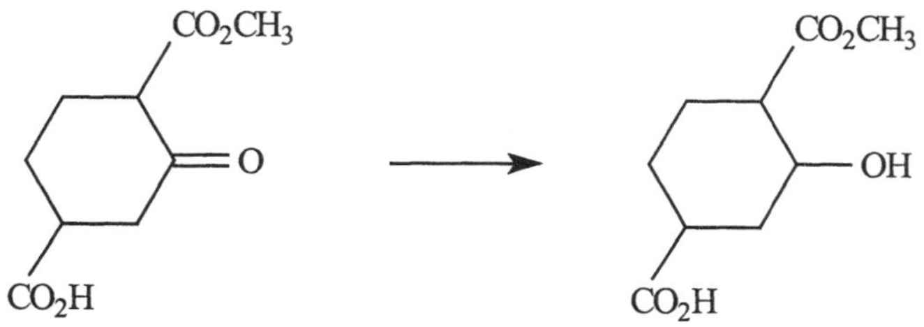 [structure: cyclohexanone with CO_2CH_3 and CO_2H substituents] ⟶ [structure: cyclohexanol with CO_2CH_3 and CO_2H substituents]

A. $LiAlH_4$, ether
B. $NaBH_4$, ethanol
C. CrO_3, pyridine
D. H_2/Pd

Answer: B.

45.

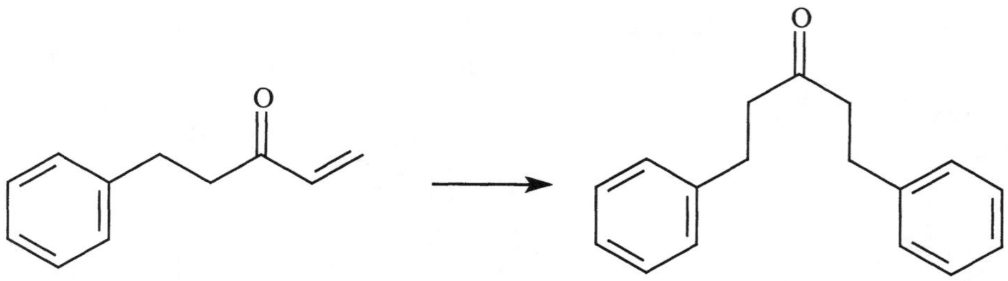

A. 1. PhMgBr, ether
   2. H_3O^+

B. 1. $PhCH_2MgBr$, ether
   2. H_3O^+

C. $(C_6H_5)_3P{=}CHC_6H_5$, THF

D. $Li(C_6H_5)_2Cu$, ether

Answer: D

46. 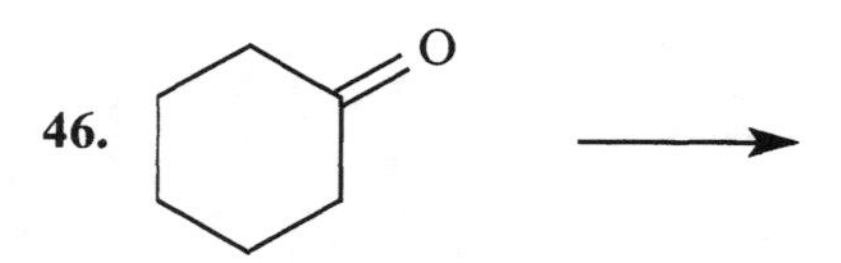

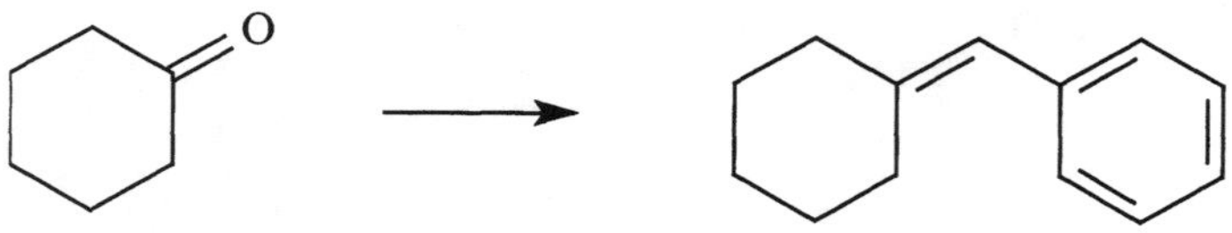

A. 1. PhMgBr, ether
   2. H_3O^+

B. 1. $PhCH_2MgBr$, ether
   2. H_3O^+

C. $(C_6H_5)_3P{=}CHC_6H_5$, THF

D. $Li(C_6H_5)_2Cu$, ether

Answer: C

47.

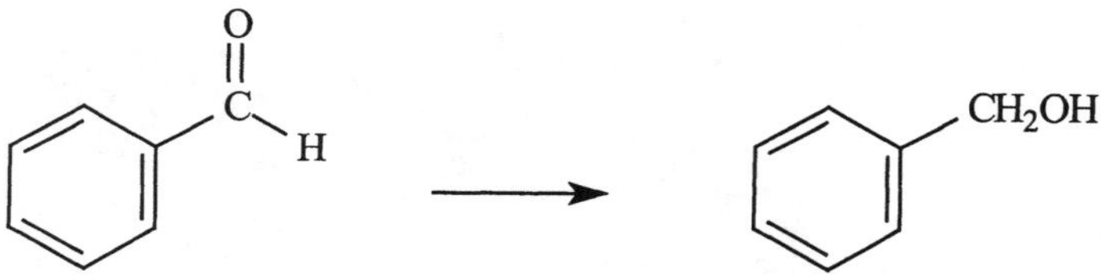

A. $NaBH_4$, ethanol

B. 1. $LiAlH_4$, ether
   2. H_3O^+

C. HCHO, NaOH, H_2O

D. All of the above

Answer: D

Show how the Wittig reaction might be used to prepare each of the following alkenes. Identify the alkyl halide and the carbonyl components that would be used in each synthesis.

48.

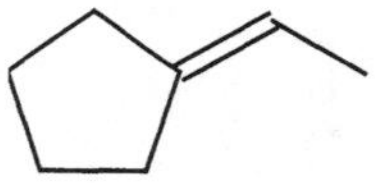

Answer:

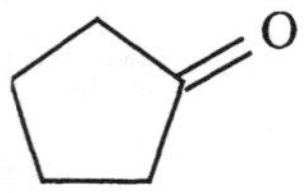

and CH_3CH_2Br

49.

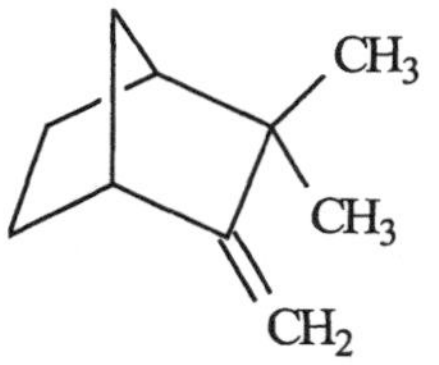

CH_3 CH_3 CH_2

camphene
(a constituent of turpentine)

Answer:

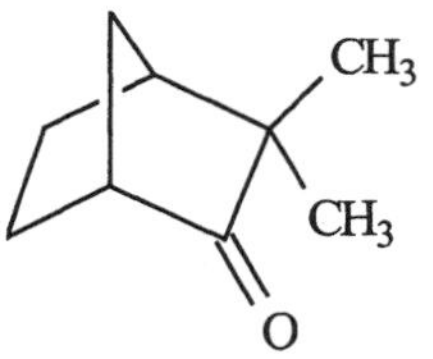

CH_3 CH_3 O

and CH_3Br

Show how the following conversions might be accomplished. Show all reagents and all intermediate structures. More than one step may be required.

50.

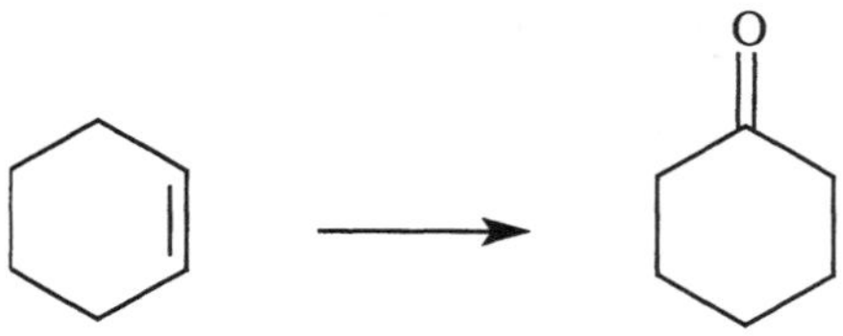

O

Answer:

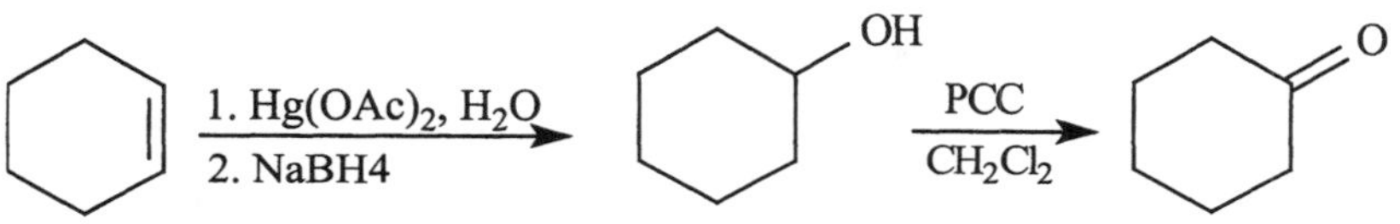

1. $Hg(OAc)_2$, H_2O
2. NaBH4

OH

PCC
CH_2Cl_2

O

51.

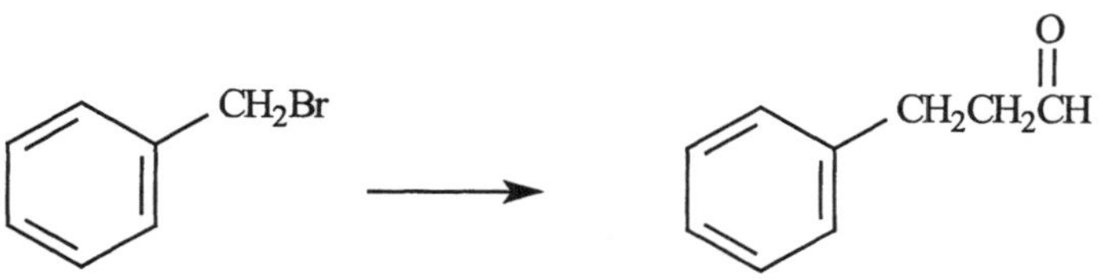

CH_2Br

O
CH_2CH_2CH

Answer:

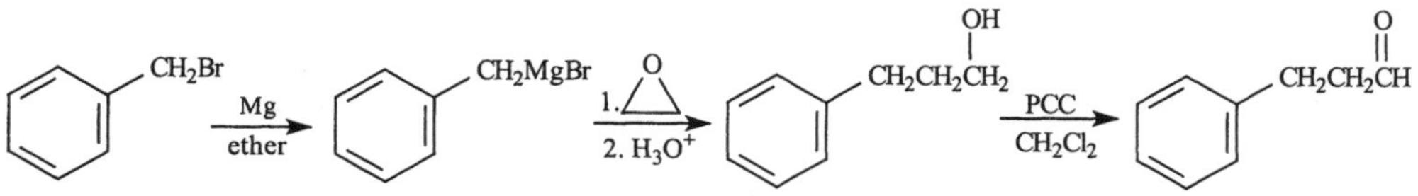

CH_2Br

Mg
ether

CH_2MgBr

1. O (epoxide)
2. H_3O^+

OH
$CH_2CH_2CH_2$

PCC
CH_2Cl_2

O
CH_2CH_2CH

52.

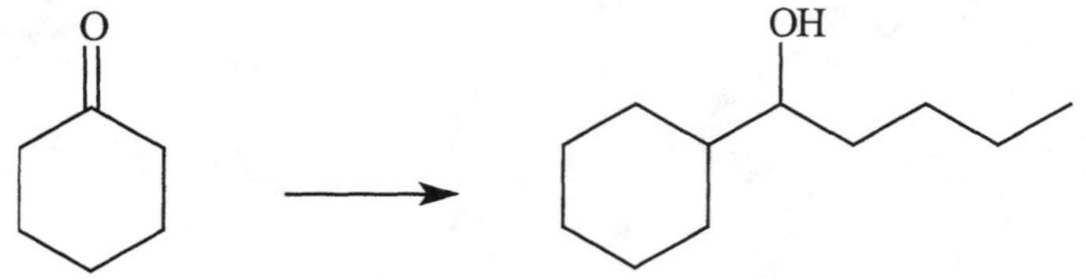

Answer:

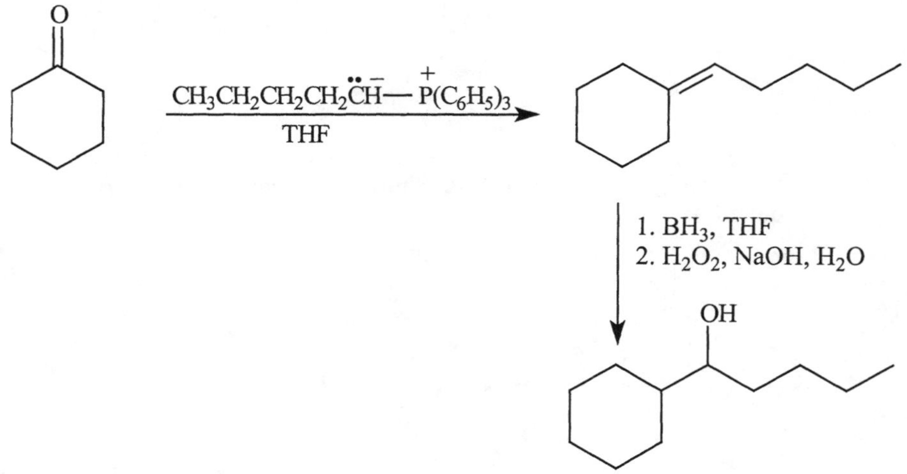

$CH_3CH_2CH_2CH_2\ddot{C}H^- - \overset{+}{P}(C_6H_5)_3$

THF

1. BH_3, THF
2. H_2O_2, NaOH, H_2O

OH

53.

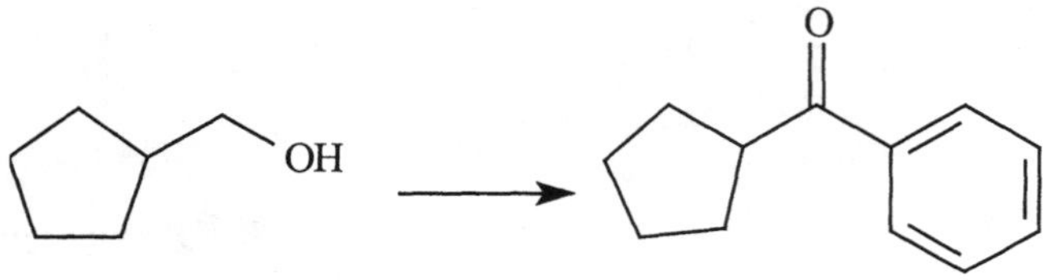

OH

Answer:

OH

PCC

CH_2Cl_2

O

H

1. MgBr, ether

2. H_3O^+

OH

PCC

CH_2Cl_2

O

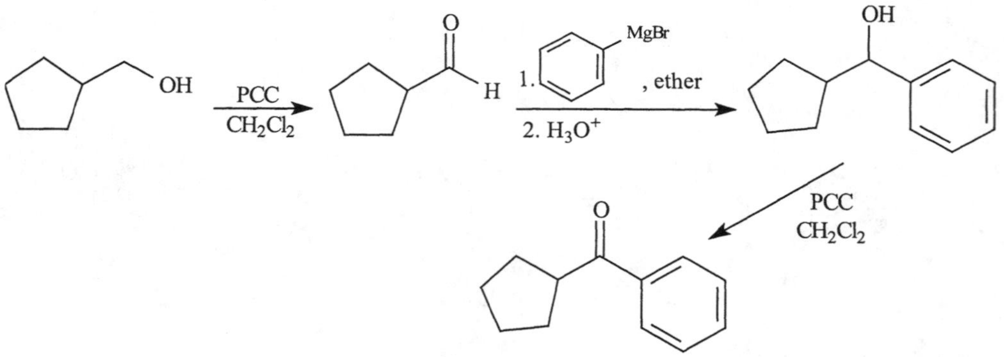

Consider the data below to answer the following questions.

$C_7H_{14}O$

IR: 1715 cm^{-1}

MS: M^+ at $m/z = 114$, α-cleavage fragment at $m/z = 71$,
McLafferty rearrangement fragment at $m/z = 86$.

^1H NMR: 0.92 δ (6H, triplet), 1.59 δ (4H, multiplet), 2.36 δ (4H, triplet)

54. Calculate the degree of unsaturation for this compound.

Answer: The base formula for $C_7H_{14}O$ is C_7H_{14}. The formula for the saturated compound is C_7H_{16}, so the compound has one degree of unsaturation.

55. What functional group is indicated by the IR data?

Answer: Absorption at 1715 cm^{-1} in the infrared spectrum indicates the presence of a carbonyl compound, most probably a ketone.

56. Interpret the mass spectral data.

Answer: A fragment at $m/z = 71$ indicates a loss of 43, or a propyl group, from α-cleavage. A fragment at $m/z = 86$ indicates a loss of 28, or an ethylene group, from McLafferty rearrangement (transfer of a hydrogen atom from the gamma carbon to the carbonyl oxygen with concommitant breaking of the bond between the alpha and beta carbon).

57. Interpret the ^1H NMR data.

Answer: The ^1H NMR indicates that there are only three different kinds of hydrogen in the molecule. The 6H triplet is due to two equivalent CH_3 groups next to two equivalent CH_2 groups, the 4H triplet is due to two equivalent CH_2 groups next to two other equivalent CH_2 groups, shifted by a C=O, and the 4H multiplet is two equivalent CH_2 groups between a CH_2 and a CH_3.

58. Propose a structure consistent with the spectral data presented above.

Answer: 4-heptanone, $CH_3CH_2CH_2COCH_2CH_2CH_3$

Consider the data below to answer the following questions.

$C_7H_{14}O$

IR: 1715 cm^{-1}

MS: M^+ at $m/z = 114$, α-cleavage fragment at $m/z = 71$,
no McLafferty rearrangement fragment

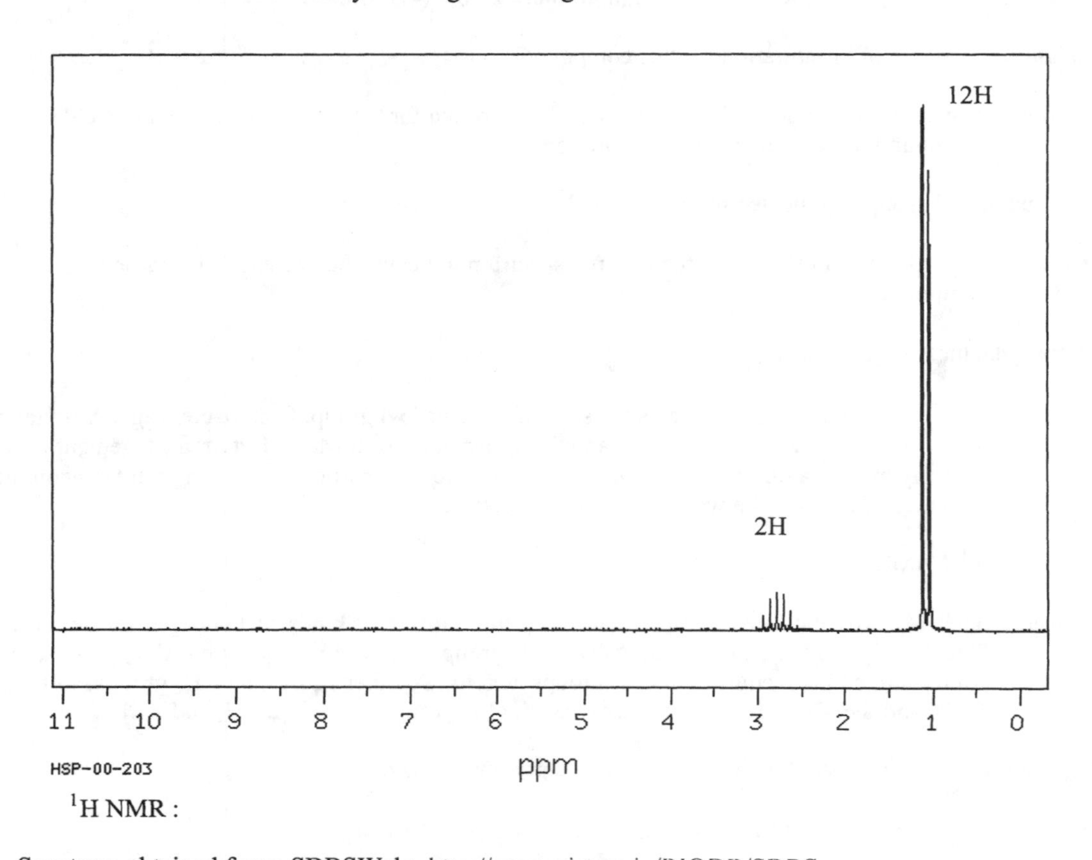

^{1}H NMR :

Spectrum obtained from: SDBSWeb: http://www.aist.go.jp/RIODB/SDBS

59. Interpret the mass spectral data for this compound.

Answer: A fragment at m/z = 71 indicates a loss of 43, or a propyl group, from α-cleavage. The absence of a McLafferty rearrangement fragment means that there is no hydrogen atom on a gamma carbon, so the propyl group must be isopropyl, and not *n*-propyl

60. Interpret the ^{1}H NMR spectrum.

Answer: The ^{1}H NMR spectrum indicates that there are only two kinds of hydrogen in this compound. The 12H doublet (one adjacent H) is most likely four equivalent methyl groups of two equivalent isopropyl groups. The 2H multiplet (many adjacent H) is consistent with two equivalent hydrogens of two isopropyl groups, too. The multiplet is shifted to about 2.77 by the adjacent C=O.

61. Propose a structure for this compound.

Answer: 2,4-dimethyl-3-pentanone, $(CH_3)_2CHCOCH(CH_3)_2$

Chapter 20 - Carboxylic Acids and Nitriles

Draw structures corresponding to each of the following IUPAC names.

1. 2-propylpentanoic acid

Answer:

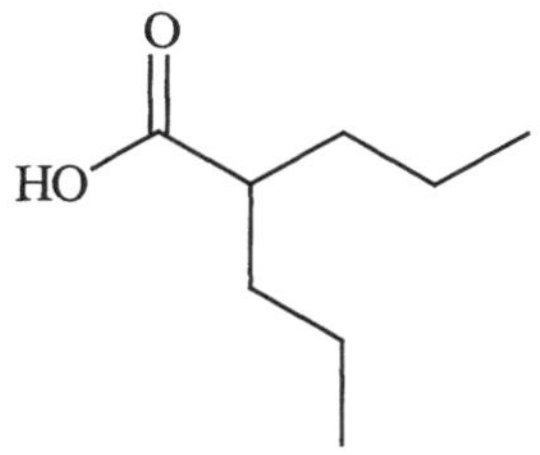

2. *cis*-1,3-cyclopentanedicarboxylic acid

Answer:

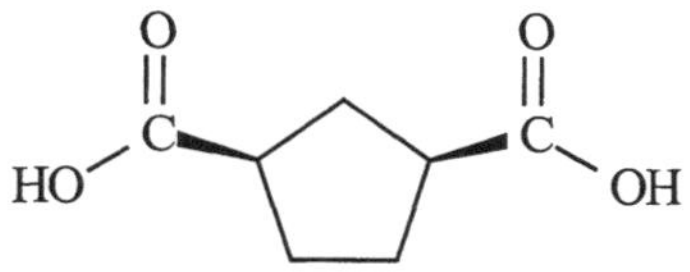

3. cyanoacetic acid

Answer: NC-CH_2COOH

4. *m*-chlorobenzoic acid

Answer:

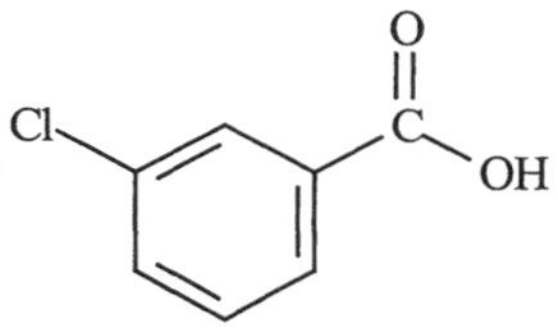

5. 2-propenenitrile

Answer: $H_2C{=}CH{-}C{\equiv}N$

Provide IUPAC names for each of the following structures.

6. $HO\overset{O}{\overset{\|}{C}}(CH_2)_3\overset{O}{\overset{\|}{C}}OH$ **glutaric acid**

Answer: pentanedioic acid

7. salicylic acid

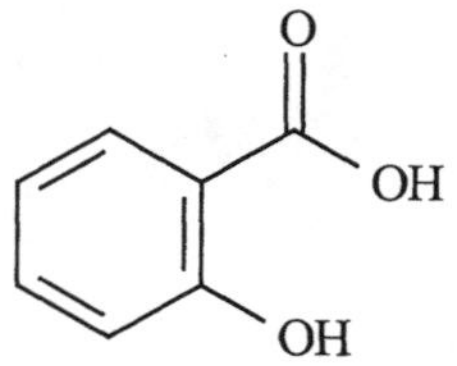

Answer: *o*-hydroxybenzoic acid

8. thujic acid

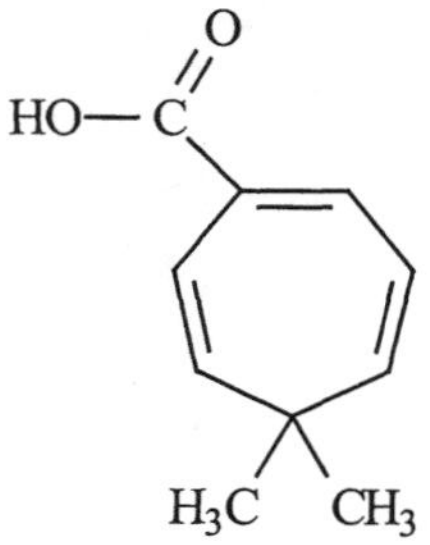

Answer: 5,5-dimethyl-1,3,6-cycloheptatriene-1-carboxylic

9. mevalonic acid

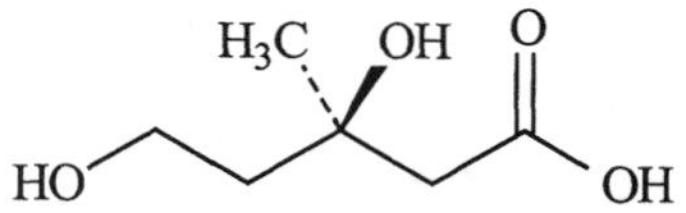

Answer: (*R*)-3,5-dihydroxy-3-methylpentanoic acid

10. tiglic acid

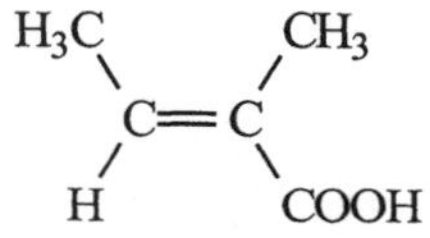

Answer: (*E*)-2-methyl-2-butenoic acid

11. 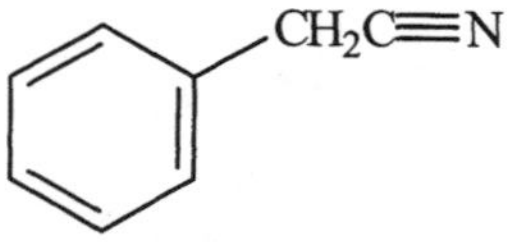 $C_6H_5CH_2C{\equiv}N$

Answer: phenylacetonitrile or 2-phenylethanenitrile

12. What is the correct name for the following structure?

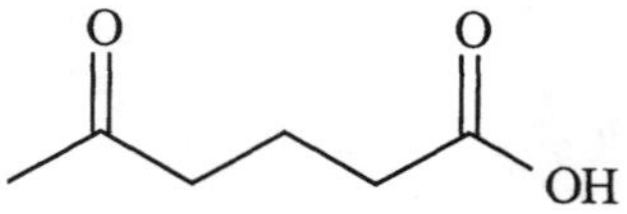

a. 2-oxohexanoic acid
b. 5-oxohexanoic acid
c. methyl butroxoketone
d. 4-ketopentanoic acid

Answer: b

Consider the data in the Table below to answer the following questions:

Acidities of Substituted Benzoic and Acetic Acids			
		$pK_a s$ at 25° C	
		$Y-C_6H_4COOH$	
Y	$Y-CH_2COOH$	*meta*	*para*
H	4.75	4.19	4.19
CN	2.47	3.64	3.55
OCH_3	3.57	4.09	4.46

13. Draw the structure of the strongest acid in the table above.

Answer: NC-CH_2-COOH

14. Which of the acids in the table above has the strongest conjugate base?

Answer: CH_3COOH

15. Explain why cyanoacetic acid and methoxyacetic acid are more acidic than their correspondingly substituted benzoic acid counterparts.

Answer: Electron-withdrawing groups, like –CN and $-OCH_3$, inductively withdraw electron density, which stabilizes the resulting carboxylate anion and, thus, increases the acidity of the carboxylic acid. These inductive effects are strongly dependent on distance. The –CN and $-OCH_3$ substituents are closer to the carboxylate in the substituted acetic acids than in the substituted benzoic acids, so their effect is greater.

16. Even through the *para* position is one carbon farther from the carboxy group than the *meta* position, *p*-cyanobenzoic acid is *more* acidic than *m*-cyanobenzoic acid. Explain the differences in acidity between *p*-cyanobenzoic acid and *m*-cyanobenzoic acid.

Answer: In *p*-cyanobenzoic acid, the negative charge of the carboxylate can be better stabilized than in the *meta* isomer because the electron-withdrawing cyano group polarizes the benzene ring and places a positive charge next to the negatively charged carboxyl group. The same polarization occurs in *m*-cyanobenzoic acid, but the effect is not as great because the charge is one carbon farther away from the carboxy group.

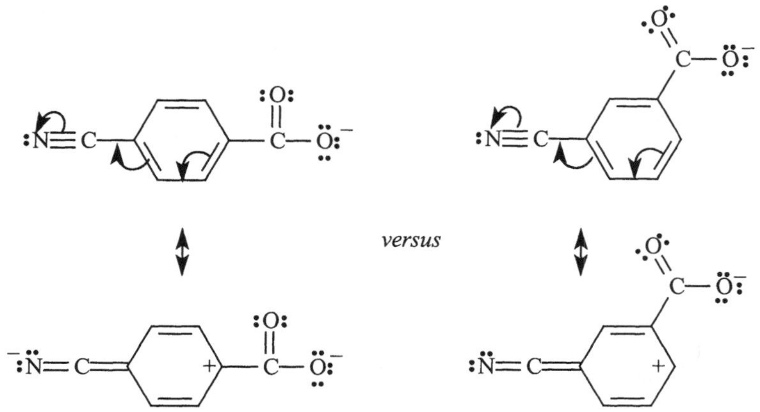

versus

17. Explain the differences in acidity between *p*-methoxybenzoic acid and *m*-methoxybenzoic acid.

Answer: *p*-Methoxybenzoic acid is less acidic than *m*-methoxybenzoic acid because the carboxyl group is directly conjugated, through the benzene ring, with the electron-donating oxygen of the methoxy group. This destabilizes the *p*-methoxybenzoate anion relative to the *m*-methoxybenzoate anion by placing two negative charges on the carboxylate group.

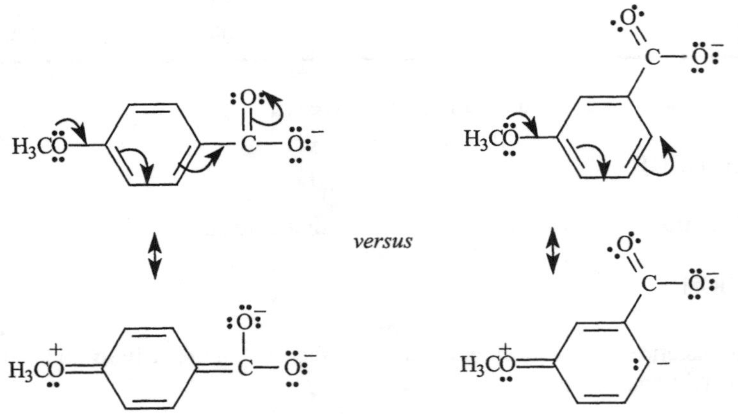

versus

Consider the data below to answer the following questions.

When CO_2 is bubbled through an ether solution of benzylmagnesium bromide, and the resulting mixture is acidified, phenylacetic acid is produced. Any unreacted benzylmagnesium bromide is converted to toluene in the acidification step.

18. Write the complete reaction sequence for the process described above.

Answer:

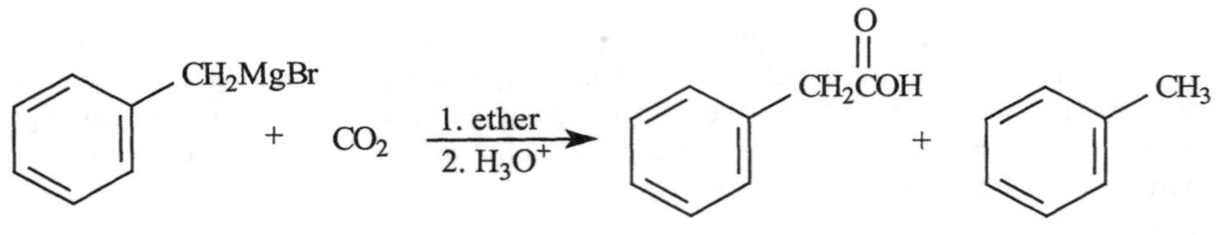

$$C_6H_5CH_2MgBr + CO_2 \xrightarrow[2.\ H_3O^+]{1.\ ether} C_6H_5CH_2COOH + C_6H_5CH_3$$

19. How could you separate phenylacetic acid from toluene?

Answer: Extract the ether solution containing the mixture of products with a dilute aqueous solution of sodium hydroxide. This converts phenylacetic acid to its carboxylate salt, which will dissolve in the aqueous layer. The toluene will remain in the ether layer. Separate the aqueous and organic layers, acidify the aqueous layer, and extract with an organic solvent to recover the phenylacetic acid.

20. This reaction is described as a ____________ process.

a. carbonylation
b. carboxylation
c. carbaniolation
d. cationation

Answer: b

What is the order of increasing acidity for the following compounds? (least to most)

21.

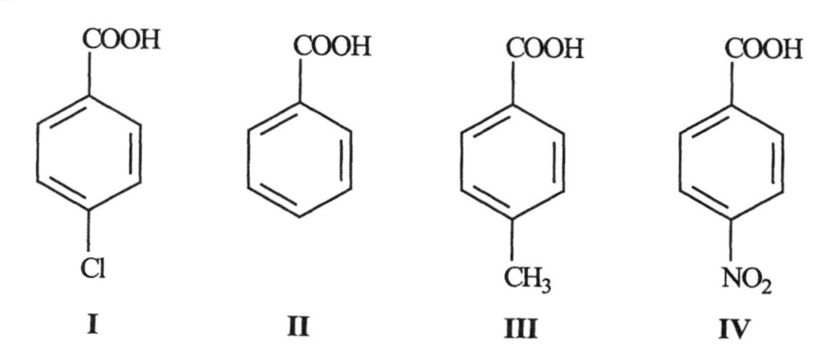

I II III IV

a. IV, I, III, II
b. III, II, I, IV
c. II, III, I, IV
d. III, II, IV, I

Answer: b

22.

COOH COOH COOH

H_3C CH_3COOH

NO_2

I II III IV

a. IV, I, III, II
b. IV, II, III, I
c. II, III, I, IV
d. I, III, II, IV

Answer: a

23. CH_3CH_2COOH $BrCH_2CH_2COOH$ $CH_3CH_2CH_2OH$ $CH_3CH(Br)COOH$

I II III IV

a. IV, II, I, III
b. I, II, IV, III
c. III, I, II, IV
d. III, IV, II, I

Answer: c

Give the major organic product(s) for each of the following reactions or sequences of reactions. Show all relevant stereochemistry.

24. 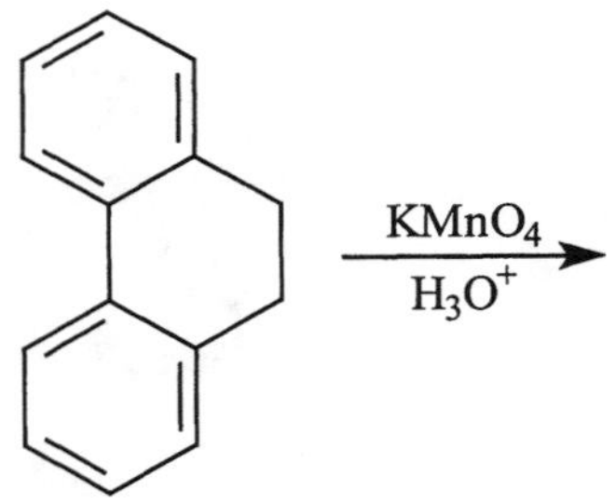 $\xrightarrow[H_3O^+]{KMnO_4}$

Answer:

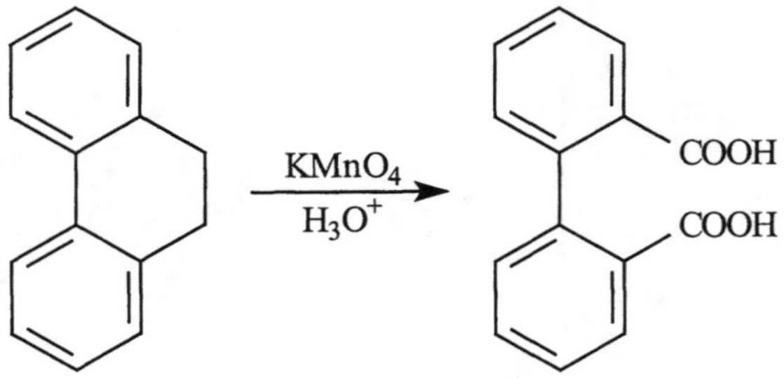

$\xrightarrow[H_3O^+]{KMnO_4}$ COOH COOH

25. 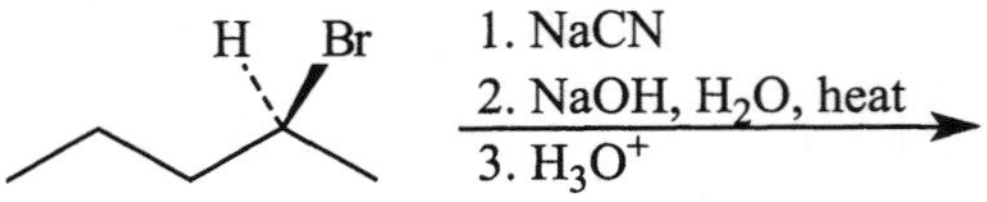 H Br 1. NaCN 2. NaOH, H_2O, heat 3. H_3O^+

Answer:

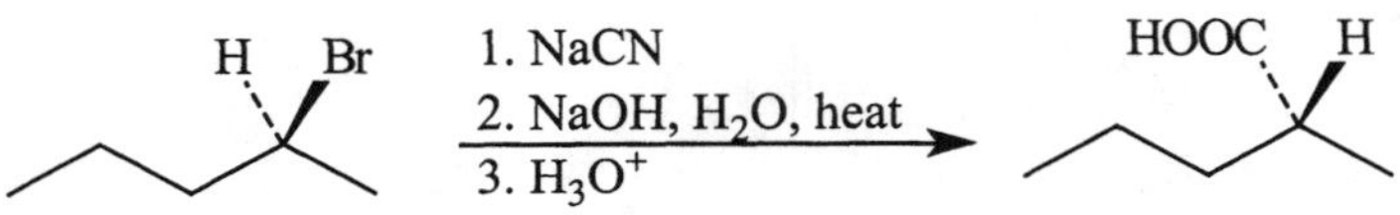

H Br 1. NaCN 2. NaOH, H_2O, heat 3. H_3O^+ → HOOC H

26. 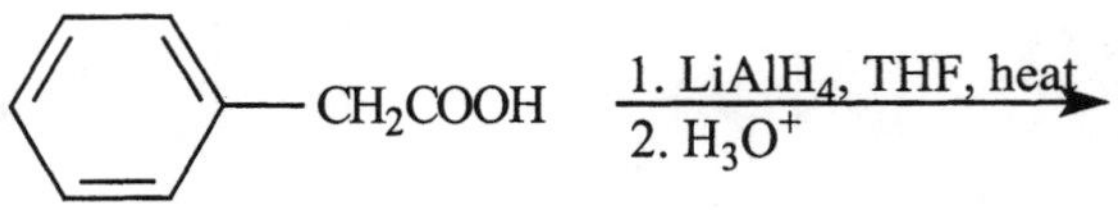 CH_2COOH 1. $LiAlH_4$, THF, heat 2. H_3O^+

Answer:

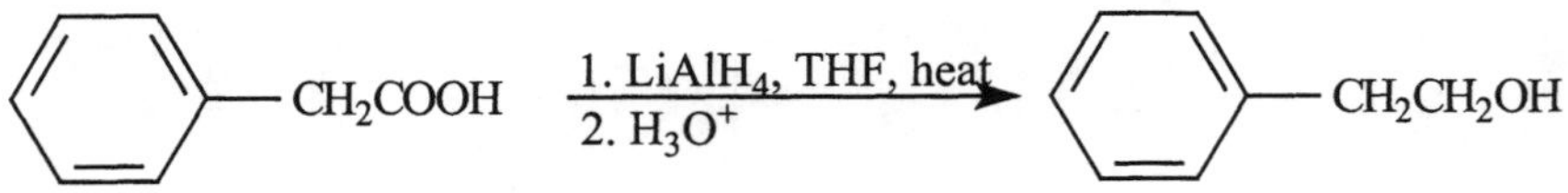

CH_2COOH 1. $LiAlH_4$, THF, heat 2. H_3O^+ → CH_2CH_2OH

27. 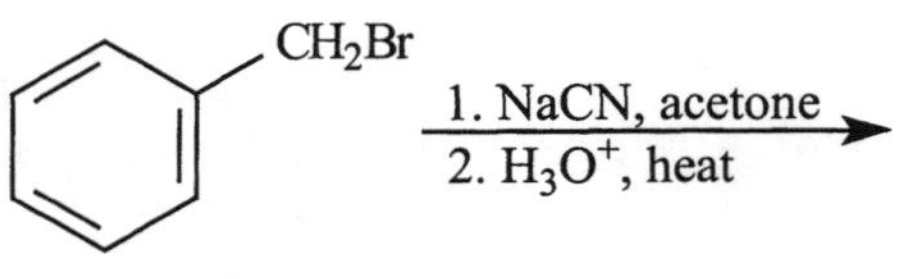 CH_2Br 1. NaCN, acetone 2. H_3O^+, heat

Answer:

$C_6H_5CH_2Br \xrightarrow[\text{2. } H_3O^+\text{, heat}]{\text{1. NaCN, acetone}} C_6H_5CH_2COOH$

28. Cyclopentane–COOH $\xrightarrow[\text{2. } H_3O^+]{\text{1. } BH_3\text{, THF}}$

Answer:

Cyclopentane–COOH $\xrightarrow[\text{2. } H_3O^+]{\text{1. } BH_3\text{, THF}}$ Cyclopentane–CH_2OH

29. $(CH_3)_2C{=}CHCH_2CH_2CH(CH_3)CH_2CH_2OH \xrightarrow{CrO_3\text{, } H_3O^+}$

Answer:

$(CH_3)_2C{=}CHCH_2CH_2CH(CH_3)CH_2CH_2OH \xrightarrow{CrO_3\text{, } H_3O^+} (CH_3)_2C{=}CHCH_2CH_2CH(CH_3)CH_2COOH$

30. $C_6H_5Br \xrightarrow[\text{2. } CO_2]{\text{1. Mg, ether}} \xrightarrow{\text{3. } H_3O^+}$

Answer:

$C_6H_5Br \xrightarrow[\text{2. } CO_2]{\text{1. Mg, ether}} \xrightarrow{\text{3. } H_3O^+} C_6H_5COOH$

31. CH_3COCH_2COOH + CH_3MgI $\xrightarrow{\text{ether}}$

Answer:

CH_3COCH_2COOH + CH_3MgI $\xrightarrow{\text{ether}}$ $CH_3COCH_2COO^- \; ^+MgI$ + CH_4

32.  (hexyl chain)–CN $\xrightarrow[\text{2. } H_3O^+]{\text{1. } LiAlH_4\text{, THF}}$

Answer:

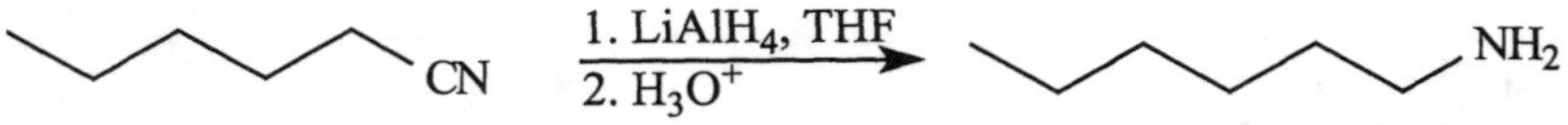

(hexyl chain)–CN $\xrightarrow[\text{2. } H_3O^+]{\text{1. } LiAlH_4\text{, THF}}$ (heptyl chain)–NH_2

33. 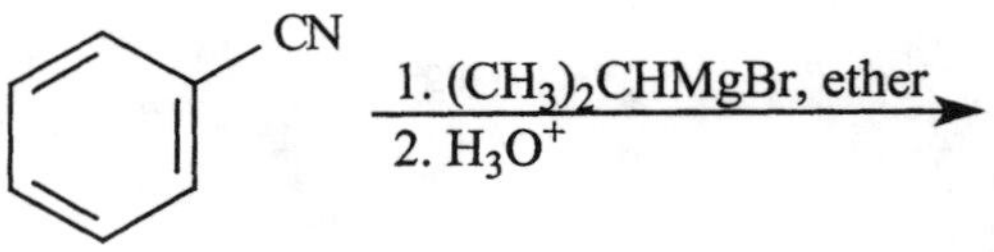 C_6H_5CN $\xrightarrow[\text{2. } H_3O^+]{\text{1. } (CH_3)_2CHMgBr\text{, ether}}$

Answer:

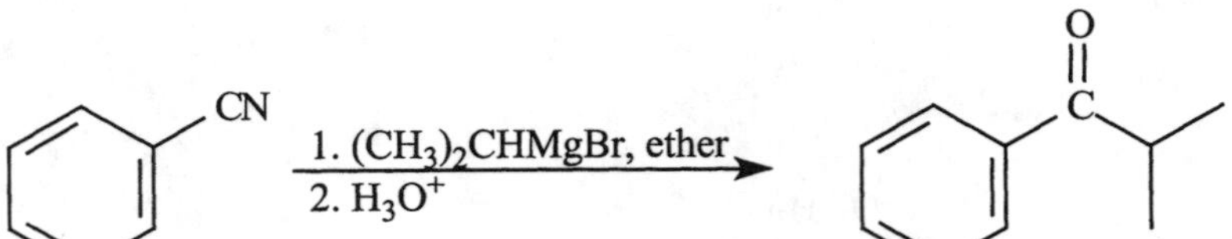

C_6H_5CN $\xrightarrow[\text{2. } H_3O^+]{\text{1. } (CH_3)_2CHMgBr\text{, ether}}$ $C_6H_5C(=O)CH(CH_3)_2$

34. 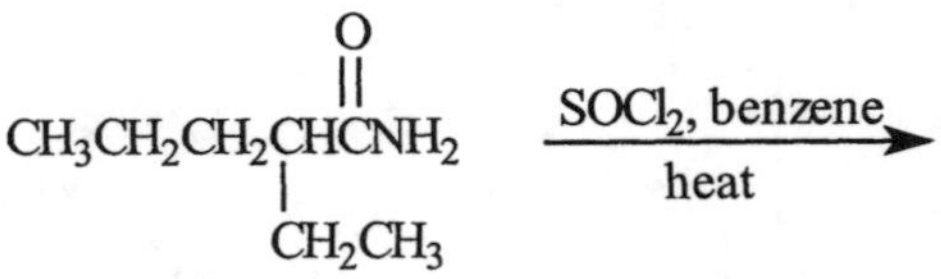 $CH_3CH_2CH_2CH(CH_2CH_3)CONH_2$ $\xrightarrow[\text{heat}]{SOCl_2\text{, benzene}}$

Answer:

$CH_3CH_2CH_2CH(CH_2CH_3)CONH_2$ $\xrightarrow[\text{heat}]{SOCl_2\text{, benzene}}$ $CH_3CH_2CH_2CH(CH_2CH_3)C{\equiv}N$

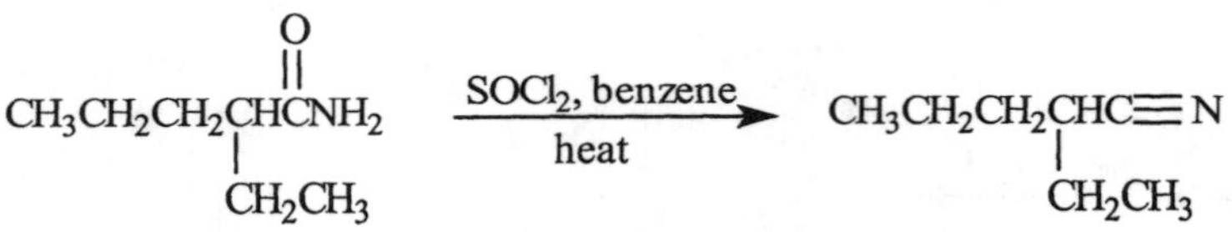

Choose the *best* reagent(s) for carrying out the following conversions from the list below. Place the letter corresponding to the best choice in the blank to the left of the conversion.

a. $KMnO_4$, H_3O^+
b. Tollens' Reagent
c. $NaBH_4$, ethanol
d. 1. BH_3 2. H_3O^+
e. 1. CH_3MgBr, ether 2. H_3O^+
f. CrO_3, H_2SO_4, H_2O
g. 1. Mg, ether 2. CO_2 3. H_3O^+
h. 1. NaCN 2. H_2SO_4, H_2, heat
i. O_3, then Zn and HOAc
j. CH_3I

35. _____ $CH_3CH{=}CHCH_2COOH \longrightarrow CH_3COOH + HOOCCH_2COOH$

Answer: a

36. ___

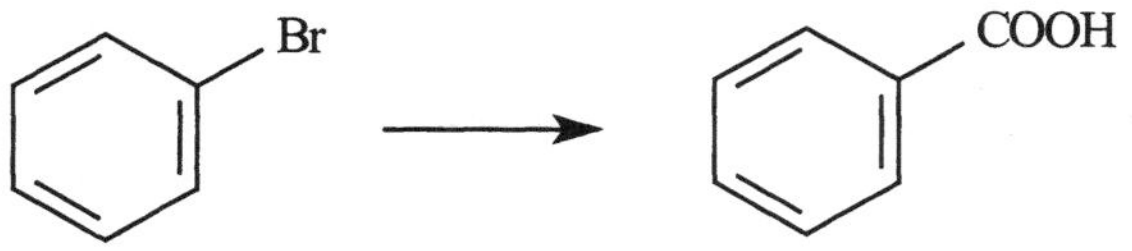

Answer: g

37. ___

Answer: d

38. ___

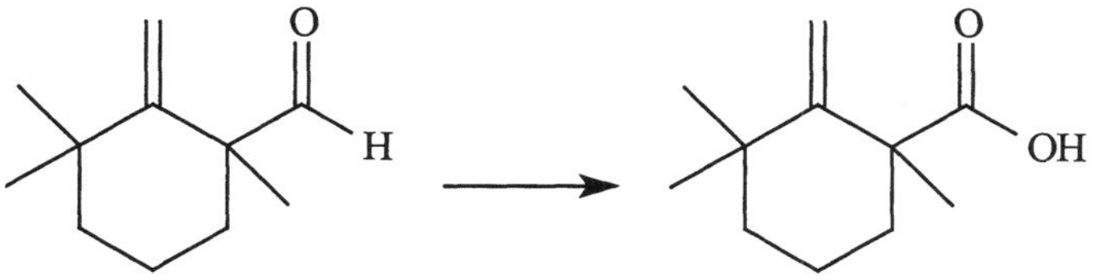

Answer: b

39. ___

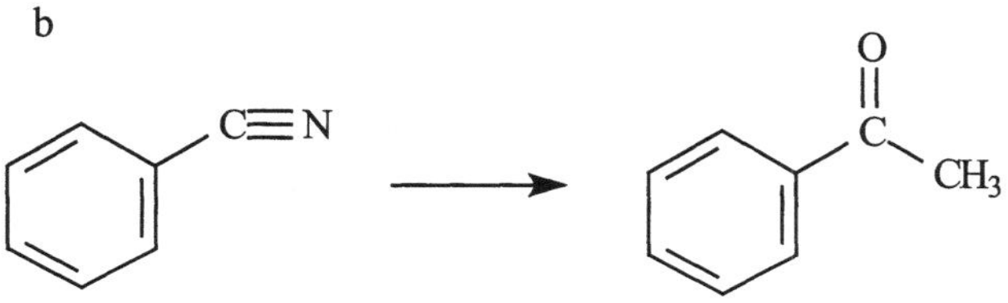

Answer: e

Carboxylic acids are synthesized from alkyl halides via Grignard reagent carboxylation or nitrile hydrolysis. Choose the best method for effecting each of the following conversions. Explain each of your choices. If neither method is appropriate, explain.

40.

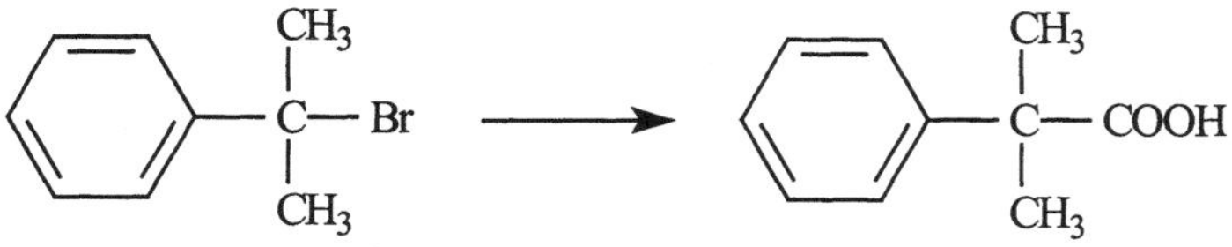

Answer: Since S_N2 displacements do not occur at tertiary alkyl halides the Grignard reagent carboxylation is the best method for carrying out this conversion.

41.  $H_2N-C_6H_4-CH_2CH_2I \longrightarrow H_2N-C_6H_4-CH_2CH_2COOH$

Answer: Amine protons interfere with the formation of Grignard reagents, so nitrile hydrolysis is the best method for carrying out this conversion.

42.  Br → COOH

Answer: Either method would be appropriate for this conversion.

43.  CHO Br → CHO COOH

Answer: Neither method of acid synthesis yields the desired product. Any Grignard reagent formed will react with the carbonyl function group present in the starting material. Reaction with cyanide occurs at the carbonyl functional group as well as at the halogen. However, if the aldehyde is first protected by forming an acetal, either method can be used to synthesize a carboxylic acid.

44. Propose a synthesis of the anti-inflammatory drug Ibuprofen from benzene. Show all reagents and all intermediate structures. Assume that *ortho* and *para* isomers can be separated.

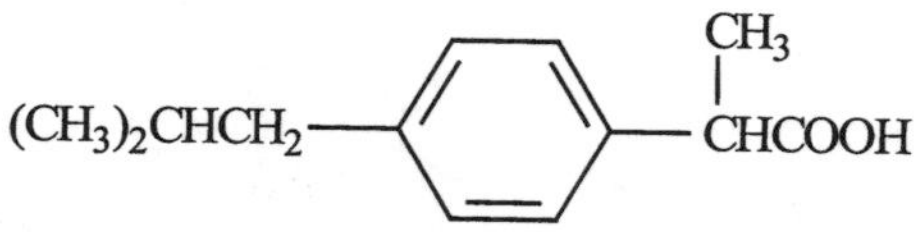

$(CH_3)_2CHCH_2$–C_6H_4–$CH(CH_3)COOH$ **Ibuprofen**

Answer:

Benzene $\xrightarrow[AlCl_3]{CH_3CH_2Cl}$ CH_2CH_3-benzene $\xrightarrow[AlCl_3]{(CH_3)_2CHCCl (O)}$ CH_2CH_3 / $C(=O)$—$CH(CH_3)_2$ $\xrightarrow[HCl]{HOCH_2CH_2OH}$ CH_2CH_3 / O—C—$CH(CH_3)_2$ (acetal, O) $\xrightarrow{NBS}$ Br—$CHCH_3$ / O—C—$CH(CH_3)_2$ (acetal, O) $\xrightarrow{1.\ Mg,\ ether;\ 2.\ CO_2;\ 3.\ H_3O^+}$ HOOC—$CHCH_3$ / $C(=O)$—$CH(CH_3)_2$ $\xrightarrow{H_2/Pd}$ HOOC—$CHCH_3$ / $CH_2CH(CH_3)_2$

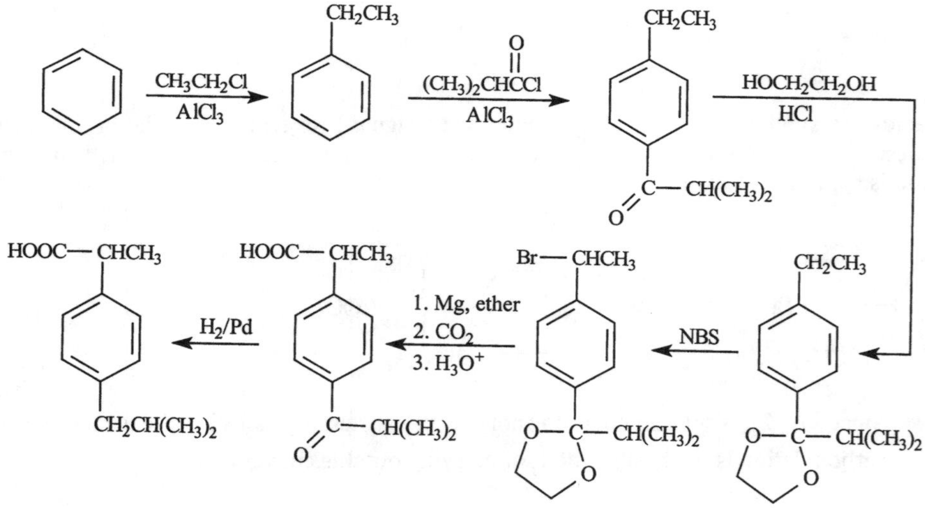

Show how you would accomplish the following transformations. More than one step may be required. Show all reagents and all intermediate structures.

45.  H Br → H CH_3 NH_2

Answer:

(2-bromopentane, H/Br wedge) $\xrightarrow[\text{ethanol}]{\text{NaCN}}$ (NC, H nitrile) $\xrightarrow[\text{2. } H_3O^+]{\text{1. } LiAlH_4\text{, ether}}$ (H, CH_3 … NH_2)

46. $CH_3CH_2C(CH_3)_2$—Br $\longrightarrow$ $CH_3CH_2C(CH_3)_2$—CN

Answer:

$CH_3CH_2C(CH_3)_2$—Br

1. Mg, ether
2. CO_2
3. H_3O^+

$CH_3CH_2C(CH_3)_2$—COOH $\xrightarrow{SOCl_2}$ $CH_3CH_2C(CH_3)_2$—COCl $\xrightarrow{2\ NH_3}$ $CH_3CH_2C(CH_3)_2$—$CONH_2$

$\xrightarrow{SOCl_2\text{, benzene, heat}}$ $CH_3CH_2C(CH_3)_2$—CN

47. The two ^1H NMR spectra below belong to acetic acid (CH_3CO_2H) and its isomer, methyl formate (HCO_2CH_3). Which spectrum corresponds to which compound? Explain your answer.

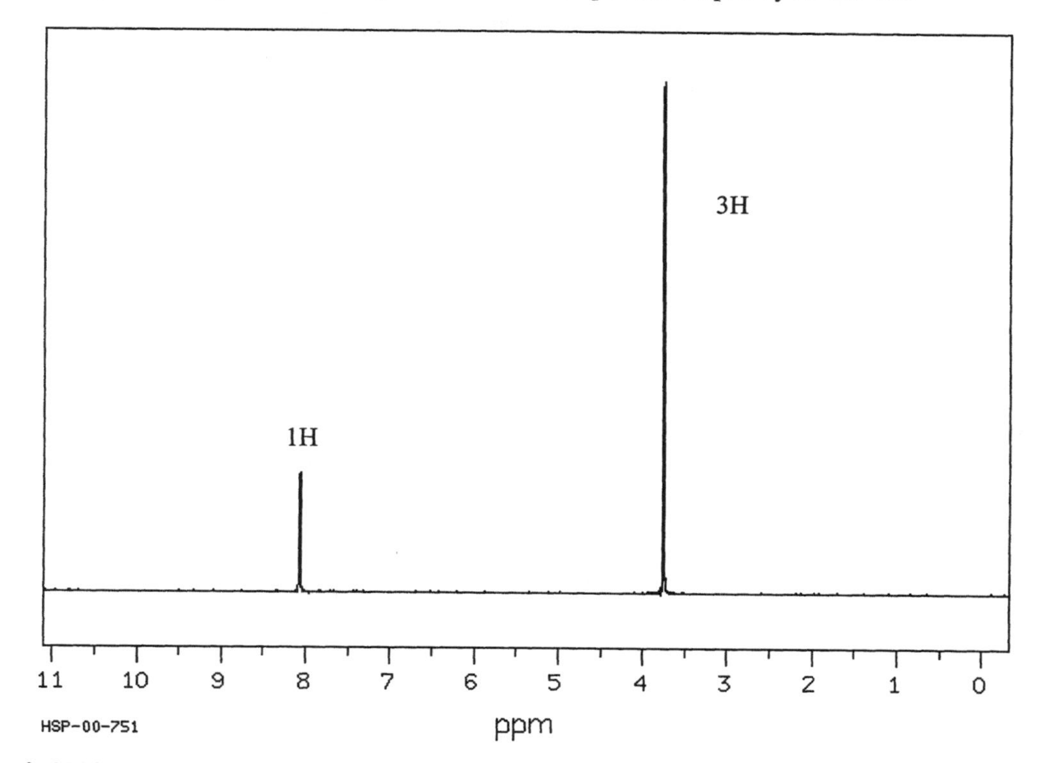

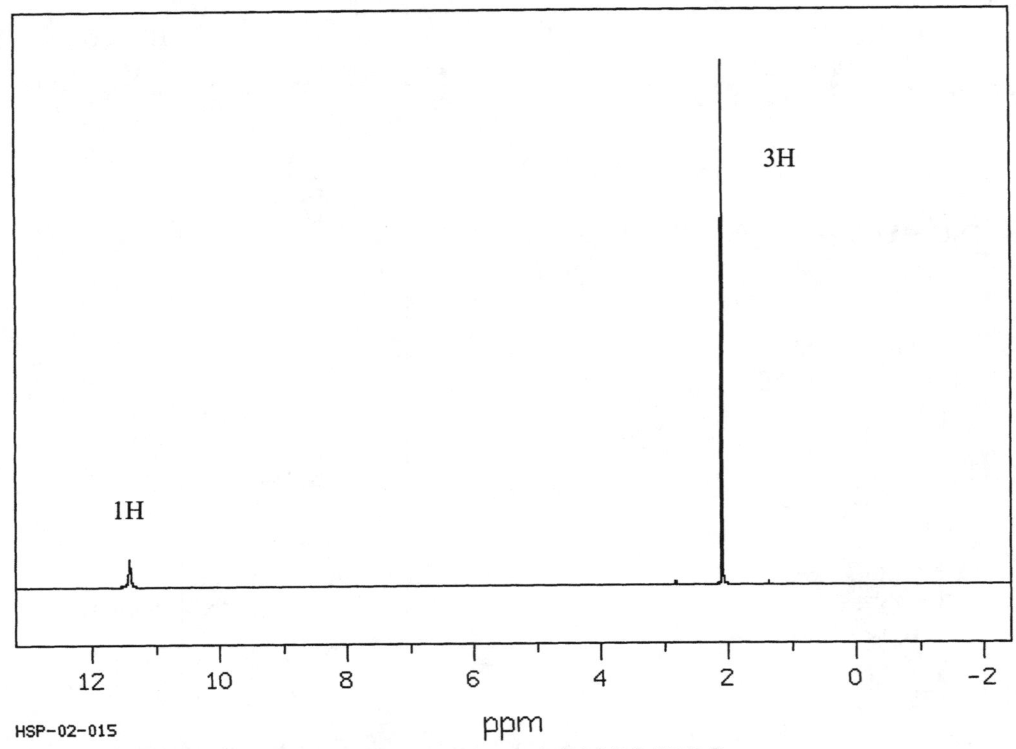

Spectra obtained from SDBSWeb: http://www.aist.go.jp/RIODB/SDBS

Answer: Both of these compounds contain two different kinds of protons. In addition, both of the protons in each compound are expected to appear as singlets. However, the position of the absorptions should be diagnostic.

The carboxylic acid proton in acetic acid should appear between 11 and 12 δ while the methyl singlet should appear between 2 and 3 δ. We see that absorptions appear in these regions in the bottom spectrum.

The aldehyde-like proton in methyl formate appears slightly upfield from "normal" aldehydes owing to the electron-donating methoxy group attached to the carbonyl. The methyl singlet in methyl formate would be predicted to appear between 3 and 4 δ, which it does.

Chapter 21 – Carboxylic Acid Derivatives and Nucleophilic Acyl Substitution Reactions

Provide IUPAC names for each of the following structures:

1. H_2N–C_6H_4–$\overset{O}{\overset{\|}{C}}OCH_2CH_3$ **benzocaine**

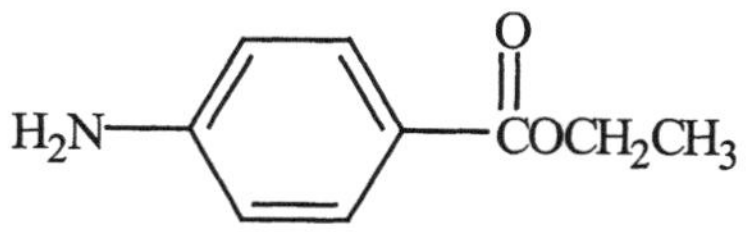

Answer: Ethyl *p*-aminobenzoate

2. [structure: two isobutyryl groups, each C=O, joined through O]

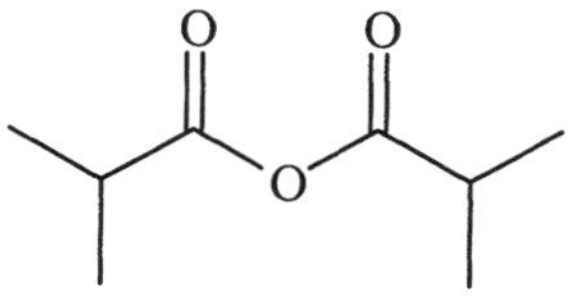

Answer: bis(2-methylpropanoic) anhydride

3. C_6H_5–$CH_2\overset{O}{\overset{\|}{C}}$—$OCH_3$

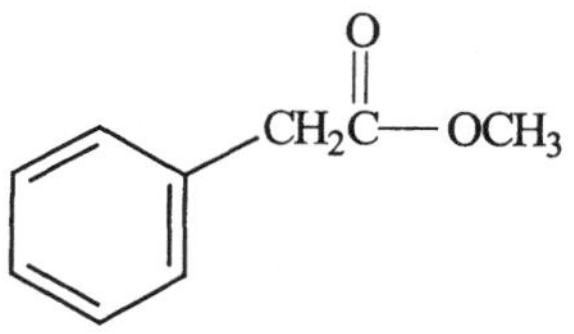

Answer: methyl phenylacetate

4. H_3C(H)C=C(H)–C(=O)Cl

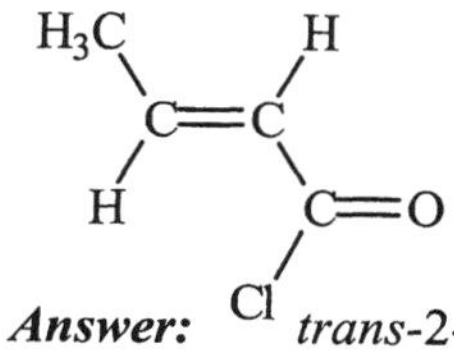

Answer: *trans*-2-butenoyl chloride

5. cyclopentyl–NH—$\overset{O}{\overset{\|}{C}}$—$CH_2CH(CH_3)_2$

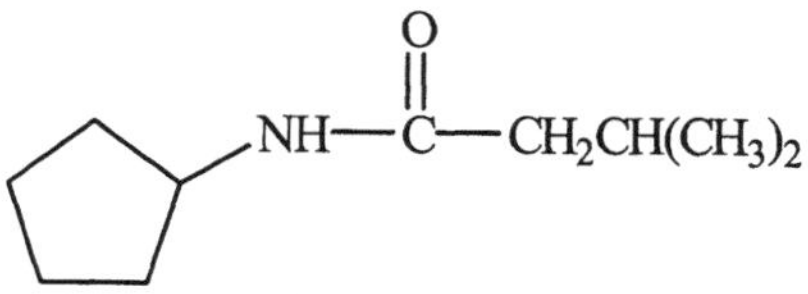

Answer: N-cyclopentyl-3-methylbutanamide

Draw structures corresponding to each of the following names:

6. 2-propenamide

Answer:

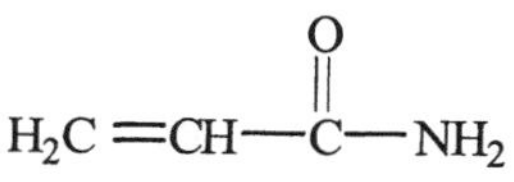

$H_2C{=}CH{-}\overset{O}{\overset{\|}{C}}{-}NH_2$

7. 3,4,5-trimethoxybenzoyl chloride

Answer:

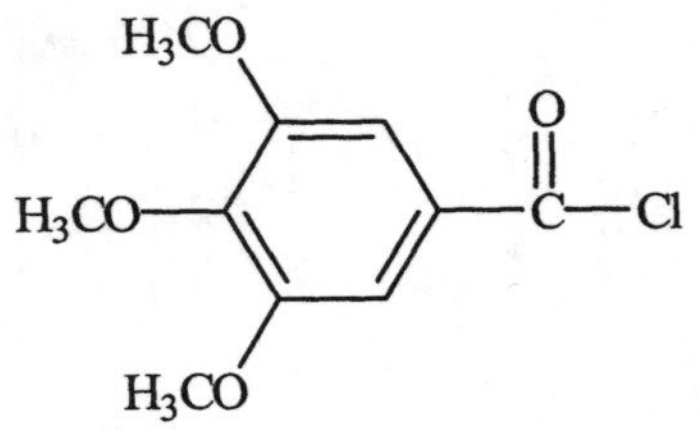

H_3CO

H_3CO — C(=O) — Cl

H_3CO

8. acetic formic anhydride

Answer: H O CH_3

O O

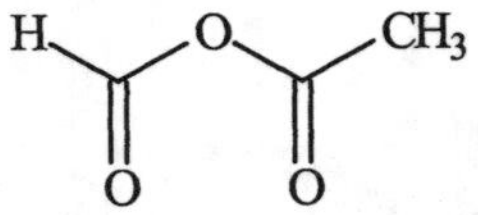

9. N,N-dimethylformamide

Answer:

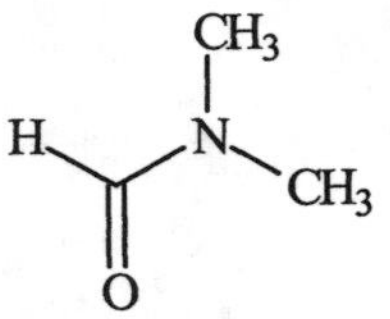

CH_3

H N CH_3

O

10. methyl *cis*-3-ethylcyclobutanecarboxylate

Answer:

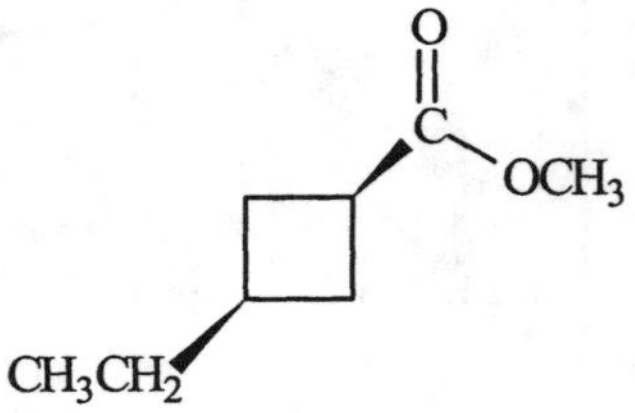

O

C OCH_3

CH_3CH_2

11. (*E*)-2,4-dimethyl-2-hexenoyl chloride

Answer:

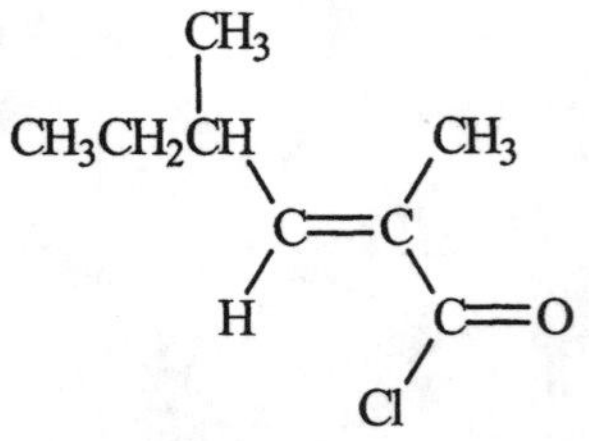

CH_3

CH_3CH_2CH CH_3

C=C

H C=O

Cl

12. What is the correct structure for phenylbenzoate?

a. $C_6H_5-C(=O)-O-C_6H_5$

b. $H_3C-C(=O)-O-C_6H_5$

c. $C_6H_5-C(=O)-O-CH_3$

d. $C_6H_5-CH_2O-C(=O)-CH_2-C_6H_5$

Answer: a

What is the order of *decreasing* reactivity towards nucleophilic acyl substitution for the carboxylic acid derivatives? (most reactive first)

13. $H_3C-C(=O)-O-C(=O)-CH_3$ (I) $H_3C-C(=O)-N(CH_3)_2$ (II) $H_3C-C(=O)-OCH_3$ (III) $(CH_3)_2CH-C(=O)-OCH_3$ (IV)

a. I, II, III, IV
b. I, III, IV, II
c. II, IV, III, I
d. II, I, III, IV

Answer: b

14. $R-C(=O)-O-C(=O)-R$ (I) $R-C(=O)-NH_2$ (II) $R-C(=O)-OR$ (III) $R-C(=O)-Cl$ (IV)

a. I, III, II, IV
b. II, III, I, IV
c. III, II, I, IV
d. IV, I, III, II

Answer: d

15. Ethyl *p*-nitrobenzoate is more reactive towards nucleophilic acyl substitution that ethyl *p*-methyoxybenzoate. Explain this reactivity difference using both words and structures.

Answer: In general, any factor that makes the carbonyl carbon more polarized will increase the reactivity of the carboxylic acid derivative. In these particular examples, both are aromatic ethyl esters. It is the substituent on the aromatic ring that is affecting the reactivity difference. The electron-withdrawing nitro group increases the polarization of the carbonyl by withdrawing electrons from it through the aromatic ring. The electron donating methoxy group decreases the polarization of the carbonyl by donating electrons to it through the aromatic ring.

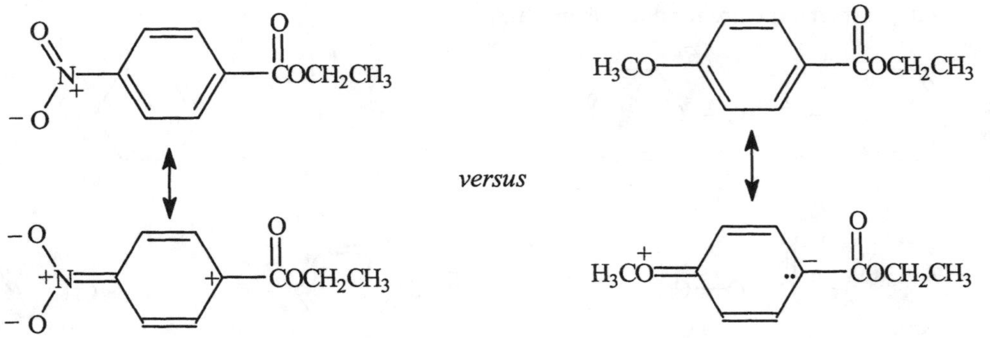

versus

16. Write the complete stepwise mechanism for the basic hydrolysis of acetamide, shown below. Show all electron flow with arrows and draw all intermediate structures.

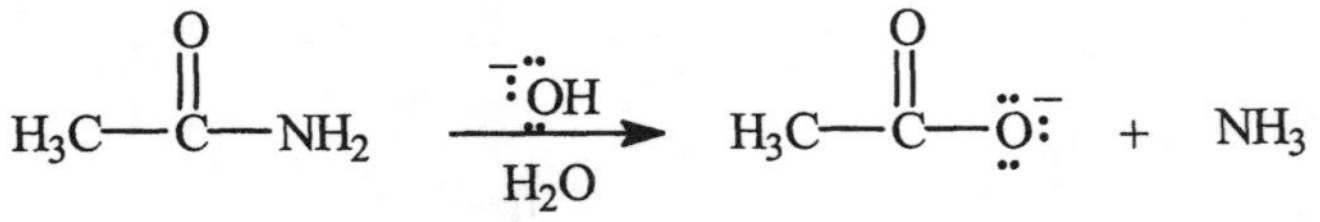

$$H_3C-C(=O)-NH_2 \xrightarrow[H_2O]{^{-}:\ddot{O}H} H_3C-C(=O)-\ddot{O}:^{-} + NH_3$$

Answer:

H₃C—C(=O)—NH₂ → (⁻:ÖH, H₂O) → H₃C—C(O⁻)(OH)(H₂N) → H₃C—C(=O)—O—H + ⁻:NH₂ → H₃C—C(=O)—Ö:⁻ + NH₃

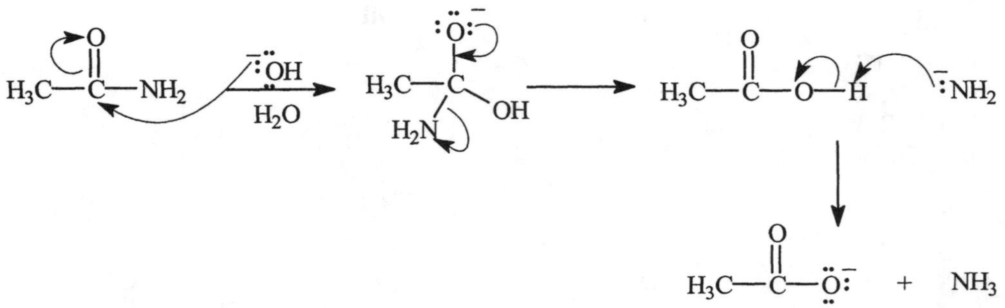

Consider the reaction below to answer the following questions:

$$CH_3CH_2-C(=O)-Cl + 2\ CH_2N_2 \longrightarrow CH_3CH_2-C(=O)-CHN_2 + CH_3Cl + N_2$$

Acid halides react with diazomethane to yield diazoketones. Excess diazomethane is used to prevent the HCl produced in the reaction from reacting with the diazoketone.

17. Diazomethane is an example of a dipolar molecule; a molecule which is neutral overall but has charges on individual atoms. One resonance form of diazomethane is drawn below. Draw the Lewis structure of the other resonance form of diazomethane. Be sure to include all formal charges.

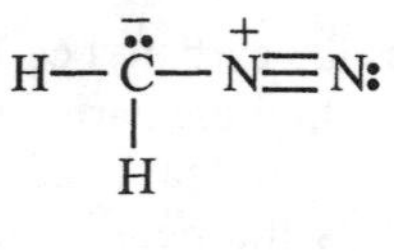

$$H-\ddot{C}^{-}H-\overset{+}{N}\equiv N:$$

Answer:

$$H-\ddot{C}^{-}H-\overset{+}{N}\equiv N: \longleftrightarrow H-CH=\overset{+}{N}=\ddot{N}:^{-}$$

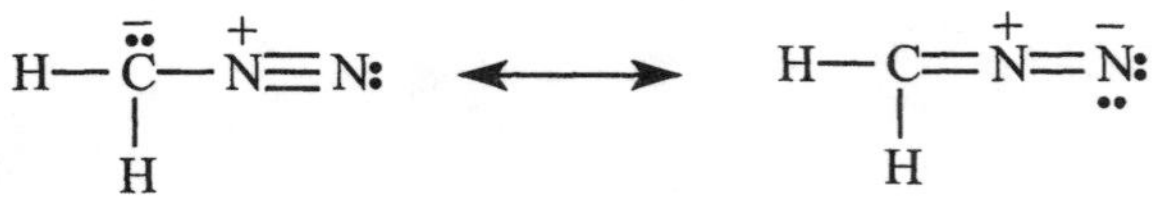

18. The intermediate structures for the mechanism for the reaction of propanyl chloride with diazomethane are provide below. Show all electron flow with arrows on these structures.

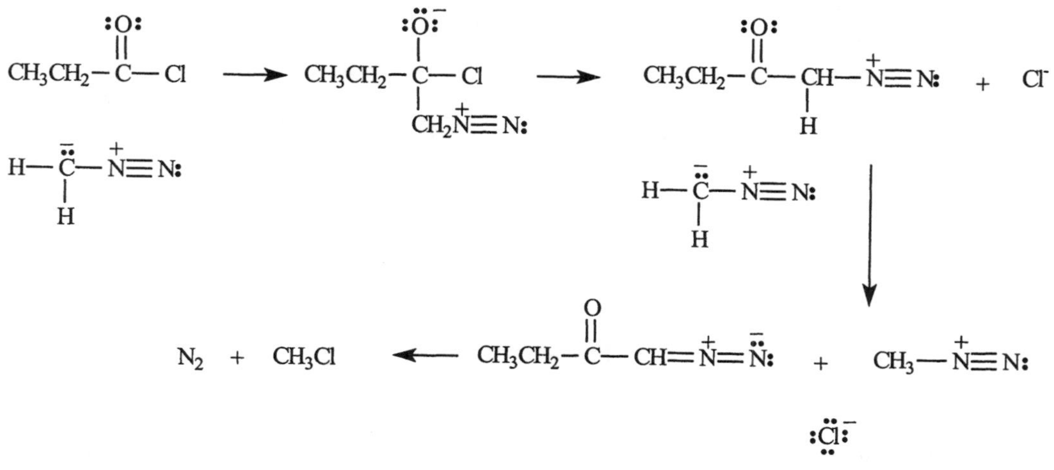

$CH_3CH_2-C(=O)-Cl$ + $H-\ddot{C}H^{-}-\overset{+}{N}\equiv N:$ $\longrightarrow$ $CH_3CH_2-C(-\ddot{O}:^{-})(-CH_2\overset{+}{N}\equiv N:)-Cl$ $\longrightarrow$ $CH_3CH_2-C(=O)-CH(H)-\overset{+}{N}\equiv N:$ + Cl^-

$CH_3CH_2-C(=O)-CH(H)-\overset{+}{N}\equiv N:$ + $H-\ddot{C}H^{-}-\overset{+}{N}\equiv N:$ $\longrightarrow$ $CH_3CH_2-C(=O)-CH=\overset{+}{N}=\ddot{N}^{-}:$ + $CH_3-\overset{+}{N}\equiv N:$ + $:\ddot{Cl}:^-$

$CH_3CH_2-C(=O)-CH=\overset{+}{N}=\ddot{N}^{-}:$ + $CH_3-\overset{+}{N}\equiv N:$ + $:\ddot{Cl}:^-$ $\longrightarrow$ N_2 + CH_3Cl

Answer:

$CH_3CH_2-C(=O)-Cl$ + $H-\ddot{C}H^{-}-\overset{+}{N}\equiv N:$ $\longrightarrow$ $CH_3CH_2-C(-\ddot{O}:^{-})(-CH_2\overset{+}{N}\equiv N:)-Cl$ $\longrightarrow$ $CH_3CH_2-C(=O)-CH(H)-\overset{+}{N}\equiv N:$ + Cl^-

$CH_3CH_2-C(=O)-CH(H)-\overset{+}{N}\equiv N:$ + $H-\ddot{C}H^{-}-\overset{+}{N}\equiv N:$ $\longrightarrow$ $CH_3CH_2-C(=O)-CH=\overset{+}{N}=\ddot{N}^{-}:$ + $CH_3-\overset{+}{N}\equiv N:$ + $:\ddot{Cl}:^-$

$CH_3CH_2-C(=O)-CH=\overset{+}{N}=\ddot{N}^{-}:$ + $CH_3-\overset{+}{N}\equiv N:$ + $:\ddot{Cl}:^-$ $\longrightarrow$ N_2 + CH_3Cl

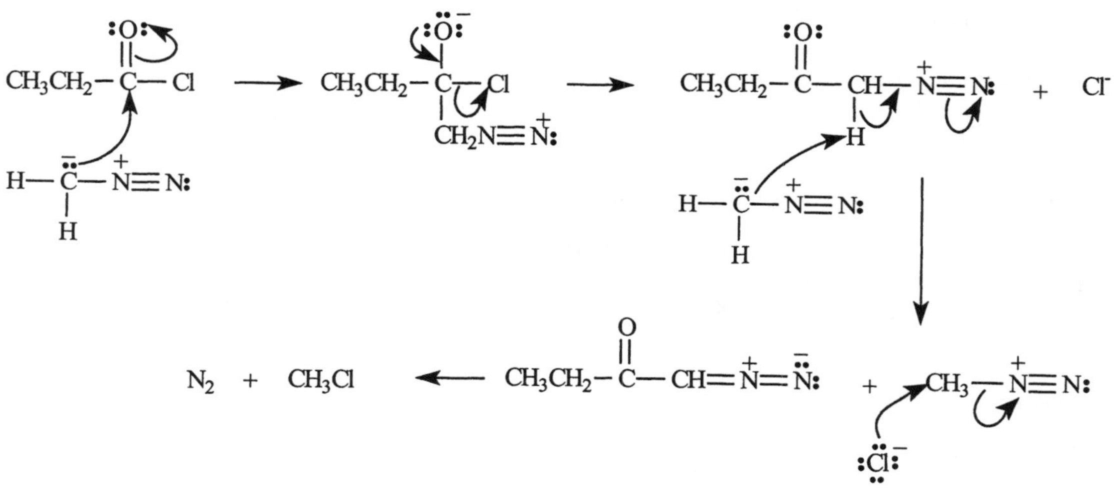

Consider the reaction below to answer the following questions:

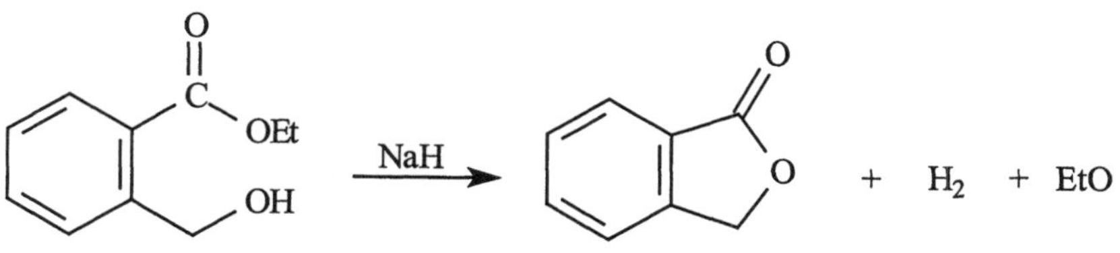

2-(hydroxymethyl)benzoate ethyl ester ($C(=O)OEt$, OH) $\xrightarrow{NaH}$ lactone (O, O) + H_2 + EtO

19. Write the complete stepwise mechanism for this reaction. Show intermediate structures and all electron flow with arrows.

Answer:

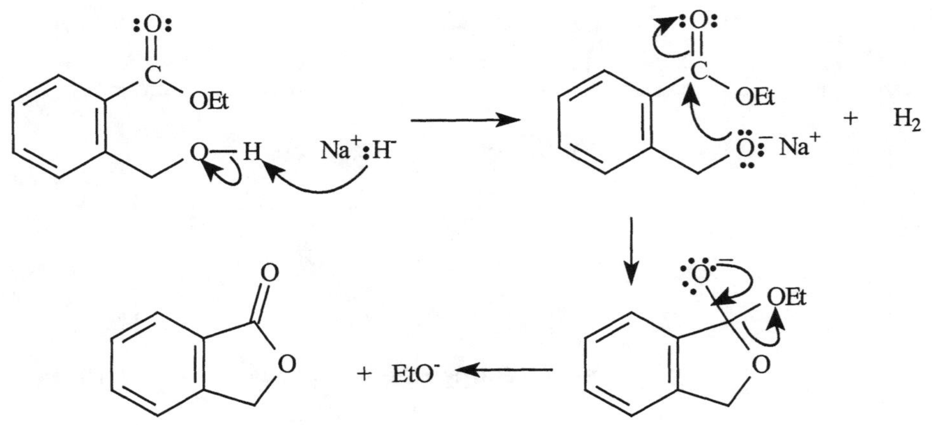

20. This reaction is an example of:

a. an *intermolecular* nucleophilic acyl substitution reaction
b. an *intramolecular* nucleophilic acyl substitution reaction
c. an *intermolecular* S_N2 reaction
d. an *intramolecular* S_N2 reaction

Answer: b

21. The purpose of the base catalyst in this reaction is:

a. to polarize the carbonyl group to make it more electrophilic
b. to convert the ester to an intermediate carboxylic acid
c. to convert the alcohol group to an alkoxide anion, which is a better nucleophile
d. all of the above

Answer: c

22. The product of this reaction is:

a. a lactone
b. an anhydride
c. a lactam
d. an ether

Answer: a

23. Methyl butanoate has been isolated from pineapple oil and can be prepared by the Fischer esterification reaction shown below. Write the complete stepwise mechanism for this reaction. Show all electron flow with arrows and include all intermediate structures.

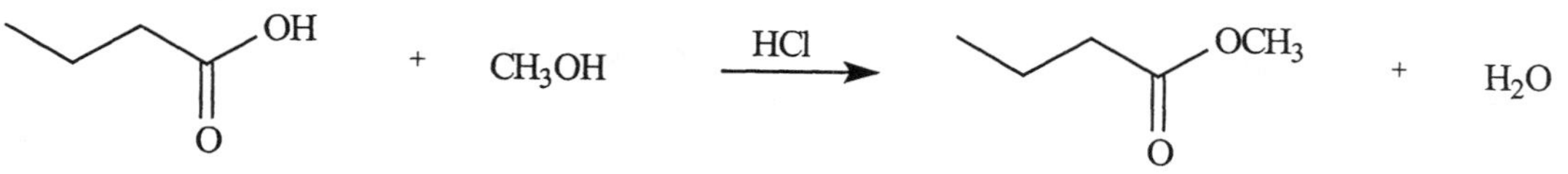

$$CH_3CH_2CH_2COOH + CH_3OH \xrightarrow{HCl} CH_3CH_2CH_2COOCH_3 + H_2O$$

Answer:

H⁺ transfer

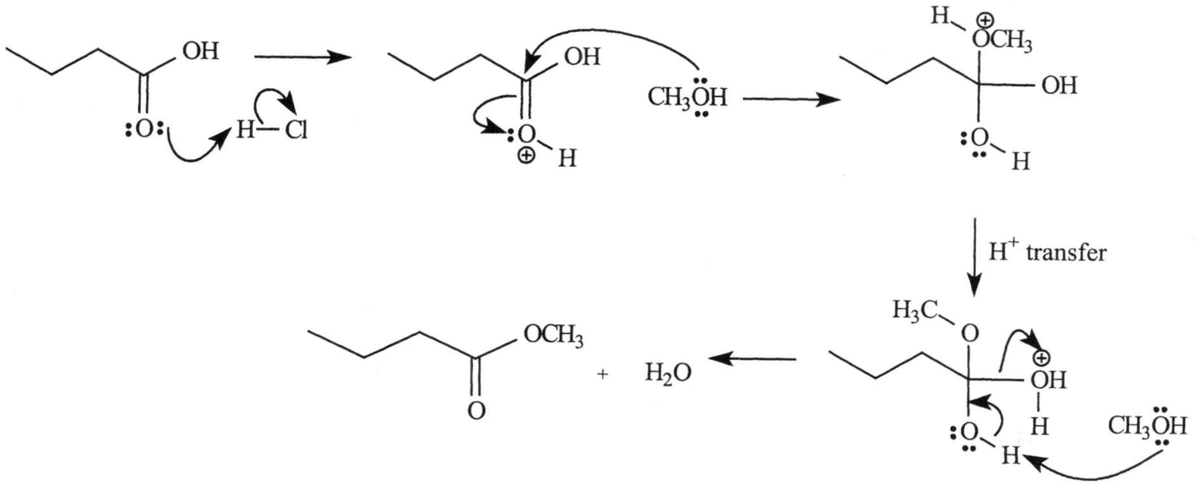

24. Write the complete stepwise mechanism for the acid-catalyzed hydrolysis of the following amide to yield mandelic acid. Show all electron flow with arrows and draw the structures of all intermediate species.

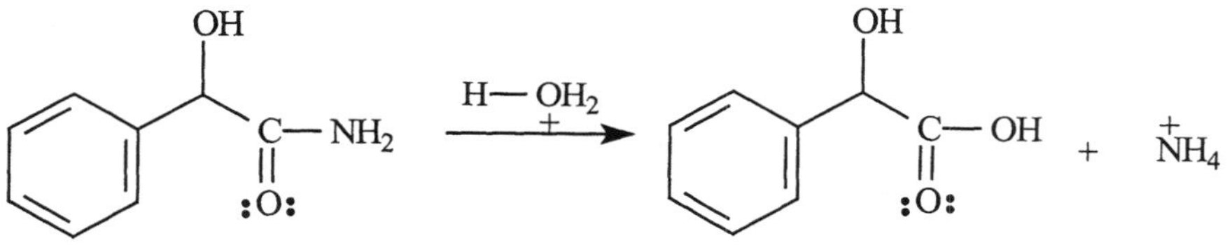

$$C_6H_5CH(OH)C(=O)NH_2 \xrightarrow{H-OH_2^+} C_6H_5CH(OH)C(=O)OH + NH_4^+$$

Answer:

H⁺ transfer

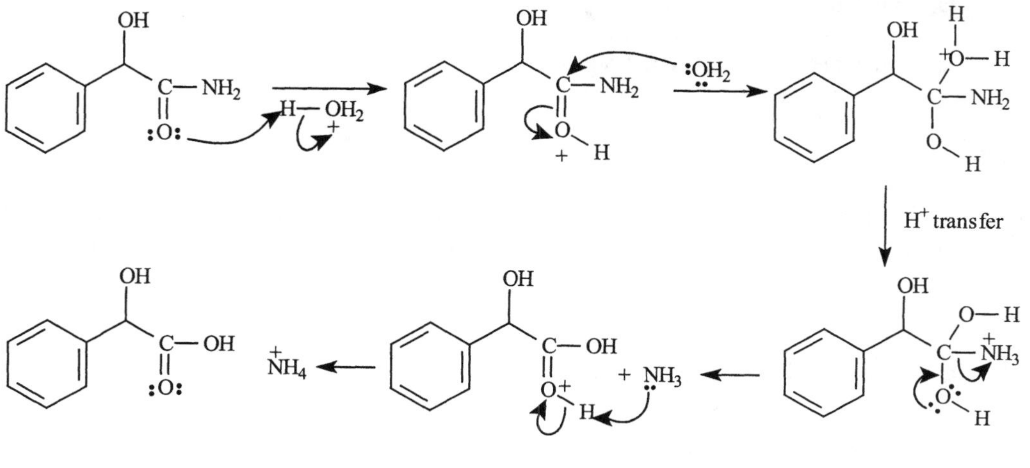

25. The purpose of the acid catalyst in the hydrolysis of an amide is:

a. to enhance the nucleophilicity of the water molecule
b. to enhance the electrophilicity of the amide carbonyl carbon
c. to enhance the electrophilicity of the water molecule
d. to shift the equilibrium of the reaction

Answer: b

Consider the information below to answer the following questions.

The reaction of a carboxylic acid with an alcohol in the presence of acid is termed *Fischer esterification.*

$$C_6H_5\text{–}C(=O)\text{–}OH + CH_3OH \xrightleftharpoons{HCl} C_6H_5\text{–}C(=O)\text{–}OCH_3 + H_2O$$

A B C

26. The *nucleophile* in this reaction is ______________.

Answer: B

27. Compound C functions as ___________ in this reaction.

a. a base scavenger
b. a solvent
c. a catalyst
d. a neutralizer

Answer: c

28. Fischer esterification is an example of:

a. nucleophilic acyl addition
b. nucleophilic acyl substitution
c. nucleophilic acyl elimination
d. nucleophilic acyl rearrangement

Answer: b

29. Write the stepwise mechanism for the Fischer esterification reaction of benzoic acid and methanol given above. Show all electron flow by using curved arrows, and include all intermediate structures.

Answer:

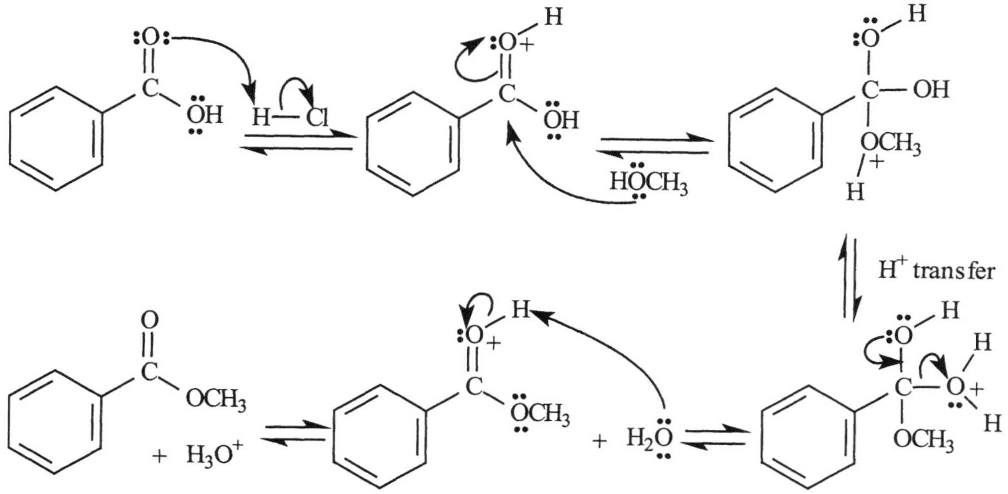

Provide structure(s) for the starting material(s), reagent(s) or the major organic product(s) of each of the following reactions or sequences of reactions. Show all relevant stereochemistry.

30.

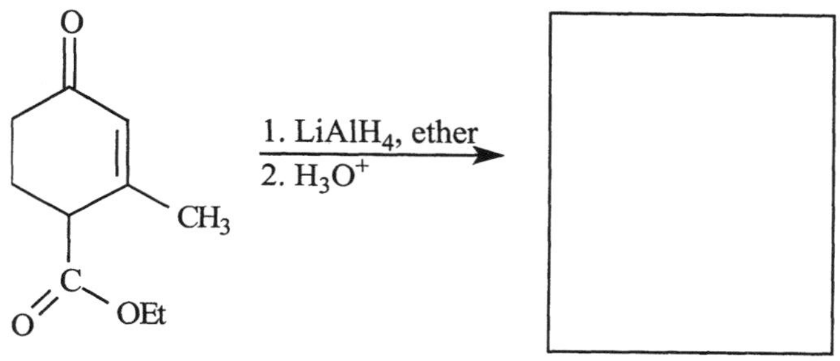

1. $LiAlH_4$, ether
2. H_3O^+

Answer:

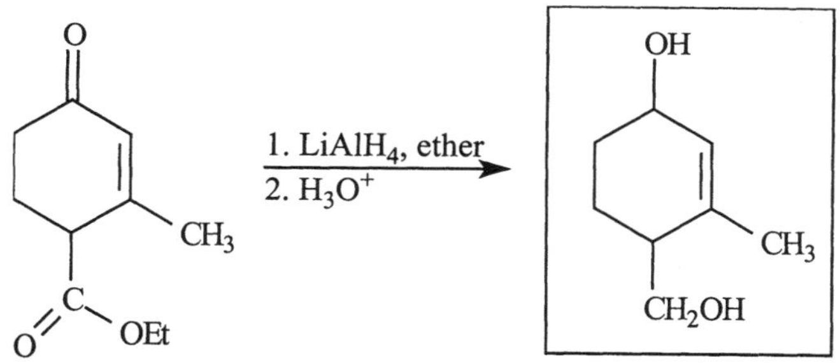

1. $LiAlH_4$, ether
2. H_3O^+

31. $(CH_3)_2CH—C(=O)—Cl$ + [ ] $\xrightarrow{\text{ether}}$ $(CH_3)_2CH—C(=O)—O—C(=O)—CH_3$

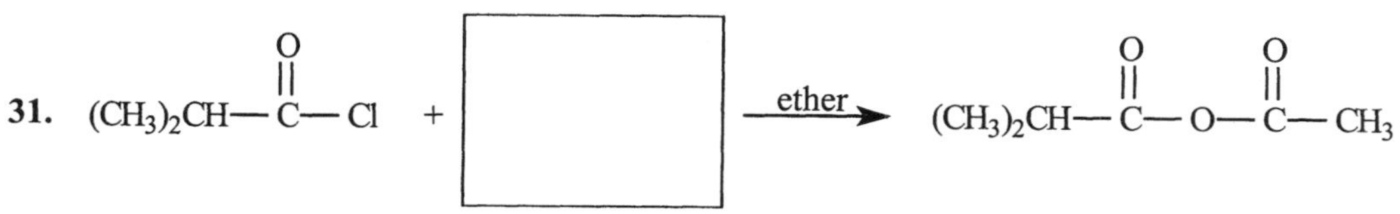

Answer:

$$(CH_3)_2CH-\overset{O}{\overset{\|}{C}}-Cl \quad + \quad \boxed{:\ddot{\underset{..}{O}}^{-}-\overset{O}{\overset{\|}{C}}-CH_3} \xrightarrow{\text{ether}} (CH_3)_2CH-\overset{O}{\overset{\|}{C}}-O-\overset{O}{\overset{\|}{C}}-CH_3$$

32. CH3 O OH → [ ] → CH3 O Cl

Answer:

CH3 O OH → $SOCl_2$ → CH3 O Cl

33. CN → 1. $(CH_3)_2CHMgBr$, ether; 2. H_3O^+ → [ ]

Answer:

CN → 1. $(CH_3)_2CHMgBr$, ether; 2. H_3O^+ → [O, C]

34. COOH OH → $(CH_3CO)_2O$; NaOH, H_2O → [ ]

Answer:

COOH OH → $(CH_3CO)_2O$; NaOH, H_2O → [COOH O O—CCH3]

35. 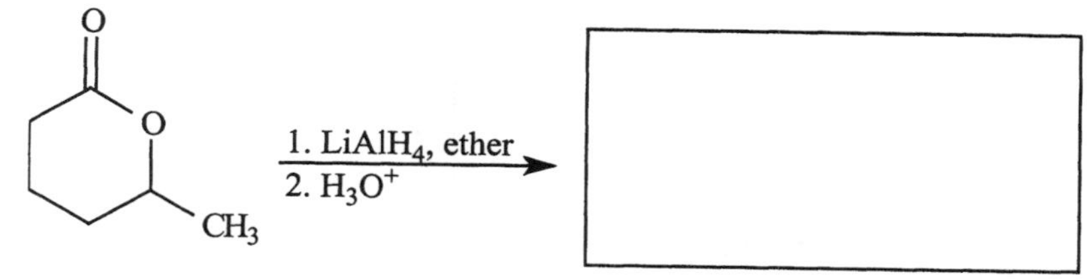

Answer:

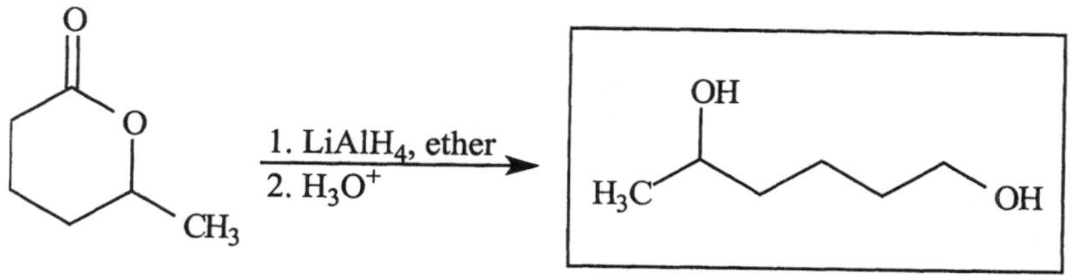

36. 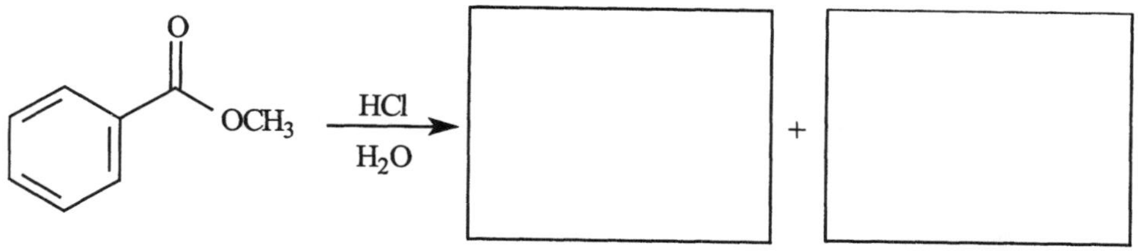

Answer:

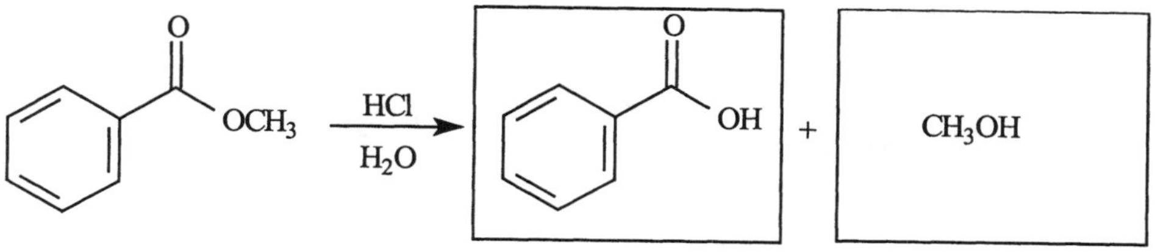

37. 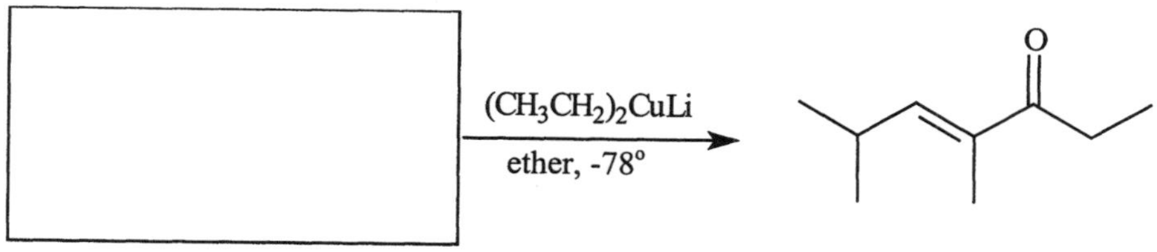

Answer:

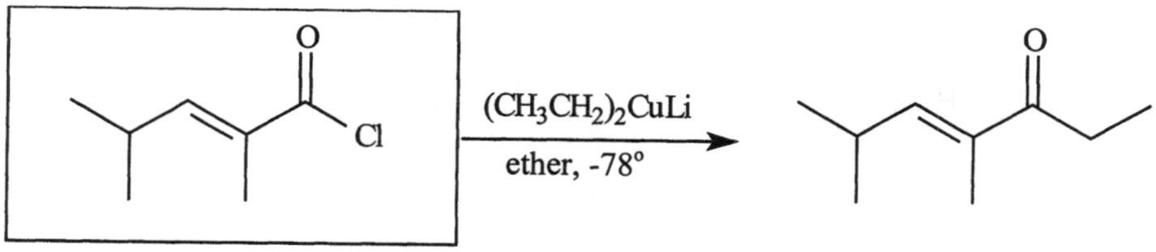

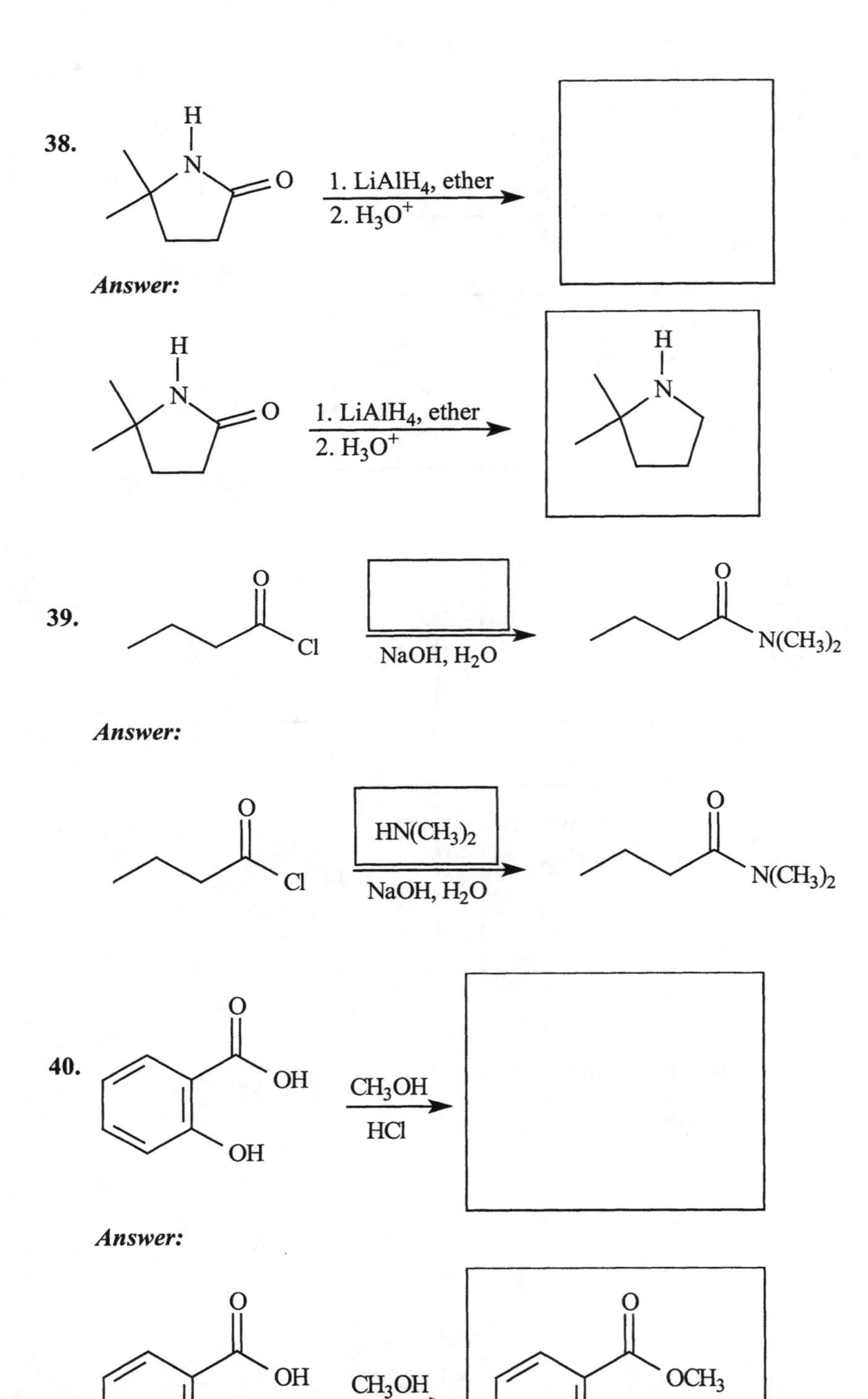

O
OH
OH
CH3OH
HCl
O
OCH3
OH

41. Benzoyl chloride + pyrrolidine $\xrightarrow{\text{pyridine}}$ [ ]

Answer:

Benzoyl chloride + pyrrolidine $\xrightarrow{\text{pyridine}}$ N-benzoylpyrrolidine

42. δ-Valerolactone $\xrightarrow[\text{2. } H_3O^+]{\text{1. DIBAH, ether}}$ [ ]

Answer:

δ-Valerolactone $\xrightarrow[\text{2. } H_3O^+]{\text{1. DIBAH, ether}}$ HO–$CH_2CH_2CH_2CH_2$–CHO (5-hydroxypentanal)

43. cis-Tetrahydrophthalic anhydride $\xrightarrow{[\ \ ]}$ monomethyl ester (COOH, CO_2CH_3)

Answer:

cis-Tetrahydrophthalic anhydride $\xrightarrow{CH_3OH}$ monomethyl ester (OH, OCH_3)

44. 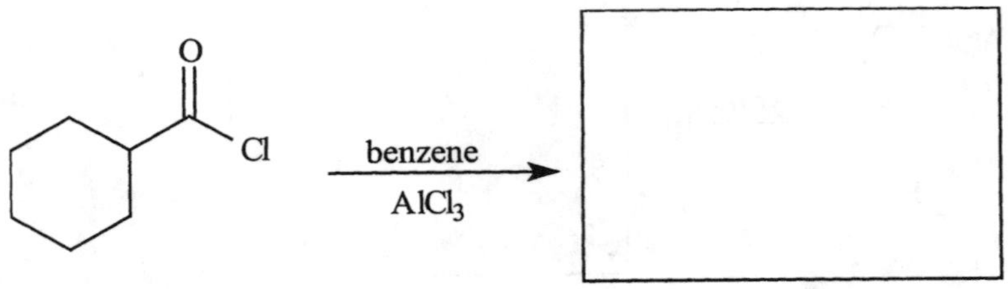 Cyclohexanecarbonyl chloride $\xrightarrow[\text{AlCl}_3]{\text{benzene}}$ [ ]

Answer:

Cyclohexanecarbonyl chloride $\xrightarrow[\text{AlCl}_3]{\text{benzene}}$ cyclohexyl phenyl ketone

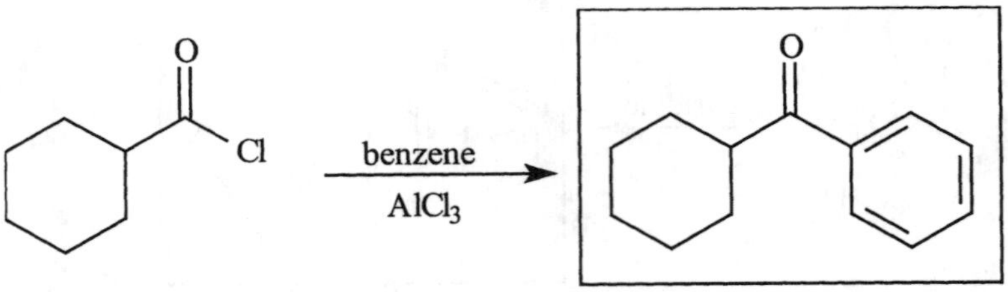

Choose the *best* reagent(s) from the list provided below for carrying out the following transformations. Place the letter corresponding to the best choice in the blank to the left of the transformation.

a. $(Ph)_2CuLi$, ether
b. $NaBH_4$, ethanol
c. 1. CH_3MgBr, ether
   2. H_3O^+
d. 1. $LiAlH_4$, THF
   2. H_3O^+
e. $(CH_3)_2CuLi$, ether
f. 1. DIBAH, toluene
   2. H_3O^+
g. 1. $(Ph)_2CHMgBr$
   2. H_3O^+
h. 1. 2 PhMgBr, ether
   2. H_3O^+

45. ____ Benzoyl chloride ⟶ triphenylmethanol

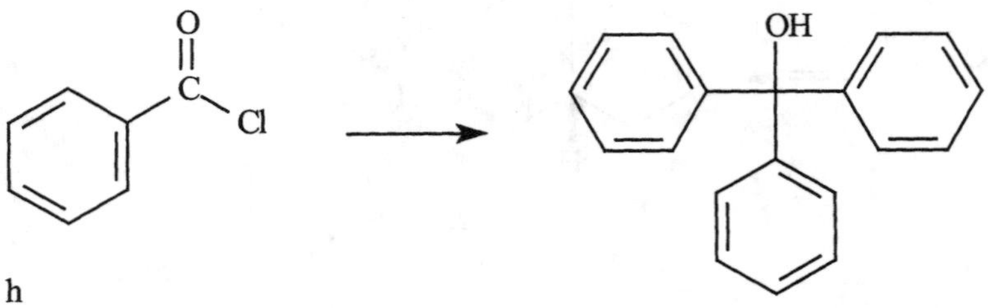

Answer: h

46. ____ Benzoyl chloride ⟶ benzophenone

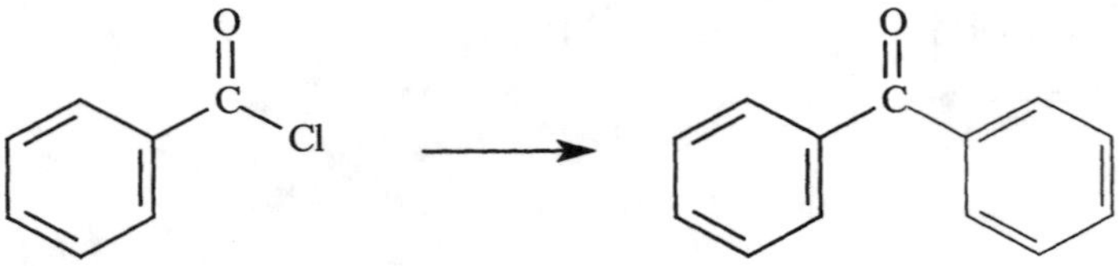

Answer: a

47. ____ O, C, Cl → CH_2OH

Answer: d

48. ____ O, C, OCH_3 → O, C, H

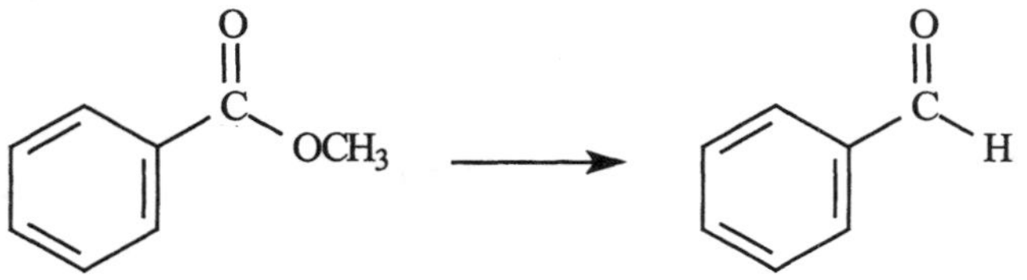

Answer: f

49. ____ $NHCH_2CH_3$, O → $NHCH_2CH_3$

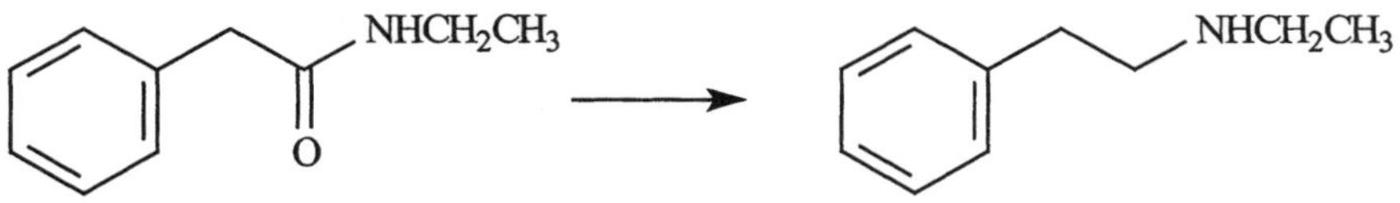

Answer: d

Show how you would accomplish each of the following transformations. More than one step may be required. Show all reagents and all intermediate structures.

50.  OH, O → OH

Answer:

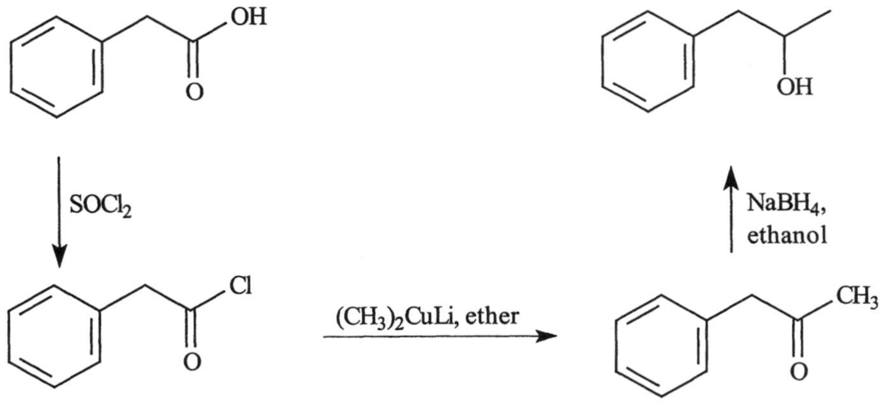

OH, O

$SOCl_2$

Cl, O

$(CH_3)_2CuLi$, ether

CH_3, O

$NaBH_4$, ethanol

OH

51. 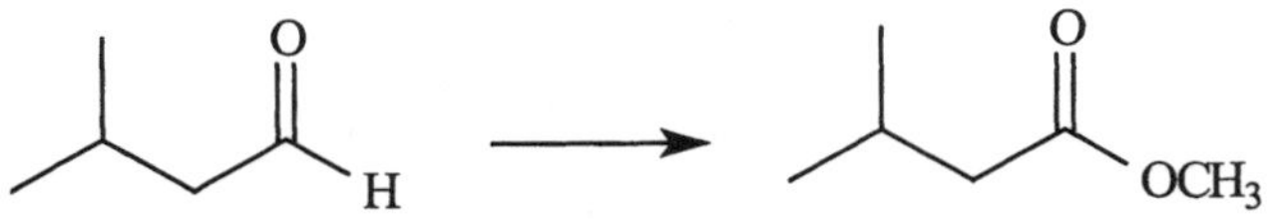 O, H → O, OCH_3

Answer:

$$\text{(CH}_3)_2\text{CHCH}_2\text{CHO} \xrightarrow[H_2O]{CrO_3,\ H_2SO_4} \text{(CH}_3)_2\text{CHCH}_2\text{COOH} \xrightarrow[HCl]{CH_3OH} \text{(CH}_3)_2\text{CHCH}_2\text{COOCH}_3$$

52. $C_6H_5CH_3 \longrightarrow C_6H_5CH_2CO_2CH_2CH_3$

Answer:

$C_6H_5CH_3$ —NBS→ $C_6H_5CH_2Br$ —(1. Mg, ether; 2. CO_2; 3. H_3O^+)→ $C_6H_5CH_2COOH$ —(CH_3CH_2OH, HCl)→ $C_6H_5CH_2CO_2CH_2CH_3$

53. cyclopentene ⟶ glutaric anhydride

Answer:

cyclopentene —($KMnO_4$, H_3O^+)→ $HOOC(CH_2)_3COOH$ —200° C→ glutaric anhydride

54. Aklomide, 2-chloro-4-nitrobenzamide, is an ingredient in veterinary antibacterial preparations. Propose a synthesis of aklomide starting with toluene. Show all reagents and all intermediate structures.

$H_3C-C_6H_5 \longrightarrow H_2N-C(=O)-C_6H_3(Cl)-NO_2$

Answer:

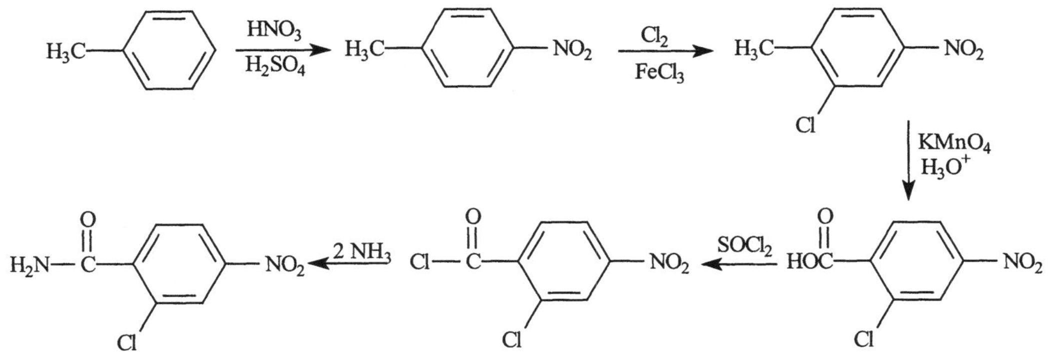

H_3C–C6H4 $\xrightarrow[H_2SO_4]{HNO_3}$ H_3C–C6H4–NO_2 $\xrightarrow[FeCl_3]{Cl_2}$ H_3C–C6H3(Cl)–NO_2 $\xrightarrow{KMnO_4,\ H_3O^+}$ HOC(=O)–C6H3(Cl)–NO_2 $\xrightarrow{SOCl_2}$ Cl–C(=O)–C6H3(Cl)–NO_2 $\xrightarrow{2\ NH_3}$ H_2N–C(=O)–C6H3(Cl)–NO_2

55. Ethyl phenylacetate is a pleasant smelling compound used in perfumery. Draw structures for each of the intermediates in the synthesis of ethyl phenylacetate below.

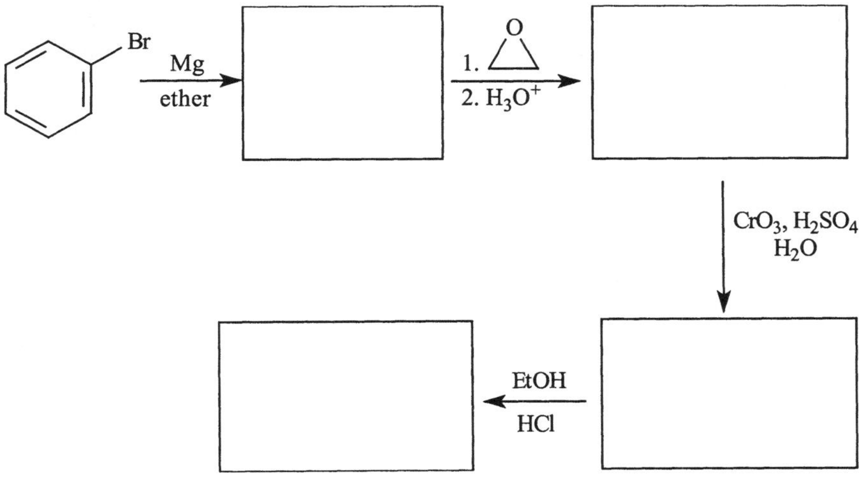

Bromobenzene (Br) $\xrightarrow[ether]{Mg}$ [ ] $\xrightarrow[2.\ H_3O^+]{1.\ \text{ethylene oxide (O)}}$ [ ] $\xrightarrow[H_2O]{CrO_3,\ H_2SO_4}$ [ ] $\xrightarrow[HCl]{EtOH}$ [ ]

Answer:

Bromobenzene (Br) $\xrightarrow[ether]{Mg}$ [C6H5–MgBr] $\xrightarrow[2.\ H_3O^+]{1.\ \text{ethylene oxide (O)}}$ [C6H5–CH_2CH_2OH] $\xrightarrow[H_2O]{CrO_3,\ H_2SO_4}$ [C6H5–CH_2CO_2H] $\xrightarrow[HCl]{EtOH}$ [C6H5–CH_2CO_2Et]

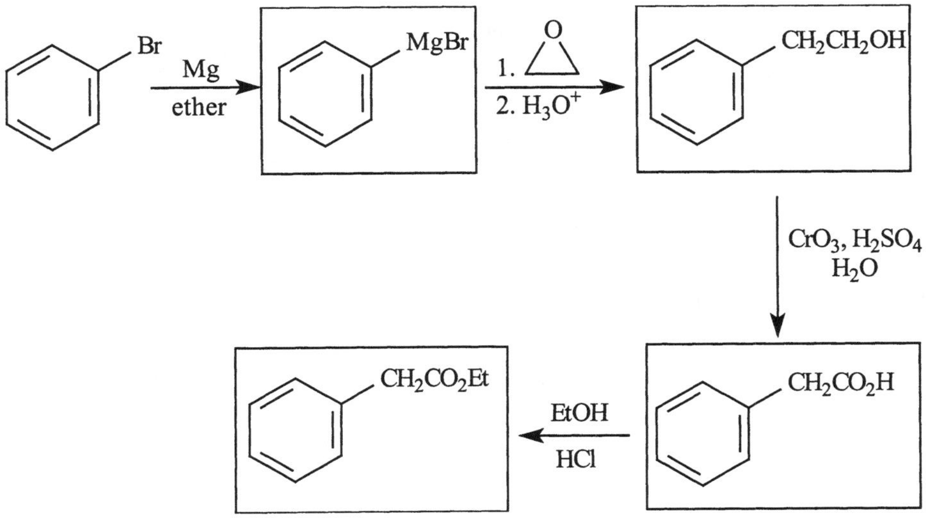

For each pair of compounds below, tell which spectroscopic technique you would use to distinguish between the two members of the pair. Tell what differences you would expect to see.

56. $N{\equiv}C{-}CH_2CH_2{-}O{-}CH_2CH_3$ *and* (N-ethyl four-membered lactam: ring C=O, N–CH_2CH_3)

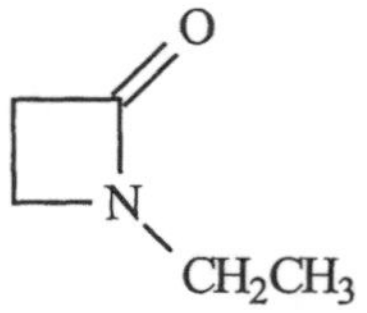

Answer:

IR	2250 cm^{-1}(nitrile)	1730 – 1760 cm^{-1} (four-membered lactam)

Although you would not be expected to know the absorption of a four-membered lactam, you should be able to predict that IR spectroscopy would differentiate these two compounds based solely on the nitrile absorption in the first compound and the fact that the lactam would have a carbonyl absorption somewhere in the region of 1660-1750 cm^{-1}.

57. 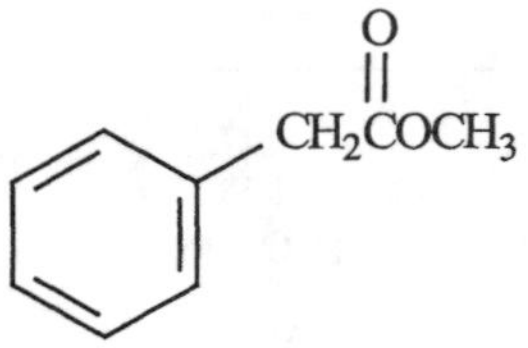 $C_6H_5CH_2COCH_3$ (O above C) *and* $C_6H_5COCH_2CH_3$ (O above C)

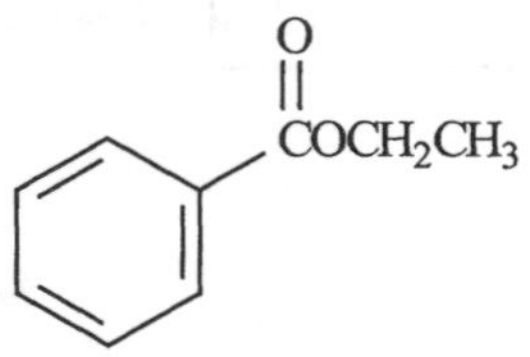

Answer:

IR	1735 cm^{-1} (aliphatic ester)	1720 cm^{-1} (aromatic ester)
^{1}H NMR	methyl singlet methylene singlet	one triplet one quartet

58. $CH_3CH_2\overset{O}{\overset{\|}{C}}O\overset{O}{\overset{\|}{C}}CH_2CH_3$ *and* $CH_3CH_2\overset{O}{\overset{\|}{C}}CH_2CH_2\overset{O}{\overset{\|}{C}}OH$

Answer:

IR	1820, 1760 cm^{-1} (anhydride)	2500 - 3300 cm^{-1} (acid–OH) 1710 - 1760 cm^{-1} (carboxyl) 1715 cm^{-1} (ketone)
^{1}H NMR	one triplet one quartet	three overlapping triplets one quartet one singlet

Refer to the data below to answer the following questions:

Kodel® is a staple and filament fiber prepared from dimethyl terephthalate and 1,4-cyclohexanedimethanol. Fabric made from Kodel® has good crease resistance.

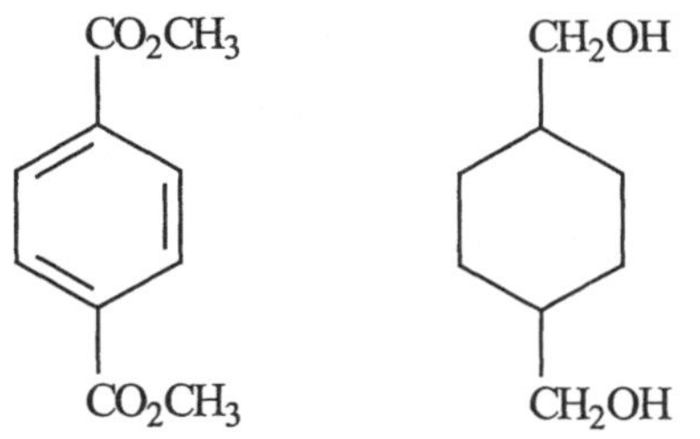

CO_2CH_3 CH_2OH

CO_2CH_3 CH_2OH

dimethyl terephthalate **1,4-cyclohexanedimethanol**

59. Draw the structure of the Kodel® polymer.

Answer:

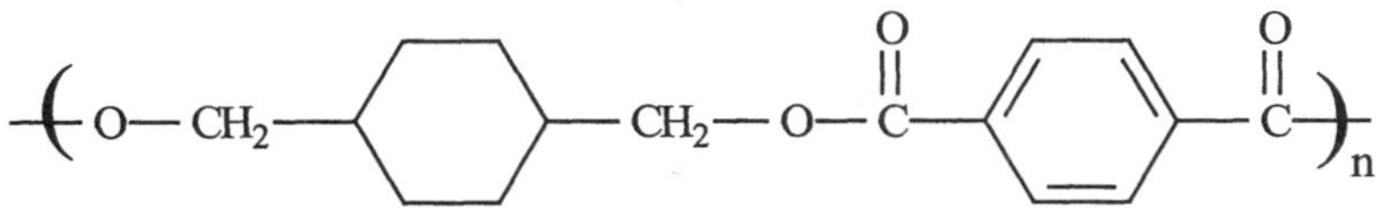

$-(O-CH_2-$ $-CH_2-O-\overset{O}{\overset{\|}{C}}-$ $-\overset{O}{\overset{\|}{C}})_n-$

60. Kodel® is an example of:

a. a polyurethane
b. a polyester
c. a polyamide
d. a polycarbonate

Answer: b

61. Poly(ethylene terephthalate), PET, is the polymeric material of Mylar® and Dacron®. What are the monomers from which PET is prepared?

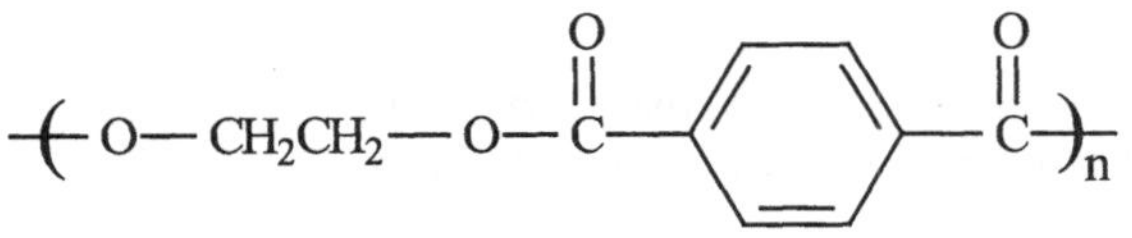

$-(O-CH_2CH_2-O-\overset{O}{\overset{\|}{C}}-$ $-\overset{O}{\overset{\|}{C}})_n-$ **PET**

Answer:

$HO-\overset{O}{\overset{\|}{C}}-$ $-\overset{O}{\overset{\|}{C}}-OH$ + $HOCH_2CH_2OH$

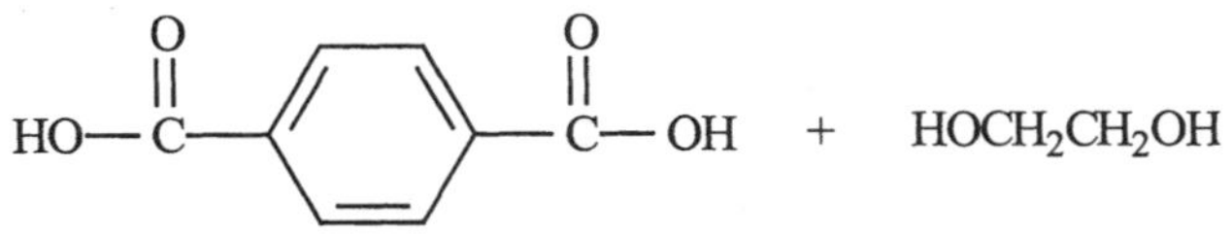

Chapter 22 – Carbonyl Alpha-Substitution Reactions

Refer to the compounds below to answer the following questions:

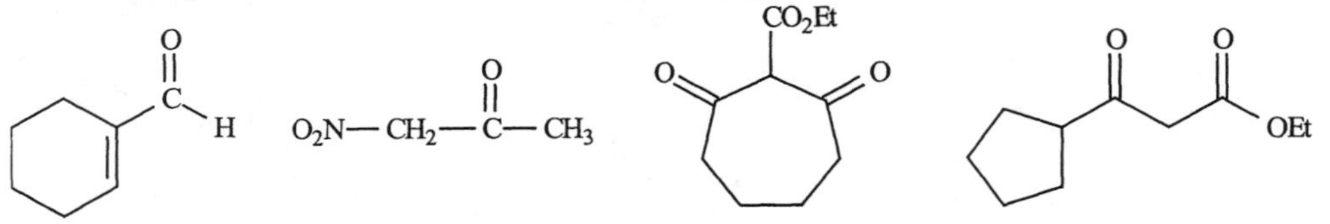

I   II   III   IV

1. Indicate all the acidic hydrogens in Compounds **I** through **IV**.

Answer: Acidic hydrogens are underlined.

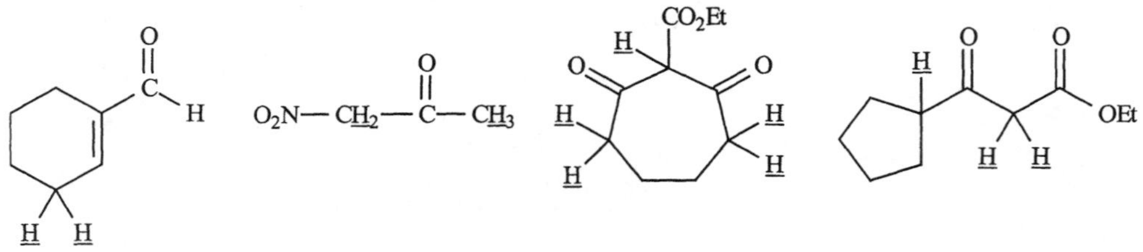

I   II   III   IV

2. Indicate which hydrogens in Compound **II** are the *most acidic*. Explain your answer.

Answer: The methylene hydrogens are the most acidic because they are flanked by two electron-withdrawing groups, $-NO_2$ and C=O. The enolate generated by their removal is highly resonance stabilized; it has three resonance forms.

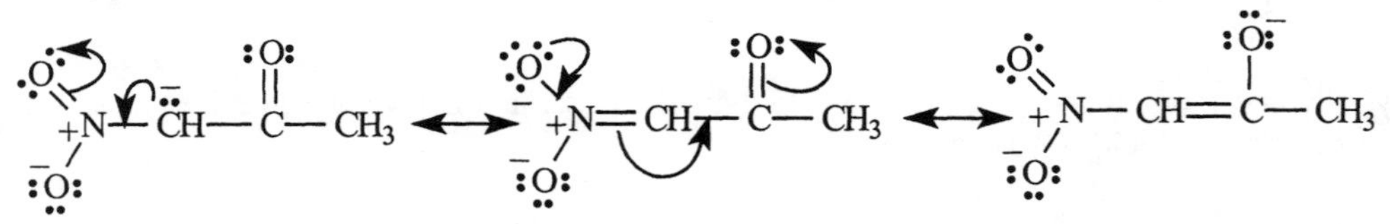

In contrast, the enolate generated by the abstraction of a methyl proton is stabilized by only one electron-withdrawing group and has two resonance forms:

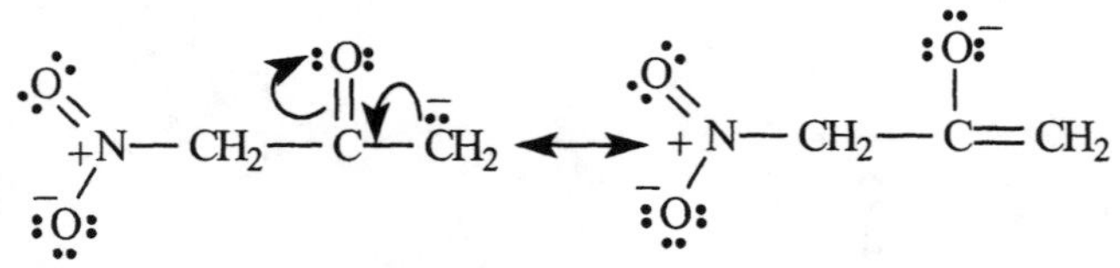

3. Choose the *most acidic* compound from Compounds **I** - **IV**. Explain your choice.

Answer: Compound **III** is the most acidic compound because the methine hydrogen is flanked by *three* carbonyl groups so the enolate ion generated by its removal has four resonance forms.

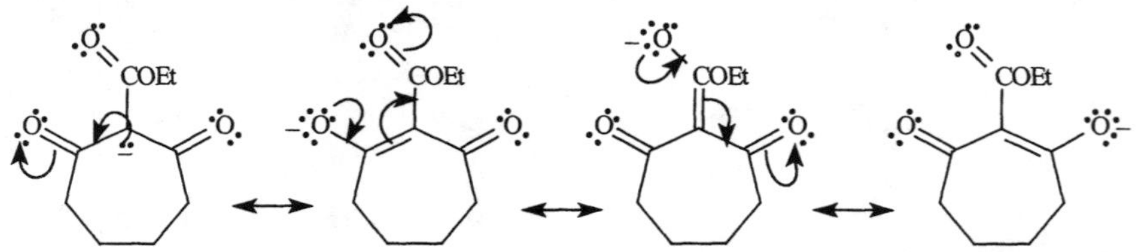

4. Draw the structures for all enols of Compound **I**.

Answer: OH, C, H

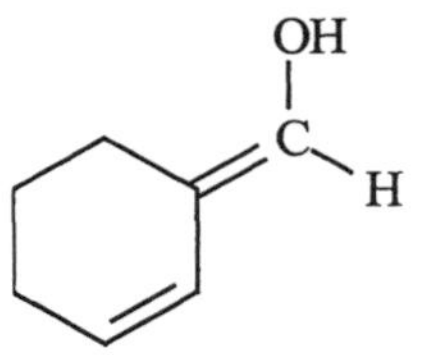

Consider the structures below to answer the following questions.

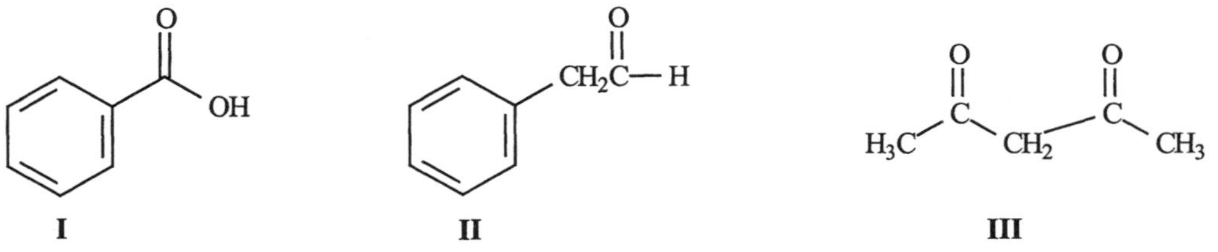

I: O, OH   II: O, CH_2C—H   III: O, O, H_3C, C, CH_2, C, CH_3

5. Indicate the ***most*** acidic hydrogens in each of the molecules.

Answer:

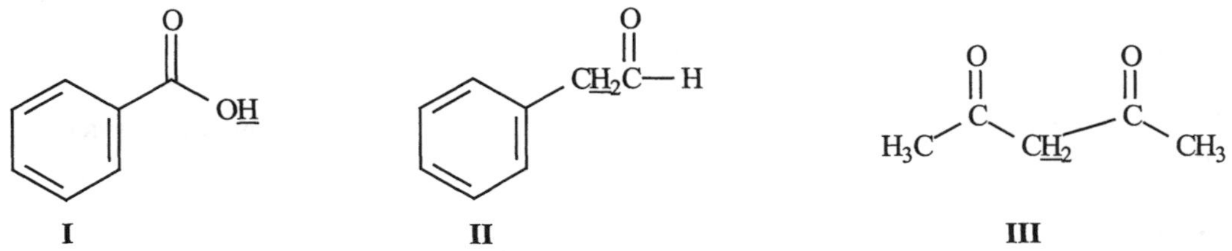

I: O, O<u>H</u>   II: O, C<u>H</u>$_2$C—H   III: O, O, H_3C, C, C<u>H</u>$_2$, C, CH_3

The most acidic hydrogens are underlined.

6. Rank the molecules above in order of ***increasing*** acidity (least acidic to most acidic).

a. III, II, I
b. II, III, I
c. I, II, III
d. II, I, III

Answer: b

7. Nitroethane [$CH_3CH_2NO_2$, pK_a = 8.6] is a much stronger acid than ethane [CH_3CH_3, p$K_a \approx 60$]. Explain.

Answer: When a proton is removed from the carbon bearing the nitro group in nitroethane, the negative charge is shared by the electron-withdrawing nitro group. Thus, the anion is stabilized by resonance between two forms.

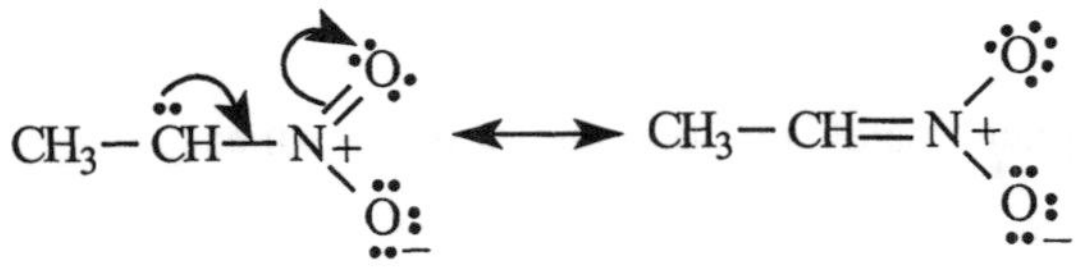

$CH_3-\ddot{C}H-N^+(=O)-O^-$ ⟷ $CH_3-CH=N^+(-O)-O^-$

When a proton is abstracted from ethane, the carbon atom must bear the full negative charge.

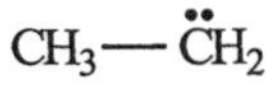

$CH_3-\ddot{C}H_2^-$

Consider the reaction below to answer the following questions.

$pK_a = 16$ (A) + B → C + D ($pK_a = 40$)

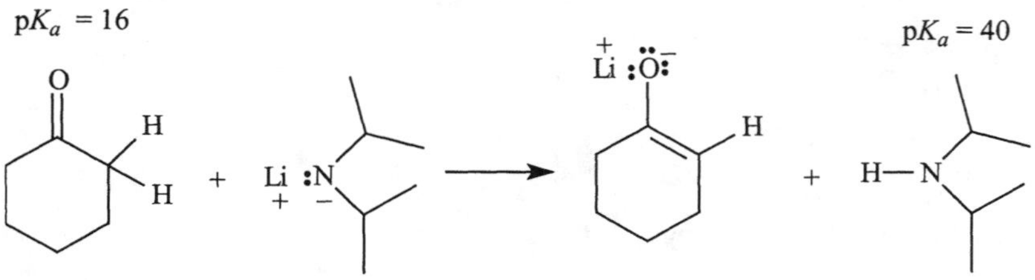

A B C D

8. The strongest base in the reaction is:

Answer: B

9. The weakest acid in the reaction is:

Answer: D

10. The enolate ion in the reaction is:

Answer: C

11. On the structures provided above, draw arrows indicating electron flow in the generation of the intermediate **C.**

Answer:

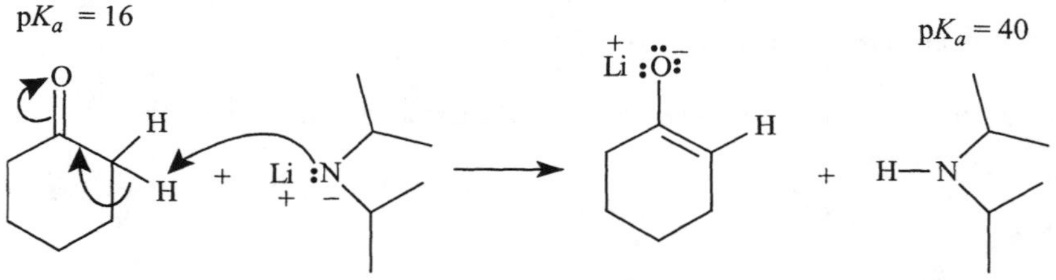

$pK_a = 16$ (A) + B → C + D ($pK_a = 40$)

A B C D

Consider the reaction sequence below to answer the following questions:

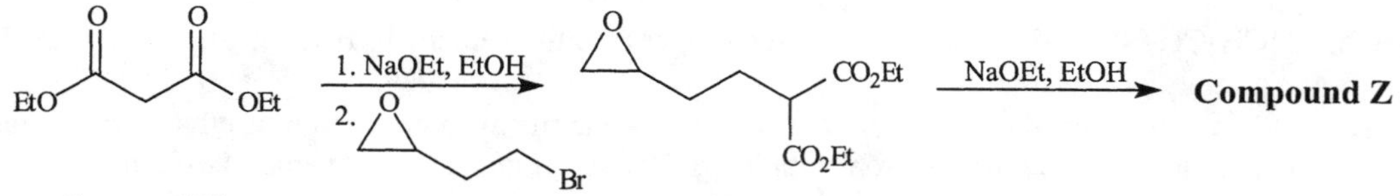

Compound X —(1. NaOEt, EtOH; 2. epoxide-Br)→ Compound Y —(NaOEt, EtOH)→ **Compound Z**

12. Compound X, diethyl propanedioate, is more commonly known as ___________.

a. ethyl acetoacetate
b. acetoacetic ester
c. oxalic ester
d. malonic ester

Answer: d

13. Write the complete stepwise mechanism for the conversion of Compound X into Compound Y. Show all electron flow with arrows and draw all intermediate structures.

Answer:

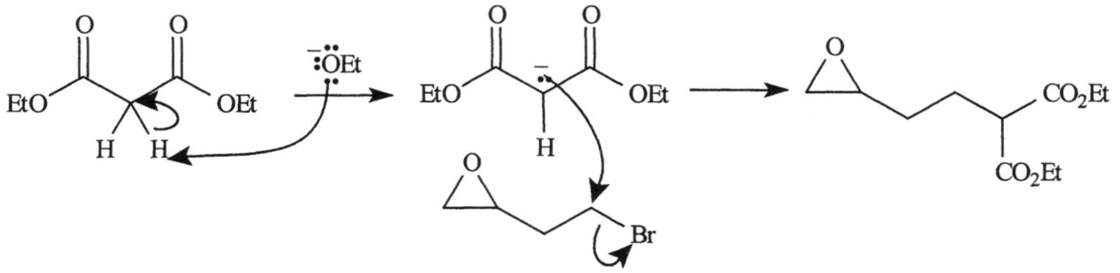

14. Below are the structures and electron flow for the conversion of Compound Y into Compound Z. Draw the structure of Compound Z. (Hint: Compound Z is an alcohol.)

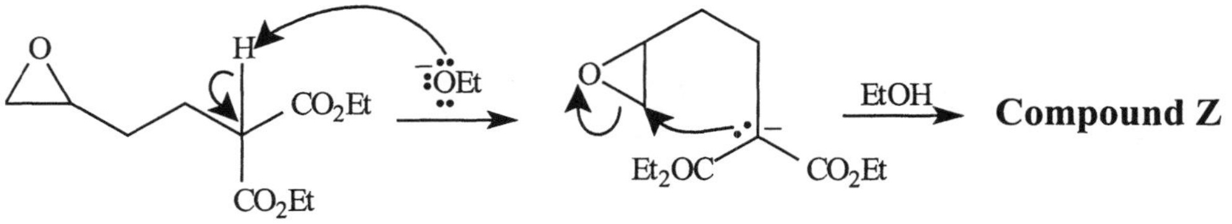

Compound Z

Answer:

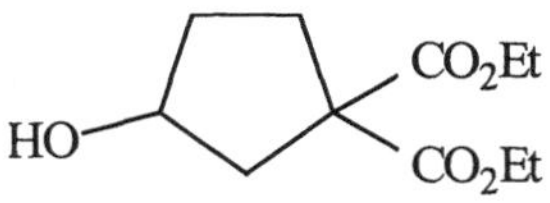

Consider the reaction sequence below to answer the following questions:

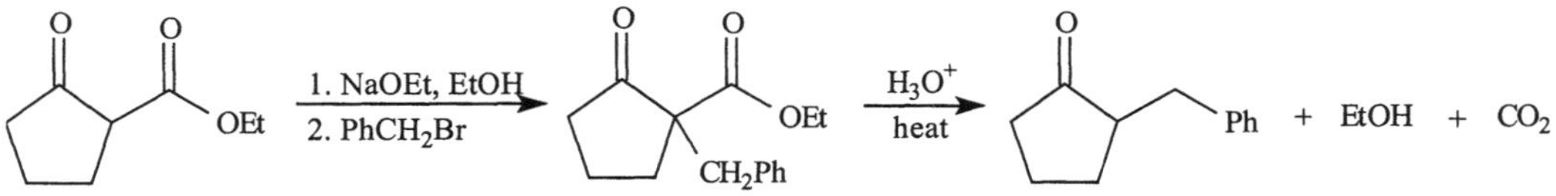

A → (1. NaOEt, EtOH; 2. $PhCH_2Br$) → B → (H_3O^+, heat) → C + EtOH + CO_2

15. The starting material **A** in this reaction sequence is called a ________.

a. β-keto ester
b. α-carboethoxy ketone
c. malonic ester
d. acetoacetic ester

Answer: a

16. Conversion of **A** into **B** is a type of reaction termed ________.

a. an acylation
b. an enolation
c. an alkylation
d. a phenylation

Answer: c

17. Conversion of **B** into **C** involves hydrolysis of the ester followed by decarboxylation. On the structures provided below, show the electron flow for the decarboxylation step.

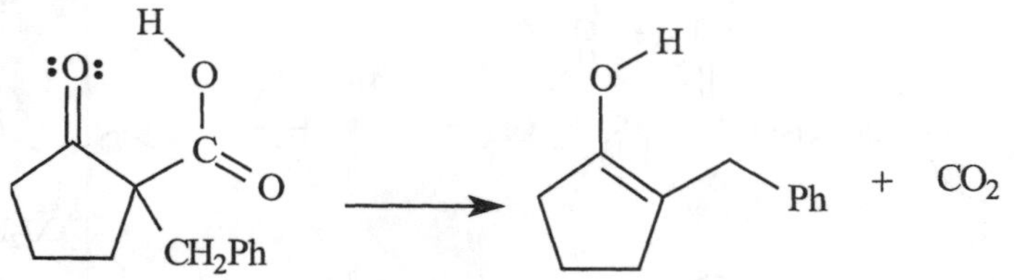

:O: H O C O CH$_2$Ph → O H Ph + CO_2

Answer:

:O: H O C O CH$_2$Ph → O H Ph + CO_2

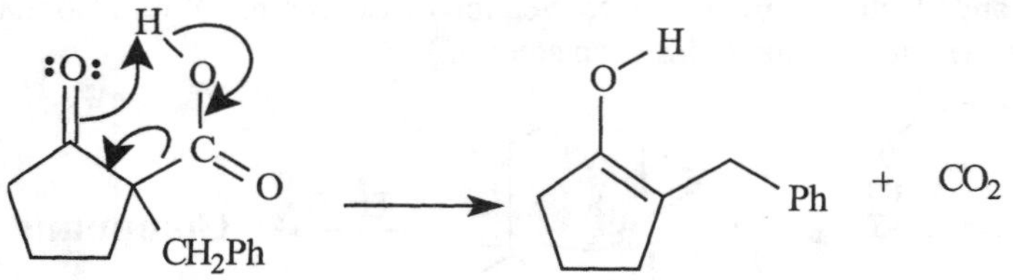

18. The initial product formed on decarboxylation is an enol, which rapidly equilibrates to its keto form under the acidic reaction conditions. Write the complete stepwise mechanism for the acid-catalyzed conversion of the enol into its keto form, Compound C.

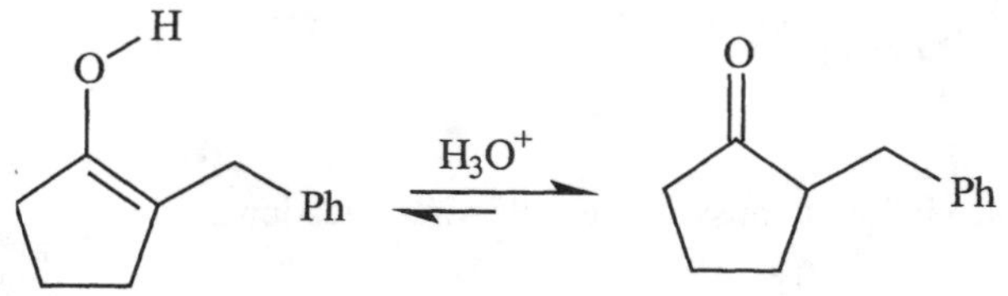

O H Ph $\xrightarrow{H_3O^+}$ O Ph

Answer:

O H Ph ⇌ H—$\overset{+}{O}H_2$ O H H + Ph $\ddot{O}H_2$ ⇌ O Ph

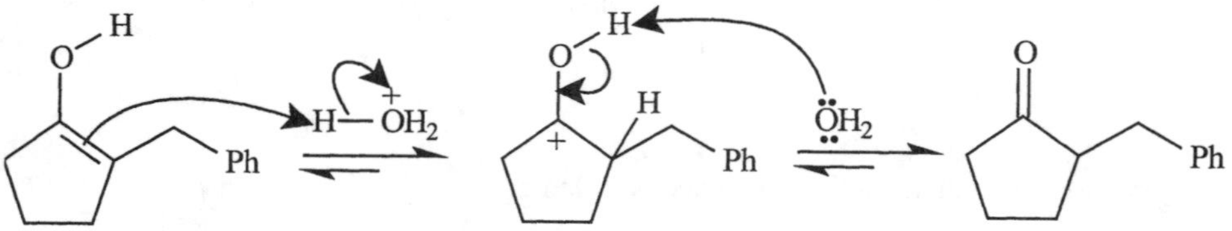

19. The decarboxylation of the β-keto acid whose structure is shown below, fails. Explain this behavior.

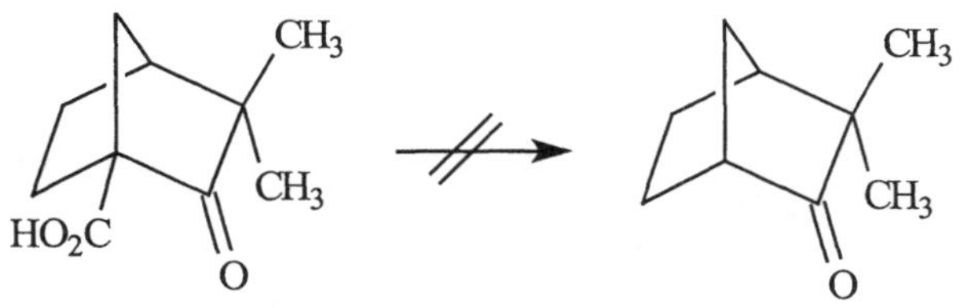
CH3
CH3
HO2C
O
CH3
CH3
O

Answer: The cyclic mechanism for the decarboxylation of β-ketoacids initially yields an enol, which tautomerizes to the more stable keto form. In this case, the enol produced would have a double bond at the "bridgehead" of the fused ring system which is highly strained and unstable. Thus, decarboxylation is not favored.

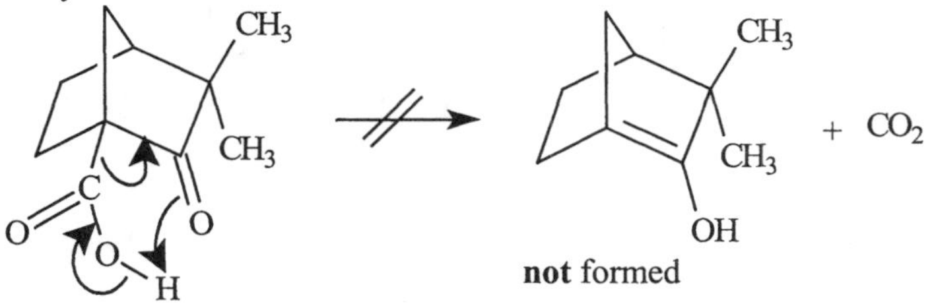
CH3
CH3
C
O
O
H
O
CH3
CH3
OH
+ CO2
not formed

Consider the reaction below to answer the following questions:

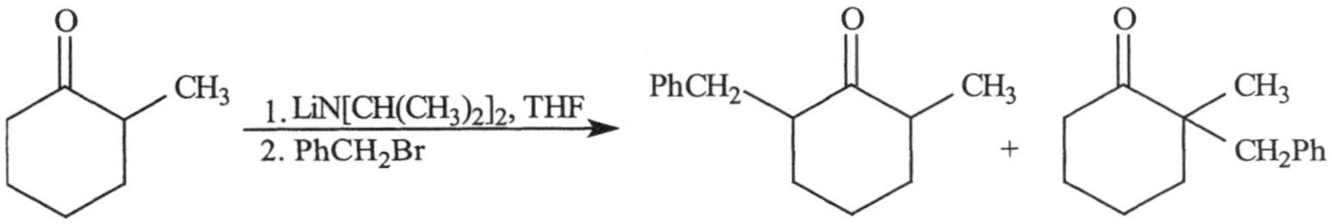
O
CH3
1. LiN[CH(CH3)2]2, THF
2. PhCH2Br
PhCH2
O
CH3
+
O
CH3
CH2Ph

90% 10%

20. Write the complete stepwise mechanism for the reaction above. Show all intermediate structures and all electron flow with arrows.

Answer:

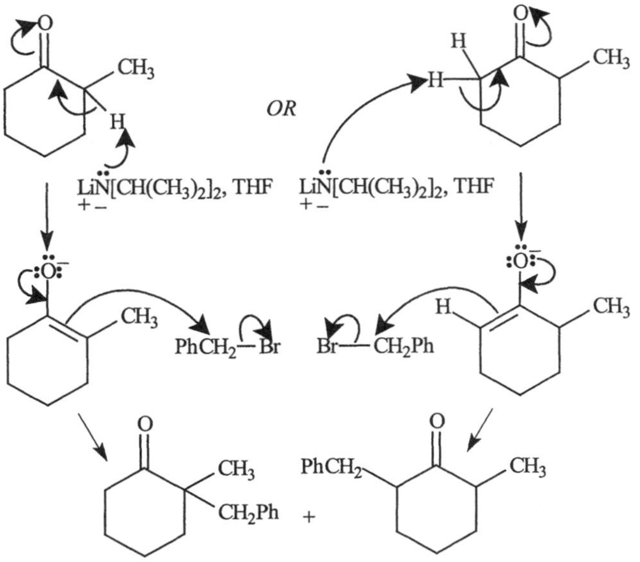
O
CH3
H
OR
H
O
CH3
H
LiN[CH(CH3)2]2, THF
LiN[CH(CH3)2]2, THF
:O:
CH3
PhCH2—Br
Br—CH2Ph
:O:
H
CH3
O
CH3
CH2Ph
+
PhCH2
O
CH3

21. Explain the product ratio in this reaction.

Answer: Lithium diisoproylamide is a sterically hindered base, so abstraction of a proton is more favorably at the less sterically crowded side of the ketone. Hence, the substitution occurs primarily at position 6 rather than position 2.

22. Write the complete stepwise mechanism for the reaction of cyclopentanone with bromine in acetic acid to give 2-bromocyclopentanone. Show all intermediate structures and all electron flow with arrows.

Answer:

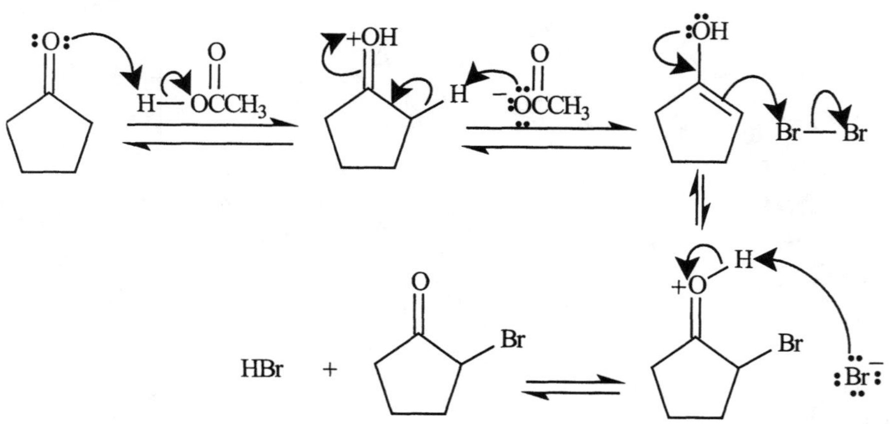

Give the major organic product(s) of each of the following reactions or sequences of reactions. Show all relevant stereochemistry.

23. 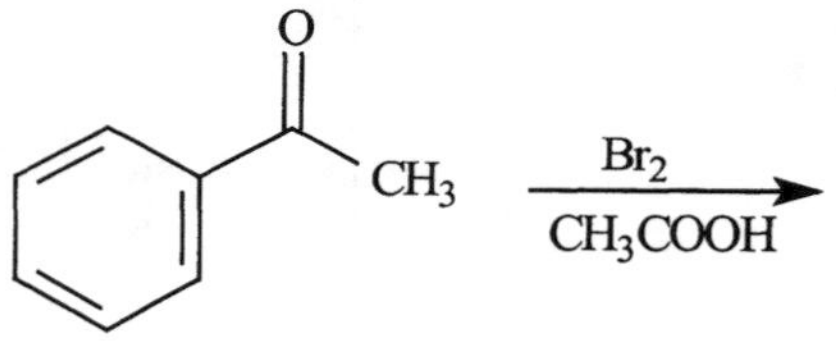

Answer:

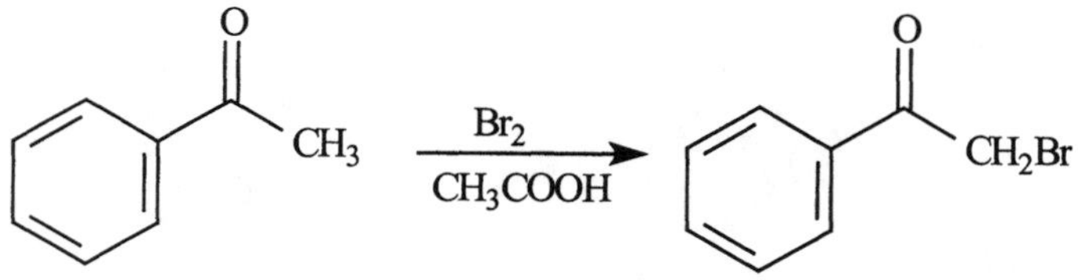

24. 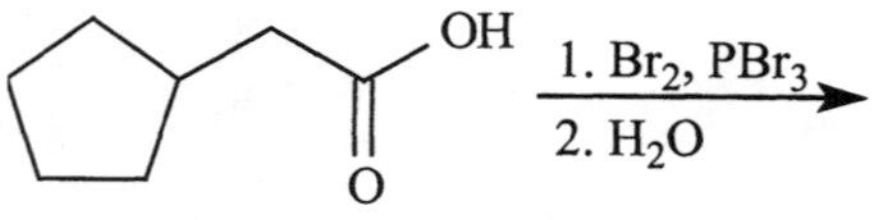

Answer:

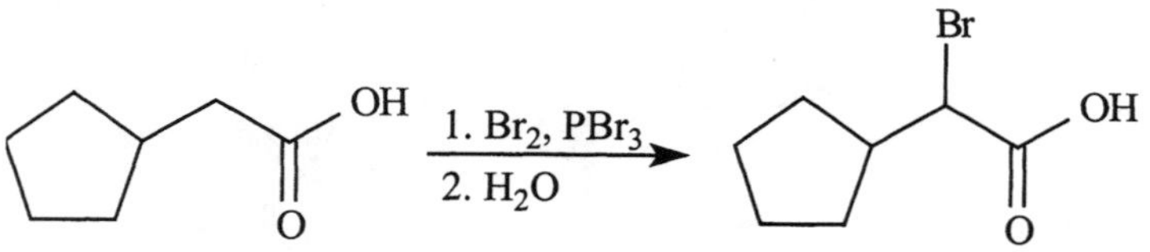

25. $H_3C-C(CH_3)_2-C(=O)-CH_3$ $\xrightarrow[H_2O]{I_2,\ NaOH}$

Answer:

$H_3C-C(CH_3)_2-C(=O)-CH_3$ $\xrightarrow[H_2O]{I_2,\ NaOH}$ $H_3C-C(CH_3)_2-C(=O)-OH$ + CHI_3

26. EtO–C(=O)–CH$_2$–C(=O)–OEt $\xrightarrow[\text{2. Br(CH}_2)_4\text{Br}]{\text{1. 2 equiv. NaOEt, EtOH}}$

Answer:

EtO–C(=O)–CH$_2$–C(=O)–OEt $\xrightarrow[\text{2. Br(CH}_2)_4\text{Br}]{\text{1. 2 equiv. NaOEt, EtOH}}$ 1,1-cyclopentane with CO_2Et, CO_2Et

27. CH_3–C(=O)–CH$_2$–C(=O)–OEt + $(CH_3)_2CHCH_2CH_2Br$ $\xrightarrow[\text{2. } H_3O^+\text{, heat}]{\text{1. NaOEt, EtOH}}$

Answer:

CH_3–C(=O)–CH$_2$–C(=O)–OEt + $(CH_3)_2CHCH_2CH_2Br$ $\xrightarrow[\text{2. } H_3O^+\text{, heat}]{\text{1. NaOEt, EtOH}}$ $CH_3C(=O)CH_2CH_2CH_2CH(CH_3)_2$ + EtOH + CO_2

28. cyclohexanone $\xrightarrow[HCl]{Cl_2}$

Answer:

cyclohexanone $\xrightarrow[HCl]{Cl_2}$ 2-chlorocyclohexanone (Cl)

29. 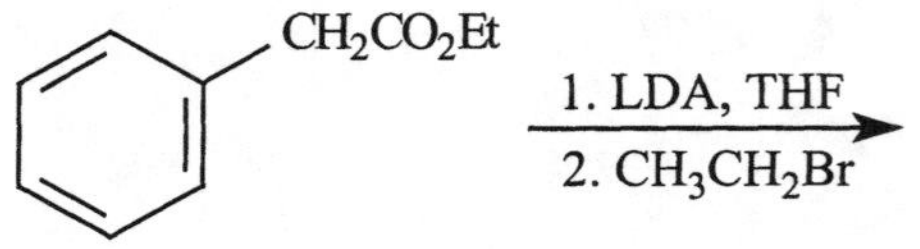 $C_6H_5CH_2CO_2Et$ $\xrightarrow[\text{2. } CH_3CH_2Br]{\text{1. LDA, THF}}$

Answer:

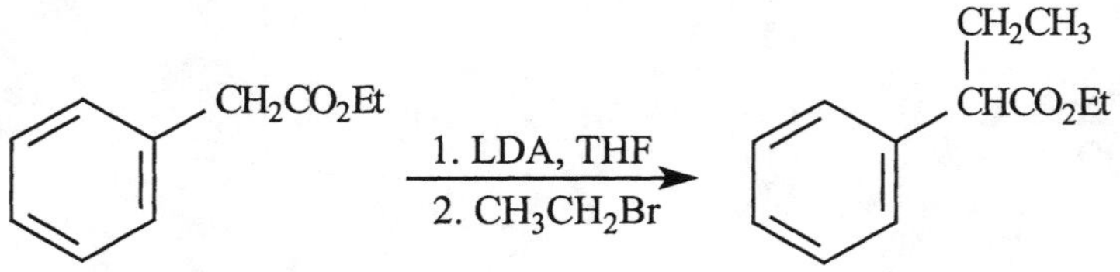

$C_6H_5CH_2CO_2Et$ $\xrightarrow[\text{2. } CH_3CH_2Br]{\text{1. LDA, THF}}$ $C_6H_5CH(CH_2CH_3)CO_2Et$

30. 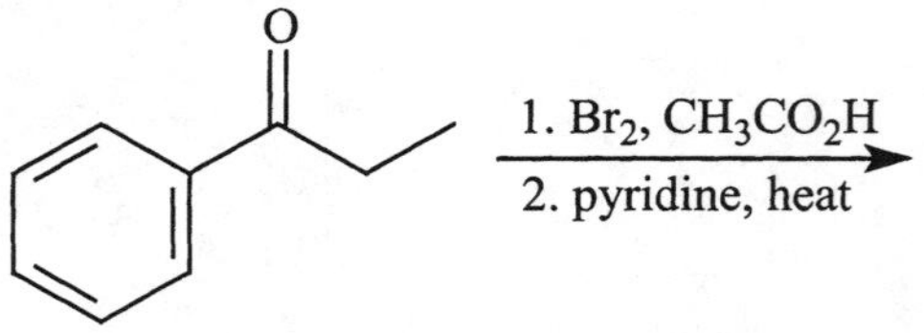 $C_6H_5COCH_2CH_3$ $\xrightarrow[\text{2. pyridine, heat}]{\text{1. } Br_2, CH_3CO_2H}$

Answer:

$C_6H_5COCH_2CH_3$ $\xrightarrow[\text{2. pyridine, heat}]{\text{1. } Br_2, CH_3CO_2H}$ $C_6H_5COCH=CH_2$

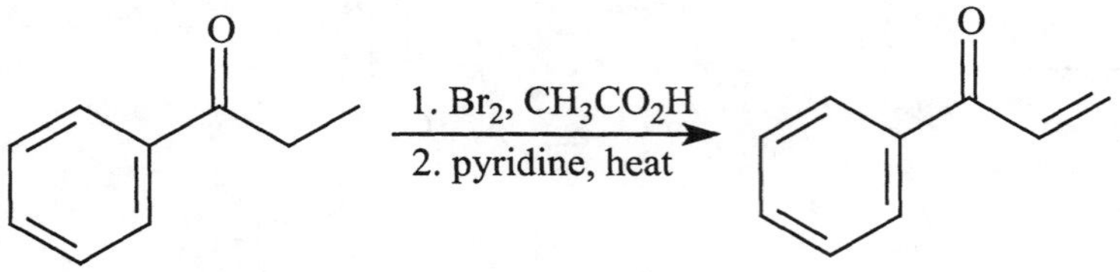

31. Diethyl malonate can be prepared by the following reaction sequence. Draw the structures of each of the missing intermediates in the boxes provided.

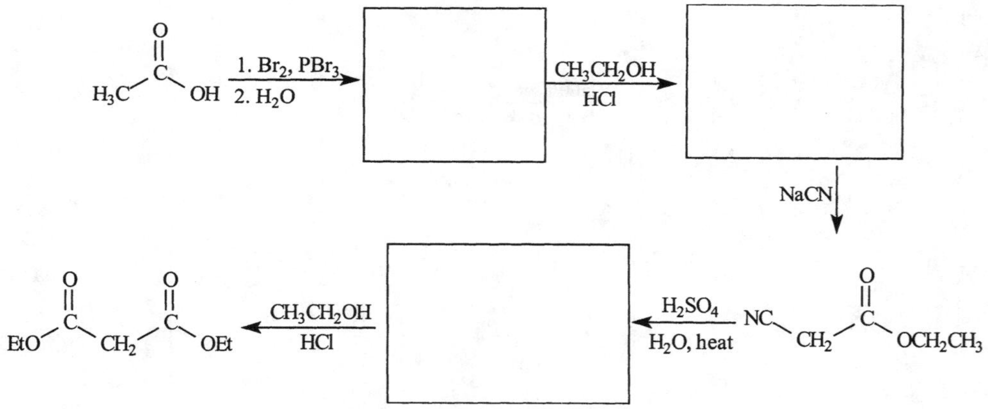

$H_3C-C(=O)-OH$ $\xrightarrow[\text{2. } H_2O]{\text{1. } Br_2, PBr_3}$ [ ] $\xrightarrow[HCl]{CH_3CH_2OH}$ [ ] $\xrightarrow{NaCN}$ $NC-CH_2-C(=O)-OCH_2CH_3$ $\xrightarrow[H_2O, \text{ heat}]{H_2SO_4}$ [ ] $\xrightarrow[HCl]{CH_3CH_2OH}$ $EtO-C(=O)-CH_2-C(=O)-OEt$

Answer:

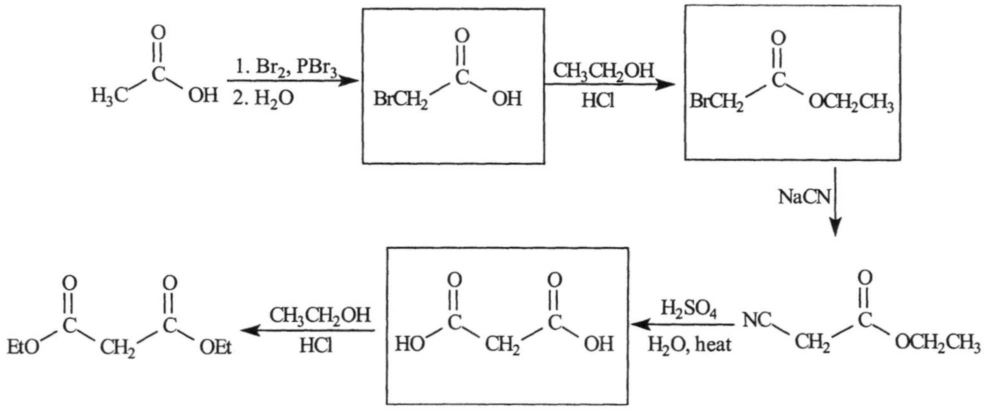

CH_3COOH —(1. Br_2, PBr_3; 2. H_2O)→ $BrCH_2COOH$ —(CH_3CH_2OH, HCl)→ $BrCH_2COOCH_2CH_3$ —(NaCN)→ $NCCH_2COOCH_2CH_3$ —(H_2SO_4, H_2O, heat)→ $HOOCCH_2COOH$ —(CH_3CH_2OH, HCl)→ $EtOOCCH_2COOEt$

How would you prepare each of the following compounds using *either* an acetoacetic ester synthesis or a malonic ester synthesis? Show all intermediate structures and all reagents.

32. COOH

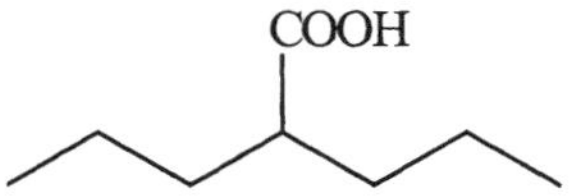

Answer:

EtO OEt —(1. NaOEt, EtOH; 2. $CH_3CH_2CH_2Br$)→ EtO OEt

—(1. NaOEt, EtOH; 2. $CH_3CH_2CH_2Br$)→ EtO OEt

—(H_3O^+, heat)→ COOH

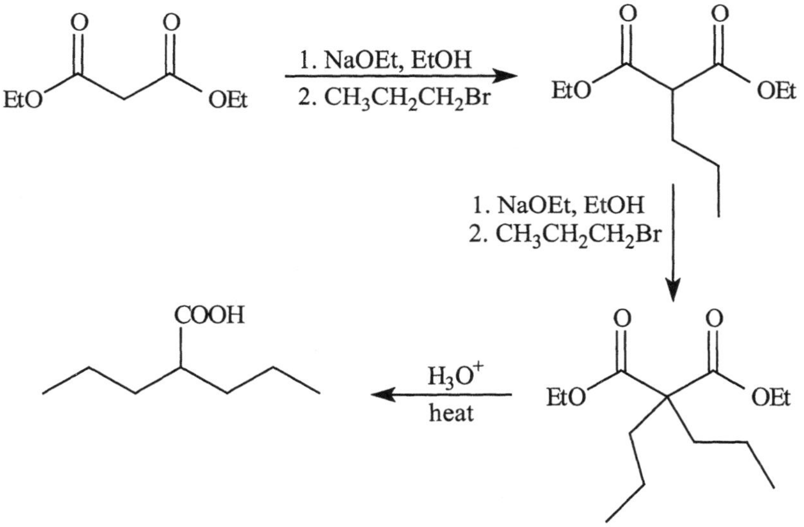

33.

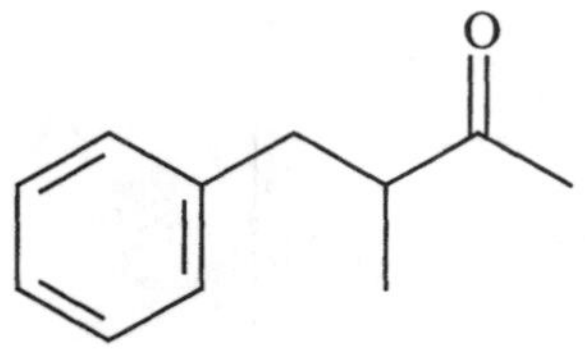

Answer:

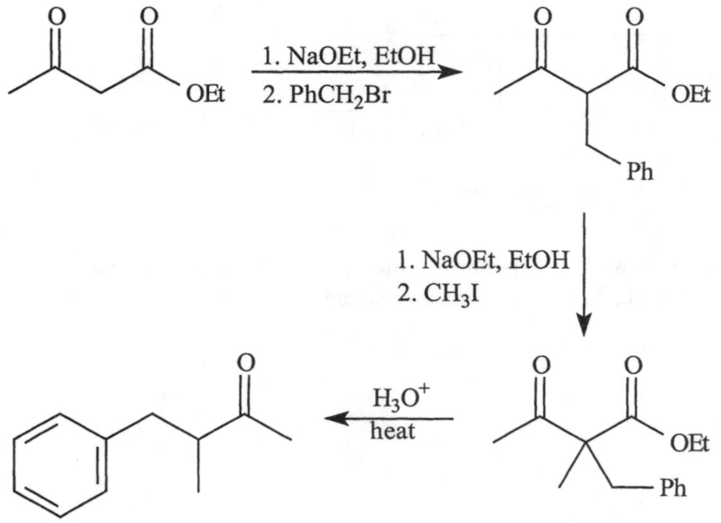

1. NaOEt, EtOH
2. $PhCH_2Br$

OEt

Ph

1. NaOEt, EtOH
2. CH_3I

H_3O^+
heat

OEt

Ph

34.

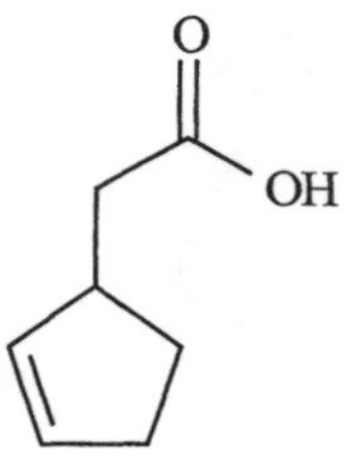

OH

Answer:

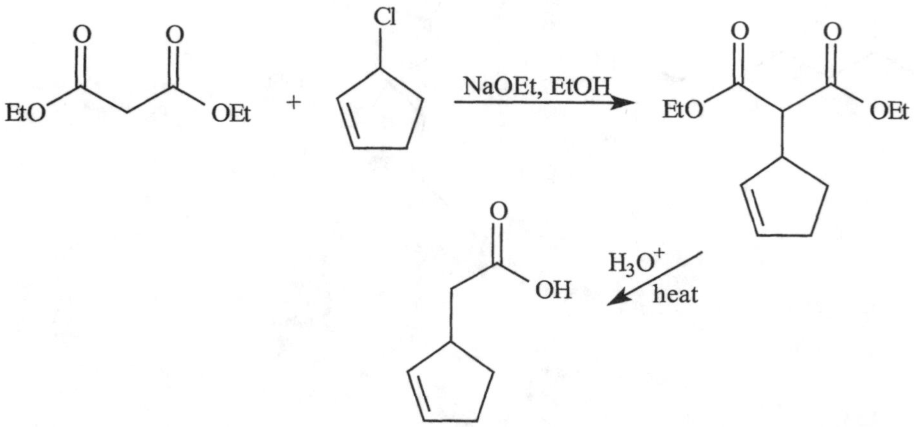

EtO OEt + Cl

NaOEt, EtOH

EtO OEt

H_3O^+
heat

OH

35. Cyclopentyl methyl ketone (cyclopentyl–C(=O)–CH_3)

Answer:

Ethyl acetoacetate ($CH_3COCH_2CO_2Et$)

1. 2 NaOEt, EtOH
2. $BrCH_2CH_2CH_2CH_2Br$

→ 1-acetyl-1-(ethoxycarbonyl)cyclopentane (cyclopentane carrying C(=O)–CH_3 and C(=O)–OEt on the same carbon)

$\xrightarrow[\text{heat}]{H_3O^+}$ cyclopentyl–C(=O)–CH_3

36. $H_2C{=}CHCH_2CH_2\overset{O}{\overset{\|}{C}}CH_3$

Answer:

$CH_3COCH_2CO_2Et$ (OEt) $\xrightarrow[\text{2. } H_2C{=}CHCH_2Br]{\text{1. NaOEt, EtOH}}$ $CH_3COCH(CH_2CH{=}CH_2)CO_2Et$

$\xrightarrow[\text{heat}]{H_3O^+}$ $H_2C{=}CHCH_2CH_2\overset{O}{\overset{\|}{C}}CH_3$

Show how you would accomplish each of the following transformations. More than one step may be required. Show all reagents and all intermediate structures.

37. 1-Bromoheptane (skeletal chain ending in Br) ⟶ Methyl non-2-enoate (skeletal chain with C=C, ending in CO_2CH_3)

Answer:

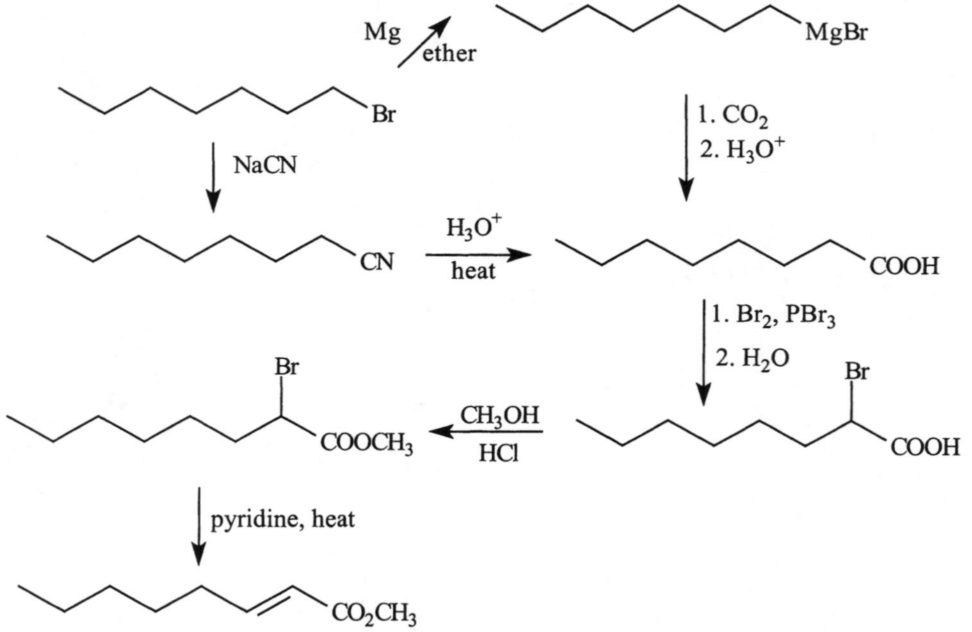

Mg, ether

MgBr

Br

NaCN

1. CO_2
2. H_3O^+

CN

H_3O^+, heat

COOH

1. Br_2, PBr_3
2. H_2O

Br

Br

$COOCH_3$

CH_3OH, HCl

COOH

pyridine, heat

CO_2CH_3

38.

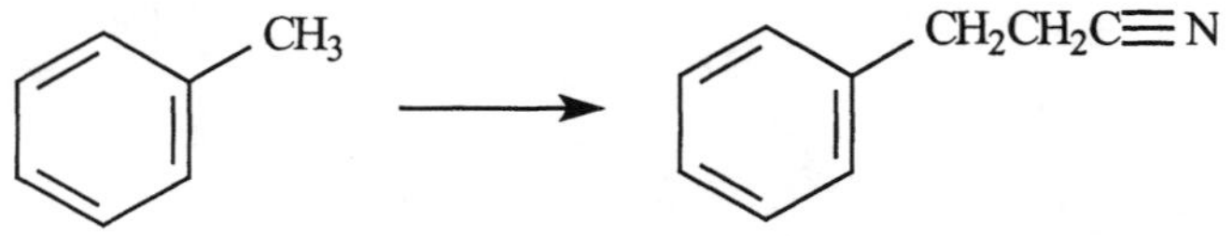

CH_3 ⟶ $CH_2CH_2C{\equiv}N$

Answer:

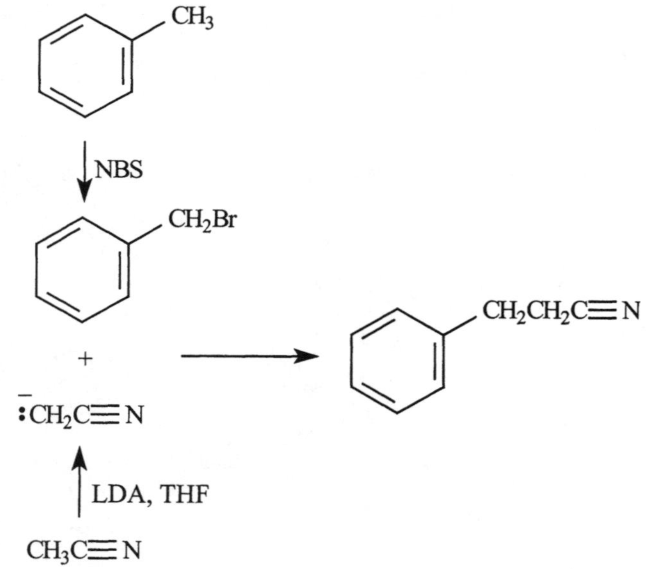

CH_3

NBS

CH_2Br

+

$:\overset{-}{C}H_2C{\equiv}N$ ⟶ $CH_2CH_2C{\equiv}N$

LDA, THF

$CH_3C{\equiv}N$

Chapter 23 – Carbonyl Condensation Reactions

Draw the structure of the aldol self-condensation product for each of the following compounds. If a compound does not undergo aldol self-condensation, explain why it does not.

1. 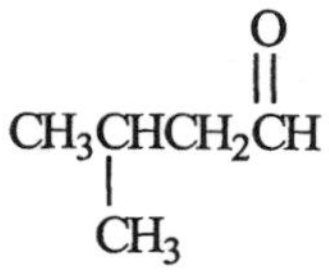 $CH_3CH(CH_3)CH_2CHO$

$$\begin{array}{l} \qquad\qquad\;\; O \\ \qquad\qquad\;\; \| \\ CH_3\underset{\underset{CH_3}{|}}{C}HCH_2CH \end{array}$$

Answer:

$$CH_3\underset{\underset{CH_3}{|}}{C}HCH_2CH{=}\underset{\underset{CH(CH_3)_2}{|}}{C}{-}\overset{\overset{O}{\|}}{C}H$$

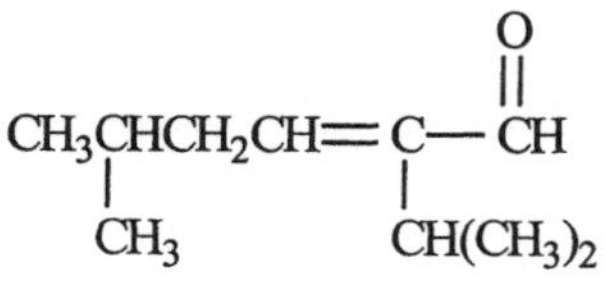

2.

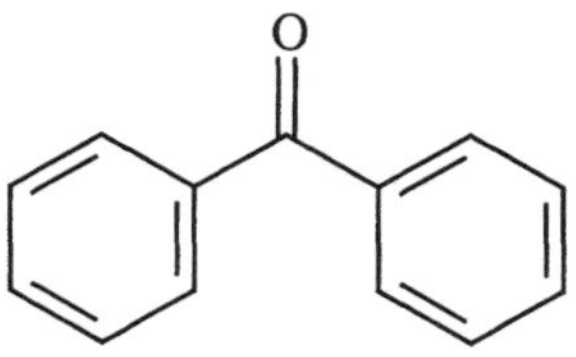

Answer: Benzophenone does not undergo aldol self-condensation because it has no α-hydrogens.

3. 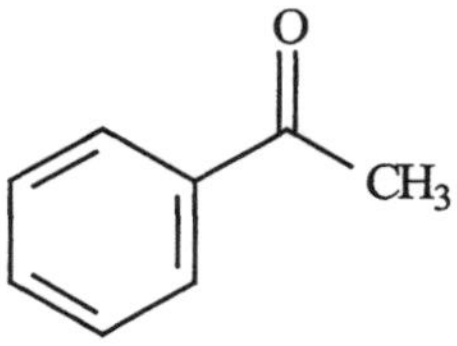 CH_3

Answer:

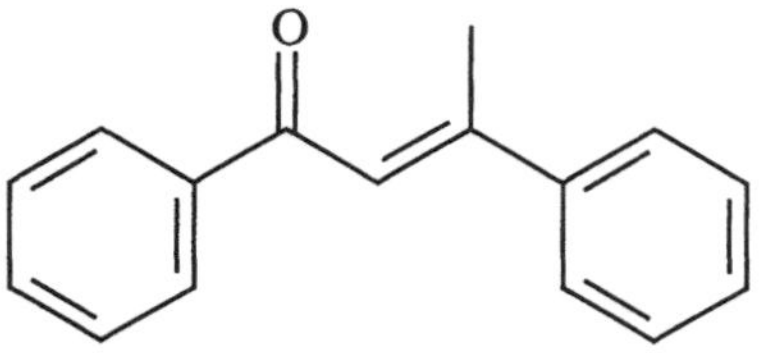

4. 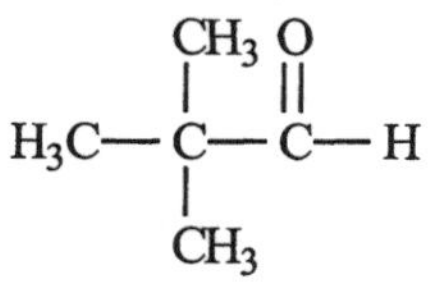 $H_3C{-}\underset{\underset{CH_3}{|}}{\overset{\overset{CH_3}{|}}{C}}{-}\overset{\overset{O}{\|}}{C}{-}H$

Answer: 2,2-Dimethylpropanal does not undergo aldol self-condensation because it has no α-hydrogens.

Consider the reaction below to answer the following question:

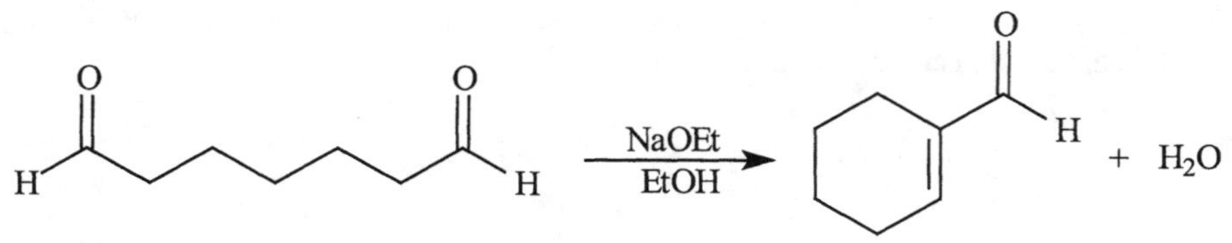

5. Write the complete stepwise mechanism for the reaction above. Show all intermediate structures and all electron flow with arrows.

Answer:

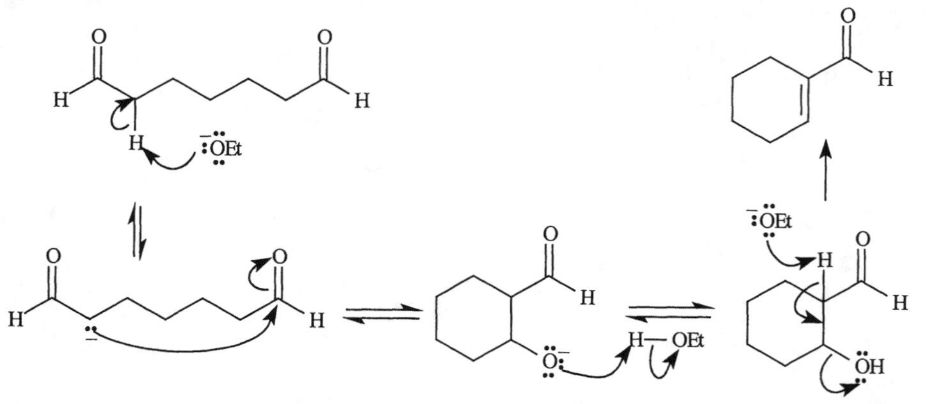

6. This reaction is an example of:

a. an intramolecular Claisen condensation
b. an intramolecular aldol condensation
c. a Robinson annulation
d. a Michael reaction

Answer: b

7. The product of this reaction is:

a. a β, γ-unsaturated aldehyde
b. a α, β-unsaturated ketone
c. an α, β-unsaturated aldehyde
d. an enol

Answer: c

Consider the data below to answer the following questions:

The Friedlander Quinoline Synthesis, first reported in 1882, is the base-catalyzed condensation of 2-aminobenzaldehydes with ketones to form quinoline derivatives.

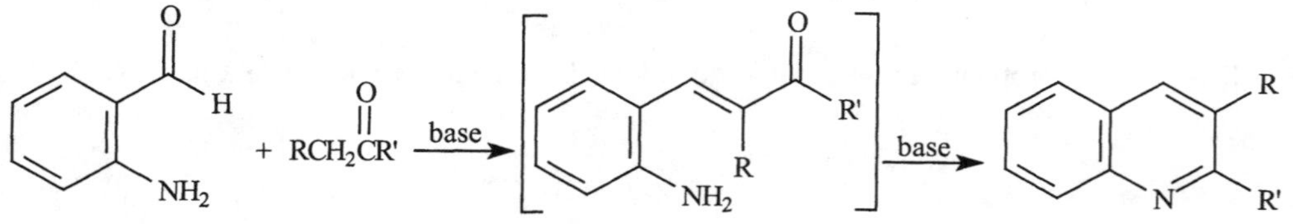

8. The first step of the Friedlander Quinoline Synthesis is a mixed aldol condensation. Write the complete stepwise mechanism for this reaction .

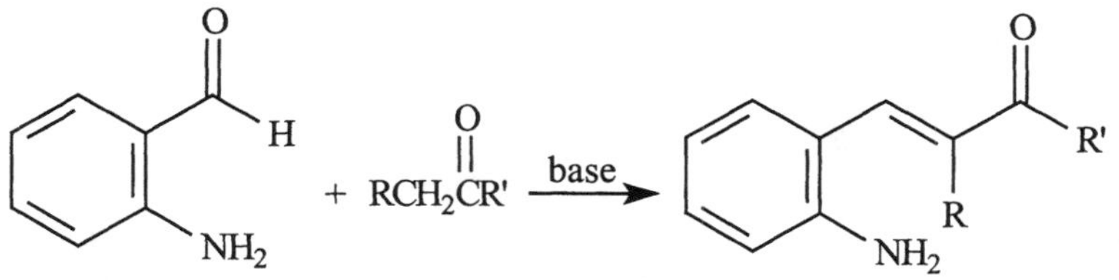

Answer:

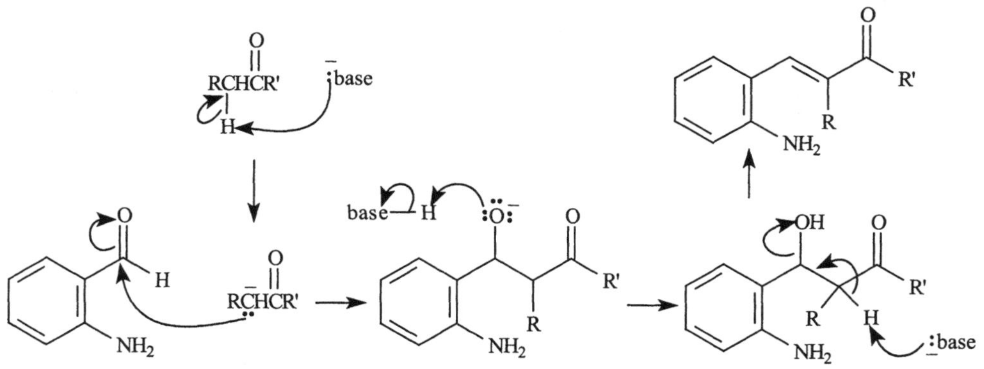

9. The second step of the Friedlander Quinoline Synthesis is a nucleophilic addition of a primary amine to a ketone yielding an imine. Write the complete stepwise mechanism for this imine forming reaction. Show all electron flow with arrows and show all intermediate structures.

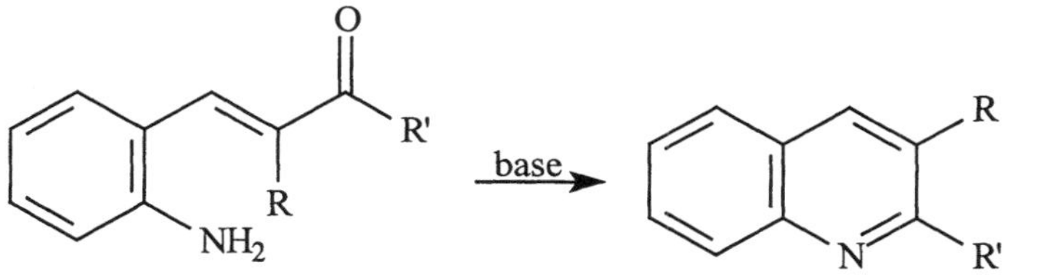

Answer:

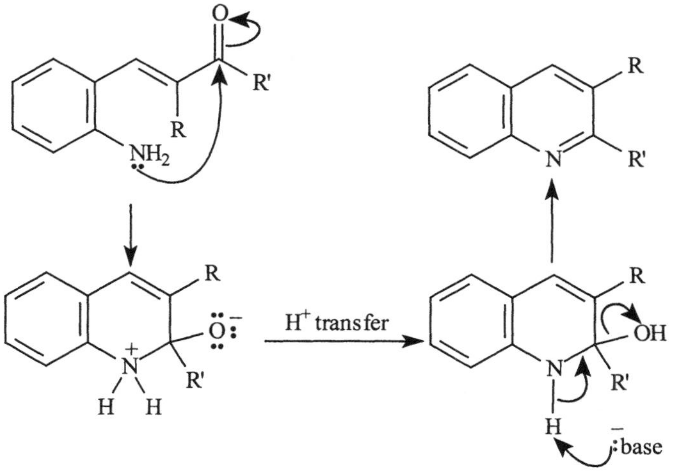

10. In the alkylation of cyclohexanone, better yields are obtained by first reacting cyclohexanone with an equivalent of lithium diisopropylamide in THF and then adding the alkyl halide, rather than mixing cyclohexanone, alkyl halide, and a catalytic amount of sodium ethoxide in ethanol. Explain this observation by pointing out what the problems with the second reaction conditions might be and how the first set of reaction conditions help alleviate the problems.

Answer: When cyclohexanone is placed in a solution of sodium ethoxide in ethanol, the enolate is generated in small amounts in the presence of large amounts of ketone-ideal conditions for an aldol self-condensation. Consequently, aldol self-condensation competes with alkylation of the enolate, and product mixtures result.

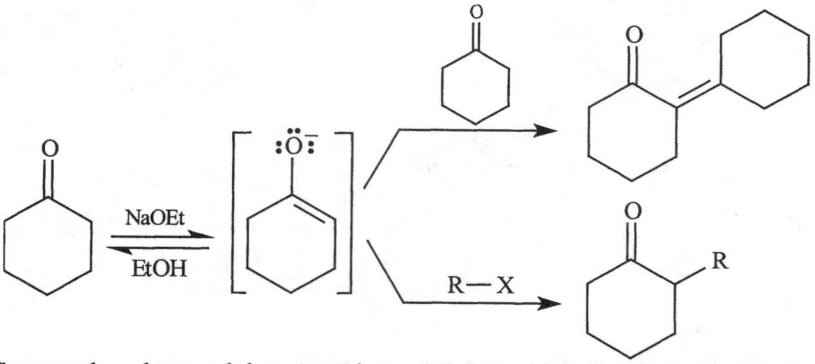

NaOEt
EtOH
R—X
R

Conversely, when cyclohexanone is treated first with an equivalent of LDA, the enolate is rapidly generated and no ketone remains. Addition of alkyl halide then yields the desired alkylated product.

Each of the following compounds can be prepared by a mixed aldol condensation reaction. Give the structures of the aldehyde and/or ketone precursors for each aldol product and formulate the reaction.

11. (2-furyl)$CH{=}CHCCH_3$ (C=O)

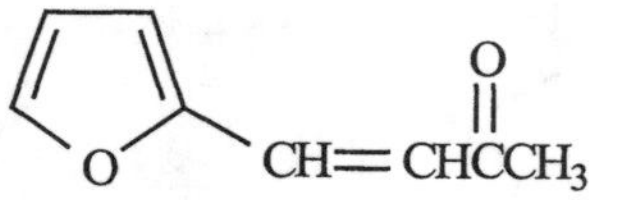

Answer:

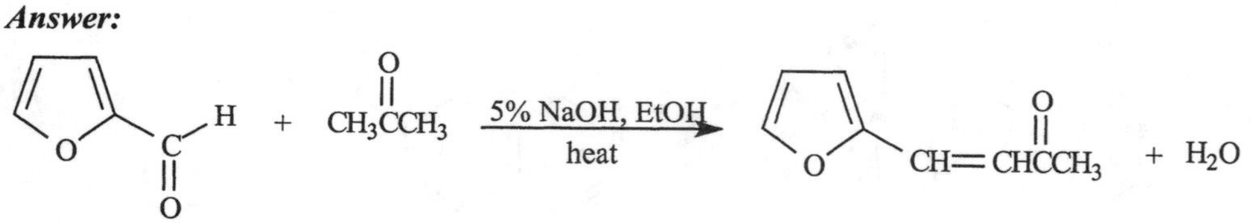

(2-furyl)CHO + CH_3CCH_3 (C=O) $\xrightarrow[\text{heat}]{\text{5\% NaOH, EtOH}}$ (2-furyl)$CH{=}CHCCH_3$ (C=O) + H_2O

12. $CH_3CCH{=}CH_2$ (C=O)

Answer:

CH_3CCH_3 (C=O) + HCH (C=O) $\xrightarrow[\text{heat}]{\text{5\% NaOH, EtOH}}$ $CH_3CCH{=}CH_2$ (C=O) + H_2O

13.

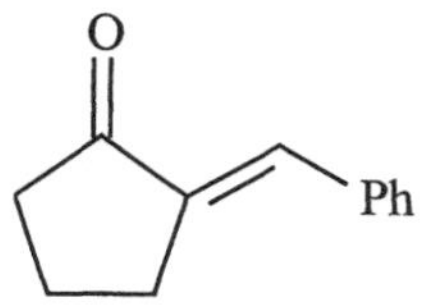

Answer:

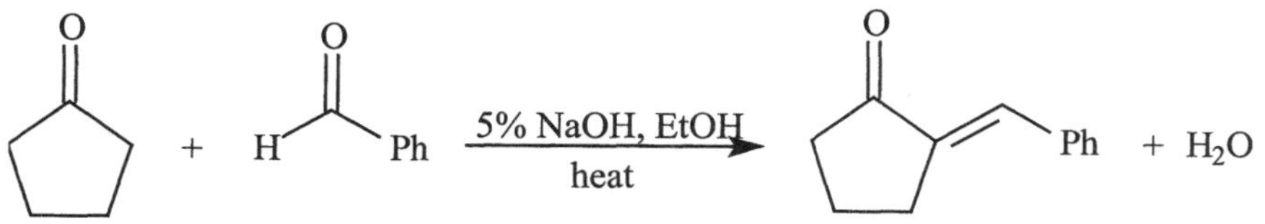

$$\text{cyclopentanone} + \text{PhCHO} \xrightarrow[\text{heat}]{5\%\ NaOH,\ EtOH} \text{2-benzylidenecyclopentanone} + H_2O$$

Consider the reaction below to answer the following questions.

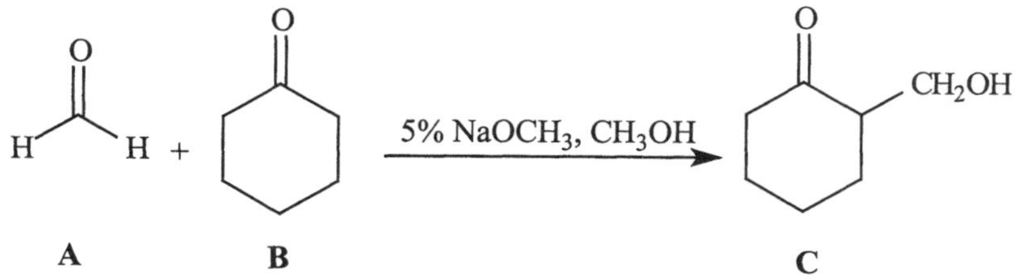

$$\underset{\textbf{A}}{HCHO} + \underset{\textbf{B}}{\text{cyclohexanone}} \xrightarrow{5\%\ NaOCH_3,\ CH_3OH} \underset{\textbf{C}}{\text{2-(hydroxymethyl)cyclohexanone}}$$

14. Which carbonyl compound functions as the *electrophile* in this reaction?

Answer: A

15. Draw the structure of the enolate ion that is generated during the course of this reaction.

Answer:

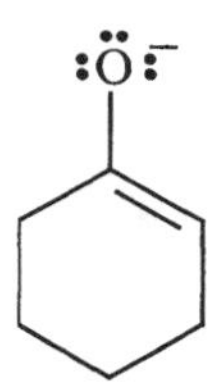

16. This reaction is an example of:

a. a mixed Claisen condensation.
b. a Dieckman condensation.
c. a Michael reaction.
d. a mixed aldol reaction.

Answer: d

Draw the structure of the product you would expect to obtain by Claisen condensation of each of the following esters. If an ester does not undergo Claisen condensation, explain why it does not.

17. 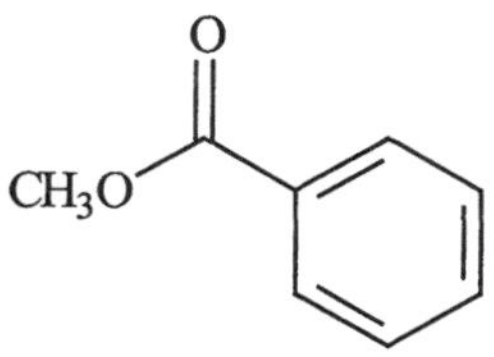 CH_3O

Answer: This ester does not undergo Claisen condensation, because it has no α-hydrogens and cannot undergo enolization.

18. 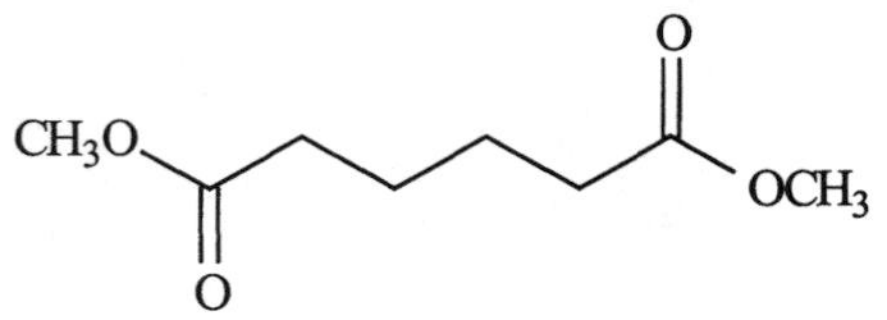 CH_3O ... OCH_3

Answer:

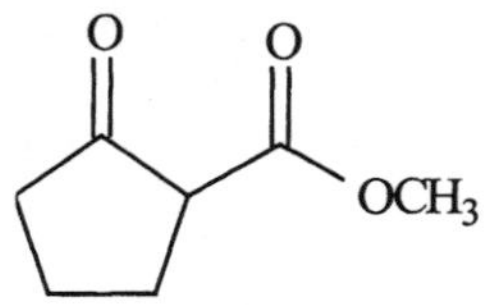

OCH_3

19. 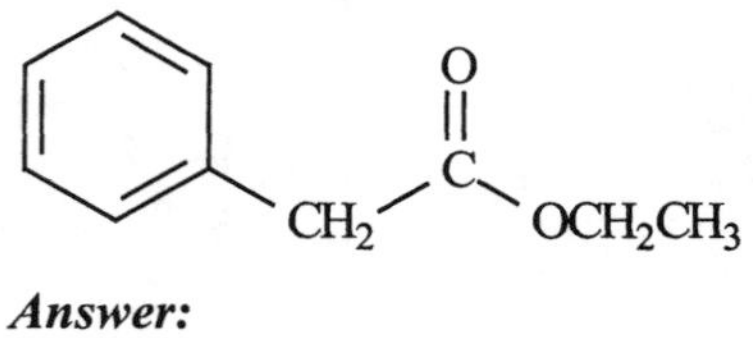 CH_2 — C(=O) — OCH_2CH_3

Answer:

CH_2 — C(=O) — CH — C(=O) — OCH_2CH_3

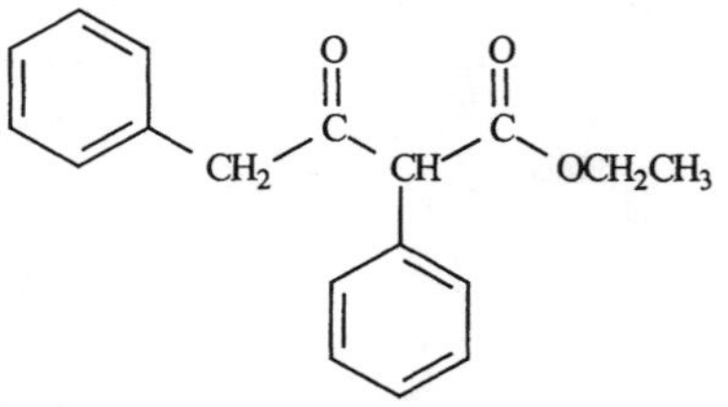

Consider the reaction below to answer the following questions:

Acetoacetic ester can be prepared by the Claisen self-condensation reaction of ethyl acetate.

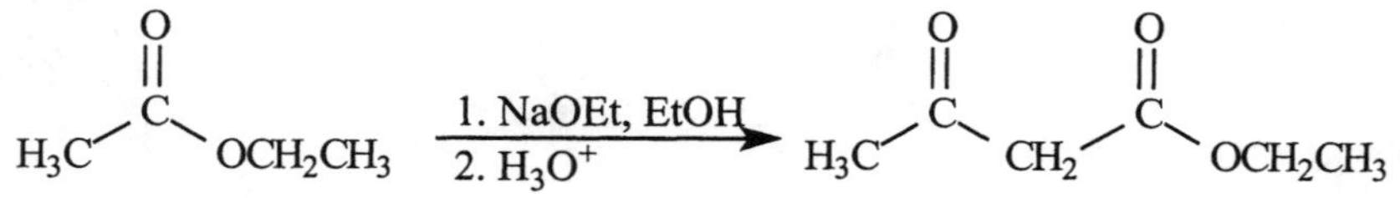

$$H_3C-C(=O)-OCH_2CH_3 \xrightarrow[2.\ H_3O^+]{1.\ NaOEt,\ EtOH} H_3C-C(=O)-CH_2-C(=O)-OCH_2CH_3$$

20. Write the complete stepwise mechanism for this reaction. Show all electron flow with arrows and draw all intermediate structures.

Answer:

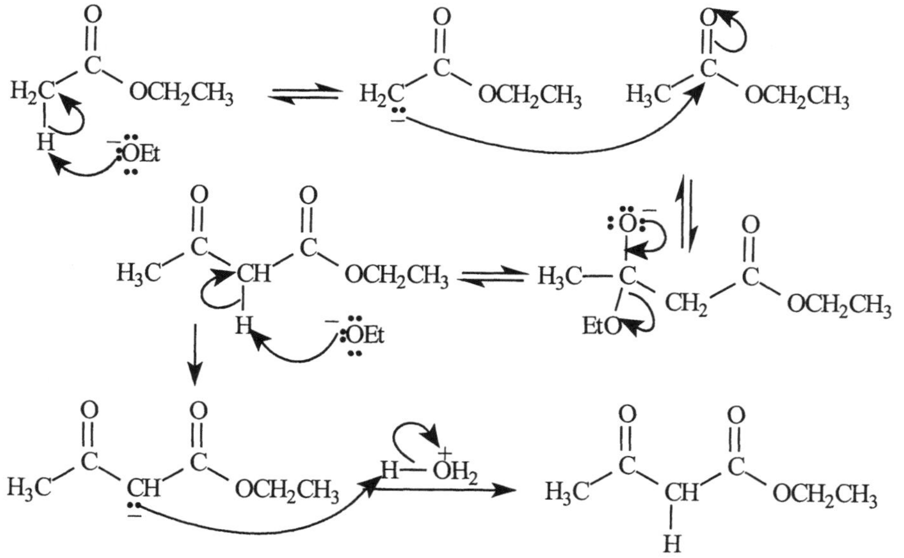

21. Ethyl acetate can be prepared from ethanol as the only organic starting material. Show all reagents and structures for all intermediates in this preparation.

Answer:

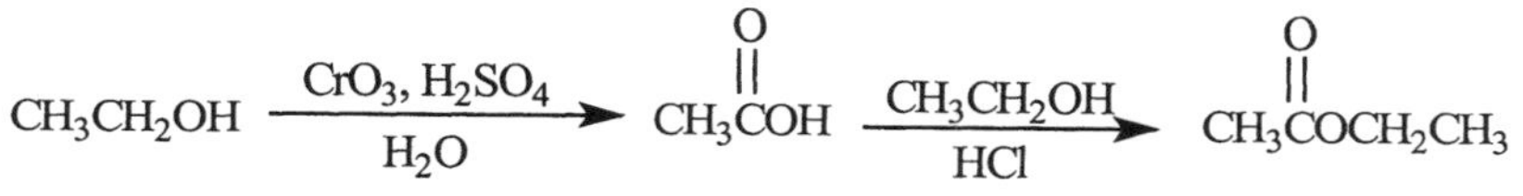

$$CH_3CH_2OH \xrightarrow[H_2O]{CrO_3,\ H_2SO_4} CH_3\overset{O}{\overset{\|}{C}}OH \xrightarrow[HCl]{CH_3CH_2OH} CH_3\overset{O}{\overset{\|}{C}}OCH_2CH_3$$

22. Give the structures of the ester precursors for the following Claisen condensation product and formulate the reaction.

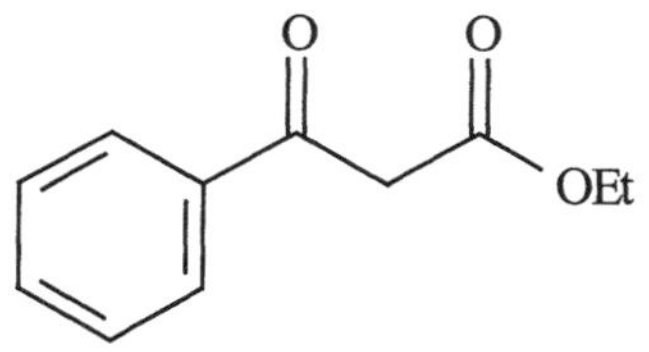

Answer:

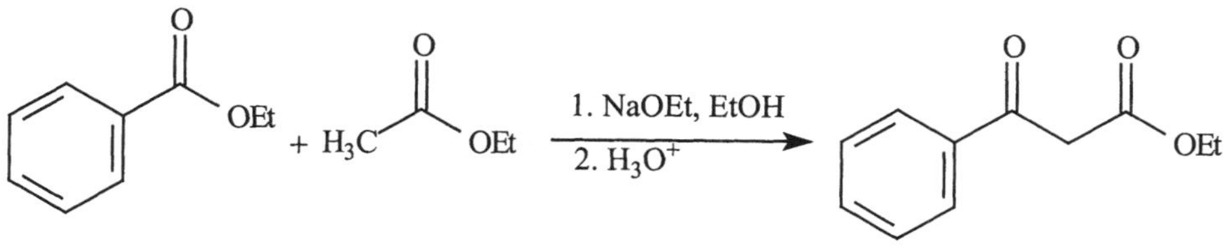

1. NaOEt, EtOH
2. H_3O^+

Consider the compound 2-methyl-2-carboethoxycyclopentanone, whose structure is shown below, to answer the following questions.

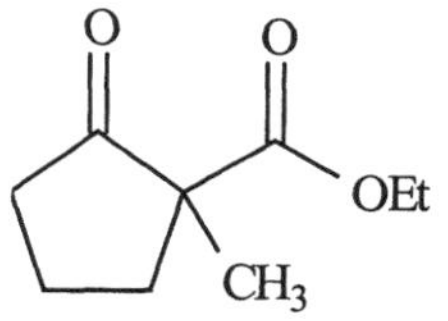

23. Formulate a synthesis of 2-methyl-2-carboethoxycyclopentanone starting with acyclic precursors using a Dieckmann cyclization as a key carbon-carbon bond forming step. show all reagents and all intermediate structures.

Answer:

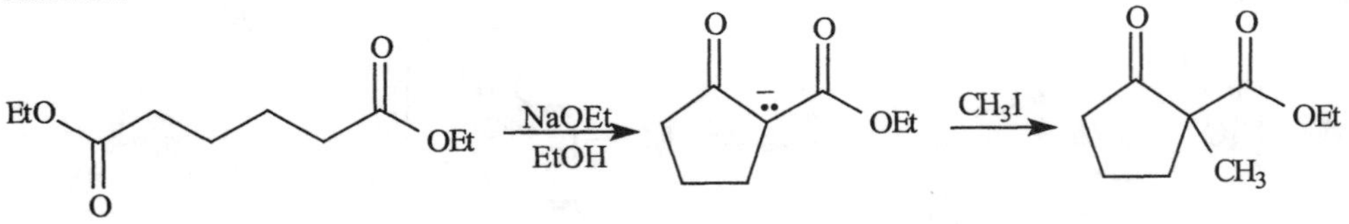

EtO O OEt O $\xrightarrow[\text{EtOH}]{\text{NaOEt}}$ O O OEt $\xrightarrow{CH_3I}$ O O OEt CH_3

24. When 2-methyl-2-carboethoxycyclopentanone is treated with sodium ethoxide in ethanol solution followed by a mild aqueous acid work-up, 5-methyl-2-carboethoxycyclopentanone is isolated as the major product. This reaction proceeds by a reverse Claisen condensation mechanism followed by a recyclization. On the structures provided below, show electron flow with arrows in this interesting reaction.

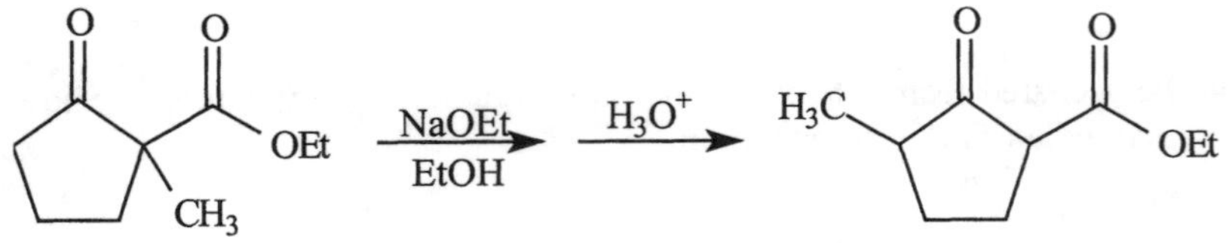

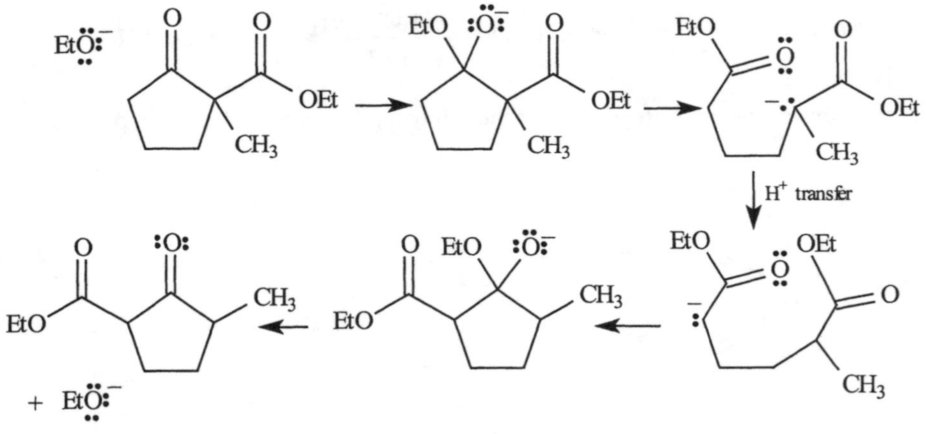

O O OEt CH_3 $\xrightarrow[\text{EtOH}]{\text{NaOEt}}$ $\xrightarrow{H_3O^+}$ H_3C O O OEt

EtÖ: O O OEt CH_3 → EtO :Ö: O OEt CH_3 → EtO Ö O OEt CH_3

↓ H^+ transfer

O :O: EtO CH_3 + EtÖ: ← O EtO :Ö: EtO CH_3 ← EtO Ö OEt O CH_3

Answer:

EtÖ: O O OEt CH_3 → EtO :Ö: O OEt CH_3 → EtO Ö O OEt CH_3

↓ H^+ transfer

O :O: EtO CH_3 + EtÖ: ← O EtO :Ö: EtO CH_3 ← EtO Ö OEt O CH_3

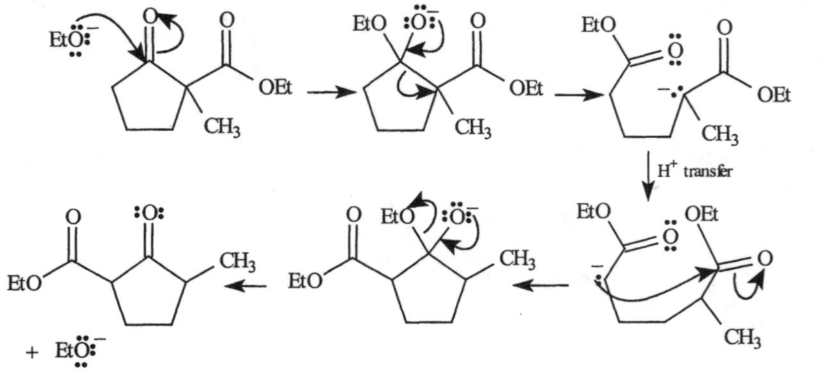

25. Oxaloacetic acid is an important intermediate in the biosynthesis of citric acid. Synthesize oxaloacetic acid using a mixed Claisen condensation as a key carbon-carbon bond forming reaction.

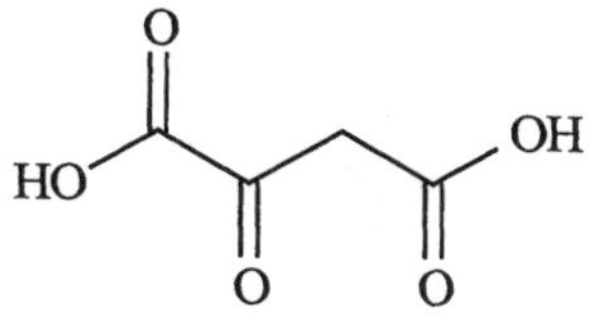

oxaloacetic acid

Answer:

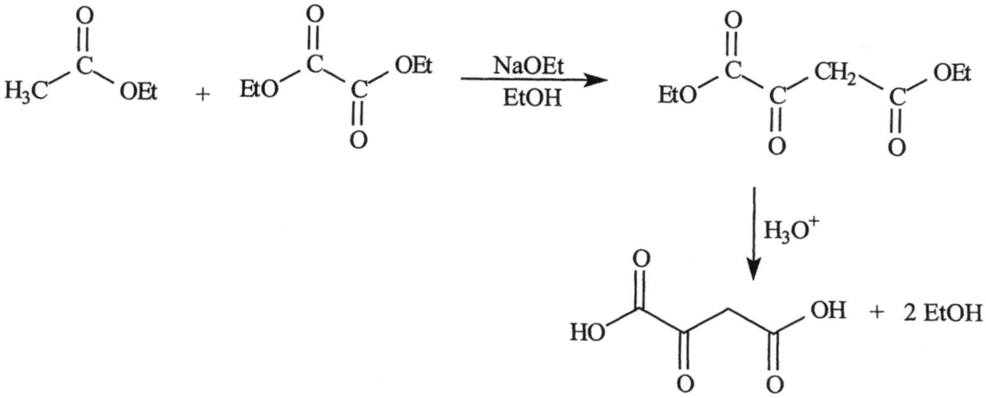

$H_3C-C(=O)-OEt$ + $EtO-C(=O)-C(=O)-OEt$ $\xrightarrow[EtOH]{NaOEt}$ $EtO-C(=O)-C(=O)-CH_2-C(=O)-OEt$

$\xrightarrow{H_3O^+}$ $HO-C(=O)-C(=O)-CH_2-C(=O)-OH$ + 2 EtOH

Draw the structures of the precursors to each of the following Michael reaction products. Label the Michael donor and the Michael acceptor in each case and formulate the reaction.

26.

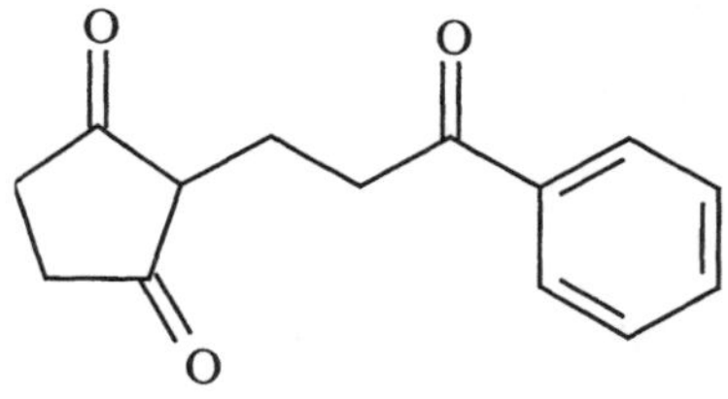

Answer:

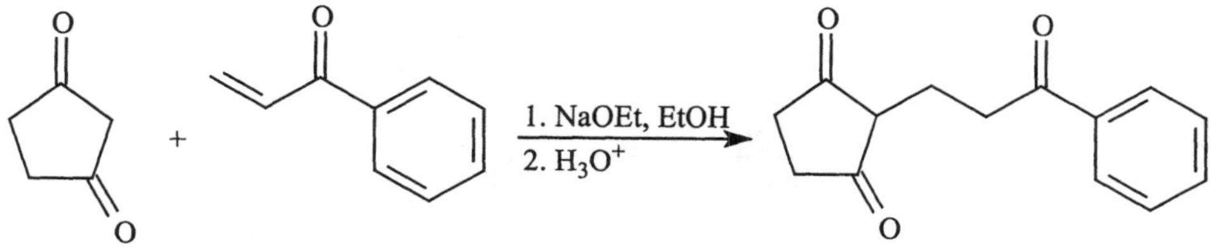

Michael donor + Michael acceptor $\xrightarrow[2.\ H_3O^+]{1.\ NaOEt,\ EtOH}$

27.

CO_2Et, $CH_2CH_2\overset{O}{\overset{\|}{C}}CH_3$, O

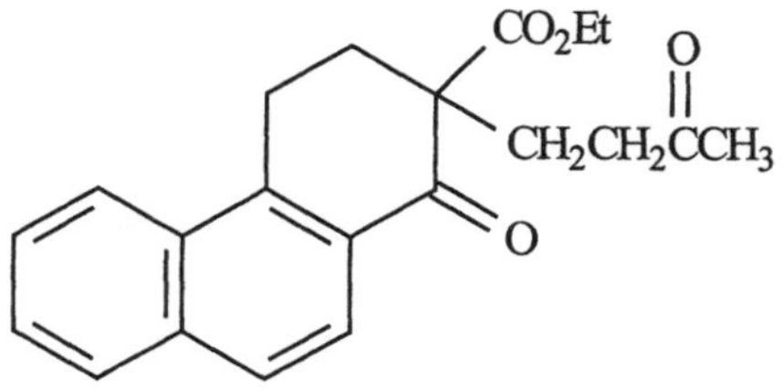

Answer:

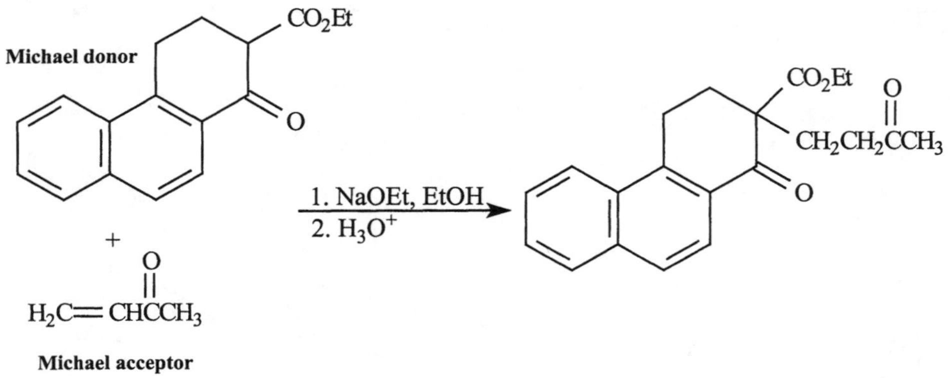

Michael donor

CO_2Et

O

+

$H_2C{=}CHCCH_3$ (with C=O)

Michael acceptor

1. NaOEt, EtOH
2. H_3O^+

CO_2Et O

$CH_2CH_2CCH_3$

O

28. 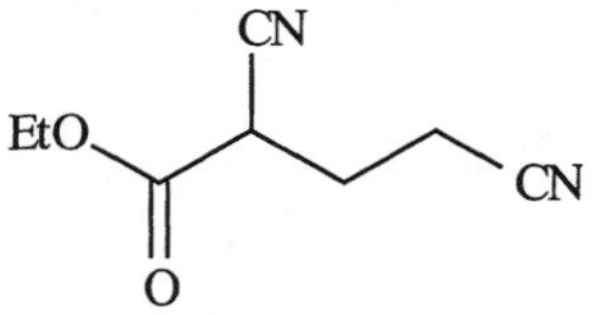 EtO, CN, CN, O

Answer:

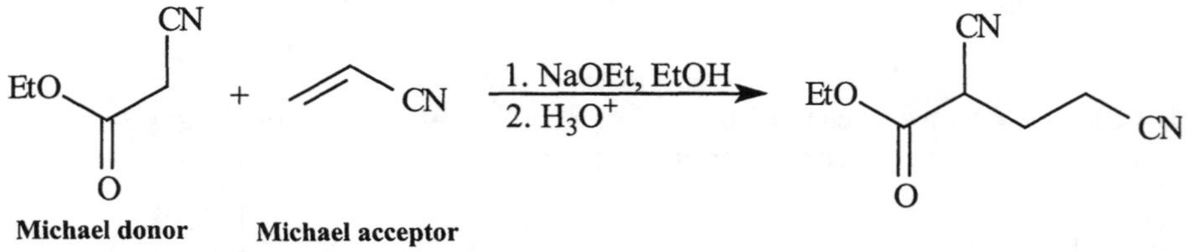

EtO, CN, O + CN → 1. NaOEt, EtOH 2. H_3O^+ → EtO, CN, CN, O

Michael donor   Michael acceptor

29. 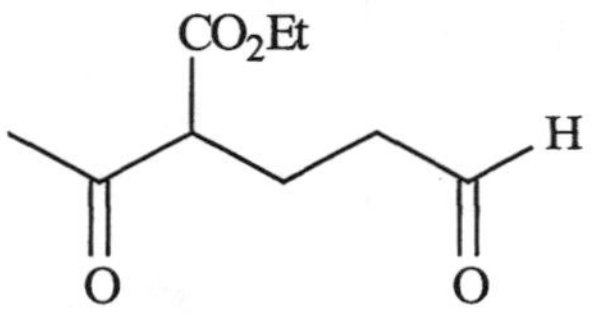 CO_2Et, H, O, O

Answer:

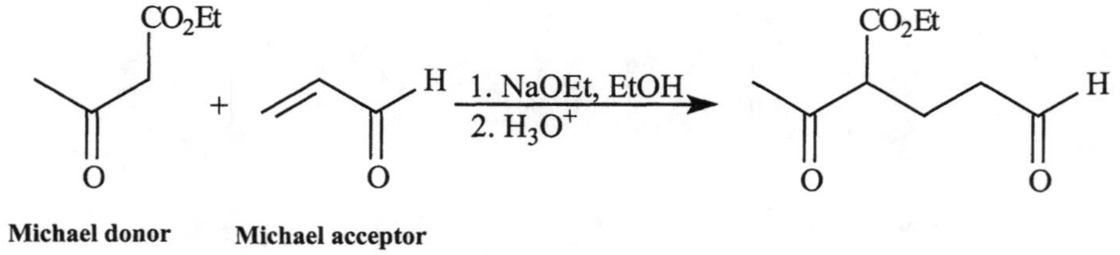

CO_2Et + H, O → 1. NaOEt, EtOH 2. H_3O^+ → CO_2Et, H, O, O

Michael donor   Michael acceptor

30. 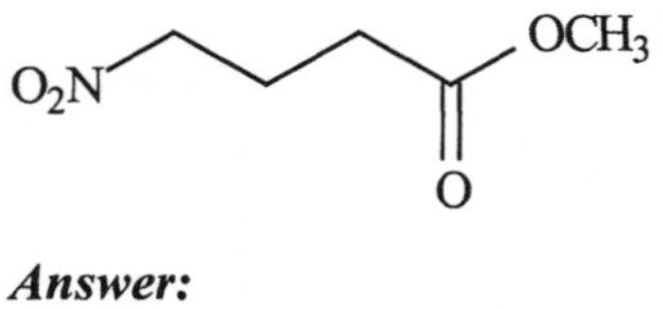 O_2N, OCH_3, O

Answer:

$O_2N{-}CH_3$ + OCH_3, O → 1. NaOEt, EtOH 2. H_3O^+ → O_2N, OCH_3, O

Michael donor   Michael acceptor

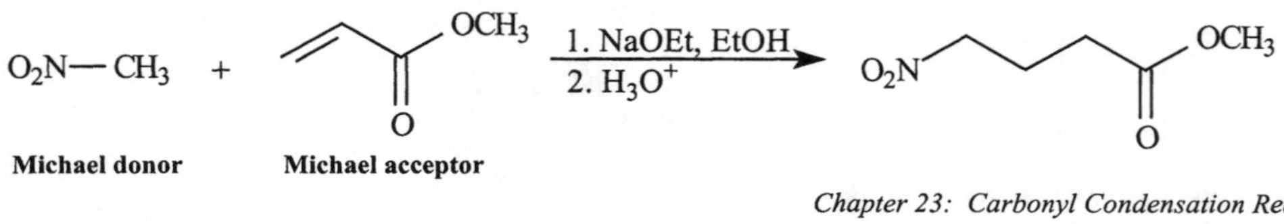

Consider the reaction below to answer the following questions.

The Stork enamine reaction is a variation on the Michael reaction which utilizes an enamine nucleophile.

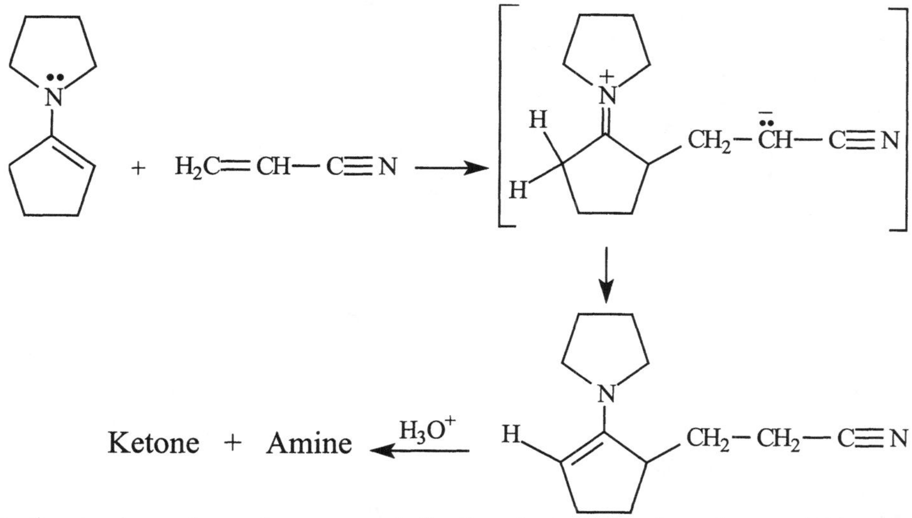

$+ \; H_2C{=}CH{-}C{\equiv}N \longrightarrow$

Ketone + Amine $\xleftarrow{H_3O^+}$

31. On the structures above, draw arrows indicating electron flow in each step of this reaction.

Answer:

Ketone + Amine $\xleftarrow{H_3O^+}$

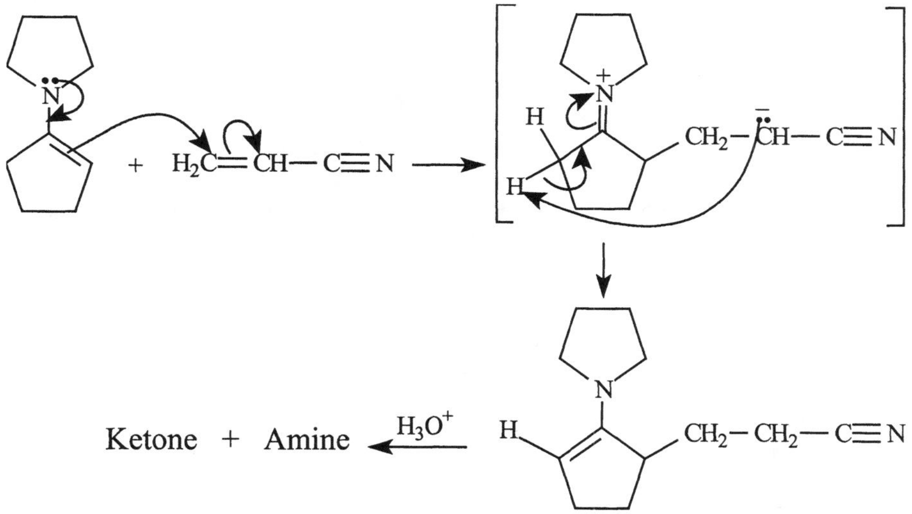

32. Draw the structures of the Ketone + Amine products of this reaction.

Answer:

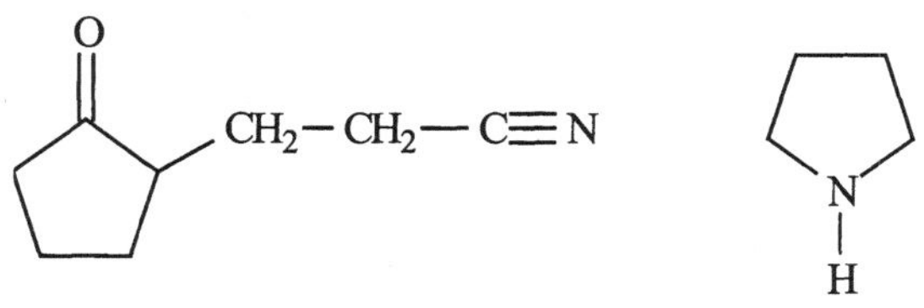

Ketone

Amine

33. Show how you might use a Stork enamine reaction to prepare the following compound.

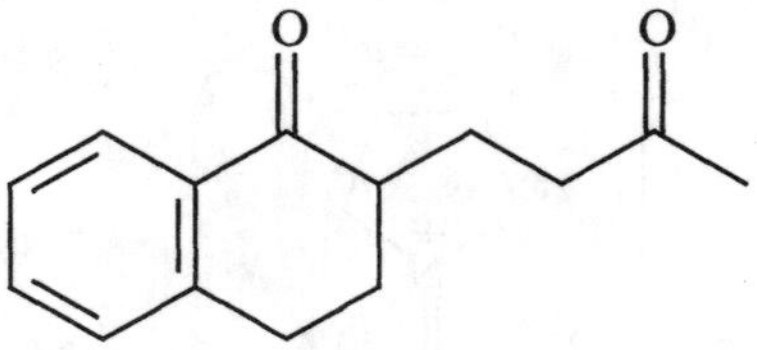

Answer:

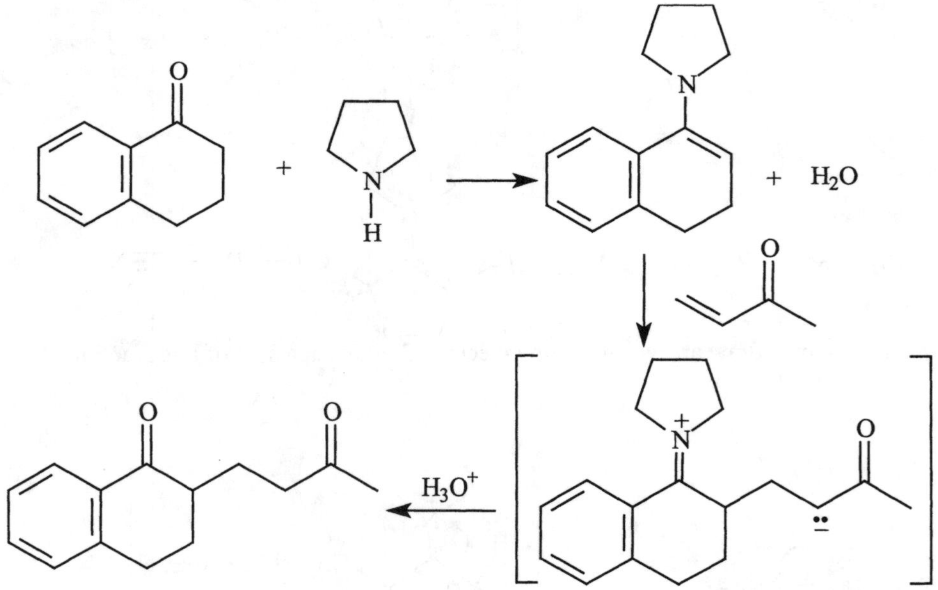

+ H_2O

H_3O^+

34. Provide the indicated starting material and intermediate in the synthetic sequence below involving a Dieckmann condensation, followed by a Robinson Annulation.

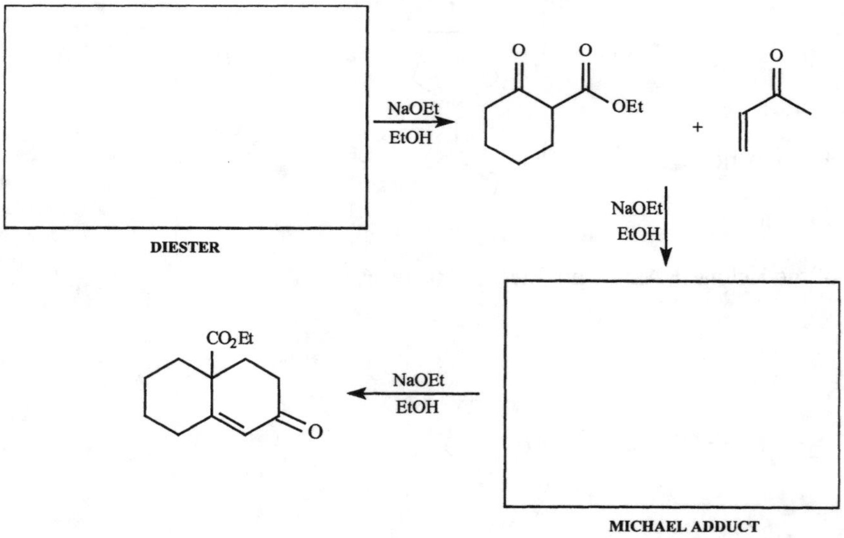

NaOEt
EtOH

OEt

+

NaOEt
EtOH

DIESTER

CO_2Et

NaOEt
EtOH

MICHAEL ADDUCT

Answer:

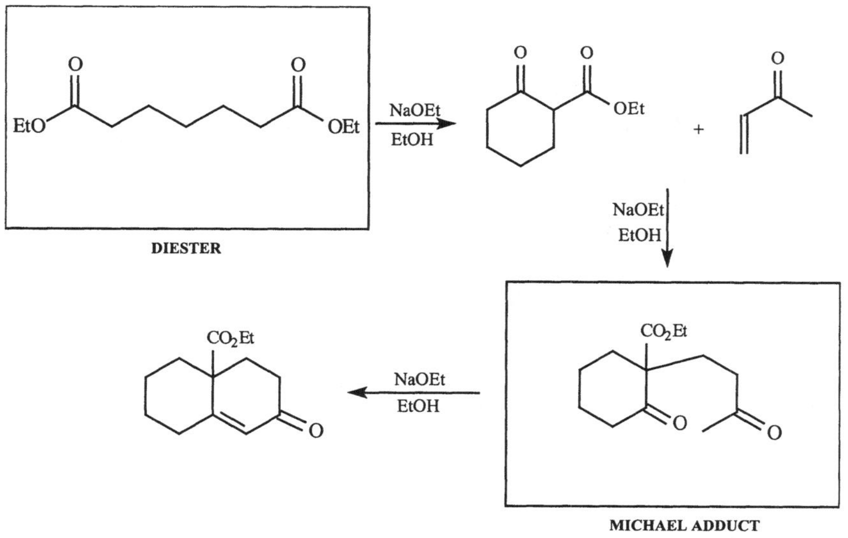

DIESTER

NaOEt, EtOH

OEt

+

NaOEt, EtOH

MICHAEL ADDUCT

CO_2Et

NaOEt, EtOH

35. Show how you might use a Robinson annulation reaction to synthesize the following compound. Draw the structures of both reactants and the structure of the intermediate Michael addition product.

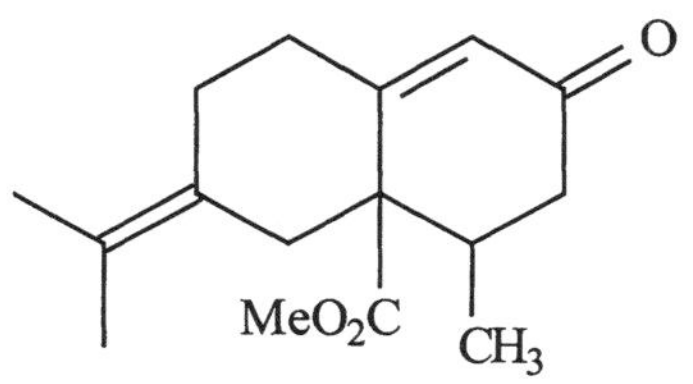

MeO_2C CH_3

Answer:

CO_2Me + H_3C CH_3 NaOMe, MeOH → MeO_2C CH_3

NaOMe, MeOH heat

+ H_2O

MeO_2C CH_3

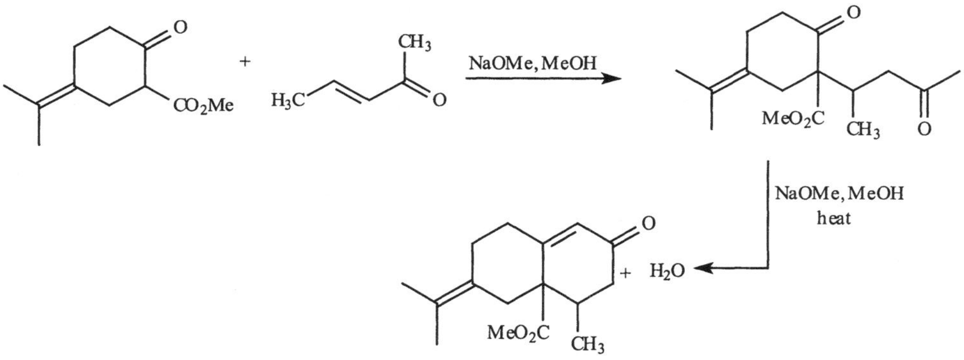

Give the major organic product(s) for each of the following reactions or reaction sequences.

36. 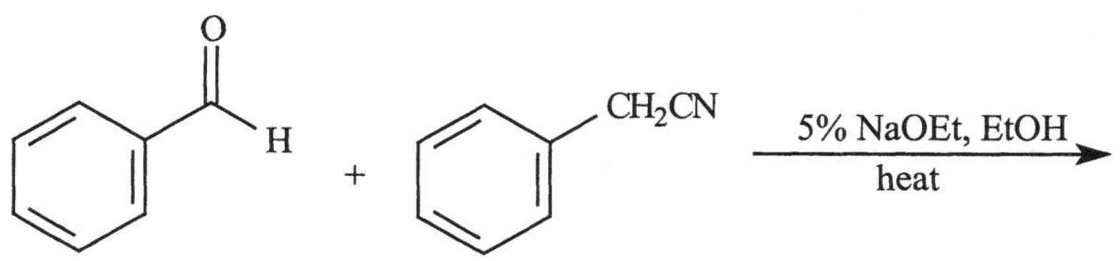 H + CH_2CN $\xrightarrow[\text{heat}]{\text{5\% NaOEt, EtOH}}$

Answer:

$$C_6H_5CHO + C_6H_5CH_2CN \xrightarrow[\text{heat}]{\text{5\% NaOEt, EtOH}} C_6H_5CH{=}C(C_6H_5)CN$$

38. cyclohexanone + pyrrolidine $\xrightarrow{\text{pH 4.5}}$ $\xrightarrow{CH_2{=}CHCOCH_3}$ $\xrightarrow{H_3O^+}$

Answer:

cyclohexanone + pyrrolidine $\xrightarrow{\text{pH 4.5}}$ $\xrightarrow{CH_2{=}CHCOCH_3}$ $\xrightarrow{H_3O^+}$ 2-(3-oxobutyl)cyclohexanone

39. 2-methyl-1,3-cyclopentanedione (CH_3) + $H_2C{=}CH{-}\overset{O}{\overset{\|}{C}}{-}CH_3$ $\xrightarrow{\text{NaOEt, EtOH}}$ **Michael adduct**

$\xrightarrow[\text{heat}]{\text{NaOEt, EtOH}}$ **Robinson annulation product**

Answer:

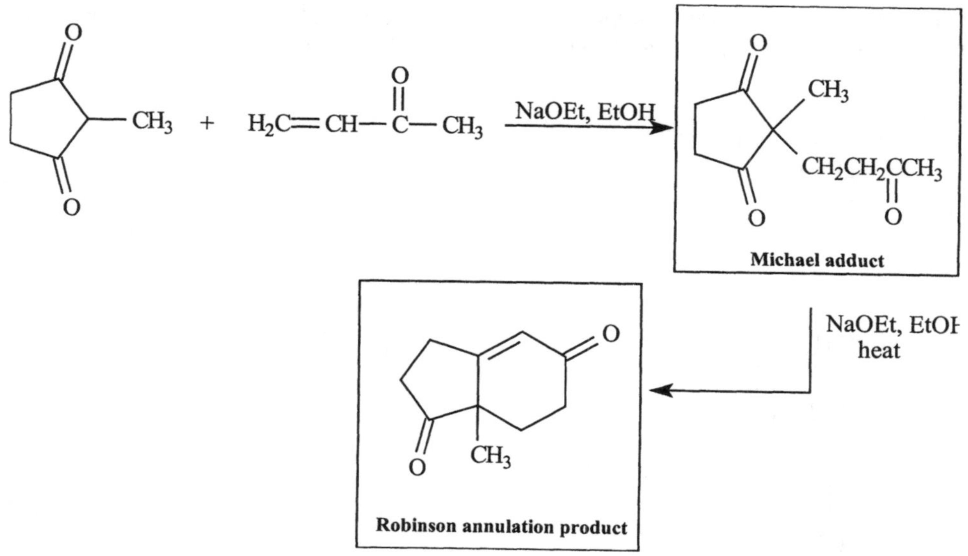

$$\text{2-methylcyclopentane-1,3-dione} + H_2C{=}CH{-}\overset{O}{\overset{\|}{C}}{-}CH_3 \xrightarrow{\text{NaOEt, EtOH}} \text{Michael adduct}$$

Michael adduct: 2-methyl-2-($CH_2CH_2CCH_3$, C=O)cyclopentane-1,3-dione

NaOEt, EtOH
heat

Robinson annulation product

40. acetophenone (CH_3) + methyl benzoate (OCH_3) $\xrightarrow[\text{2. } H_3O^+]{\text{1. NaOCH}_3\text{, CH}_3\text{OH}}$

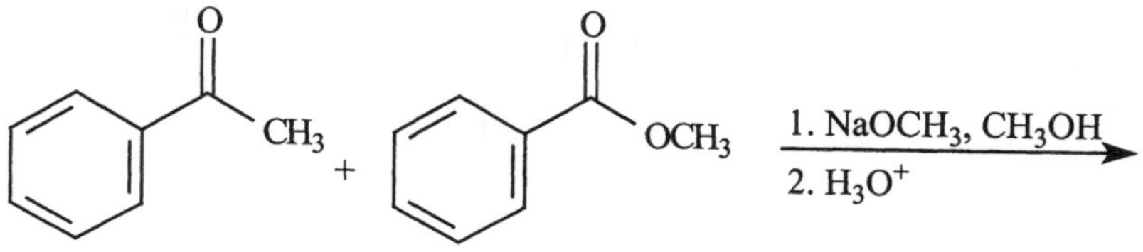

Answer:

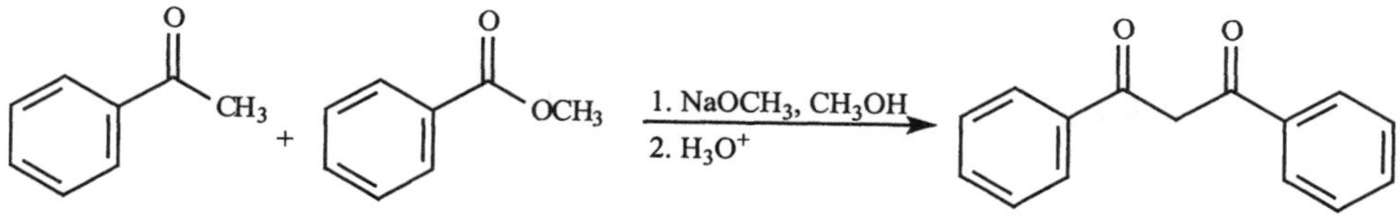

acetophenone (CH_3) + methyl benzoate (OCH_3) $\xrightarrow[\text{2. } H_3O^+]{\text{1. NaOCH}_3\text{, CH}_3\text{OH}}$ 1,3-diphenyl-1,3-propanedione

41. ethyl 1-methyl-2-(2-oxopropyl)cyclopentanecarboxylate (H_3C, O, OEt, CH_3, O) $\xrightarrow[\text{EtOH}]{\text{NaOEt}}$

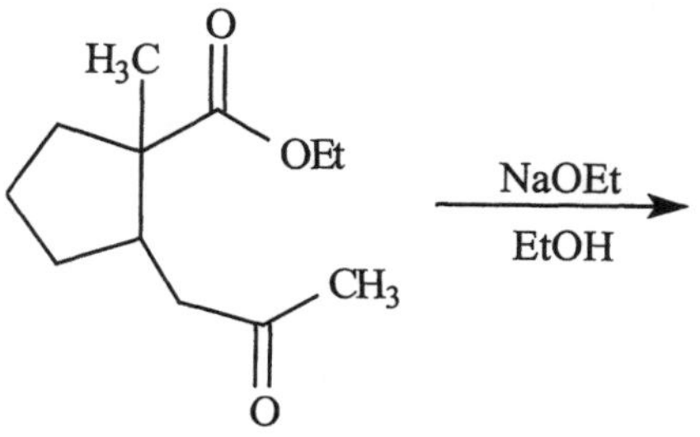

Answer:

(H_3C, O, OEt, CH_3, O) $\xrightarrow[\text{EtOH}]{\text{NaOEt}}$ bicyclic dione (H_3C, O, O)

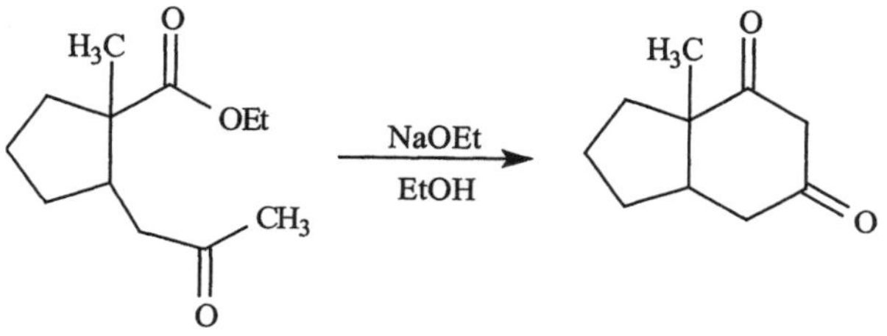

42. A multistep synthesis can be used to prepare 3,3-dimethylindanone. From the list provided below, choose the best reagent(s) for each step in this sequence. Place the letter in the box over the reaction arrow.

a. Cl_2, HOAc
b. 0.05 equiv. NaOEt, ethanol, heat
c. 1. PhMgBr, ether
   2. H_3O^+
d. 1. Mg, ether
   2. CO_2
   3. H_3O^+
e. I_2, NaOH, H_2O
f. H_2SO_4, Δ
g. 1. $(Ph)_2CuLi$, ether
   2. H_3O^+
h. 1. LDA, THF
   2. $(CH_3)_2CHBr$
i. $SOCl_2$, $CHCl_3$

O, C, H_3C, CH_3 → CH_3, O, H_3C, CH_3 → H_3C CH_3, O, CH_3 → H_3C CH_3, O, OH → H_3C CH_3, O, Cl → (AlCl$_3$) H_3C, CH_3, O

Answer: step 1 = b; step 2 = g; step 3 = e; step 4 = i

Chapter 24 - Amines

Classify each of the following nitrogen atoms in the following compounds as primary, secondary, tertiary, or quaternary.

1. 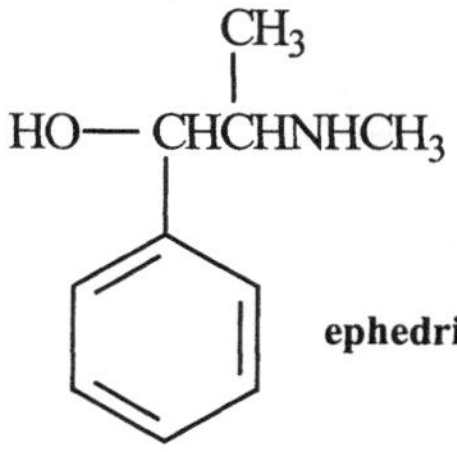 $HO-CH(C_6H_5)CH(CH_3)NHCH_3$ **ephedrine**

Answer: The nitrogen atom in ephedrine is secondary.

2. 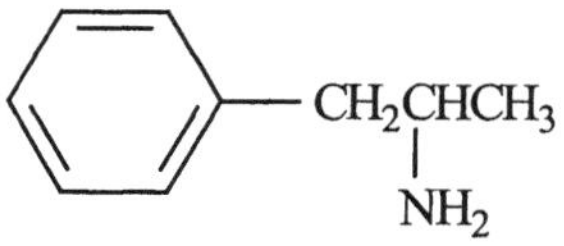 $C_6H_5-CH_2CH(NH_2)CH_3$ **amphetamine**

Answer: The nitrogen atom in amphetamine is primary.

3. 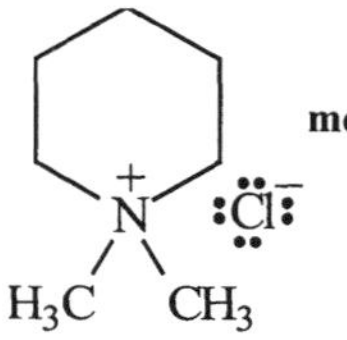 **mepiquat chloride**

Answer: The nitrogen in mepiquat chloride is a quaternary ammonium salt.

4. 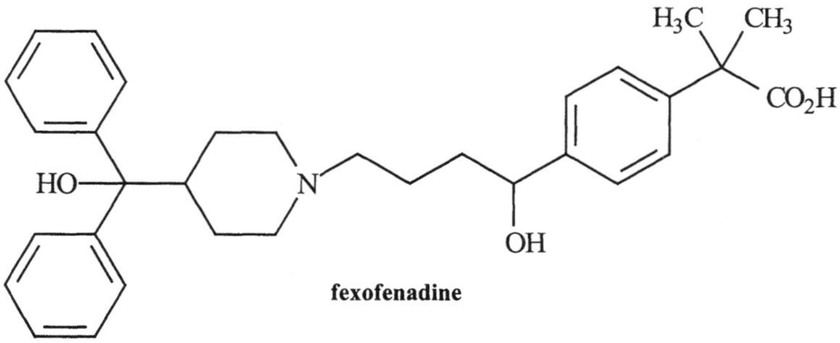 **fexofenadine**

Answer: The nitrogen atom in fexofenadine is tertiary

Draw structures corresponding to each of the following IUPAC names:

5. diisopropylamine

Answer:

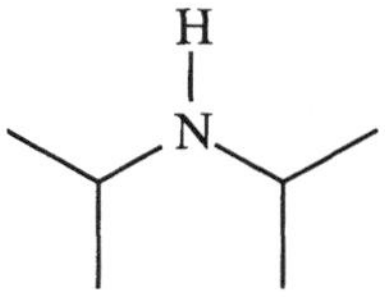

6. *N,N*-dimethylcyclopentanamine

Answer:

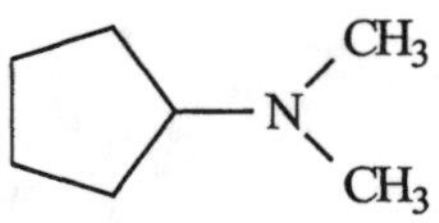

7. 1,4-butanediamine

Answer: $H_2NCH_2CH_2CH_2CH_2NH_2$

8. *p*-methoxyaniline

Answer:

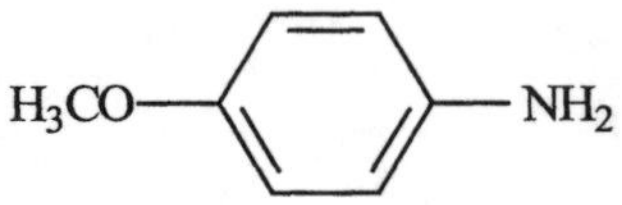

Name each of the following compounds by IUPAC rules.

9.

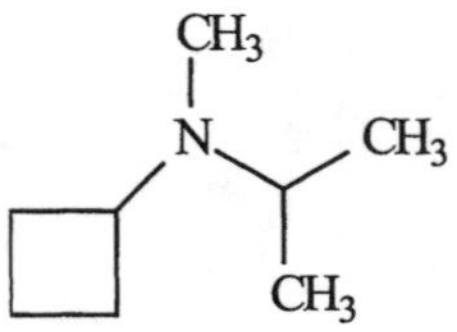

Answer: *N*-methyl-*N*-isopropylcyclobutylamine

10.

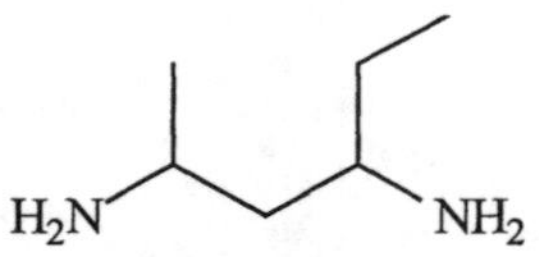

Answer: 2,4-hexanediamine

11.

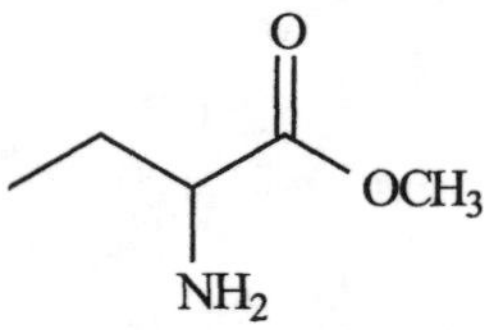

Answer: methyl-2-aminobutanoate

12.

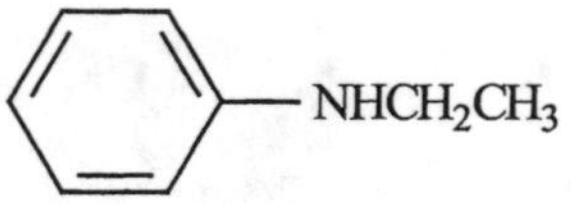

Answer: *N*-ethylaniline

13.

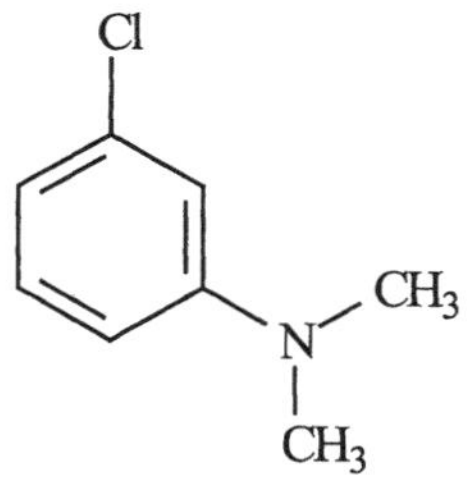

Answer: *m*-chloro-*N,N*-dimethylaniline

14.  O_2N–C_6H_4–NH_2

Answer: *p*-nitroaniline

Consider the reaction below to answer the following questions.

Methamphetamine can be synthesized by reacting phenyl-2-propanone with methylamine in the presence of H_2/Ni.

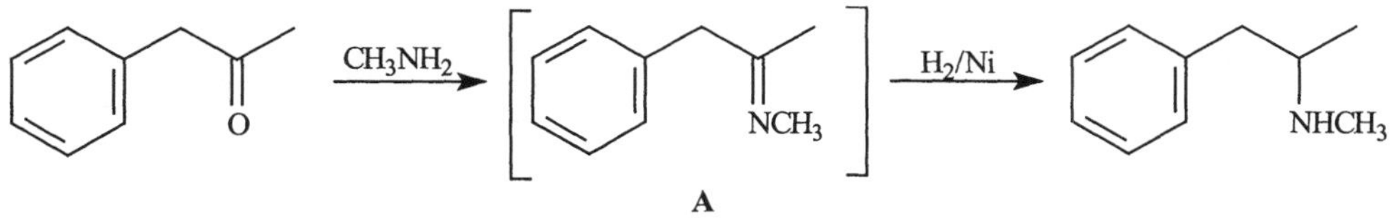

O —CH_3NH_2→ [NCH_3] —H_2/Ni→ $NHCH_3$

A

15. Identify the nucleophile in the initial reaction of phenyl-2-propanone to yield intermediate **A**.

Answer: The nucleophile is methylamine.

16. Intermediate **A** is an example of:

a. an imine
b. an enamine
c. an iminium ion
d. an imide

Answer: a

17. Although the yield of methamphetamine is good, some unreacted phenyl-2-propanone remains after the reaction is complete. Describe how methamphetamine can be separated from phenyl-2-propanone.

Answer: Dissolve the reaction mixture containing the ketone and amine in ether and extract with aqueous HCl. The basic amine will dissolve in the aqueous layer as its hydrochloric salt. The neutral ketone will remain in the ether layer. Separate the two layers and neutralize the aqueous layer with NaOH. Extract the neutralized layer with ether. The purified amine will dissolve in the ether.

Refer to the Table of pK_as below to answer the following questions:

pK_as of Some Arylammonium Ions

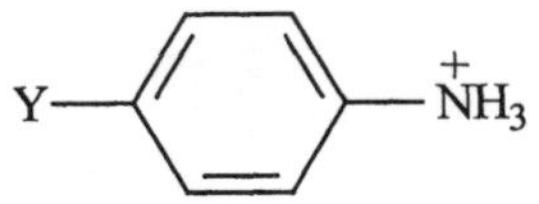

Y	pK_a
–H	4.63
–C ≡ N	1.74
$–NH_2$	6.15

18. Based on the pK_as for their corresponding ammonium ions, which arylamine above is the strongest base?

Answer: *p*-aminoaniline

19. Explain the difference in acidity between *p*-cyanoanilinium ion and anilinium ion. Use both words and structures.

Answer: *p*-Cyanoanilinium ion is a stronger acid (pK_a = 1.74) than anilinium ion (pK_a = 4.63). *p*-Cyanoanilinium ion gives up a proton on nitrogen more readily than anilinium ion because the electron-withdrawing cyano group polarizes the benzene ring and thus decreases the stability of the positively charged ion.

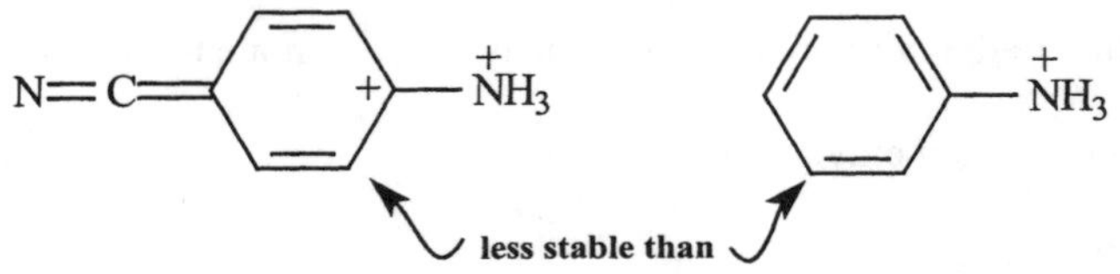

less stable than

20. Explain the difference in acidity between *p*-aminoanilinium ion and anilinium ion. Use both words and structures.

Answer: *p*-Aminoanilinium ion (pK_a = 6.15) is less acidic than anilinium ion (pK_a = 4.63) because *p*-aminoanilinium ion is stabilized by the electron-donating amino group. The *p*-amino group donates electron density to the benzene ring, which helps stabilize the positive charge on nitrogen.

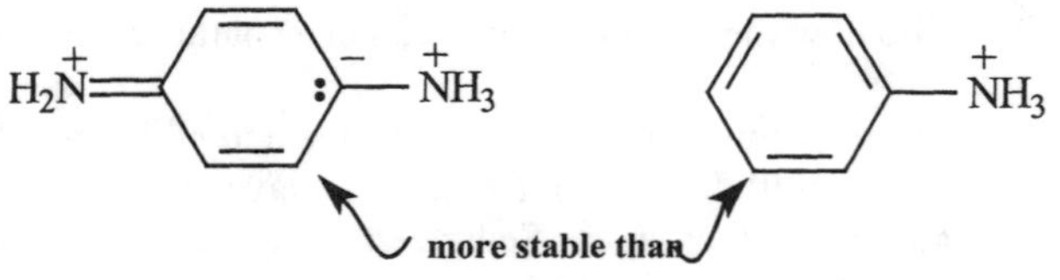

more stable than

21. Rank the following compounds in order of increasing basicity. Label the least basic compound "1" and the most basic compound "4". Place the number corresponding to the compound's rank in the blank below the compound.

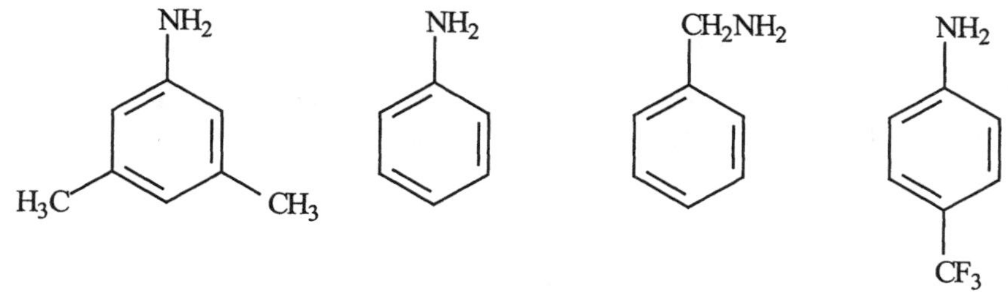

3,5-dimethylaniline (NH_2; H_3C, CH_3) ____ aniline (NH_2) ____ benzylamine (CH_2NH_2) ____ 4-(trifluoromethyl)aniline (NH_2; CF_3) ____

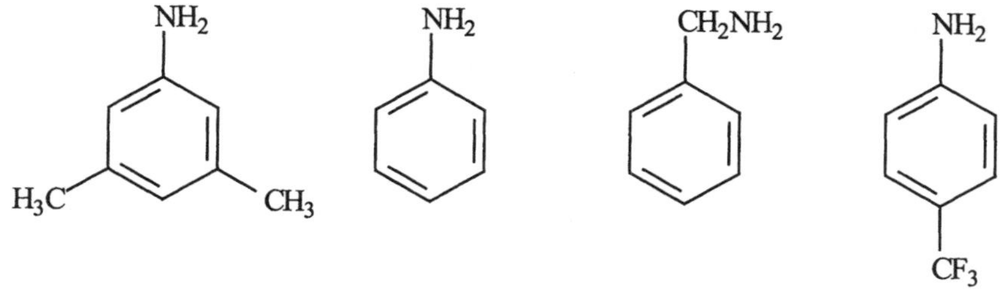

Answer:

3,5-dimethylaniline (NH_2; H_3C, CH_3) __3__ aniline (NH_2) __2__ benzylamine (CH_2NH_2) __4__ 4-(trifluoromethyl)aniline (NH_2; CF_3) __1__

22. When a THF solution of phenyl-2-propanone and bromobutane is treated with 50% aqueous NaOH, poor yields of 3-phenyl-2-heptanone result. However, when a small amount of benzyltriethylammonium chloride is added to the reaction mixture, the yield of 3-phenyl-2-heptanone increases to 90%. Explain these results.

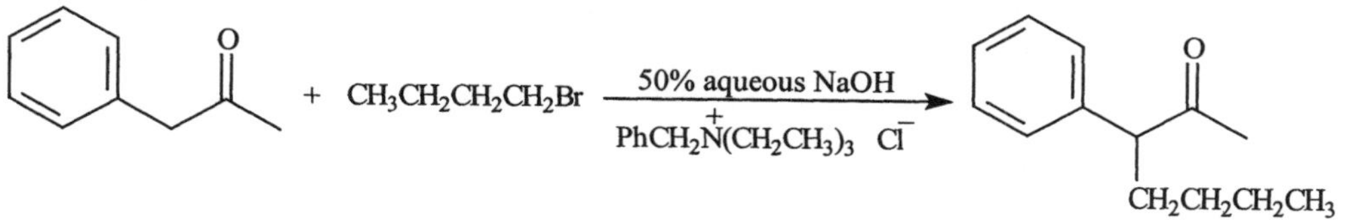

$$\text{phenyl-2-propanone} + CH_3CH_2CH_2CH_2Br \xrightarrow[PhCH_2\overset{+}{N}(CH_2CH_3)_3\ \overset{-}{Cl}]{\text{50\% aqueous NaOH}} \text{3-phenyl-2-heptanone } (CH_2CH_2CH_2CH_3)$$

Answer: The reaction that is occurring is a carbonyl α-substitution reaction. Hydroxide ion abstracts a proton from Cl on phenyl-2-propanone to generate an enolate ion, which then undergoes S_N2 attack at the primary carbon of bromobutane. However, since the organic layer and water layer are immiscible, the hydroxide is unable to come into contact with the ketone in the organic phase, so there is little or no reaction.

When the quaternary ammonium salt is added, it dissolves in both the aqueous and organic layers. When it moves into the organic layer, it takes hydroxide ion with it, to preserve the charge neutrality. Once in the organic layer, hydroxide ion reacts with the ketone to generate the enolate, which then undergoes S_N2 displacement of bromide to give the carbonyl α-substitution product.

Refer to the reaction below to answer the following questions:

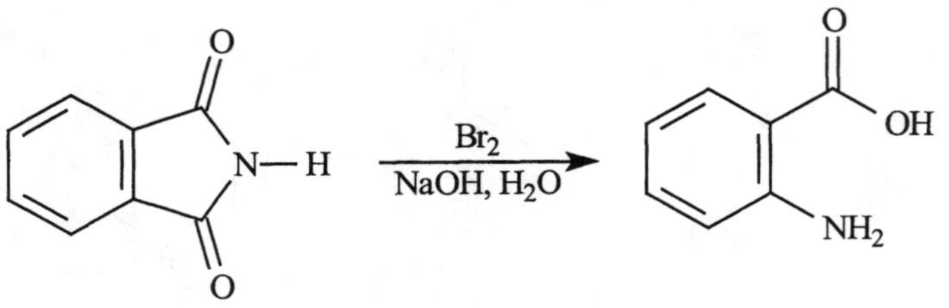

23. Draw arrows on the structures provided below which show electron flow in the complete stepwise mechanism for the reaction above.

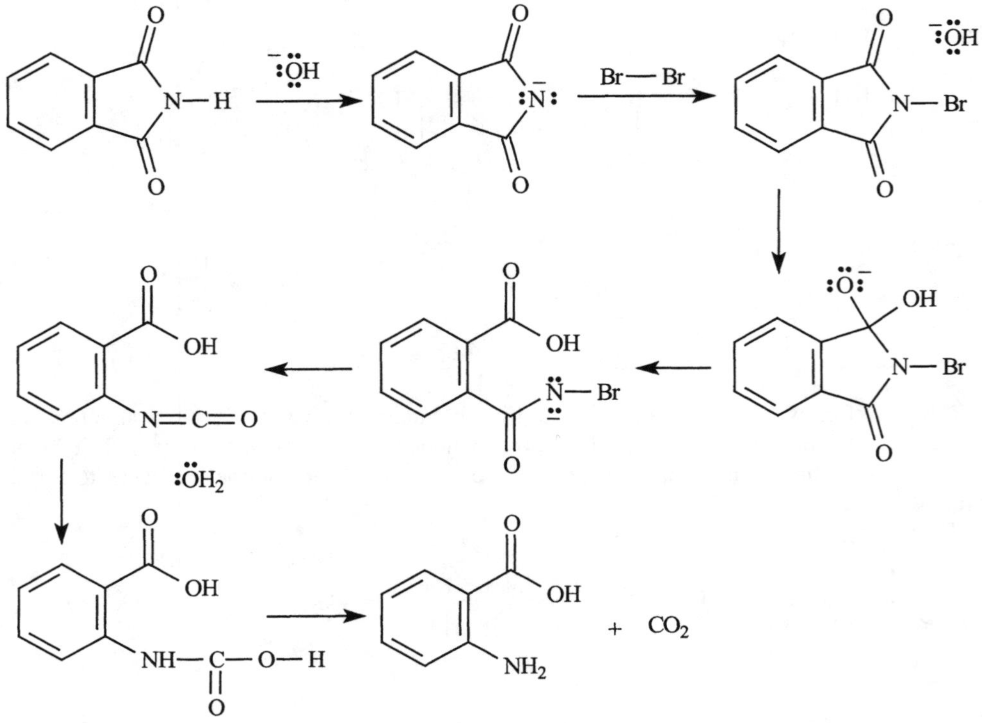

Answer:

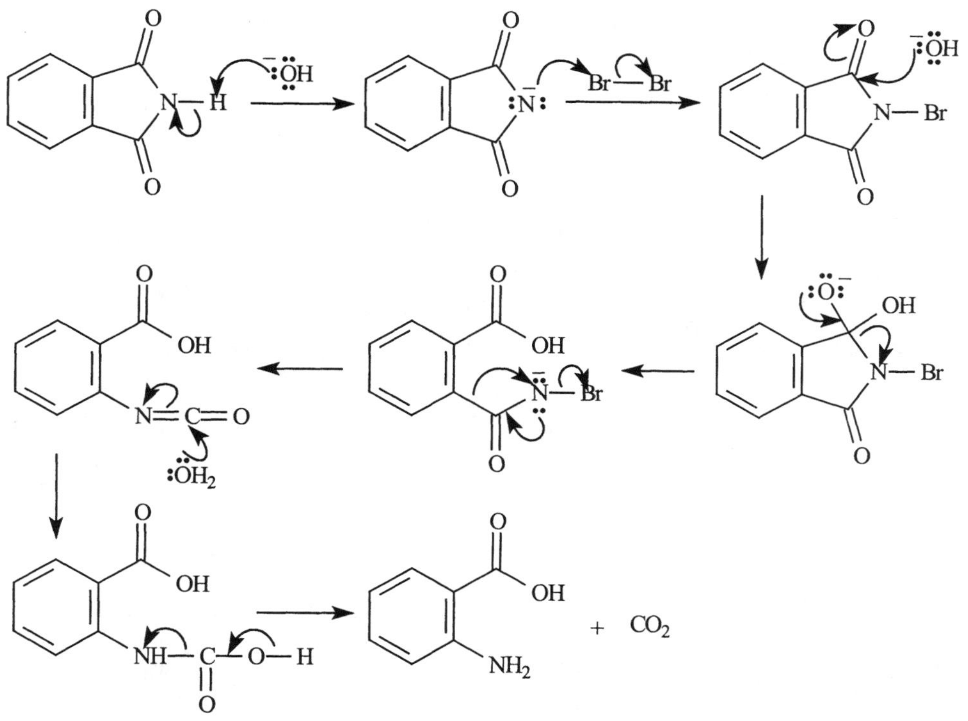

24. This reaction is an example of:

a. a Curtius rearrangement
b. a Hofmann elimination reaction
c. a Gabriel synthesis
d. a Hofmann rearrangement

Answer: d

Give the major organic product(s) of each of the following reactions or sequences of reactions. Show all relevant stereochemistry.

25. Toluene (CH_3) $\xrightarrow[H_2SO_4]{HNO_3}$ $\xrightarrow[\text{ethanol}]{H_2/Pt}$

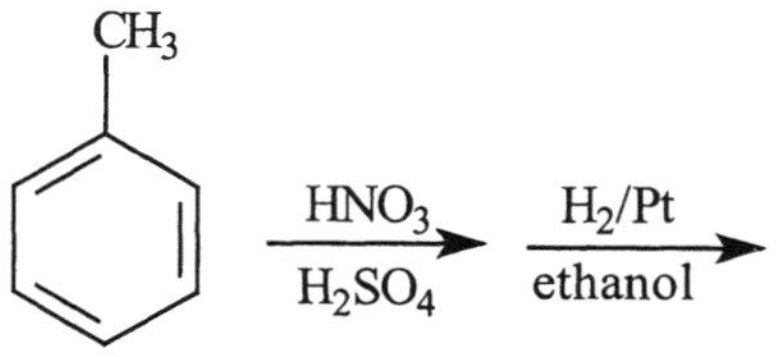

Answer:

Toluene (CH_3) $\xrightarrow[H_2SO_4]{HNO_3}$ $\xrightarrow[\text{ethanol}]{H_2/Pt}$ p-toluidine (CH_3, NH_2) + o-toluidine (CH_3, NH_2)

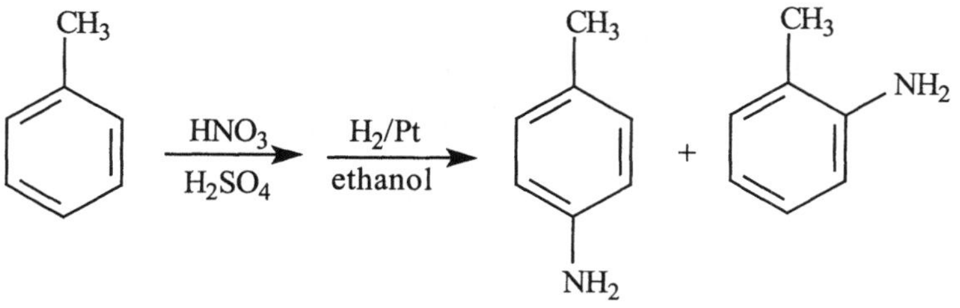

26. $H_2N-C_6H_4-CH_3$ $\xrightarrow[\text{pyridine}]{(CH_3CO)_2O}$ $\xrightarrow{Br_2,\ H_2O}$

Answer:

$H_2N-C_6H_4-CH_3$ $\xrightarrow[\text{pyridine}]{(CH_3CO)_2O}$ $\xrightarrow{Br_2,\ H_2O}$ $H_3C\overset{O}{\overset{\|}{C}}HN$–(ring with Br)–$CH_3$

27. (branched alkyl) Br $\xrightarrow{NaN_3}$ $\xrightarrow[\text{2. } H_2O]{\text{1. } LiAlH_4\text{, ether}}$

Answer:

(branched alkyl) Br $\xrightarrow{NaN_3}$ $\xrightarrow[\text{2. } H_2O]{\text{1. } LiAlH_4\text{, ether}}$ (branched alkyl) NH_2

28. $C_6H_5-NH\overset{O}{\overset{\|}{C}}CH_3$ $\xrightarrow[AlCl_3]{CH_3\overset{O}{\overset{\|}{C}}Cl}$ $\xrightarrow[H_2O]{NaOH}$

Answer:

$C_6H_5-NH\overset{O}{\overset{\|}{C}}CH_3$ $\xrightarrow[AlCl_3]{CH_3\overset{O}{\overset{\|}{C}}Cl}$ $\xrightarrow[H_2O]{NaOH}$ $CH_3\overset{O}{\overset{\|}{C}}-C_6H_4-NH_2$

29. (cyclohexanone) =O + (isopropyl) NH_2 $\xrightarrow{H_2/Pd}$

Answer:

(cyclohexanone) =O + (isopropyl) NH_2 $\xrightarrow{H_2/Pd}$ (cyclohexyl)–N(H)–(isopropyl)

30. 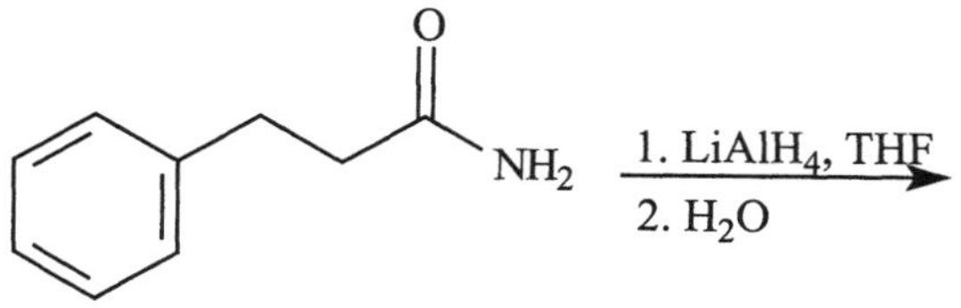 O NH_2 $\xrightarrow[\text{2. } H_2O]{\text{1. } LiAlH_4\text{, THF}}$

Answer:

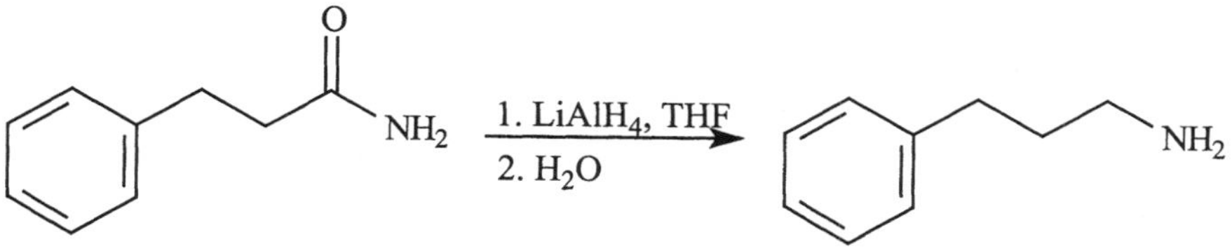

O NH_2 $\xrightarrow[\text{2. } H_2O]{\text{1. } LiAlH_4\text{, THF}}$ NH_2

31. 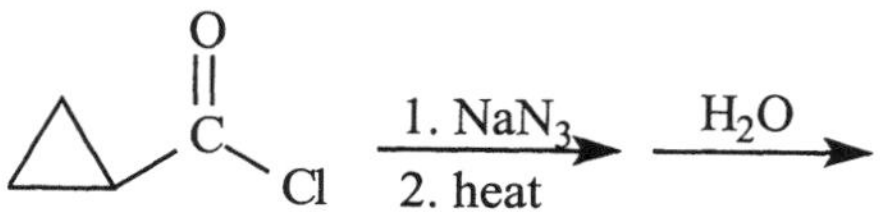 O C Cl $\xrightarrow[\text{2. heat}]{\text{1. } NaN_3}$ $\xrightarrow{H_2O}$

Answer:

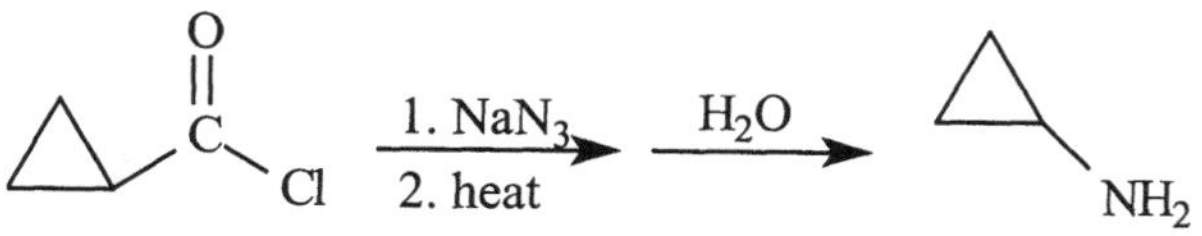

O C Cl $\xrightarrow[\text{2. heat}]{\text{1. } NaN_3}$ $\xrightarrow{H_2O}$ NH_2

32. 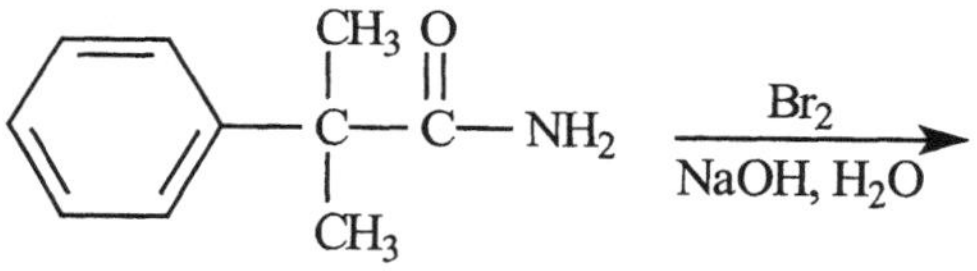 CH_3 O C—C—NH_2 CH_3 $\xrightarrow[NaOH\text{, } H_2O]{Br_2}$

Answer:

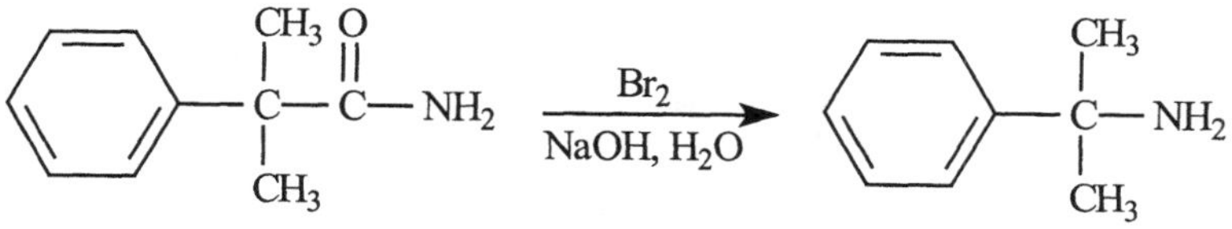

CH_3 O C—C—NH_2 CH_3 $\xrightarrow[NaOH\text{, } H_2O]{Br_2}$ CH_3 C—NH_2 CH_3

33. 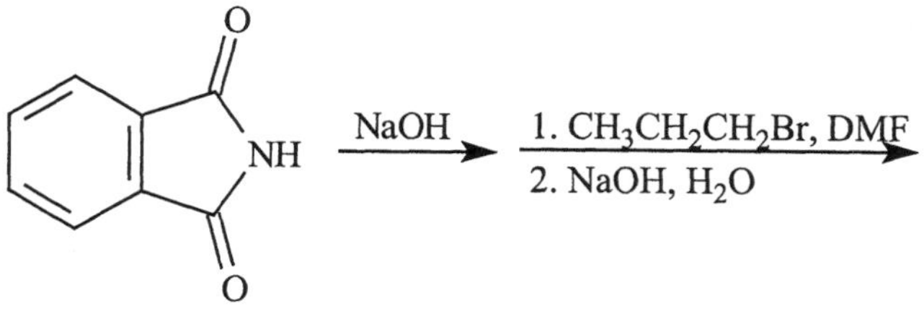 O NH O $\xrightarrow{NaOH}$ $\xrightarrow[\text{2. NaOH, } H_2O]{\text{1. } CH_3CH_2CH_2Br\text{, DMF}}$

Answer:

O NH O $\xrightarrow{NaOH}$ $\xrightarrow[\text{2. NaOH, } H_2O]{\text{1. } CH_3CH_2CH_2Br\text{, DMF}}$ $CH_3CH_2CH_2NH_2$

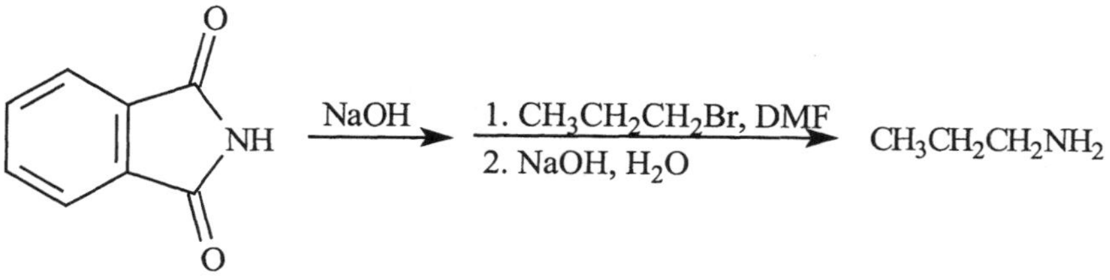

34. 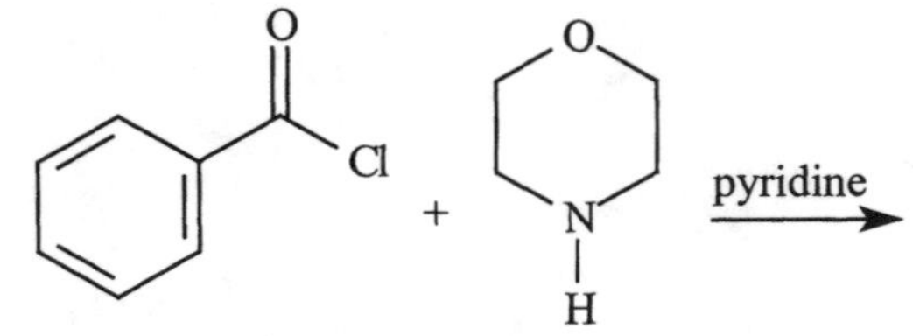 + pyridine $\longrightarrow$

O
Cl
O
N
H

Answer:

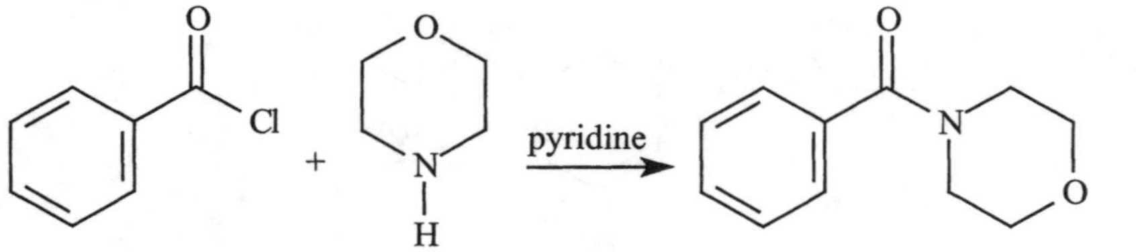

O
Cl
+
O
N
H
pyridine $\longrightarrow$
O
N
O

35. 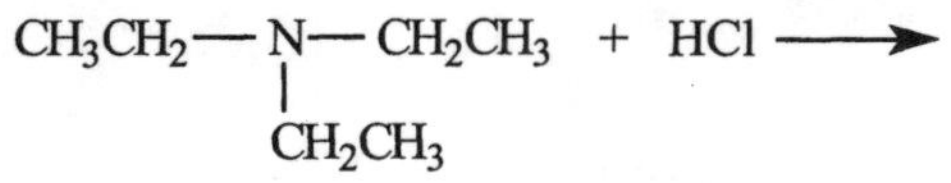 $CH_3CH_2—N—CH_2CH_3$ + HCl $\longrightarrow$
CH_2CH_3 (on N)

Answer:

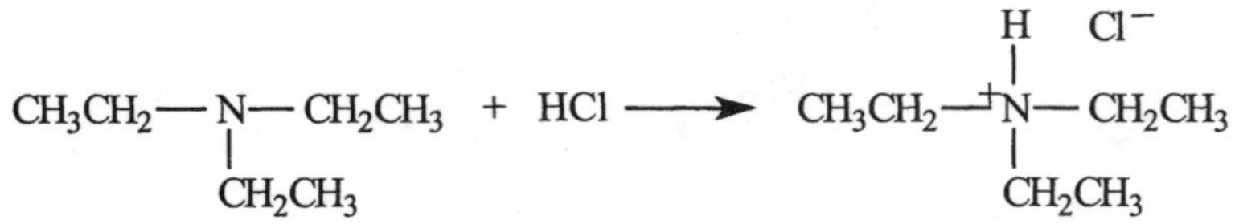

$CH_3CH_2—N—CH_2CH_3$ + HCl $\longrightarrow$ $CH_3CH_2—\overset{+}{N}H—CH_2CH_3$ Cl^-
CH_2CH_3 (on N, reactant and product)

36.

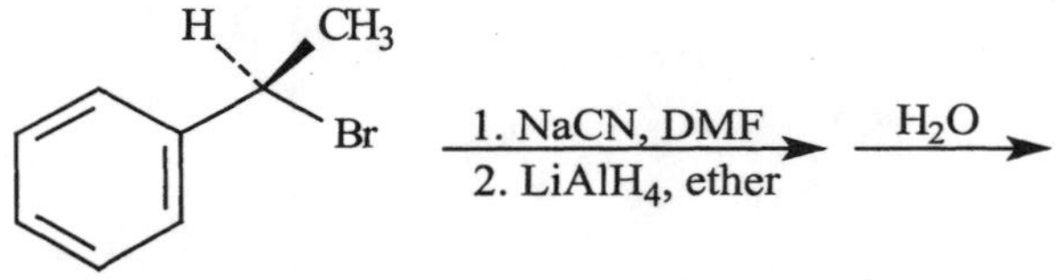

H CH_3
Br
1. NaCN, DMF
2. $LiAlH_4$, ether
H_2O

Answer:

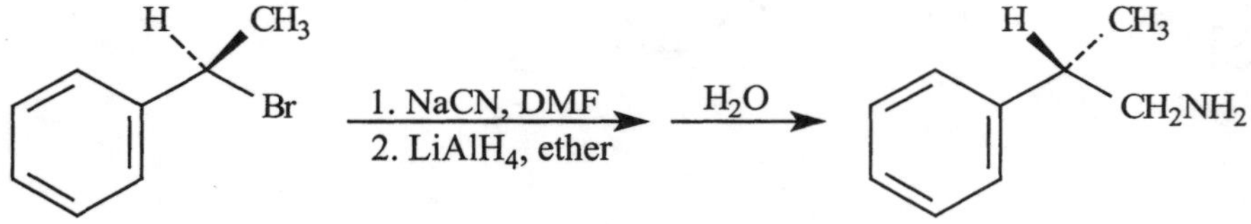

H CH_3
Br
1. NaCN, DMF
2. $LiAlH_4$, ether
H_2O
H CH_3
CH_2NH_2

37.

CH_3
N
H
1. CH_3I (excess)
2. Ag_2O, H_2O
3. heat

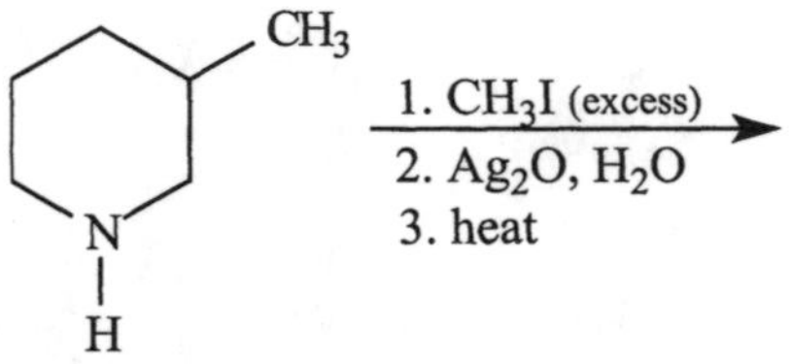

Answer:

CH_3
N
H
1. CH_3I (excess)
2. Ag_2O, H_2O
3. heat
CH_3
N
CH_3
CH_3

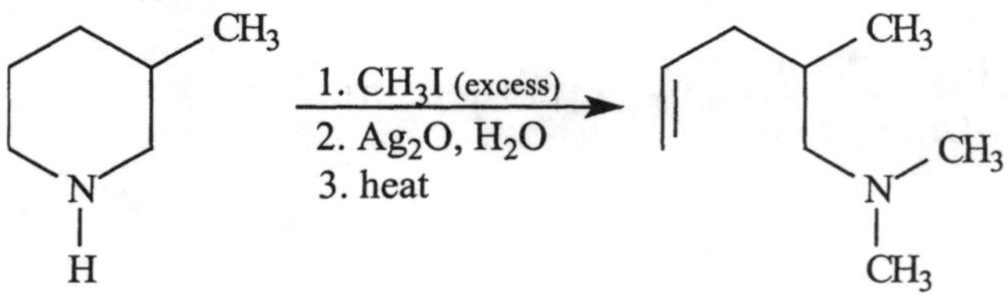

38. [2,6-dibromo-4-methylaniline: NH_2, Br, Br, CH_3] $\xrightarrow[H_2SO_4]{HNO_2}$ $\xrightarrow{CuCl}$

Answer:

[NH_2, Br, Br, CH_3] $\xrightarrow[H_2SO_4]{HNO_2}$ $\xrightarrow{CuCl}$ [Cl, Br, Br, CH_3]

39. [C6H5–$NHCOCH_3$ (O)] $\xrightarrow[2.\ NH_3,\ H_2O]{1.\ HOSO_2Cl}$

Answer:

[C6H5–$NHCOCH_3$ (O)] $\xrightarrow[2.\ NH_3,\ H_2O]{1.\ HOSO_2Cl}$ $H_2N—S(O)(O)$–C6H4–$NHCOCH_3$ (O)

40. [NH_2, CH_3] $\xrightarrow[2.\ NaI]{1. HNO_2,\ H_2SO_4}$

Answer:

[NH_2, CH_3] $\xrightarrow[2.\ NaI]{1. HNO_2,\ H_2SO_4}$ [I, CH_3]

41. [Br, Cl, Cl, NH_2] $\xrightarrow[2.\ H_3PO_2]{1.\ HNO_2,\ H_2SO_4}$

Answer:

Br–C6H2(Cl)2–NH2 (4-bromo-2,6-dichloroaniline) $\xrightarrow[\text{2. } H_3PO_2]{\text{1. } HNO_2,\ H_2SO_4}$ Br–C6H3(Cl)2 (1-bromo-3,5-dichlorobenzene)

42. O_2N–C6H4–NH_2 $\xrightarrow[\text{2. } C_6H_5OH]{\text{1. } HNO_2,\ H_2SO_4}$

Answer:

O_2N–C6H4–NH_2 $\xrightarrow[\text{2. } C_6H_5OH]{\text{1. } HNO_2,\ H_2SO_4}$ O_2N–C6H4–N=N–C6H4–OH

43. H_3C–C6H4–$\overset{+}{N}\equiv N$ HSO_4^- $\xrightarrow[CuCN]{KCN}$

Answer:

H_3C–C6H4–$\overset{+}{N}\equiv N$ HSO_4^- $\xrightarrow[CuCN]{KCN}$ H_3C–C6H4–CN

44. 3-methylaniline (NH_2, CH_3) $\xrightarrow[H_2SO_4]{HNO_2}$ $\xrightarrow{CuBr}$

Answer:

3-methylaniline (NH_2, CH_3) $\xrightarrow[H_2SO_4]{HNO_2}$ $\xrightarrow{CuBr}$ 3-bromotoluene (Br, CH_3)

45. 3-chloroaniline (Cl, NH_2) $\xrightarrow[H_2SO_4]{HNO_2}$ $\xrightarrow[Cu(NO_3)_2,\ H_2O]{Cu_2O}$

Answer:

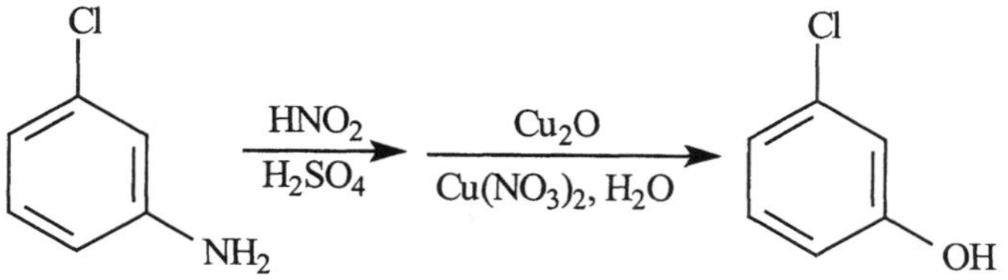

Cl, NH_2 (3-chloroaniline) $\xrightarrow[H_2SO_4]{HNO_2}$ $\xrightarrow[Cu(NO_3)_2,\ H_2O]{Cu_2O}$ Cl, OH (3-chlorophenol)

Show how each of the following transformations might be best accomplished. More than one step may be required. Show all reagents and all intermediate structures.

46. $CH_3CH_2—C(CH_3)_2—Br \longrightarrow CH_3CH_2—C(CH_3)_2—NH_2$

Answer:

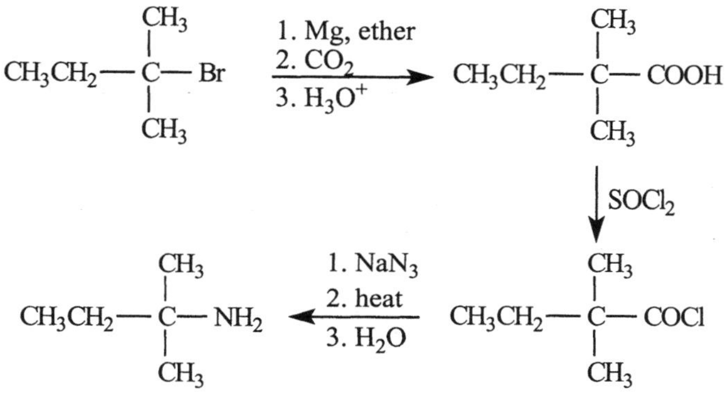

$CH_3CH_2—C(CH_3)_2—Br$ $\xrightarrow{\text{1. Mg, ether; 2. } CO_2\text{; 3. } H_3O^+}$ $CH_3CH_2—C(CH_3)_2—COOH$

$\downarrow SOCl_2$

$CH_3CH_2—C(CH_3)_2—COCl$ $\xrightarrow{\text{1. } NaN_3\text{; 2. heat; 3. } H_2O}$ $CH_3CH_2—C(CH_3)_2—NH_2$

47. (benzoic acid: O, OH) $\longrightarrow$ (dibenzylamine: N, H)

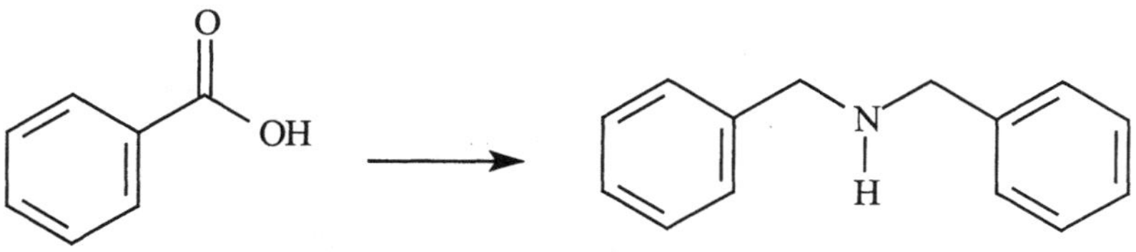

only source of carbon

Answer:

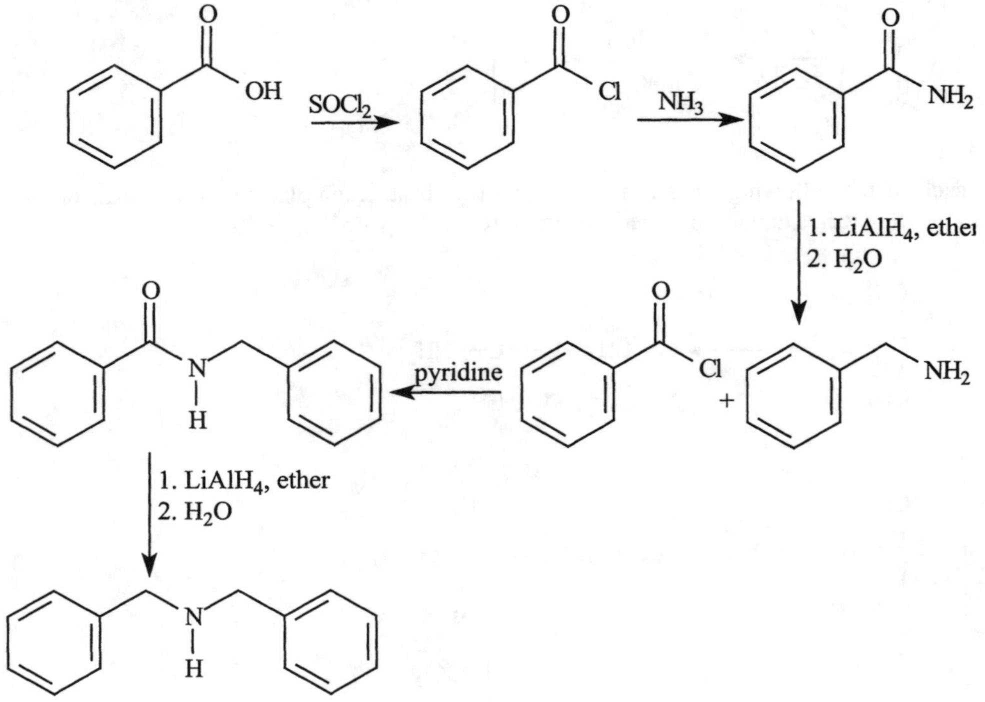

SOCl$_2$ → NH$_3$ → 1. LiAlH$_4$, ether 2. H$_2$O

O OH Cl NH$_2$

pyridine

O N H Cl + NH$_2$

1. LiAlH$_4$, ether
2. H$_2$O

N H

48. OH → NH$_2$

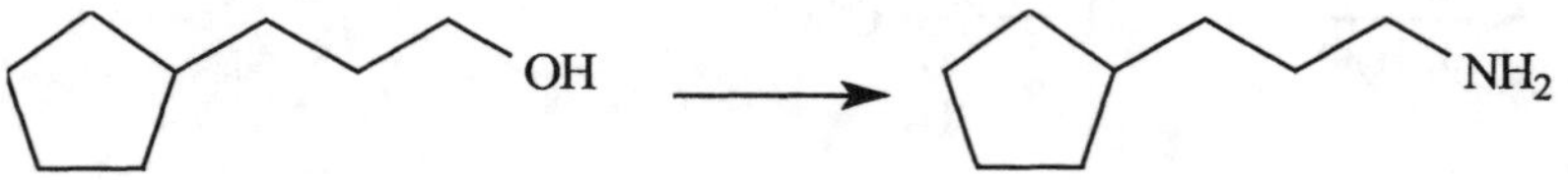

Answer:

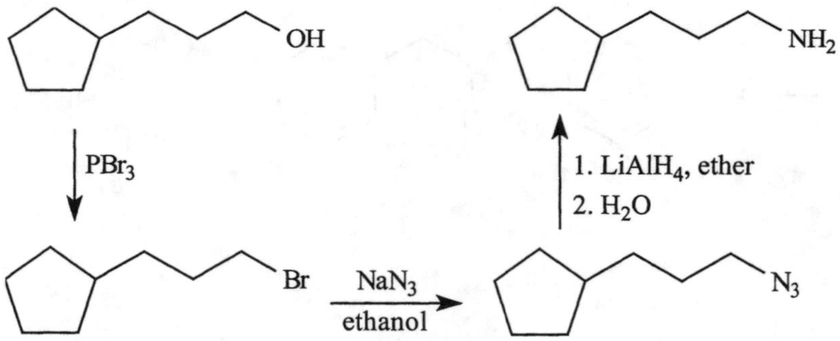

OH NH$_2$

PBr$_3$

1. LiAlH$_4$, ether
2. H$_2$O

Br NaN$_3$ ethanol → N$_3$

49. CH$_3$ → CH$_3$ CN

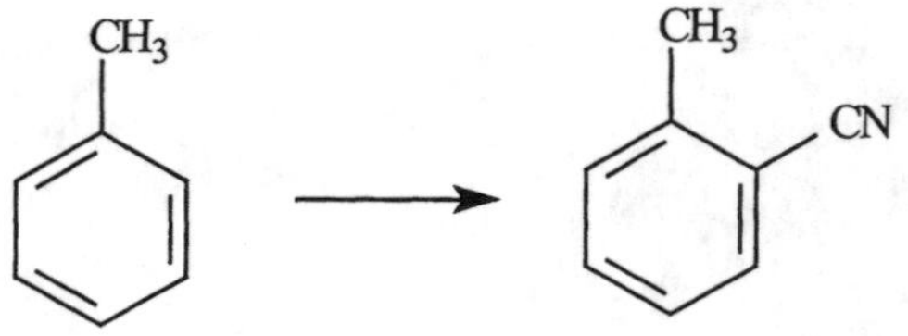

Answer:

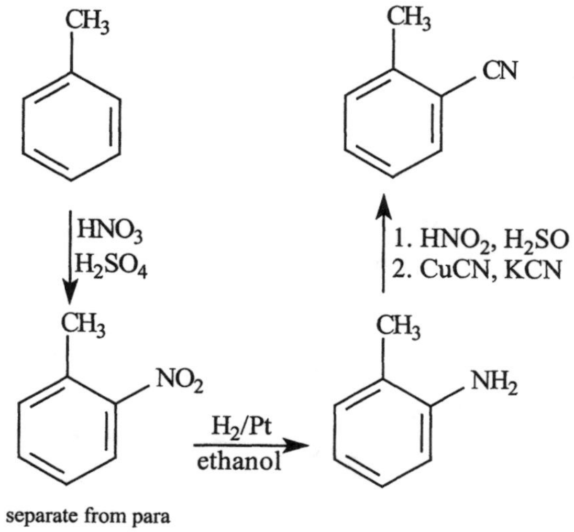

CH_3 → HNO_3, H_2SO_4 → CH_3, NO_2 (separate from para) → H_2/Pt, ethanol → CH_3, NH_2 → 1. HNO_2, H_2SO 2. CuCN, KCN → CH_3, CN

separate from para

50. → Cl, Cl

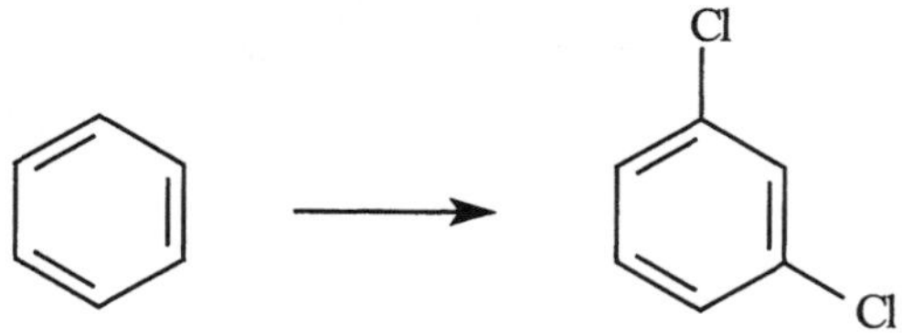

Answer:

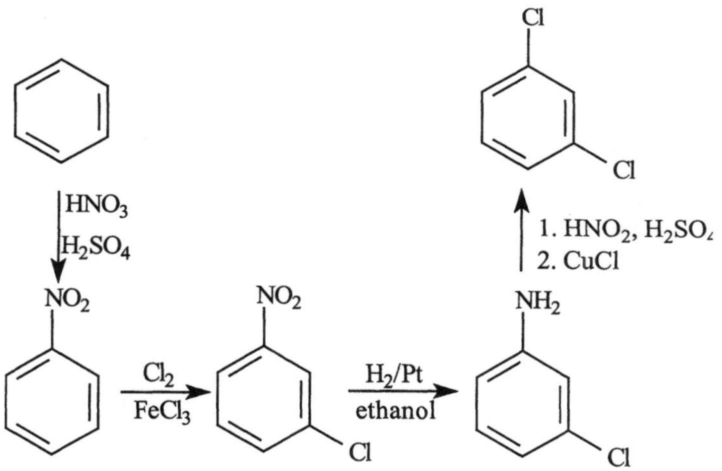

HNO_3, H_2SO_4 → NO_2 → Cl_2, $FeCl_3$ → NO_2, Cl → H_2/Pt, ethanol → NH_2, Cl → 1. HNO_2, H_2SO_4 2. CuCl → Cl, Cl

Choose the ***best*** series of reactions for accomplishing each conversion below.

51. Benzene $\longrightarrow$ 3-chlorobenzylamine (ring with Cl and CH_2NH_2 meta)

A. $\xrightarrow[FeCl_3]{Cl_2}$ $\xrightarrow[KCN]{CuCN}$ $\xrightarrow[Ni]{H_2}$

B. $\xrightarrow[H_2SO_4]{HNO_3}$ $\xrightarrow[HCl]{Fe}$ $\xrightarrow[FeCl_3]{Cl_2}$ $\xrightarrow[2.\ CuCN,\ KCN]{1.\ HNO_2,\ H_2SO_4}$ $\xrightarrow{H_3O^+}$

C. $\xrightarrow[H_2SO_4]{HNO_3}$ $\xrightarrow[FeCl_3]{Cl_2}$ $\xrightarrow[HCl]{Fe}$ $\xrightarrow[2.\ CuCN,\ KCN]{1.\ HNO_2,\ H_2SO_4}$ $\xrightarrow[2.\ H_2O]{1.\ LiAlH_4}$

D. $\xrightarrow[FeCl_3]{Cl_2}$ $\xrightarrow[H_2SO_4]{HNO_3}$ $\xrightarrow[HCl]{Fe}$

Answer: C

52. Benzene $\longrightarrow$ 3-bromoaniline (ring with Br and NH_2 meta)

A. $\xrightarrow[FeBr_3]{Br_2}$ $\xrightarrow[H_2SO_4]{HNO_3}$ $\xrightarrow[Ni]{H_2}$

B. $\xrightarrow[H_2SO_4]{HNO_3}$ $\xrightarrow[HCl]{Fe}$ $\xrightarrow[FeBr_3]{Br_2}$

C. $\xrightarrow[H_2SO_4]{HNO_3}$ $\xrightarrow[FeBr_3]{Br_2}$ $\xrightarrow[HCl]{Fe}$

D. $\xrightarrow[H_2SO_4]{HNO_3}$ $\xrightarrow[HCl]{Fe}$ $\xrightarrow[H_2SO_4]{HNO_3}$ $\xrightarrow[2.\ CuBr,\ HBr]{1.\ HNO_2,\ H_2SO_4}$

Answer: C

53. (toluene, CH_3) ⟶ (m-iodobenzoic acid, I, COOH)

A. $\xrightarrow{KMnO_4}$ $\xrightarrow[H_2SO_4]{HNO_3}$ $\xrightarrow[HCl]{Fe}$ $\xrightarrow[2.\ NaI]{1.\ HNO_2,\ H_2SO_4}$

B. $\xrightarrow[H_2SO_4]{HNO_3}$ $\xrightarrow{KMnO_4}$ $\xrightarrow[HCl]{Fe}$ $\xrightarrow[2.\ NaI]{1.\ HNO_2,\ H_2SO_4}$

C. $\xrightarrow[H_2SO_4]{HNO_3}$ $\xrightarrow[HCl]{Fe}$ $\xrightarrow[2.\ NaI]{1.\ HNO_2,\ H_2SO_4}$ $\xrightarrow{KMnO_4}$

D. $\xrightarrow[H_2SO_4]{HNO_3}$ $\xrightarrow[HCl]{Fe}$ $\xrightarrow{KMnO_4}$ $\xrightarrow[2.\ NaI]{1.\ HNO_2,\ H_2SO_4}$

Answer: A

54. Mescaline is a hallucinogenic alkaloid isolated from peyote cactus. Synthesize mescaline from 3,4,5-trimethoxytoluene. Show all reagents and all intermediate structures.

(H_3CO, H_3CO, H_3CO — CH_3) ⟶ (H_3CO, H_3CO, H_3CO — $CH_2CH_2NH_2$) **mescaline**

Answer:

(H_3CO)$_3$-aryl — CH_3 $\xrightarrow{NBS}$ (H_3CO)$_3$-aryl — CH_2Br $\xrightarrow[ethanol]{NaCN}$ (H_3CO)$_3$-aryl — CH_2CN $\xrightarrow[2.\ H_2O]{1.\ LiAlH_4,\ ether}$ (H_3CO)$_3$-aryl — $CH_2CH_2NH_2$

Refer to the data below to answer the following questions:

Triclocarbon is a disinfectant prepared from 3,4-dichloroaniline and 4-chlorophenylisocyanate.

Cl— —N=C=O + H_2N— —Cl, Cl

↓

Cl— —NH—C(=O)—NH— —Cl, Cl

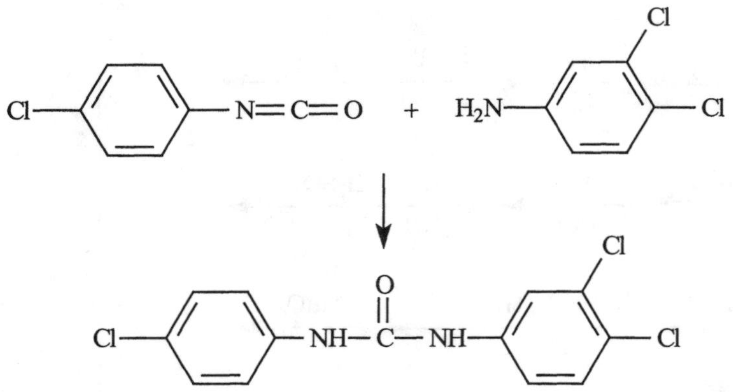

Triclocarban

55. Prepare 4-chlorophenylisocyanate from toluene.

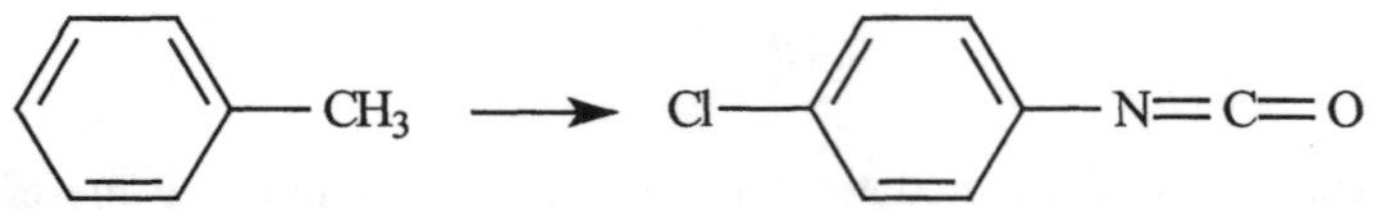

—CH_3 ⟶ Cl— —N=C=O

Answer:

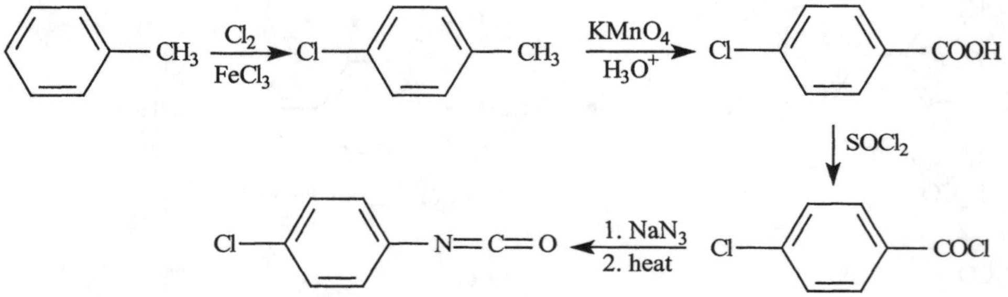

—CH_3 $\xrightarrow[FeCl_3]{Cl_2}$ Cl— —CH_3 $\xrightarrow[H_3O^+]{KMnO_4}$ Cl— —COOH

↓ $SOCl_2$

Cl— —N=C=O $\xleftarrow[2.\ heat]{1.\ NaN_3}$ Cl— —COCl

56. Prepare 3,4-dichloroaniline from benzene.

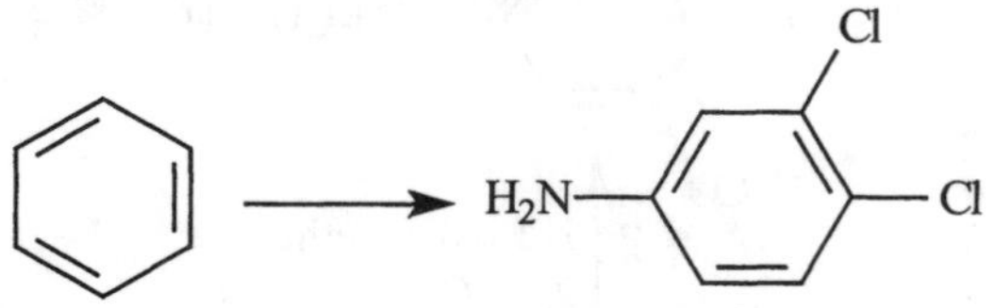

⟶ H_2N— —Cl, Cl

Answer:

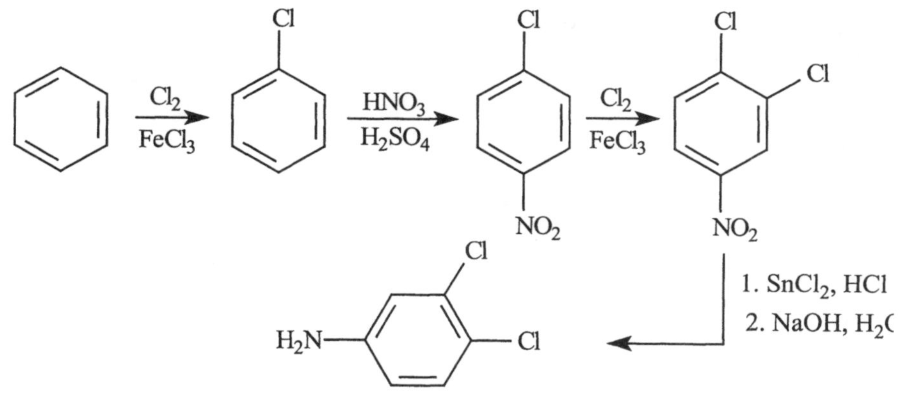

$\xrightarrow[FeCl_3]{Cl_2}$ $\xrightarrow[H_2SO_4]{HNO_3}$ $\xrightarrow[FeCl_3]{Cl_2}$

1. $SnCl_2$, HCl
2. NaOH, H_2O

57. Propose a mechanism for the reaction of 3,4-dichloroaniline and 4-chlorophenylisocyanate to yield Triclocarban.

Answer:

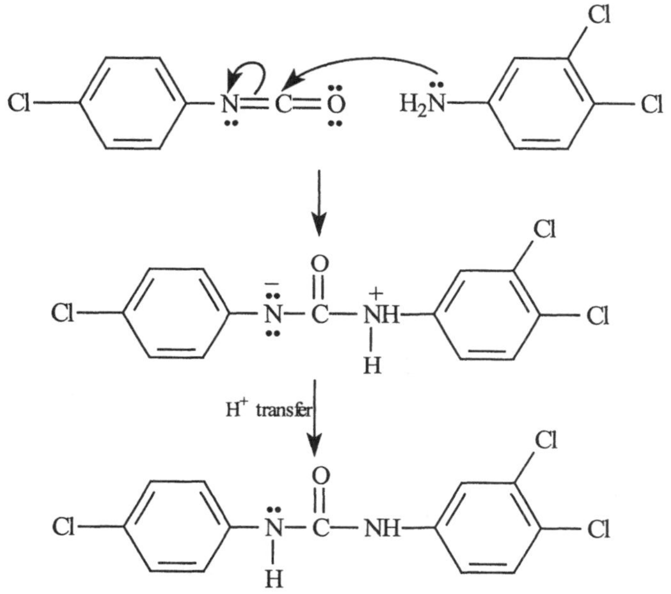

H^+ transfer

58. From the list provided below, choose the best reagent(s) for each step in the following synthesis. There is only one answer for each reaction.

a. $NaBH_4$, ethanol
b. KCN, acetone
c. 1. $LiAlH_4$, THF
   2. H_2O
d. 1. HNO_2, H_2SO_4
   2. CuCN
e. 1. $SnCl_2$, H_3O^+
   2. NaOH, H_2O
f. HNO_3, H_2SO_4

CH_3 / NO_2 → step 1 → CH_3 / NH_2 → step 2 → CH_3 / CN → step 3 → CH_3 / CH_2NH_2

Answer: step 1 = e; step 2 = d; step 3 = c

59. Draw the structures for each of the intermediates in the boxes provided for the synthesis below.

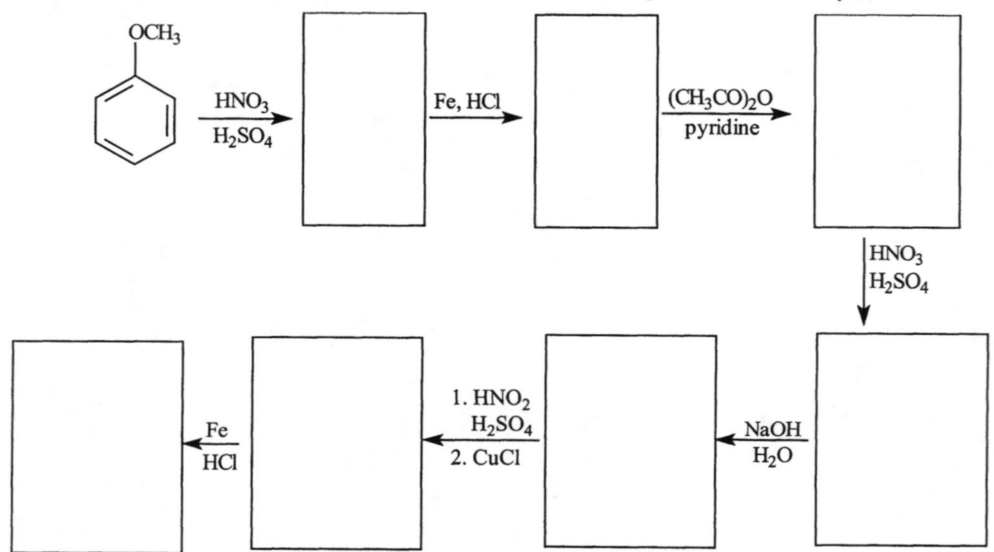

Answer:

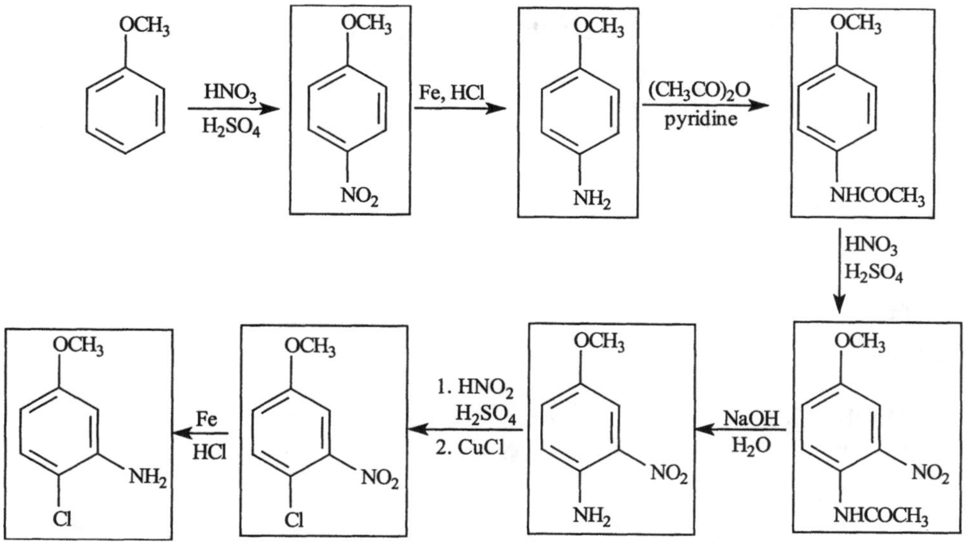

OCH_3 (benzene ring) $\xrightarrow[H_2SO_4]{HNO_3}$ OCH_3 / NO_2 $\xrightarrow{Fe,\ HCl}$ OCH_3 / NH_2 $\xrightarrow[pyridine]{(CH_3CO)_2O}$ OCH_3 / $NHCOCH_3$

$\downarrow$ HNO_3, H_2SO_4

OCH_3 / NO_2 / $NHCOCH_3$ $\xrightarrow[H_2O]{NaOH}$ OCH_3 / NO_2 / NH_2 $\xrightarrow[2.\ CuCl]{1.\ HNO_2,\ H_2SO_4}$ OCH_3 / NO_2 / Cl $\xrightarrow[HCl]{Fe}$ OCH_3 / NH_2 / Cl

60. Propose a structure that is consistent with the following spectral data:
MS: M^+ at $m/z = 77$
IR: 3350 cm^{-1} (weak, single band)
^1H NMR: δ1.05 (br s, 1H), δ1.15 (t, 6H), δ2.65 (q, 4H)

Answer: diethylamine, $(CH_3CH_2)_2NH$

Chapter 25 – Biomolecules: Carbohydrates

Convert the following Fischer projections into tetrahedral representations, and assign *R* or *S* stereochemistry to each.

1.

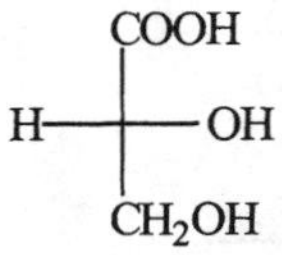

COOH
H — + — OH
CH_2OH

Answer:

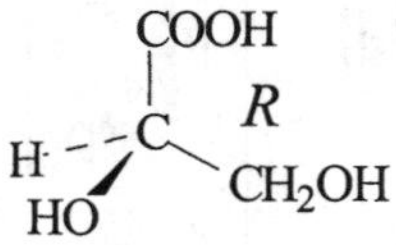

COOH
H - - C — CH_2OH
HO
R

2.

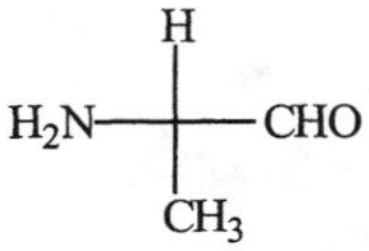

H
H_2N — + — CHO
CH_3

Answer:

H
H_2N - - C — CH_3
OHC
R

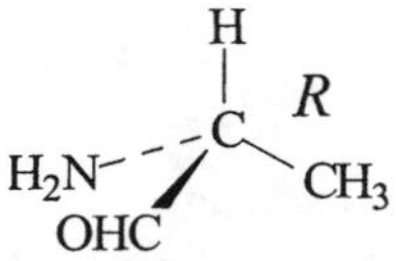

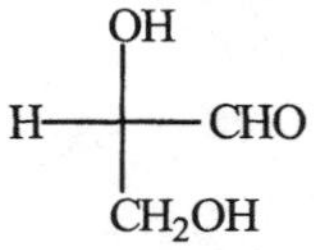

3.

OH
H — + — CHO
CH_2OH

Answer:

OH
H - - C — CH_2OH
OHC
S

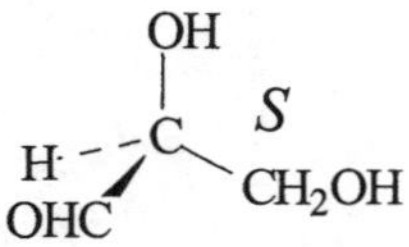

Label each pair of stereoisomers below as:

a. enantiomers b. diastereomers c. identical

Place the letter of the correct answer in the blank to the left of the pair of stereoisomers.

4.

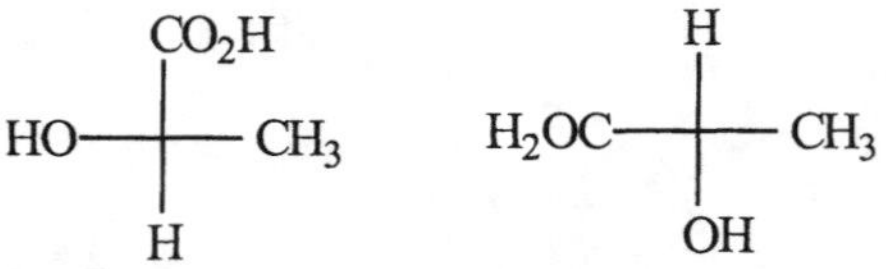

CO_2H
HO — + — CH_3
H

H
H_2OC — + — CH_3
OH

Answer: c

5.

CHO | CHO
HO—H | H—OH
H—OH | H—OH
H—OH | H—OH
CH_2OH | CH_2OH

Answer: b

6.

H; CH_3CH_2; C; CH_3; Cl

H; CH_3CH_2—CH_3; Cl

Answer: a

7. Draw a Fischer projection of (*2R,3S*) -dibromobutane.

Answer:

CH_3
Br—H
Br—H
CH_3

Refer to the monosaccharides below to answer each of the following questions:

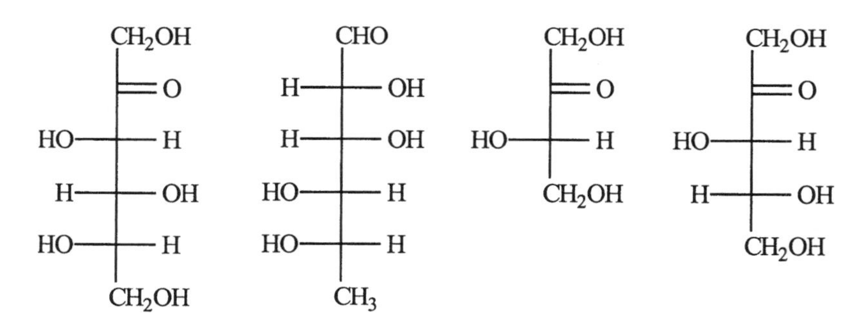

a. Sorbose b. Rhamnose c. Erythrulose d. Xylulose

Classify each sugar by type; for example, glucose is an aldohexose.

8. Xylulose is _____ .

Answer: a ketopentose

9. Erythrulose is _____ .

Answer: a ketotetrose

10. Sorbose is _____ .

Answer: a ketohexose

From the sugars above, choose the one that best fits each description below. Place the letter of the sugar in the blank to the left of the description. There is only one correct answer for each question.

11. _____ a D-sugar.

Answer: d

12. _____ a deoxy sugar.

Answer: b

13. _____ a sugar with three chirality centers.

Answer: a

14. _____ a sugar which yields a single alditol upon reduction.

Answer: b

15. Assign *R* or *S* configuration to each chirality center in sorbose.

Answer:

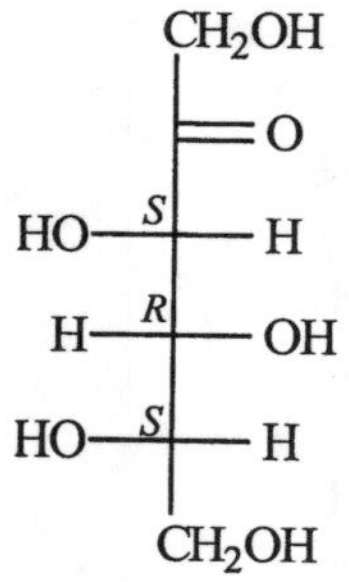

16. Name sorbose systematically.

Answer: (3*S*, 4*R*, 5*S*)-1,3,4,5,6-pentahydroxy-2-hexanone

17. Draw *both* chair conformations of the α-anomer of rhamnose in its pyranose form. Circle the *more* stable conformation.

Answer:

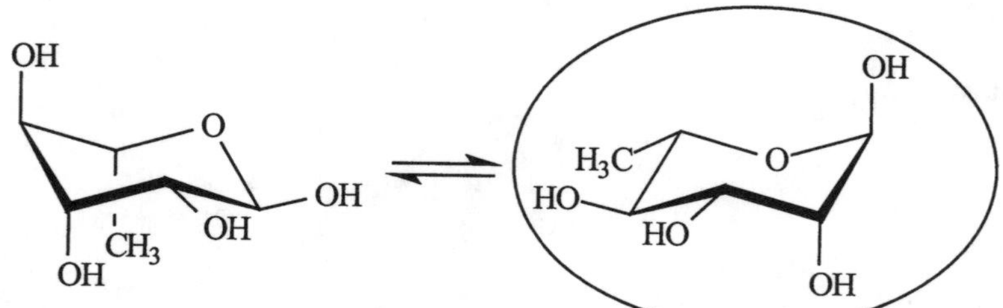

18. Provide the complete name for the α-anomer of rhamnose in its pyranose form.

Answer: α-L-Rhamnopyranose

Refer to the equilibrium below to answer the following questions.

ribose

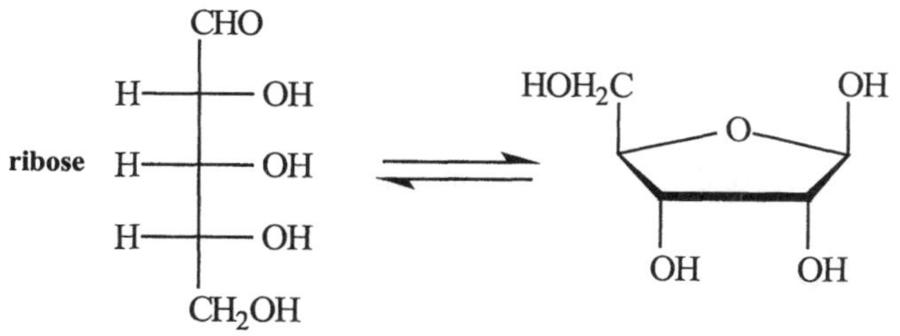

19. Classify ribose by carbonyl type and number of carbons.

Answer: Ribose is an aldopentose.

20. Which enantiomer of ribose is drawn, D or L?

Answer: D

21. The correct name for the cyclic structure is_______.

a. α-L-ribofuranose
b. β-D-ribofuranose
c. α-L-ribopyranose
d. β-D-ribopyranose

Answer: b

Refer to the sugars below to answer the following questions. Choose the sugar that best fits each description and place the letter of the sugar in the blank to the left of the description. There is only one correct answer for each question, but sugars may be used more than once.

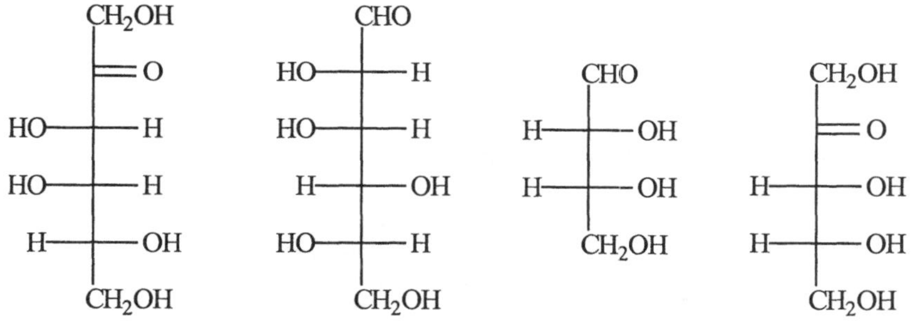

a. (-)-tagatose b. (+)- gulose c. (-)-erythrose d. (-)-ribulose

22. _____ a D-ketohexose

Answer: a

23. _____ oxidizes to an optically inactive aldaric acid

Answer: c

24. _____ a dextrorotary hexose

Answer: b

25. _____ a ketose with two chirality centers

Answer: d

26. The Fischer projection for D-idose corresponds to which pyranose below?

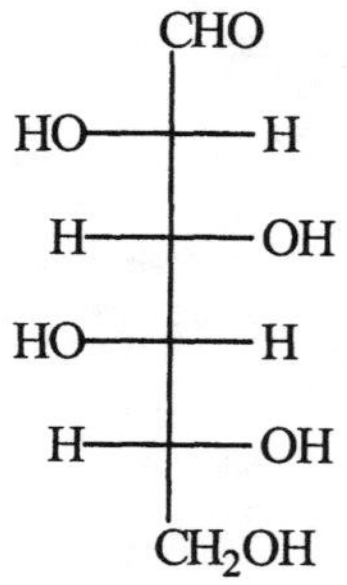

CHO
HO H
H OH
HO H
H OH
CH_2OH

D-iodose

a. 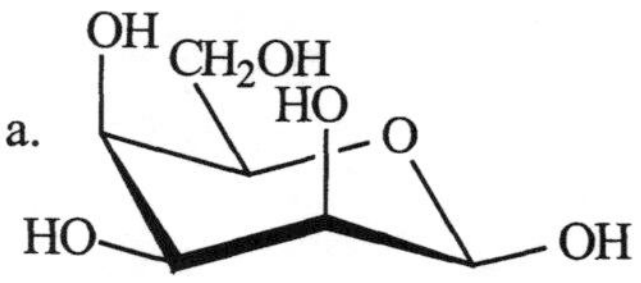

OH
CH_2OH
HO
O
HO
OH

b. 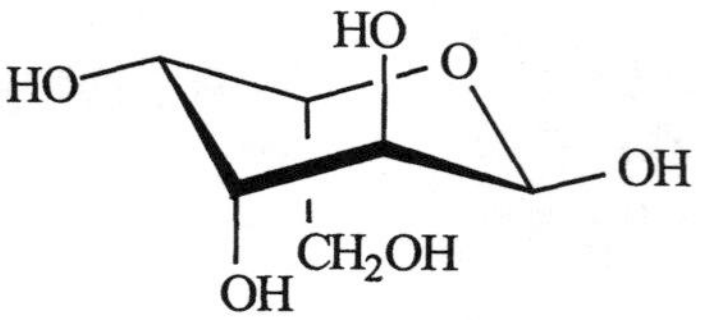

HO
HO
O
OH
CH_2OH
OH

c. 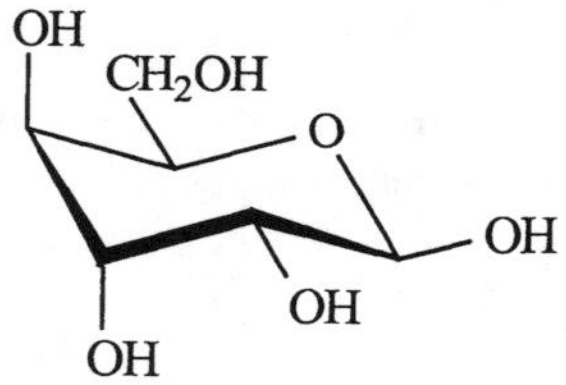

OH
CH_2OH
O
OH
OH
OH

d. 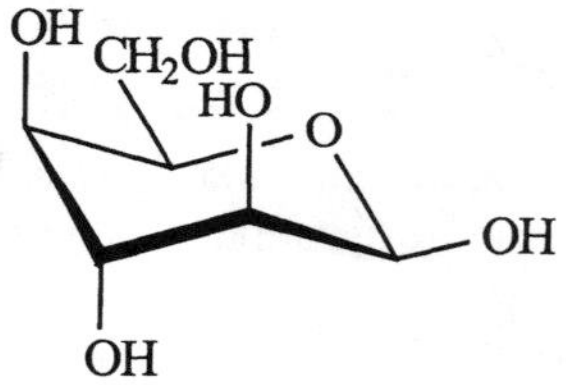

OH
CH_2OH
HO
O
OH
OH

Answer: d

27. What is the correct structure for α-D-glucopyranose?

a. 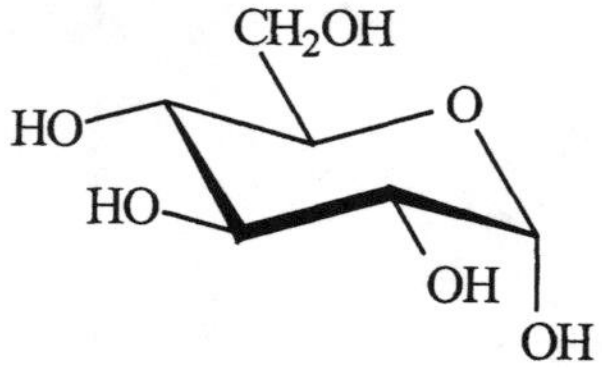

CH_2OH
HO
O
HO
OH
OH

b. 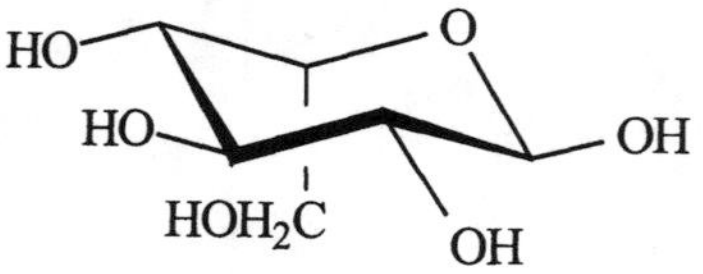

HO
O
HO
OH
HOH_2C
OH

c. 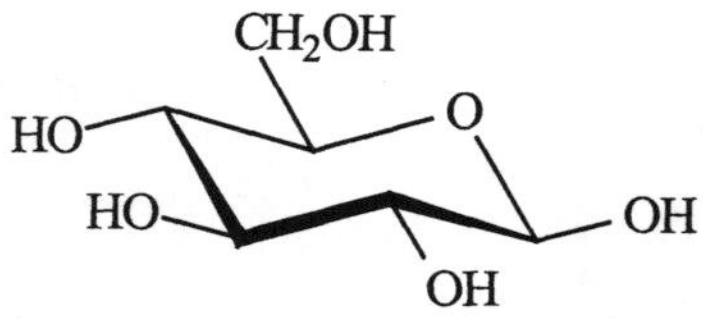

CH_2OH
HO
O
HO
OH
OH

d. 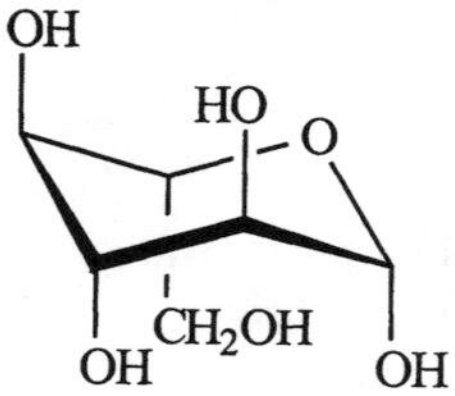

OH
HO
O
CH_2OH
OH
OH

Answer: a

What is the relationship between the following compounds?

28.

CHO | H–C–OH | H–C–OH | CH_2OH CHO | HO–C–H | HO–C–H | CH_2OH

a. anomers
b. meso compounds
c. enantiomers
d. equivalent structures

Answer: c

29.

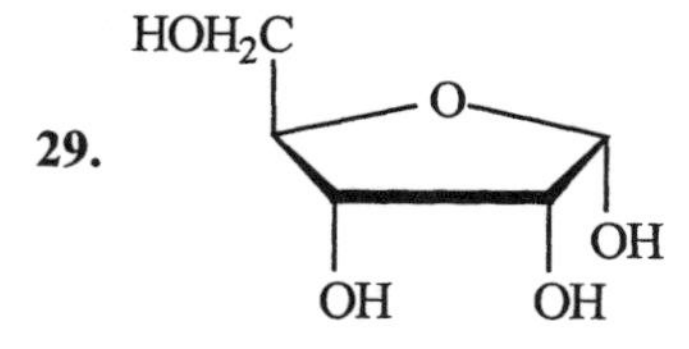

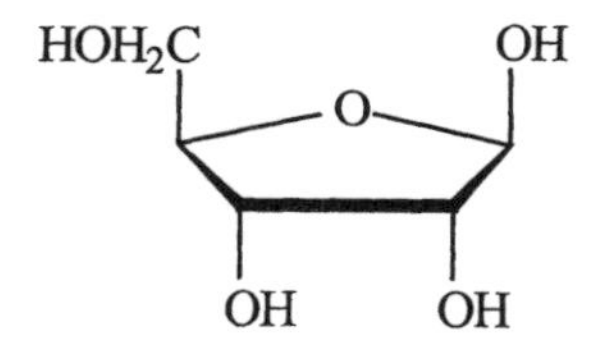

a. anomers
b. meso compounds
c. enantiomers
d. equivalent structures

Answer: a

Draw structures for the products you would expect to obtain from reaction of β-D-galactopyranose with each of the following reagents. Be sure to include all relevant stereochemistry.

HO, CH_2OH, O, HO, OH, OH

β-D-galactopyranose

30. CH_3I, Ag_2O

Answer:

H_3CO, CH_2OCH_3, O, H_3CO, OCH_3, OCH_3

31. warm dilute HNO_3

Answer:

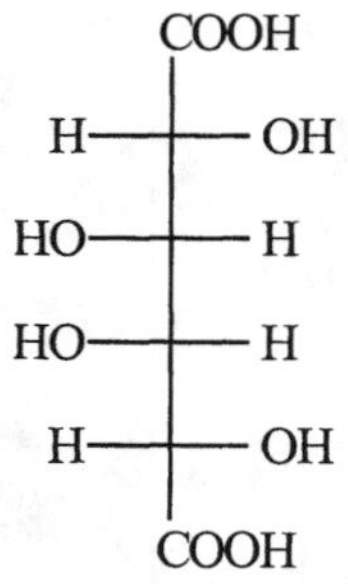

COOH
H— —OH
HO— —H
HO— —H
H— —OH
COOH

32. $(CH_3CO)_2O$, pryridine

Answer:

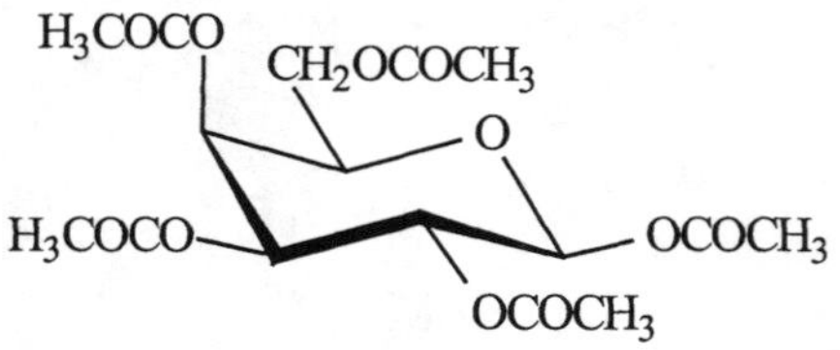

H_3COCO CH_2OCOCH_3 O
H_3COCO $OCOCH_3$
$OCOCH_3$

33. $NaBH_4$ in H_2O

Answer:

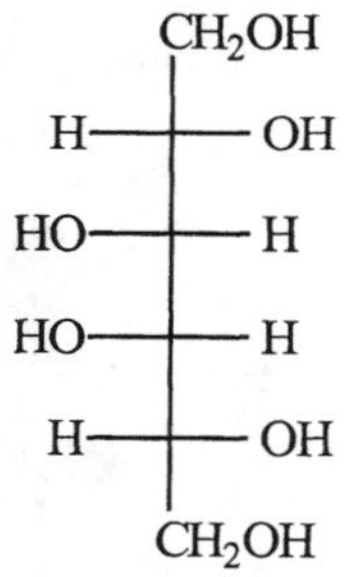

CH_2OH
H— —OH
HO— —H
HO— —H
H— —OH
CH_2OH

34. CH_3OH, HCl

Answer:

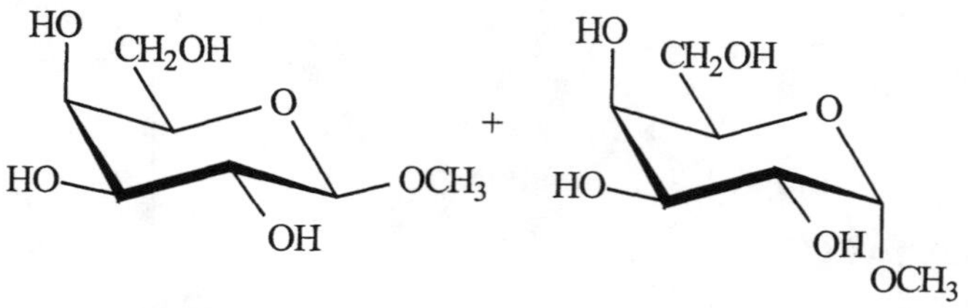

HO CH_2OH O
HO OCH_3
OH

\+

HO CH_2OH O
HO
OH OCH_3

35. 1. HCN
2. H_2, Pd/$BaSO_4$
3. H_3O^+

Answer:

```
         CHO                 CHO
    H ────┼──── OH     HO ────┼──── H
    H ────┼──── OH      H ────┼──── OH
   HO ────┼──── H   +  HO ────┼──── H
   HO ────┼──── H      HO ────┼──── H
    H ────┼──── OH      H ────┼──── OH
        CH2OH               CH2OH
```

36. Br_2, H_2O

Answer:

```
        COOH
    H ────┼──── OH
   HO ────┼──── H
   HO ────┼──── H
    H ────┼──── OH
        CH2OH
```

37. 1. H_2NOH
2. $(CH_3CO)_2O$, CH_3CO_2Na
3. $NaOCH_3$

Answer:

```
         CHO
   HO ────┼──── H
   HO ────┼──── H
    H ────┼──── OH
        CH2OH
```

Choose a structure from the list provided below that best fits each of the following descriptions. Place the letter of the structure in the blank to the left of the description. There is only one correct answer for each question.

A.

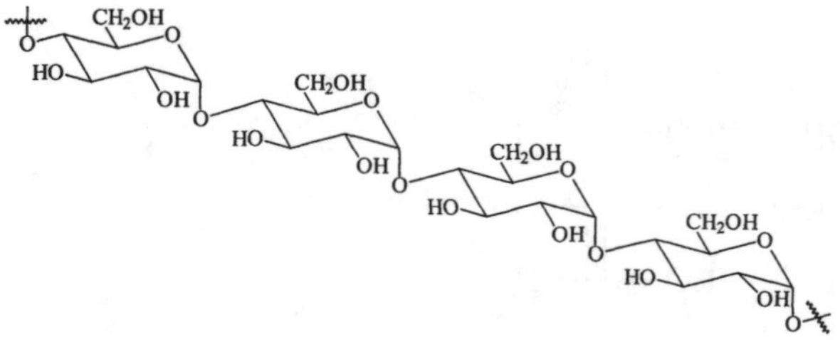

B.

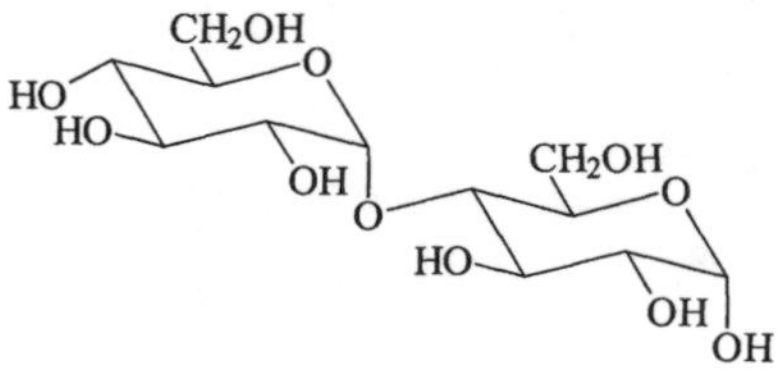

C.

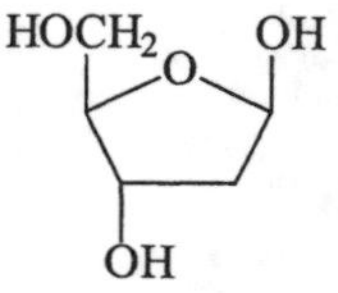

D.

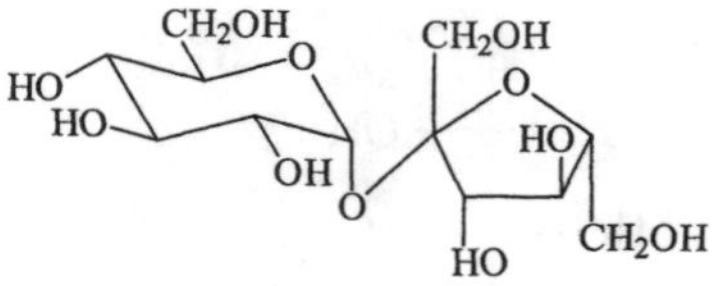

E.

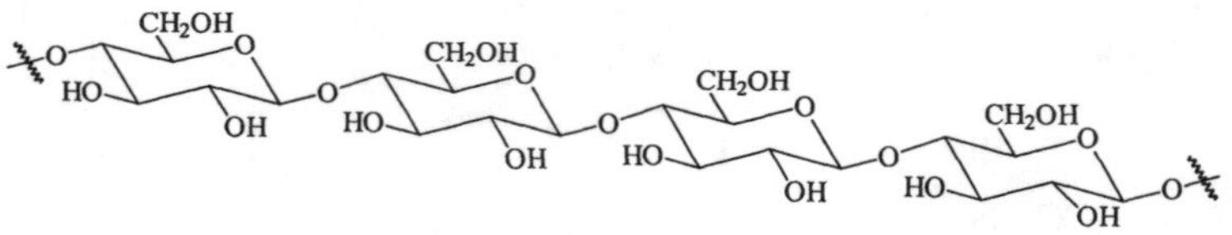

F.

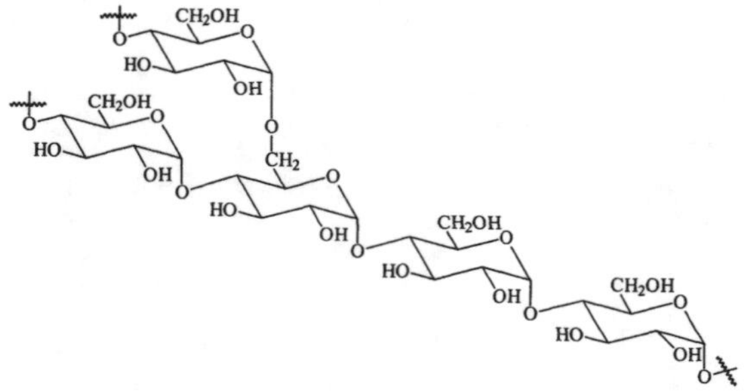

38. _____ a reducing monosaccharide

Answer: c

39. _____ a non-reducing disaccharide

Answer: d

40. _____ amylopectin

Answer: f

41. _____ a 1,4' β-glycoside

Answer: e

42. _____ cellulose

Answer: e

Choose a structure from the list provided below that best fits each of the following descriptions. Place the letter of the structure in the blank to the left of the description. There is only one correct answer for each question.

a. starch

b. cellulose

c. (chair structure: CH_2OH, O, HO, HO, HO, OH)

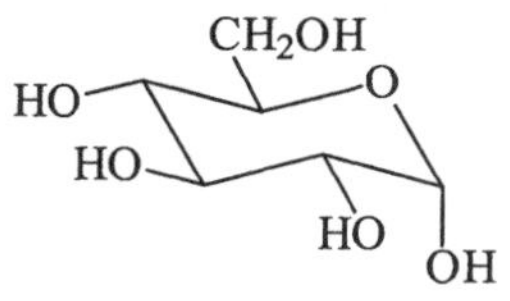

d. (Haworth structure: CH_2OH, O, OH, HO, OH, OH)

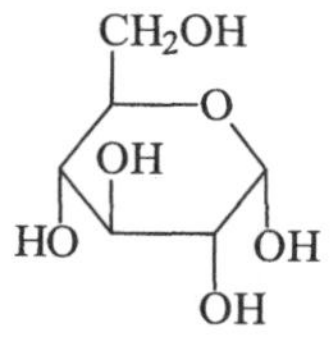

e. (Haworth structure: CH_2OH, O, H, OH, HO, OCH_3, OH)

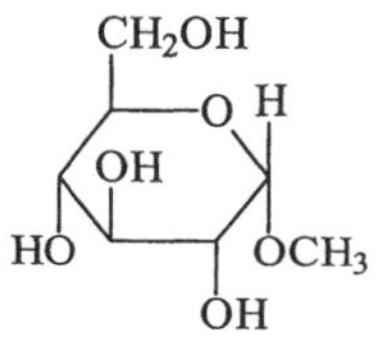

f. sucrose

43. _____ a monosaccharide that give a negative Benedict's Test.

Answer: e

44. _____ a β-1,4'-glycoside

Answer: b

45. _____ α-D-glucopyranose in a Haworth projection.

Answer: d

46. _____ a disaccharide

Answer: f

47. Fructose reduces Tollens' reagent even though it contains no aldehyde group. This occurs because fructose is readily isomerized to an aldose in basic solution. Write the complete stepwise mechanism for the base-catalyzed isomerization of fructose to an aldohexose. Show all intermediate structures and all electron flow with arrows.

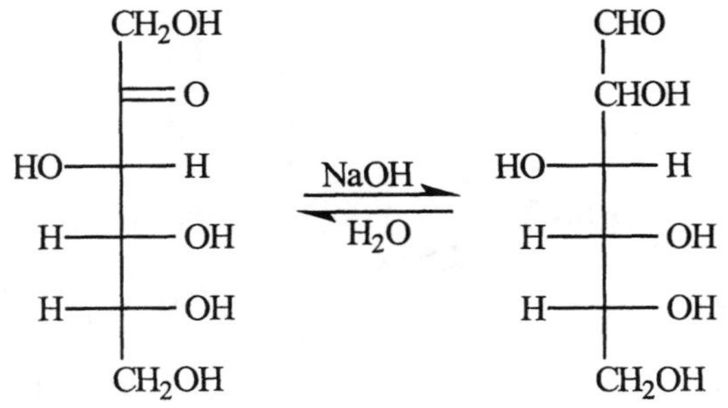

CH_2OH, C=O, HO–H, H–OH, H–OH, CH_2OH $\underset{H_2O}{\overset{NaOH}{\rightleftharpoons}}$ CHO, CHOH, HO–H, H–OH, H–OH, CH_2OH

Answer:

H, CHOH, C=O, HO–H, H–OH, H–OH, CH_2OH; :$\ddot{O}H^-$ $\rightleftharpoons$ CHOH, C–$\ddot{O}$:$^-$, HO–H, H–OH, H–OH, CH_2OH; H–OH

$\rightleftharpoons$

CH–O–H, C–$\ddot{O}H$, HO–H, H–OH, H–OH, CH_2OH; HO–H; :$\ddot{O}H^-$ $\rightleftharpoons$ CHO, CHOH, HO–H, H–OH, H–OH, CH_2OH

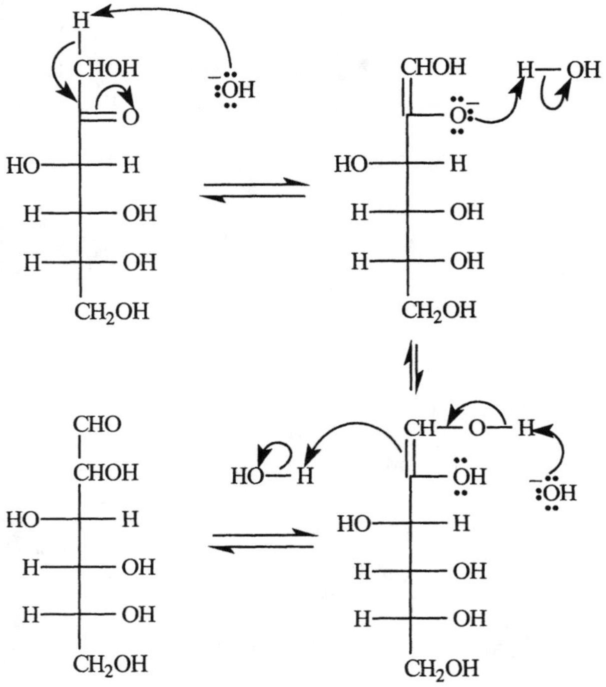

48. Melibiose is a reducing disaccharide that forms D-glucose and D-galactose on hydrolysis. Reaction of melibiose with iodomethane and silver iodide yields an octamethyl derivative, which can be hydrolyzed with aqueous acid to give one equivalent of 2,3,4,6-tera-*O*-methyl-D-galactopyranose and one equivalent of 2,3,4,-tri-*O*-methyl-D-glucopyranose. If melibiose contains an α-glycosidic bond, what is its structure?

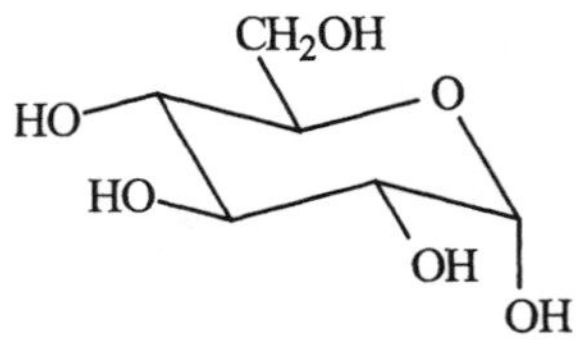

CH_2OH, O, HO, HO, OH, OH

α–D-glucopyranose

OH, CH_2OH, O, HO, OH, OH

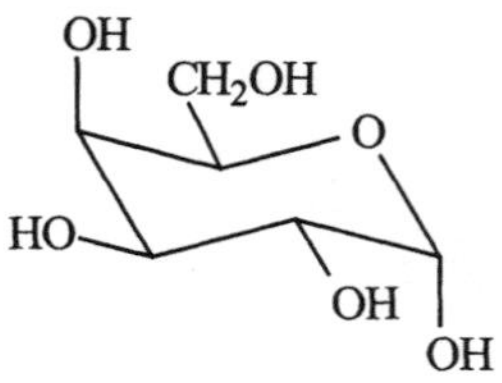

α–D-galactopyranose

Answer:

OH
CH_2OH
O
HO
OH
O
CH_2
O
HO
HO
OH
OH

Melibiose

6-O-(α-D-galactopyranosyl)-D-glucopyranose

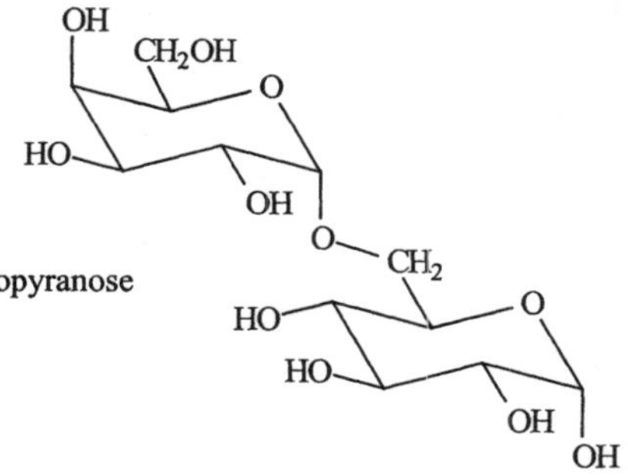

49. Compound U is an aldotetrose that can be oxidized to an optically active aldaric acid, compound V. On Wohl degradation, compound U is converted into D-glyceraldehyde. On Kiliani-Fischer chain extension, compound U is converted into compounds W and X. Compound W can be oxidized to an optically inactive aldaric acid, compound Y, but compound X is oxidized to an optically active aldaric acid Z. What are the structures of compounds U-Z?

Answer:

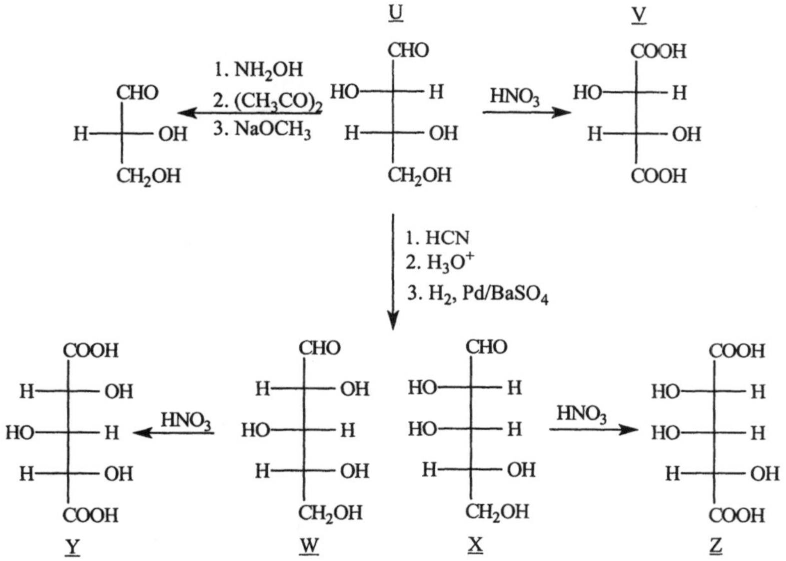

D-glyceraldehyde: CHO; H—OH; CH_2OH

← 1. NH_2OH 2. $(CH_3CO)_2$ 3. $NaOCH_3$

U: CHO; HO—H; H—OH; CH_2OH

HNO_3 →

V: COOH; HO—H; H—OH; COOH

↓ 1. HCN 2. H_3O^+ 3. H_2, $Pd/BaSO_4$

Y: COOH; H—OH; HO—H; H—OH; COOH

← HNO_3

W: CHO; H—OH; HO—H; H—OH; CH_2OH

X: CHO; HO—H; HO—H; H—OH; CH_2OH

HNO_3 →

Z: COOH; HO—H; HO—H; H—OH; COOH

Consider the reaction below to answer the following questions.

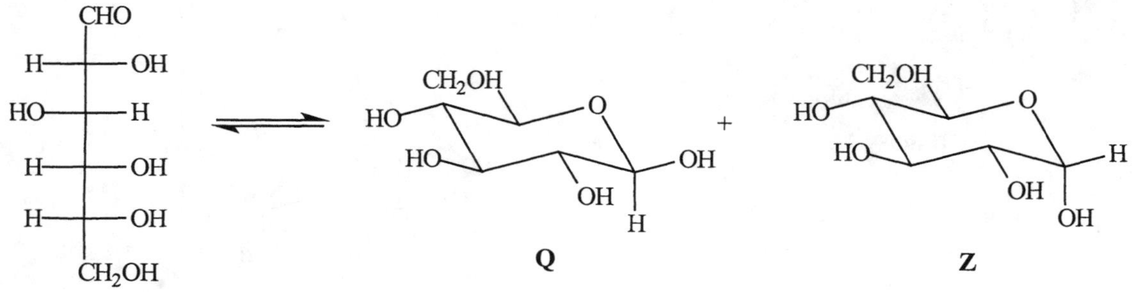

$$\text{Fischer projection (CHO; H–OH; HO–H; H–OH; H–OH; CH}_2\text{OH)} \rightleftharpoons \mathbf{Q} + \mathbf{Z}$$

(Structures: Q and Z are chair pyranose forms bearing CH_2OH, HO, HO, OH, and ring O; in Q the anomeric carbon bears OH equatorial and H axial; in Z the anomeric carbon bears H equatorial and OH axial.)

Q **Z**

50. Place a triangle around the anomeric carbon in compound **Q**.

Answer:

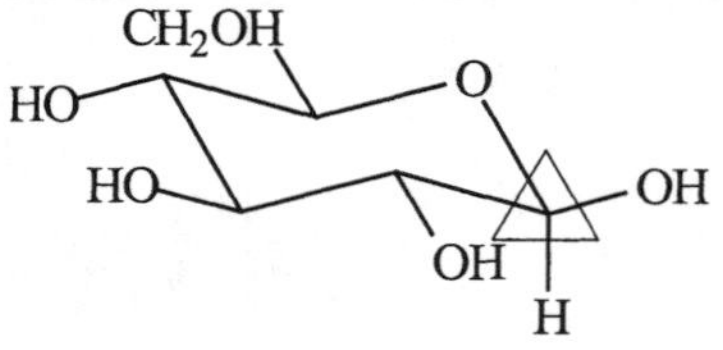

(Structure Q with a triangle around the anomeric carbon: CH_2OH, HO, HO, O, OH, OH, H)

Q

51. Compound **Z** is:

a. the D-anomer.

c. the α-anomer.

c. the β-anomer.

d. the L-anomer.

Answer: c

52. Which anomer is the ***LEAST*** stable?

Q *or* **Z**

***Answer:* Z**

53. The process by which anomer **Q** is converted into a mixture of both anomers is called:

a. anomeric rotation.

b. glycosidation.

c. pyranorotation.

d. mutarotation.

Answer: d

54. **Q** and **Z** are cyclic examples of:

a. acetals

b. hemiacetals

c. alditols

d. hemialditols

Answer: b

55. This cyclization is an example of an intramolecular nucleophilic addition of an alcohol with an aldehyde. This process is catalyzed by mild acid. On the structures provided below **draw arrows indicating electron flow** in this reaction mechanism.

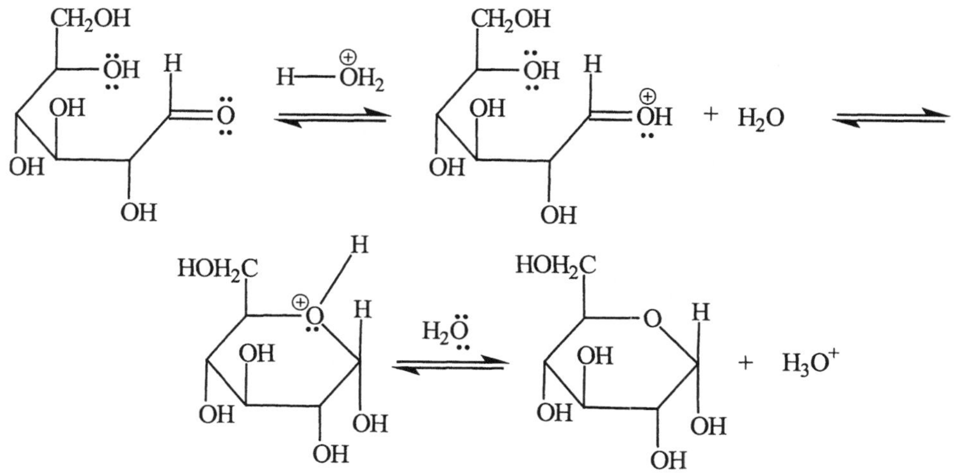

Answer:

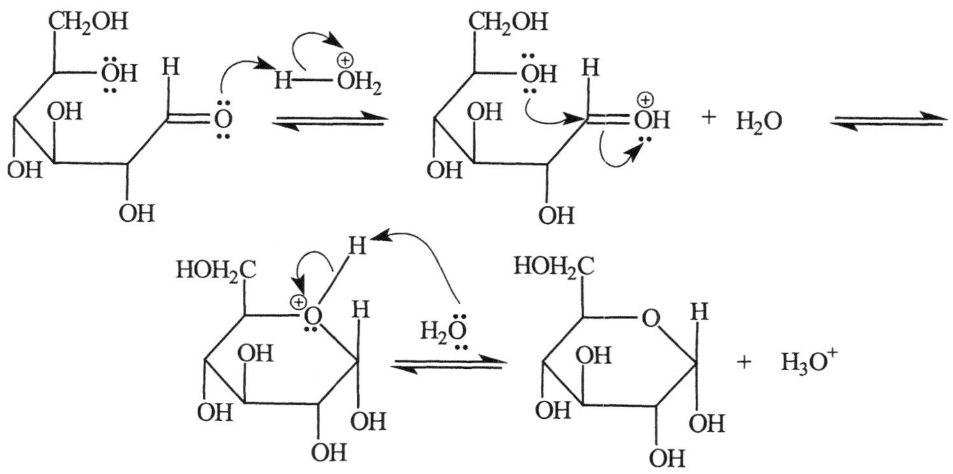

Below is the structure of the antigenic determinant for the blood group B. Use this structure to answer the following questions.

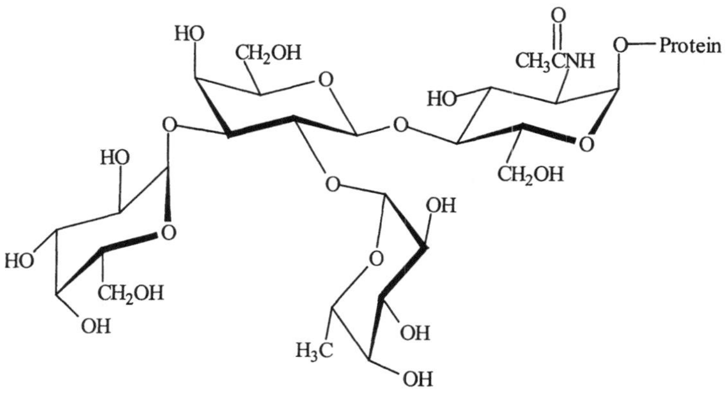

56. Put a **BOX** around the 1,3'-glycosidic linkage.

Answer:

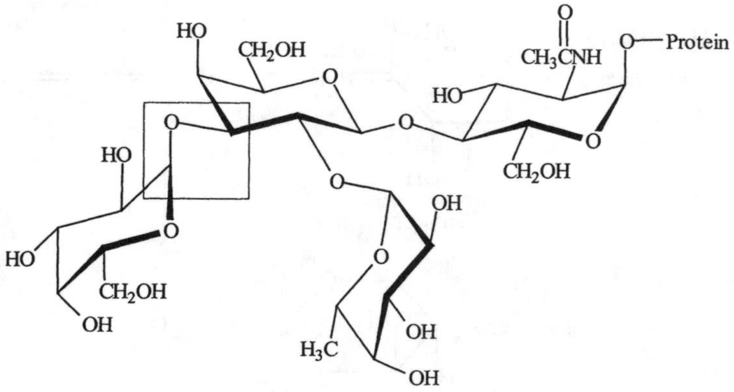

57. One of the monosaccharides is an unusual deoxy sugar called L-fucose. **CIRCLE** the L-fucose moiety.

Answer:

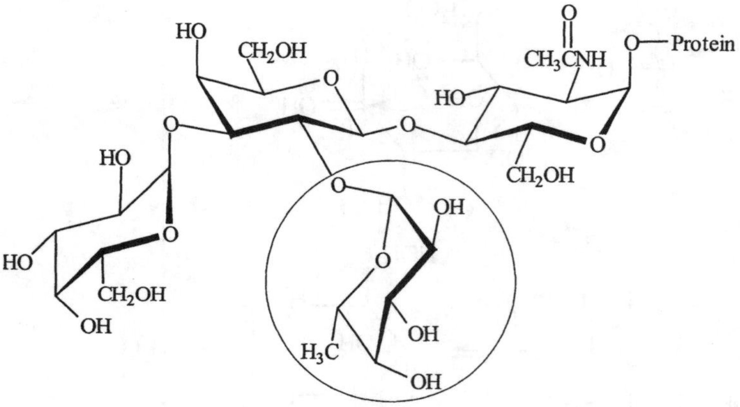

Chapter 26 – Biomolecules: Amino Acids, Peptides, and Proteins

Refer to the data below to answer the following questions:

Leucine is an essential amino acid with the systematic name 2-amino-3-methylpentanoic acid. It has pK_{a1} = 2.36 and $pK_{a2} = 9.60$.

1. Draw the condensed structure for leucine, and label all chirality centers with an asterisk.

Answer:

CH_3 (on C3) ; * (on C2)

$CH_3CHCH_2CHCOOH$

NH_2 (on C2)

2. How many possible stereoisomers of leucine are there?

Answer: Since leucine has one chirality center, there are 2^1, or 2 possible leucine stereoisomers.

3. Draw a Fischer projection of L-leucine and label the chirality center(s) as *R* or *S*.

Answer:

COOH

H_2N — *S* — H

$CH_2CH(CH_3)_2$

4. What is the p*I* of leucine?

Answer: The p*I* is the isoelectric point and is the average of pK_{a1} and pK_{a2}. For valine:

$$pI = \frac{2.36 + 9.60}{2} = 5.98$$

5. Draw the structure of the predominant form of leucine at pH = 10.00.

Answer:

CH_3 ; O (double-bonded)

$CH_3CHCH_2CHC{-}\ddot{O}{:}^-$

NH_2

6. Draw the structure of the predominant form of leucine at pH = 1.50.

Answer:

CH_3 ; O (double-bonded)

$CH_3CHCH_2CHC{-}\ddot{O}H$

$+NH_3$

7. Leucine is described as an *essential* amino acid. What does this mean?

Answer: Humans are able to synthesize only 10 of the 20 amino acids necessary for protein synthesis. The remaining 10 are called *essential* amino acids since they must be obtained from dietary sources. Failure to include an adequate dietary supply of these essential amino acids can lead to severe deficiency diseases.

8. Show how leucine might be synthesized using the Knowles enantioselective synthesis.

Answer:

$(CH_3)_2CH{-}CH{=}C(CO_2H)(NHCO_2CH_3)$ $\xrightarrow[\text{2. NaOH, } H_2O]{\text{1. } H_2\text{, [Rh/DiPAMP)(COD)]}^+ BF_4^-}$ $(CH_3)_2CHCH_2CH(NH_2)CO_2H$

9. Show the alkyl halide you would use to prepare leucine by the amidomalonate method.

Answer:

$CH_3{-}CH(CH_3){-}CH_2{-}Br$

MATCH a structure from the list below to each of the following terms. Place the letter of the structure in the blank to the left of the term which it describes.

10. ______ an octapeptide with a C-terminal valine.

Answer: f

11. ______ an amino acid in its zwitterionic form.

Answer: b

12. ______ a polypeptide which gives four fragments on treatment with chymotrypsin.

Answer: c

13. ______ the product of an Edman degradation.

Answer: j

14. ______ a carboxyl-protected amino acid.

Answer: d

15. ______ a peptide coupling reagent.

Answer: h

16. ______ small organic molecules which act as coenzymes.

Answer: m

A. $[(CH_3)_3COC(=O)]_2O$

B. $CH_3CH(^{+}NH_3)CO_2^{-}$

C. Val-Phe-Leu-Met-Tyr-Pro-Gly-Trp-Cys-Glu

D. $(CH_3)_2CHCH(NH_2)COCH_2Ph$ (with C=O)

E. $CH_3CH(NH_2)COOH$

F. Asp-Tyr-Ile-His-Pro-Phe-Arg-Val

G. apoenzyme

H. 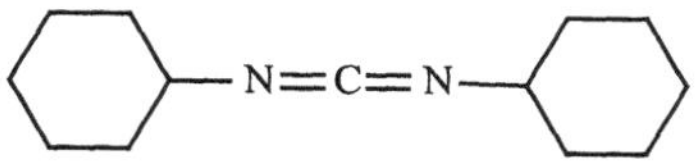 (cyclohexyl)–N=C=N–(cyclohexyl)

I. $(CH_3)_3COC(=O)NHCH(CH_3)COOH$

J. 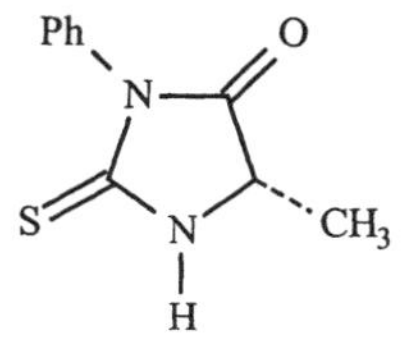 Ph, O, S, N, N, H, CH_3

K. 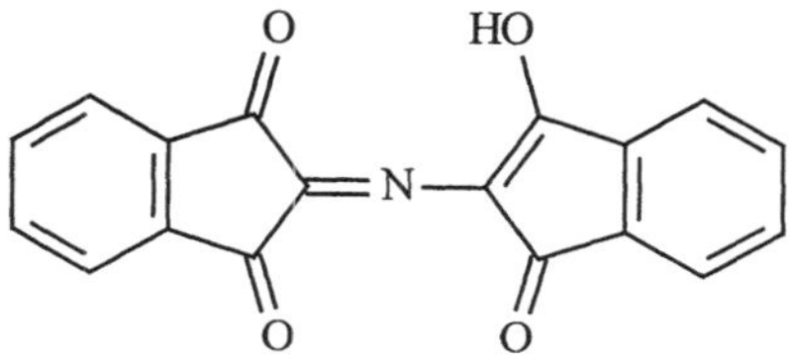 O, HO, N, O, O

L. Val-Lys-Phe-Gly-Arg-Met-Arg-Phe

M. vitamins

Refer to the data below to answer the following questions:

Amino Acid	Isoelectric point
Arginine	10.76
Glutamic Acid	3.22
Tryptophan	5.89

17. At what pH would you carry out an electrophoresis experiment if you wanted to separate a mixture of lysine, aspartic acid and phenylalanine? Explain.

Answer: The optimum pH for the electrophoresis of three amino acids occurs at the isoelectric point of the amino acid intermediate in acidity. At this pH, one amino acid migrates toward the cathode (the least acidic), one migrates toward the anode (the most acidic), and the amino acid intermediate in acidity does not migrate. In this example, electrophoresis at 5.89 allows the maximum separation of the three amino acids.

18. Define isoelectric point.

Answer: The isoelectric point is the pH at which an amino acid is exactly balanced between anionic and cationic forms and exists primarily as the neutral, dipolar zwitterion.

19. The most basic amino acid is _____ .

Answer: Arginine

20. The most acidic amino acid is ____.

Answer: Glutamic acid

Refer to the data below to answer the following questions:

Porcine dynorphin is a neuropeptide having 17 amino acid residues. Its structure is shown below.

Tyr–Gly–Gly–Phe–Leu–Arg–Arg–Ile–Arg–Pro–Lys–Leu–Lys–Trp–Asp–Asn–Gln

21. Leu^5-enkephalin is a pentapeptide contained as the N-terminal sequence of dynorphin. Write the structure of Leu^5-enkephalin using both the three letter and one letter abbreviations for the amino acids.

Answer: Tyr–Gly–Gly–Phe–Leu and Y-G-G-F-L

22. What fragments would result if dynorphin were cleaved by trypsin?

Answer: Trypsin catalyzes the hydrolysis of peptides as the carboxyl side of arginine and lysine. Consequently, the fragments resulting from trypsin hydrolysis of dynorphin are:

Tyr–Gly–Gly–Phe–Leu–Arg
Arg
Ile–Arg
Pro–Lys
Leu–Lys
Trp–Asp–Asn–Gln

23. What fragments would result if dynorphin were cleaved by chymotropsin?

Answer: Chymotropsin catalyzes the hydrolysis of peptides at the carboxyl side of the aryl-substituted amino acids phenylalanine, tyrosine, and tryptophan. Thus, the fragments resulting from chymotropsin hydrolysis of dynorphin are:

Tyr
Gly–Gly–Phe
Leu–Arg–Arg–Ile–Arg–Pro–Lys–Leu–Lys–Trp
Asp–Asn–Gln

Refer to the data below to answer the following questions:

The octapeptide saralasin is a specific antagonist of angiotensin II. A derivative of saralasin is used therapeutically as an antihypertensive. Amino acid analysis of saralasin show the presence of the following amino acids:

Ala, Arg, His, Pro, Sar, Tyr, Val_2

24. Sar is the abbreviation for sarcosine, N-methyl aminoethanoic acid. Draw the structure of sarcosine.

Answer:

$$CH_3NHCH_2\overset{\overset{\displaystyle O}{||}}{C}OH$$

25. N-Terminal analysis by the Edman method shows saralasin contains sarcosine at the N-terminus. Partial hydrolysis of saralasin with dilute hydrochloric acid yields the following fragments:

Tyr–Val–His
Sar–Arg–Val
His–Pro–Ala
Val–Tyr–Val
Arg–Val–Tyr

What is the structure of saralasin?

Answer: Sar–Arg–Val
Arg–Val–Tyr
Val–Tyr–Val
Tyr–Val–His
His–Pro–Ala

The complete sequence: Sar–Arg–Val–Tyr–Val–His–Pro–Ala

26. Show the steps involved in a synthesis of F-G-I using the Merrifield procedure.

Answer:

1. $[(CH_3)_3COC(=O)]_2O$ + **I** $\xrightarrow{(CH_3CH_2)_3N:}$ $(CH_3)_3COC(=O)$—**I** [BOC-**I**]
2. BOC-**I** + $ClCH_2$Polymer ⟶ BOC-**I**-O-CH_2-Polymer
3. BOC-**I**-O-CH_2-Polymer $\xrightarrow[\text{2. } CF_3COOH]{\text{1. wash}}$ **I**-O-CH_2-Polymer
4. BOC-**G** + **I**-O-CH_2-Polymer $\xrightarrow[\text{2. wash}]{\text{1. DCC}}$ BOC-**G**-**I**-O-CH_2-Polymer
5. BOC-**G**-**I**-O-CH_2-Polymer $\xrightarrow{CF_3COOH}$ **G**-**I**-O-CH_2-Polymer
6. BOC-**F** + **G**-**I**-O-CH_2-Polymer $\xrightarrow[\text{2. wash}]{\text{1. DCC}}$ BOC-**F**-**G**-**I**-O-CH_2-Polymer
7. BOC-**F**-**G**-**I**-O-CH_2-Polymer $\xrightarrow{HF}$ **F**-**G**-**I** + HO-CH_2-Polymer

27. BOC protecting groups are generally removed by treatment with trifluoroacetic acid.

$$(CH_3)_3COC(=O)NHCH(CH_2CH(CH_3)_2)C(=O)NHCH(CH_3)C(=O)OCH_3 \xrightarrow{CF_3COOH} H_2N\text{—}CH(CH_2CH(CH_3)_2)C(=O)NHCH(CH_3)C(=O)OCH_3 + CO_2 + (CH_3)_2C{=}CH_2$$

On the structures provided below, draw arrows consistent with electron flow in the mechanism of this reaction.

$$(CH_3)_3C\ddot{O}C(=O)NHCH(CH_2CH(CH_3)_2)C(=O)NHCH(CH_3)C(=O)OCH_3$$

$$\downarrow \quad H{-}OC(=O)CF_3$$

$$(CH_3)_3C{-}\overset{+}{\ddot{O}}(H)C(=O)NHCH(CH_2CH(CH_3)_2)C(=O)NHCH(CH_3)C(=O)OCH_3$$

$$\downarrow$$

$$(CH_3)_2\overset{+}{C}{-}CH_2{-}H \quad H{-}O{-}C(=O){-}NHCH(CH_2CH(CH_3)_2)C(=O)NHCH(CH_3)C(=O)OCH_3$$

$$\downarrow$$

$$(CH_3)_2C{=}CH_2 + CO_2 + H_2N{-}CH(CH_2CH(CH_3)_2)C(=O)NHCH(CH_3)C(=O)OCH_3$$

Answer:

$$(CH_3)_3C\ddot{O}C(=O)NHCH(CH_2CH(CH_3)_2)C(=O)NHCH(CH_3)C(=O)OCH_3$$

$$\downarrow \quad H{-}OC(=O)CF_3$$

$$(CH_3)_3C{-}\overset{+}{\ddot{O}}(H)C(=O)NHCH(CH_2CH(CH_3)_2)C(=O)NHCH(CH_3)C(=O)OCH_3$$

$$\downarrow$$

$$(CH_3)_2\overset{+}{C}{-}CH_2{-}H \quad H{-}O{-}C(=O){-}NHCH(CH_2CH(CH_3)_2)C(=O)NHCH(CH_3)C(=O)OCH_3$$

$$\downarrow$$

$$(CH_3)_2C{=}CH_2 + CO_2 + H_2N{-}CH(CH_2CH(CH_3)_2)C(=O)NHCH(CH_3)C(=O)OCH_3$$

28. During peptide synthesis, the carboxylic acid group may be protected as the methyl ester. Aqueous base hydrolysis is utilized to remove the ester protecting group.

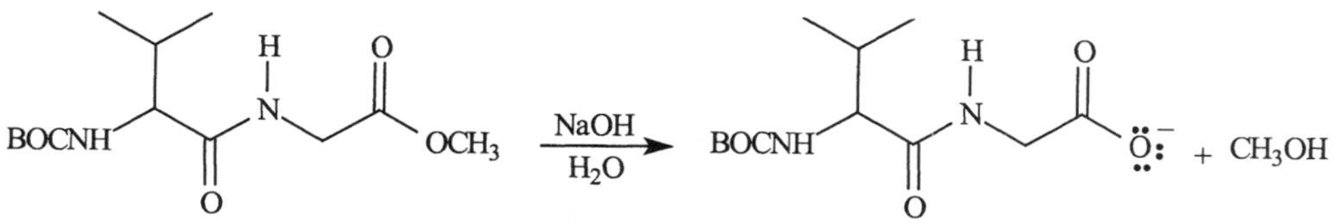

BOCNH–Val–Gly–OCH_3 $\xrightarrow[H_2O]{NaOH}$ BOCNH–Val–Gly–O^- + CH_3OH

Write the complete stepwise mechanism for the hydrolysis of the methyl ester of BOC–Val–Gly–OCH_3, above. Show all intermediate structures and all electron flow with arrows.

Answer:

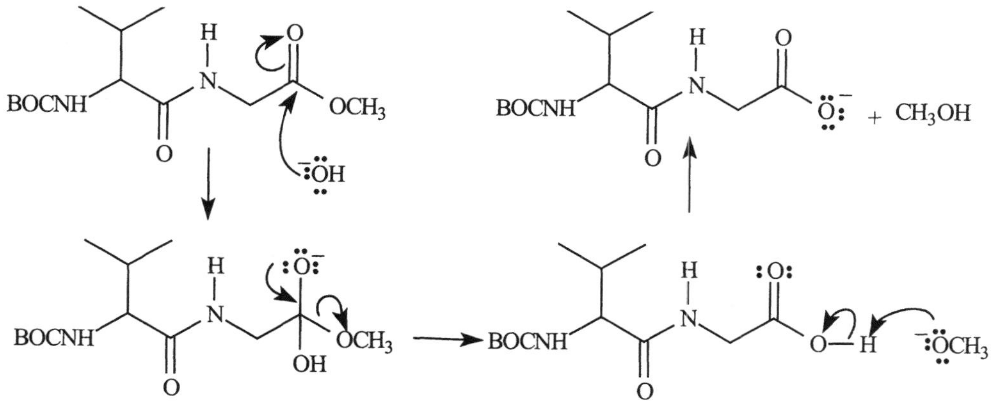

BOCNH–Val–Gly–OCH_3 + $:\ddot{O}H^-$ → tetrahedral intermediate ($:\ddot{O}:^-$, OH, OCH_3) → BOCNH–Val–Gly–O–H + $:\ddot{O}CH_3^-$ → BOCNH–Val–Gly–$\ddot{O}:^-$ + CH_3OH

29. The reaction above is an example of:

a. nucleophilic addition
b. electrophilic addition
c. nucleophilic acyl substitution
d. electrophilic substitution

Answer: c

MATCH a term from the list below to each definition. Place the letter of the term in the blank to the left of the definition.

a. Ligases
b. Fibrous proteins
c. Conjugated protein
d. Hydrolases
e. Simple protein
f. Globular proteins
g. Lyases
h. Transferases

30. ______ Proteins which yield other compounds in addition to amino acids on hydrolysis.

Answer: c

31. ______ Proteins which are tough and insoluble in water.

Answer: b

32. _____ Enzymes which catalyze the breaking away of a small molecule such as H_2O from a substrate.

Answer: g

33. _____ Enzymes which catalyze the bonding together of two substrates.

Answer: a

Chapter 27 – Biomolecules: Lipids

MATCH each of the following terms to a structure from the list below. There is only one correct structure for each term, and structures may be used more than once. Place the letter of the structure in the blank to the left of the corresponding term.

A. 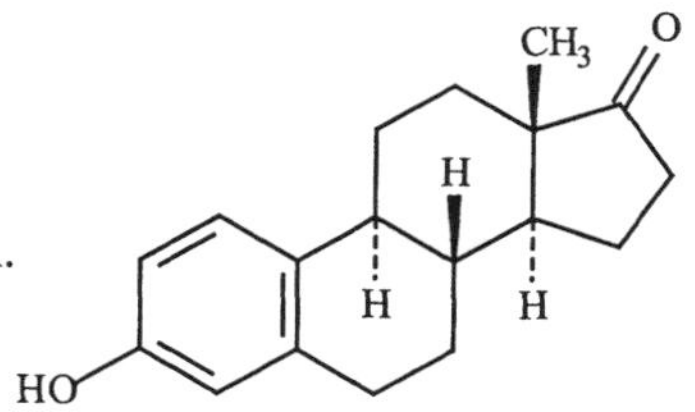 CH_3 O H HO H H

B. 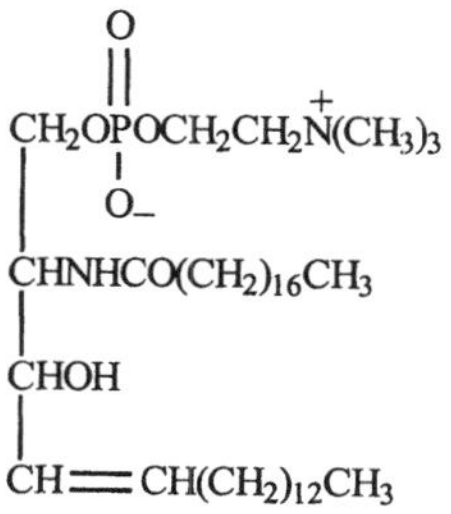 $CH_2OP(=O)(O^-)OCH_2CH_2\overset{+}{N}(CH_3)_3$ — $CHNHCO(CH_2)_{16}CH_3$ — $CHOH$ — $CH{=}CH(CH_2)_{12}CH_3$

C. 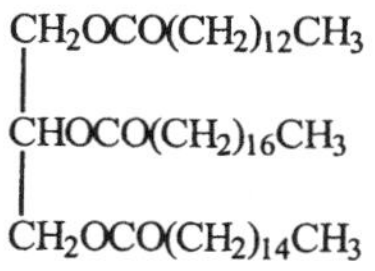 $CH_2OCO(CH_2)_{12}CH_3$ — $CHOCO(CH_2)_{16}CH_3$ — $CH_2OCO(CH_2)_{14}CH_3$

D. 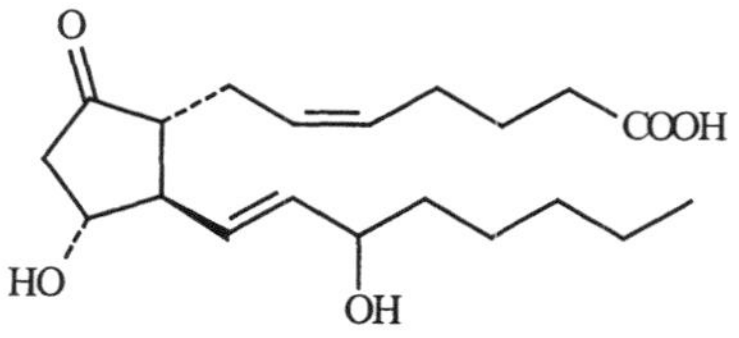 O COOH HO OH

E. 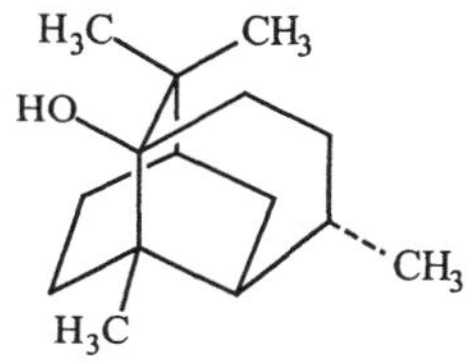 H_3C CH_3 HO CH_3 H_3C

F. 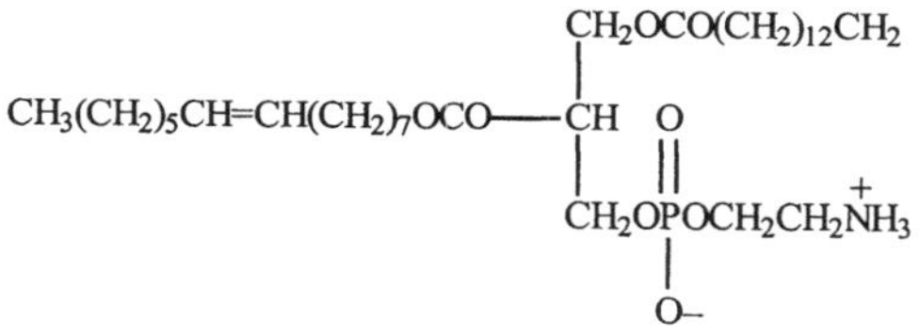 $CH_3(CH_2)_5CH{=}CH(CH_2)_7OCO$—$CH$, with $CH_2OCO(CH_2)_{12}CH_2$ and $CH_2OP(=O)(O^-)OCH_2CH_2\overset{+}{N}H_3$

G. Malonyl ACP

H. $CH_3(CH_2)_4CH{=}CHCH_2CH{=}CH(CH_2)_2\overset{O}{\overset{||}{C}}O^-Na^+$

I. $CH_3—\overset{O}{\overset{||}{C}}—SCoA$

J. 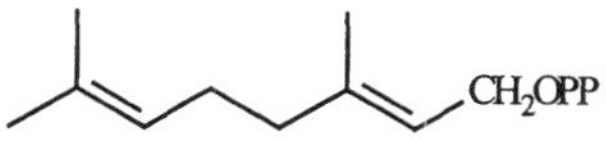 CH_2OPP

1. _____ starting material for fatty acid biosynthesis.

Answer: i

2. _____ a phosphoglyceride

Answer: f

3. _____ a prostaglandin

Answer: d

4. _____ monoterpene precursor

Answer: j

5. _____ a triglyceride

Answer: c

6. _____ a sphingolipid

Answer: b

7. _____ a soap

Answer: h

8. _____ a cephalin

Answer: f

9. _____ a steroid

Answer: a

10. _____ a sesquiterpene

Answer: e

11. Bolecic acid, $C_{18}H_{26}O_2$, yields stearic acid, $CH_3(CH_2)_{16}COOH$, on catalytic hydrogenation. Ozonolysis of bolecic acid yields the following products:

CH_2O HOOC-COOH $HOOC(CH_2)_7COOH$ $OHC(CH_2)_4COOH$

Propose a structure for bolecic acid.

Answer: There are two possible structures for bolecic acid:

$CH_2{=}CH(CH_2)_4C{\equiv}C{-}C{\equiv}C(CH_2)_7COOH$ or $CH_2{=}CH(CH_2)_4C{\equiv}C(CH_2)_7C{\equiv}CCOOH$

Refer to the structures of the terpenes below to answer the following questions:

Show the positions of the isoprene units in each of the indicated terpenes.

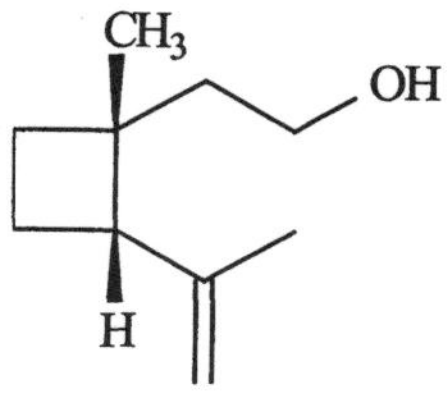

grandisol

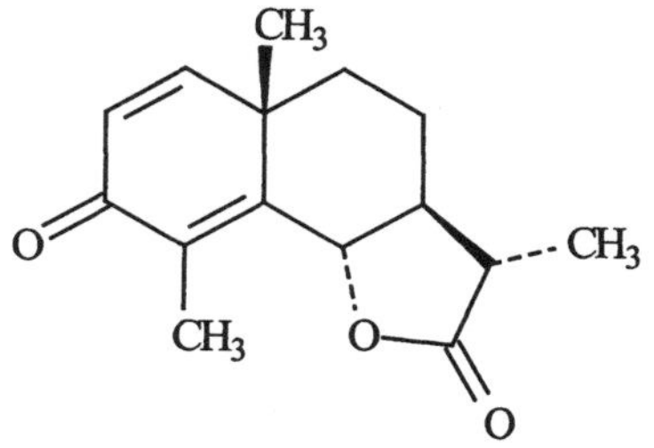

α-santonin

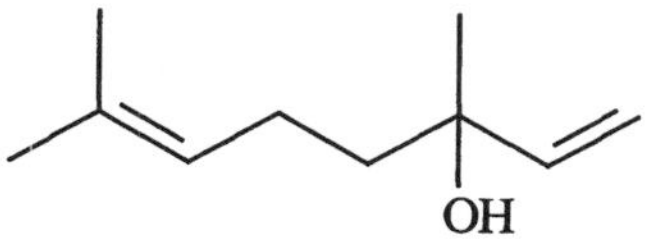

linalool

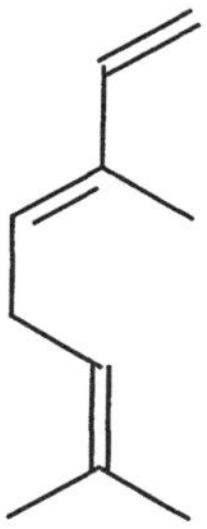

ocimene

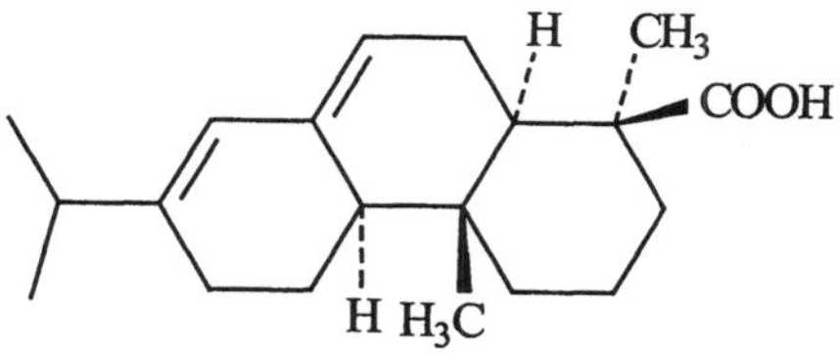

abietic acid

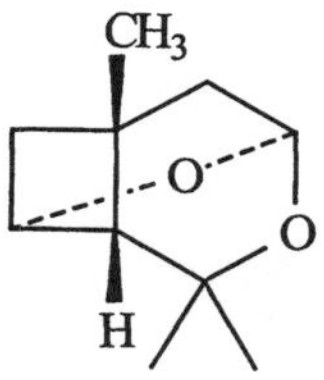

lineatin

12. grandisol

Answer:

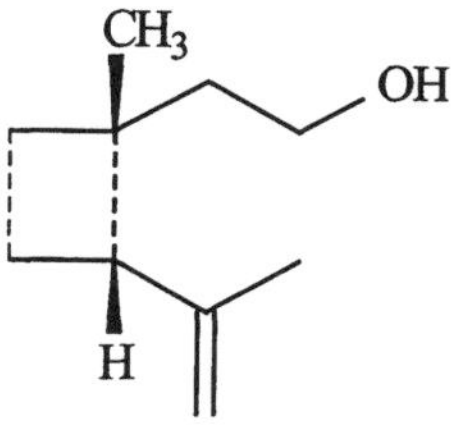

13. *α*-santonin

Answer:

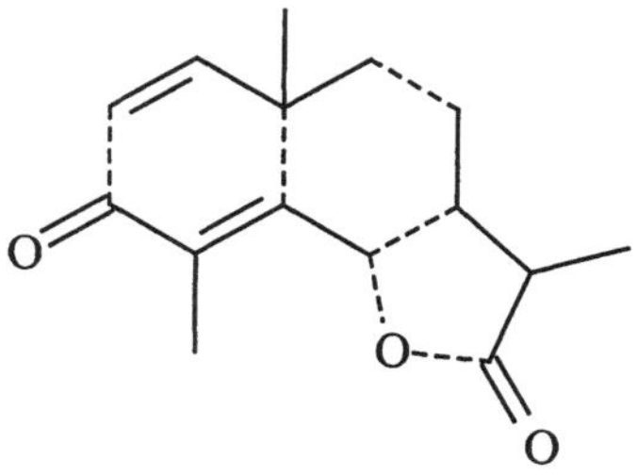

14. abietic acid

Answer:

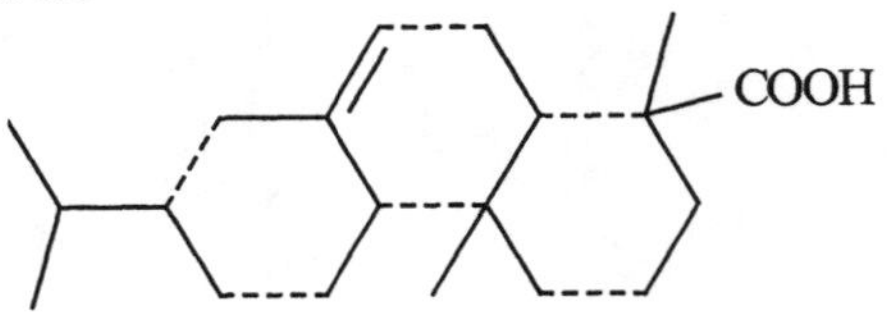

COOH

15. linalool

Answer:

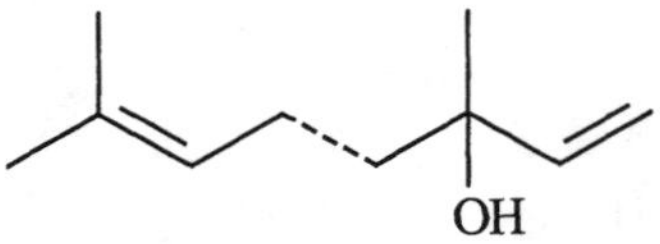

OH

16. ocimene

Answer:

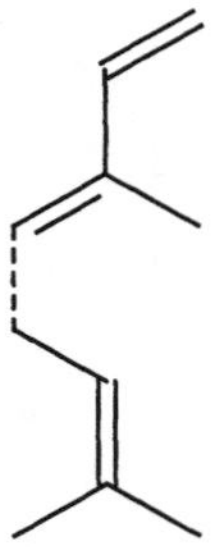

17. lineatin

Answer:

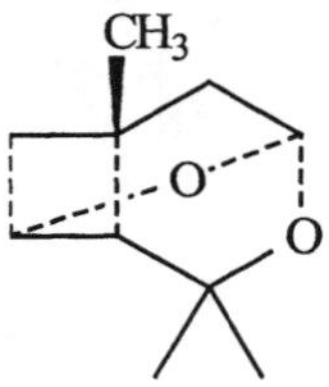

CH_3

O

O

Indicate by asterisks the stereogenic centers present in each of the indicated terpenes.

18. grandisol

Answer:

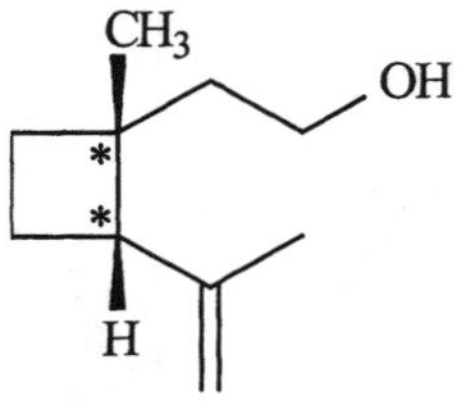

CH_3

OH

*

*

H

19. α-santonin

Answer:

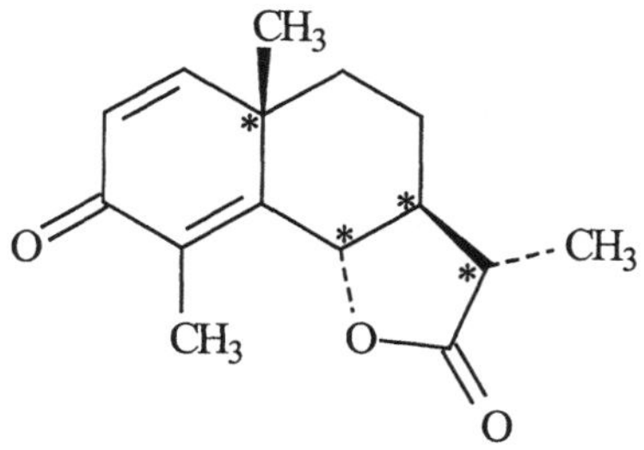

20. abietic acid

Answer:

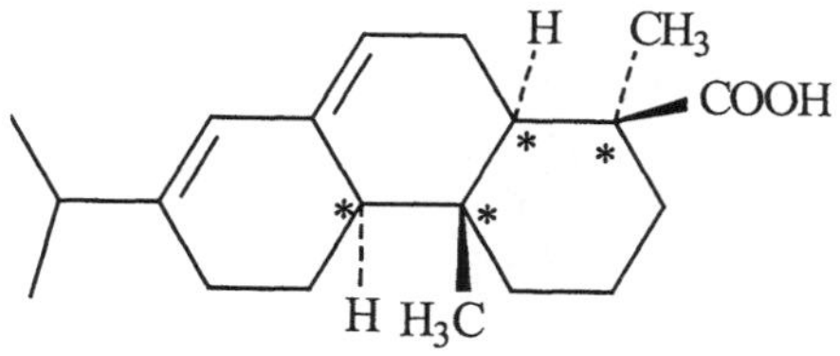

21. linalool

Answer:

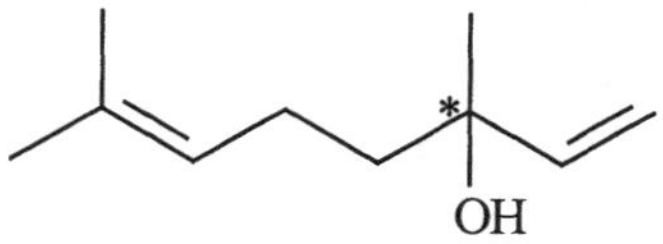

22. lineatin

Answer:

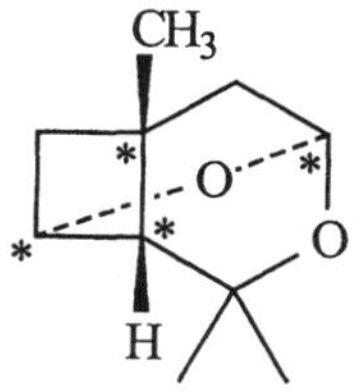

23. Abietic acid is an example of:

a. a monoterpene
b. a sesquiterpene
c. a diterpene
d. a sesterterpene

Answer: c

24. Suggest a mechanism by which caryophyllene is transformed into humulene by treatment with acid.

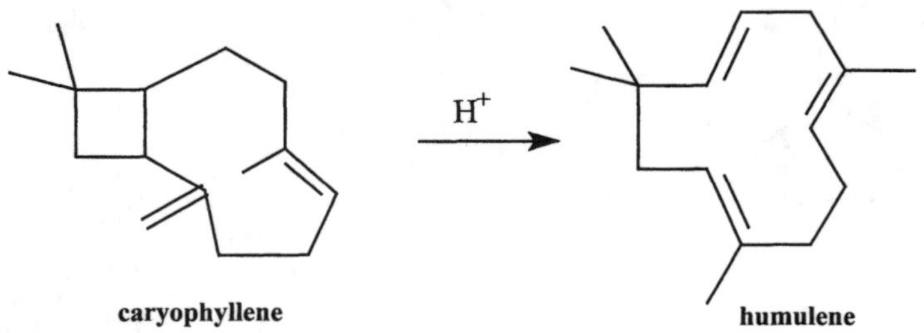

H^+

caryophyllene **humulene**

Answer:

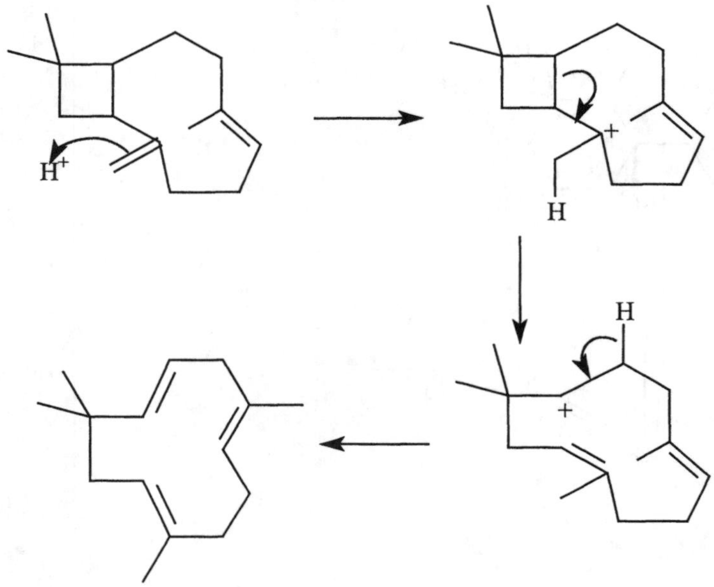

H^+ H H +

25. Draw the most stable chair conformation of terpin hydrate.

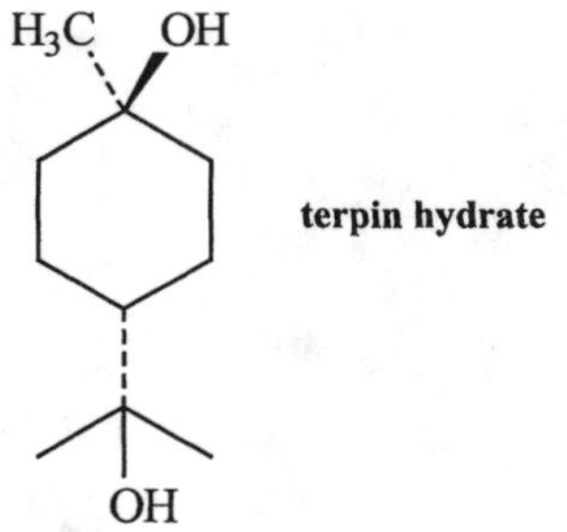

H_3C OH

terpin hydrate

OH

Answer:

CH_3 OH OH

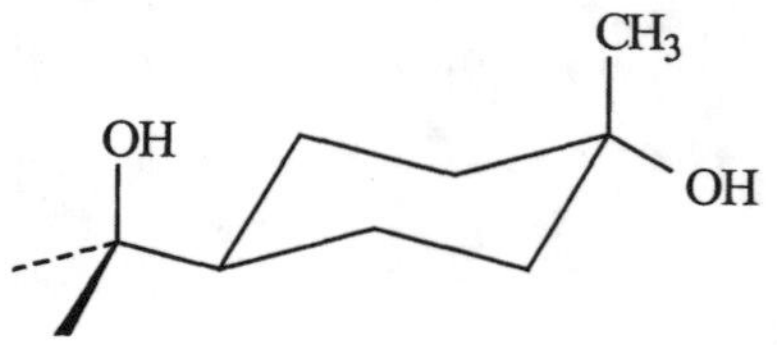

Draw the structures of the major organic product(s) you would expect to obtain from reaction of androsterone with each of the following reagents.

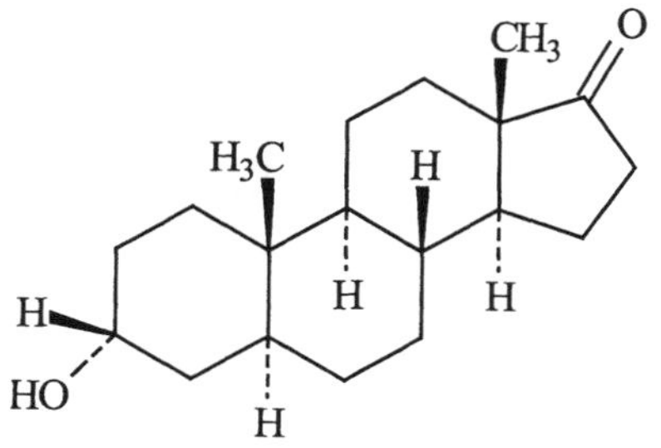

CH_3 O
H_3C H
H H
H
HO
H

androsterone

26. PCC

Answer:

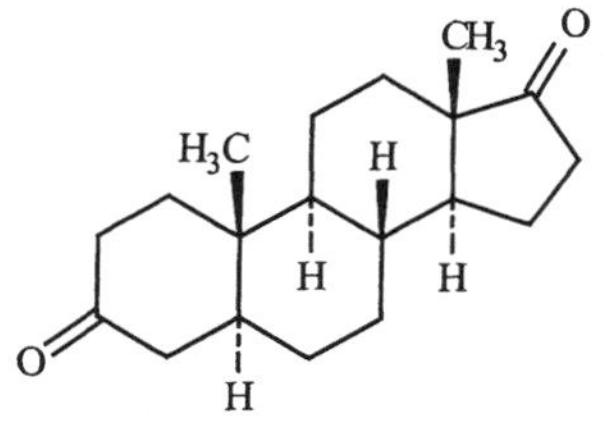

CH_3 O
H_3C H
H H
O
H

27. $NaBH_4$, ethanol

Answer:

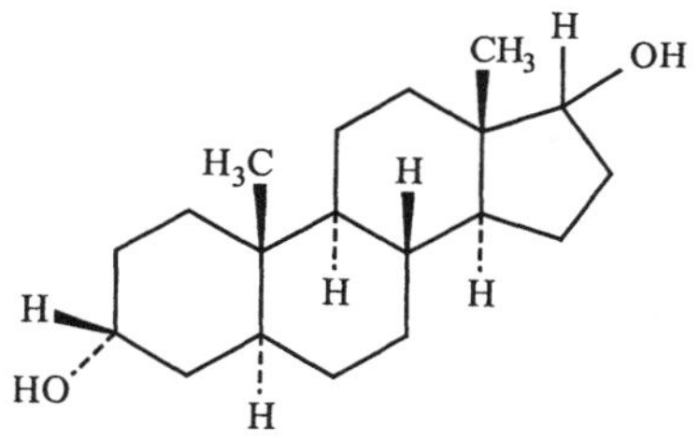

CH_3 H OH
H_3C H
H H
H
HO
H

28. CH_3COCl , pyridine

Answer:

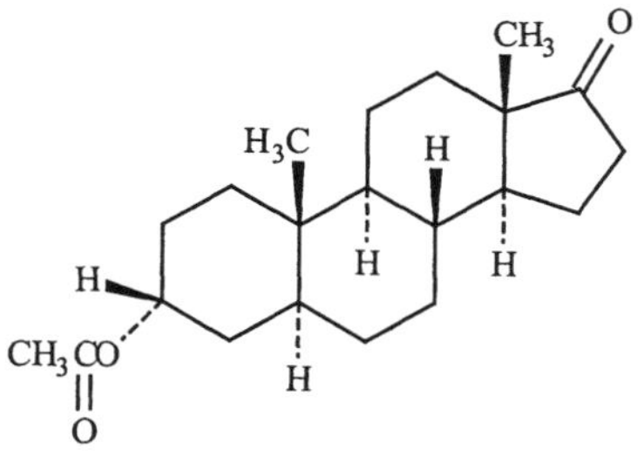

CH_3 O
H_3C H
H H
H
CH_3CO
O
H

29. $POCl_3$, pyridine

Answer:

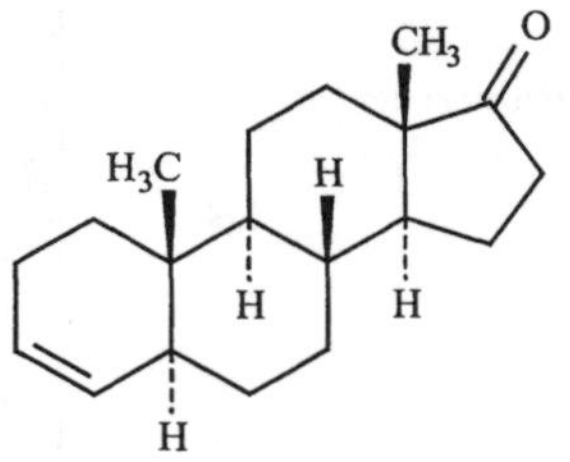

30. NaH, then CH_3I

Answer:

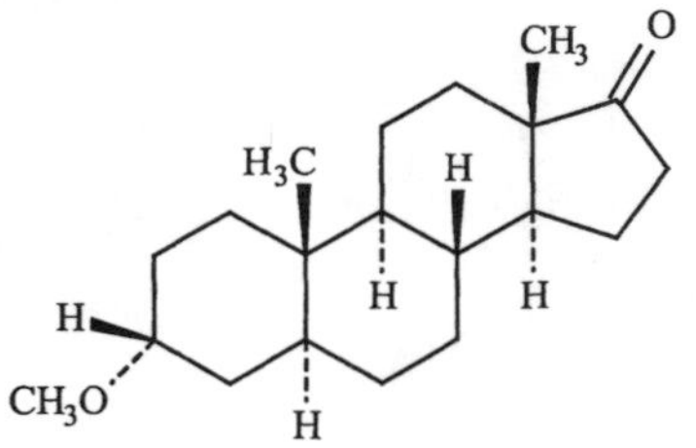

31. Mixtures of esters of long-chain carboxylic acids with long-chain alcohols are called:

a. waxes
b. fats and oils
c. fatty acids
d. soaps

Answer: a

32. Chemically, these are triacylglycerols, triesters of glycerol with three long-chain carboxylic acids.

a. waxes
b. fats and oils
c. fatty acids
d. soaps

Answer: b

33. The major lipid components of cell membranes are:

a. sphingolipids
b. prostaglandins
c. phosphoglycerides
d. terpenoids

Answer: c

34. A group of C_{20} lipids that contain a five-membered ring with two long side chains.

a. sphingolipids
b. prostaglandins
c. phosphoglycerides
d. terpenoids

Answer: b

35. Plant extracts, called essential oils, are largely a mixture of these lipids.

a. sphingolipids
b. prostaglandins
c. phosphoglycerides
d. terpenoids

Answer: d

36. When soaps disperse in water, the long hydrocarbon tails cluster together in a hydrophobic ball, while the ionic heads on the surface of the cluster stick out into the water. These spherical clusters are called:

a. fatty acid esters
b. triacylglycerols
c. lipid bilayers
d. micelles

Answer: d

37. Cell membranes, which form an effective barrier to the passage of ions and other components into and out of the cell, are:

a. fatty acid esters
b. tricacylglycerols
c. lipid bilayers
d. micelles

Answer: d

38. Male sex hormones like testosterone are called:

a. androgens
b. estrogens
c. progestins
d. glucocorticoids

Answer: a

39. In humans, most steroids function as:

a. enzymes
b. hormones
c. nucleic acids
d. proteins

Answer: b

Chapter 28 – Biomolecules: Heterocycles and Nucleic Acids

MATCH each of the following terms to a structure from the list below. There is only one correct structure for each term and structures may be used more than once. Place the letter of the structure in the blank to the left of the corresponding term.

A. Sanger dideoxy method

B. GAUCGUAAA

C. Watson-Crick

D. translation

E. 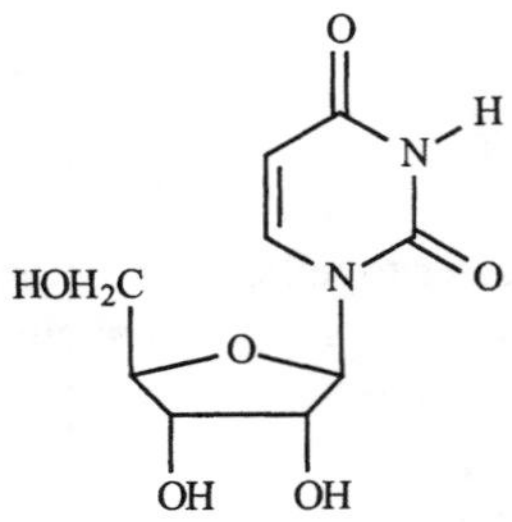 HOH_2C O N O N H O OH OH

F. 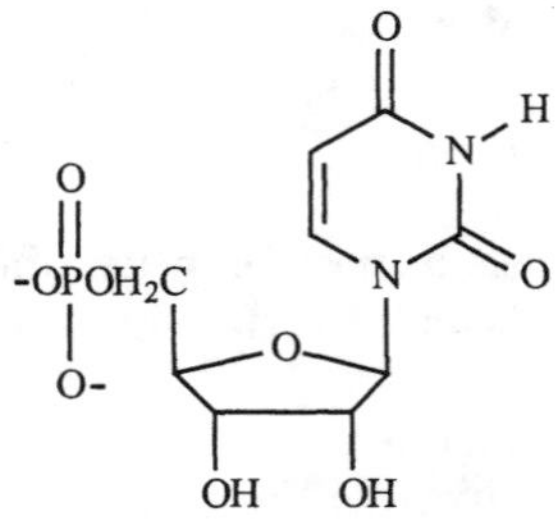 $-OPOH_2C$ O O- O N O N H O OH OH

G. transcription

H. Maxam-Gilbert method

I. AUGGCUGAG

J. replication

K. 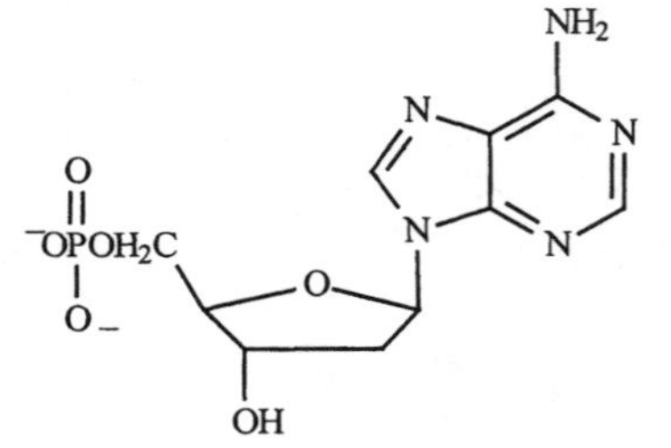 $^{-}OPOH_2C$ O O_{-} O N N N N NH_2 OH

L. 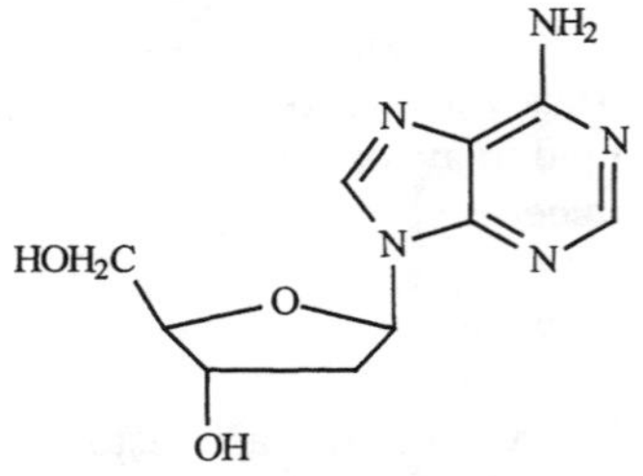 HOH_2C O N N N N NH_2 OH

M. AGATCGCTC

1. _____a pyrimidine nucleotide

Answer: E

2. _____ RNA base sequence with guanine at the 3' end.

Answer: I

3. _____ DNA base sequence with cytosine at the 3' end.

Answer: M

4. _____ uridine

Answer: E

5. _____ a purine nucleoside

Answer: L

6. _____ DNA sequencing method for the human genome

Answer: A

7. _____ RNA base sequence complementary to the DNA base sequence which codes for Leu–Ala–Phe:

   CTAGCATTT

Answer: B

8. _____ 2'-deoxyadenosine 5'-phosphate

Answer: K

9. _____ process by which mRNA directs protein synthesis

Answer: D

10. The process invented in 1986 which allows multiple copies of a given DNA sequence to be produced is:

a. the polymerase chain reaction.
b. the Sanger dideoxy method.
c. the Maxam-Gilbert method.
d. the restriction endonuclease reaction.

Answer: a

11. When pyrrole is heated with chloroform in an alkaline solution dichlorocarbene is generated and adds to pyrrole to generate an intermediate dichlorocyclopropane which rearranges to 3-chloropyridine. This reaction is called the Ciamician-Dennstedt Rearrangement. Propose a mechanism for the rearrangement of the dichlorocyclopropane intermediate.

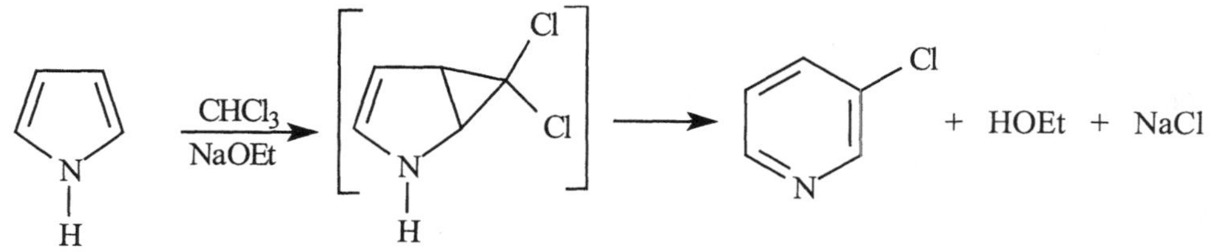

Answer:

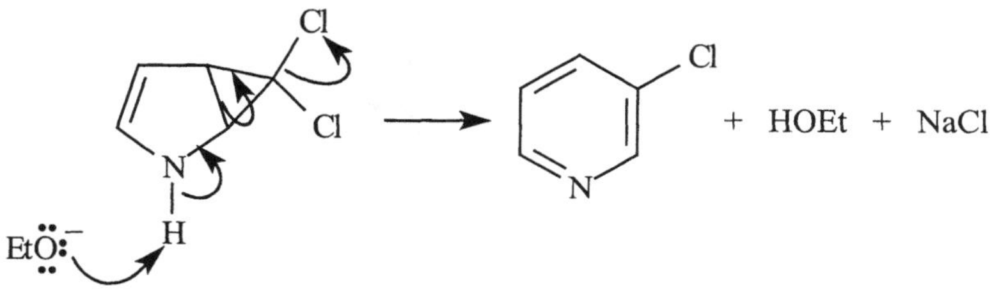

Refer to the data below to answer the following questions:

Indole derivatives may be synthesized by reaction of arylamines with α-haloacid chlorides followed by cyclization of the resulting amides with aluminum chloride in a process known as the Stollé Synthesis.

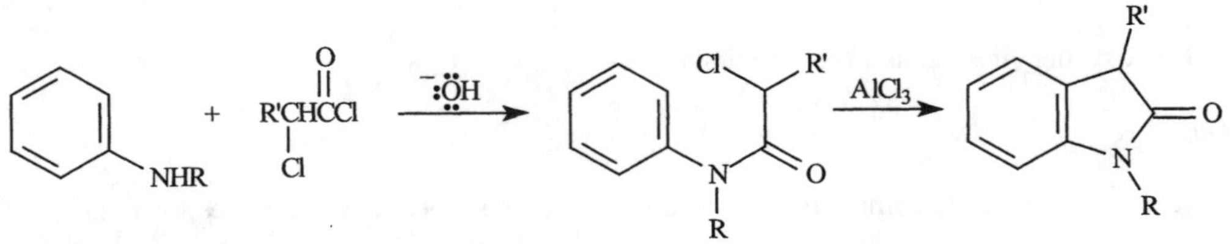

R'CHCCl(=O)Cl; $^{-}$:ÖH; $AlCl_3$

12. Write the complete stepwise mechanism for the first step of the Stollé Synthesis. Show all intermediate structures and all electron flow with arrows.

Answer:

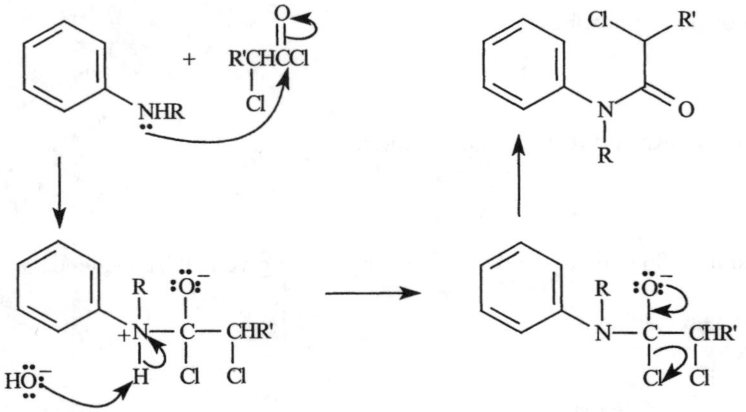

13. The first step of the Stollé Synthesis is an example of:

a. an electrophilic aromatic substitution reaction
b. a nucleophilic acyl substitution reaction
c. a nucleophilic aromatic substitution reaction
d. a S_N2 reaction

Answer: b

14. Write the complete stepwise mechanism for the second step of the Stollé Synthesis. Show all intermediate structures and all electron flow with arrows.

Answer:

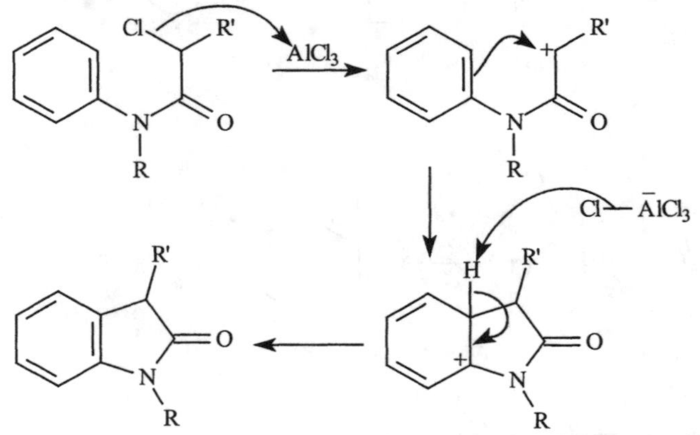

15. The second step of the Stollé Synthesis is an example of:

a. an electrophilic aromatic substitution reaction
b. a nucleophilic acyl substitution reaction
c. a nucleophilic aromatic substitution reaction
d. a S_N2 reaction

Answer: a

16. Thiophene carboxylic acid derivatives may be prepared from 1,2-diketones and dialkyl thiodiacetate.

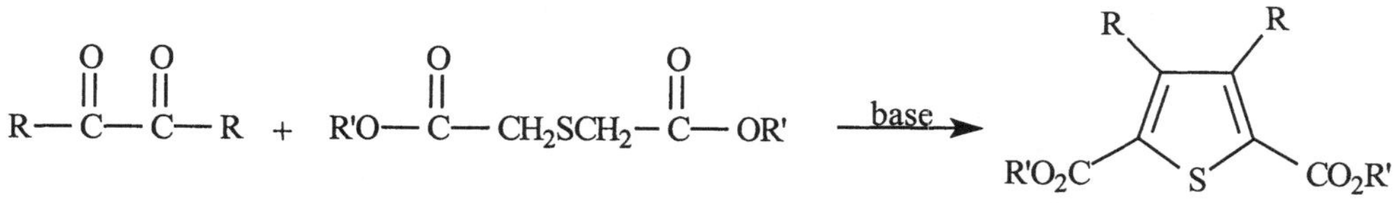

R—C(=O)—C(=O)—R + R'O—C(=O)—CH_2SCH_2—C(=O)—OR' —base→ (thiophene: R, R, $R'O_2C$, S, CO_2R')

Draw arrows indicating electron flow on the intermediate structures provided below for the mechanism for this reaction.

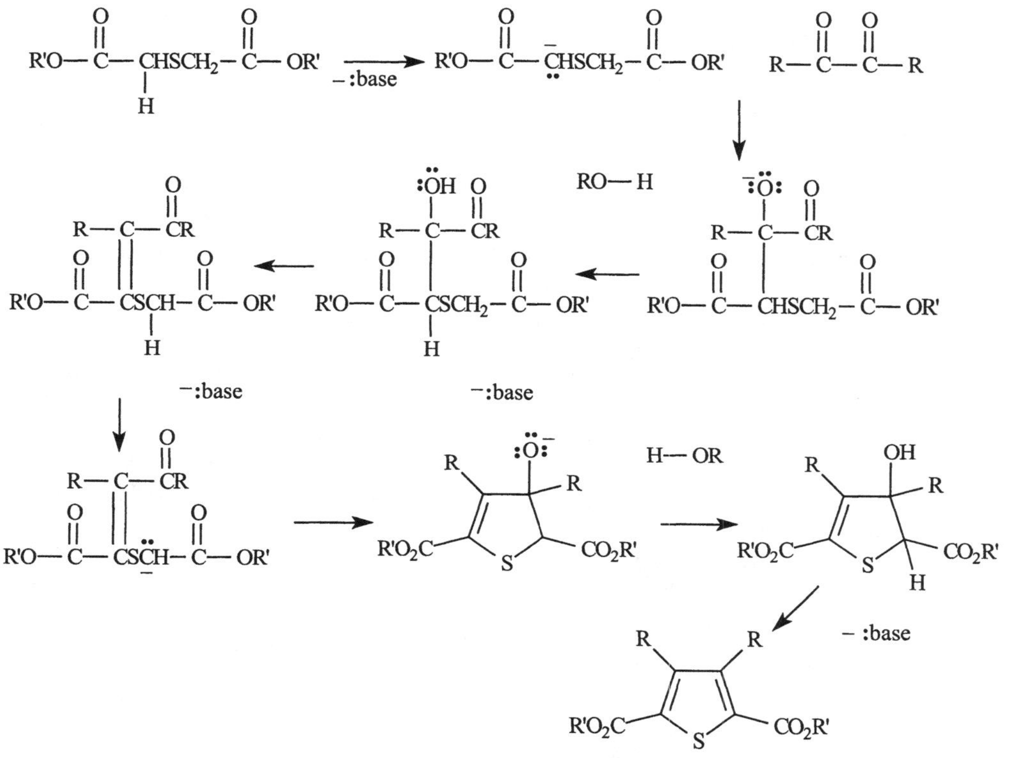

R'O—C(=O)—CHSCH$_2$—C(=O)—OR' (H) —(−:base)→ R'O—C(=O)—$\overset{-}{\text{C}}$HSCH$_2$—C(=O)—OR' + R—C(=O)—C(=O)—R

↓

R—C(—$\bar{O}$:)—CR(=O) on R'O—C(=O)—CHSCH$_2$—C(=O)—OR' (RO—H) → R—C(:OH)—CR(=O) on R'O—C(=O)—CSCH$_2$—C(=O)—OR' (H) (−:base) → R—C—CR(=O) on R'O—C(=O)—CSCH—C(=O)—OR' (H) (−:base)

↓

R—C—CR(=O) on R'O—C(=O)—CS$\ddot{\text{C}}$H—C(=O)—OR' → (ring: R, :$\ddot{\text{O}}$:⁻, R, $R'O_2C$, S, CO_2R') (H—OR) → (ring: R, OH, R, $R'O_2C$, S, CO_2R', H) (− :base) → (thiophene: R, R, $R'O_2C$, S, CO_2R')

Answer:

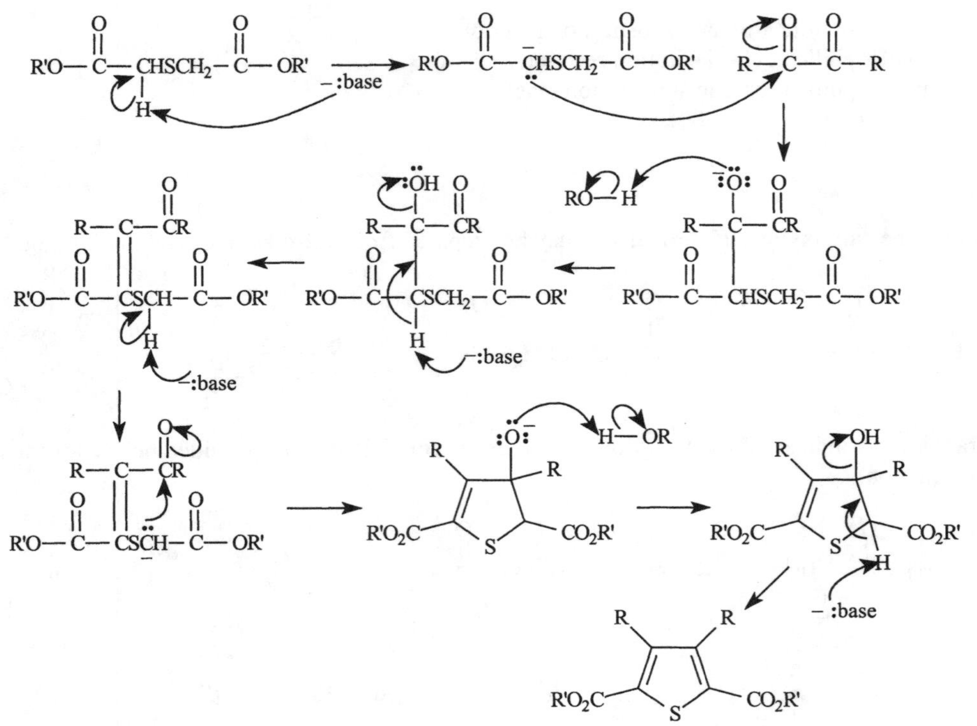

R'O—C(=O)—CHSCH$_2$—C(=O)—OR' —(−:base)→ R'O—C(=O)—$\bar{C}$HSCH$_2$—C(=O)—OR' + R—C(=O)—C(=O)—R

R'O—C(=O)—CHSCH$_2$—C(=O)—OR' (with R—C(—:Ö:$^-$)—CR(=O)) + RO—H

R—C(OH)—CR(=O) on R'O—C(=O)—CSCH$_2$—C(=O)—OR' (H, :base)

R—C—CR(=O) on R'O—C(=O)—CSCH—C(=O)—OR' (H, :base)

R—C—CR(=O) on R'O—C(=O)—CS$\ddot{C}$H$^-$—C(=O)—OR' → :Ö:$^-$ (R, R, R'O$_2$C, CO$_2$R', S) + H—OR → OH (R, R, R'O$_2$C, CO$_2$R', S, H, − :base)

→ R, R, R'O$_2$C, S, CO$_2$R' (thiophene)

17. Describe in general terms, the steps involved in the automated synthesis of the DNA sequence GCT.

Answer:		
	Step 1	Attachment of 5'-DMT-*N*-benzoyl-2'-deoxyaguanosine to the polymer support by a 3' ester linkage.
	Step 2	Deprotection of the 5'-hydroxyl by cleavage of the DMT ether with dichloroacetic acid in CH_2Cl_2.
	Step 3	Phosphite formation between the free 5'-hydroxyl of the polymer-bound N-protected 2'-deoxyguanosine and the phosphoramidite protected 5'-DMT-2'-deoxycytidine in the presence of tetrazole followed by oxidation to the phosphate triester with I_2.
	Step 4	Repeat step 2 to deprotect the 5'-hydroxyl of the polymer–GC.
	Step 5	Repeat step 3 to form the phosphate triester between 5'-hydroxyl of 2'-deoxycytidine residue and phosphoramidite protected 5'-DMT-*N*-benzoyl-2'-deoxythymidine.
	Step 6	Cleave all protecting groups from the heterocyclic bases from the phosphates, as well as cleave the ester bond holding the DNA to the silica by treatment with aqueous ammonia.

Give the major organic product(s) of each of the following reactions.

18. (furan-2-CHO) —HNO_3 / H_2SO_4→

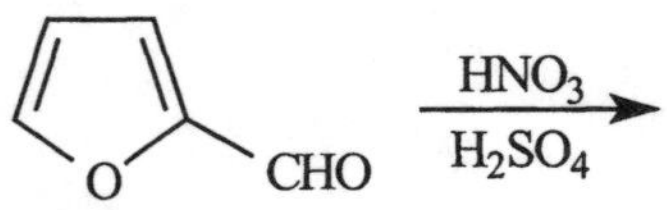

Answer:

(furan-2-CHO) —HNO_3 / H_2SO_4→ O_2N—(furan)—CHO

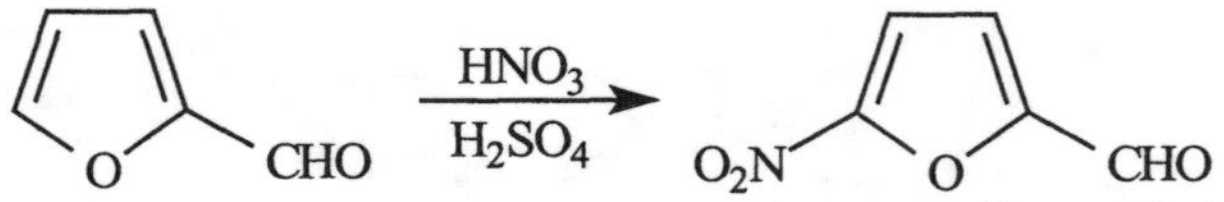

19. 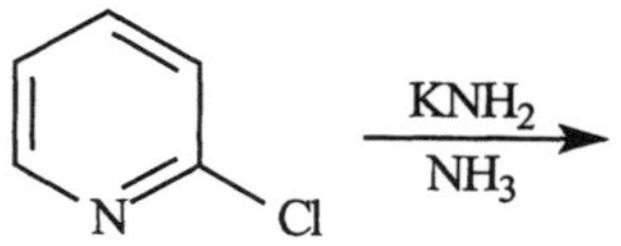 N Cl $\xrightarrow[NH_3]{KNH_2}$

Answer:

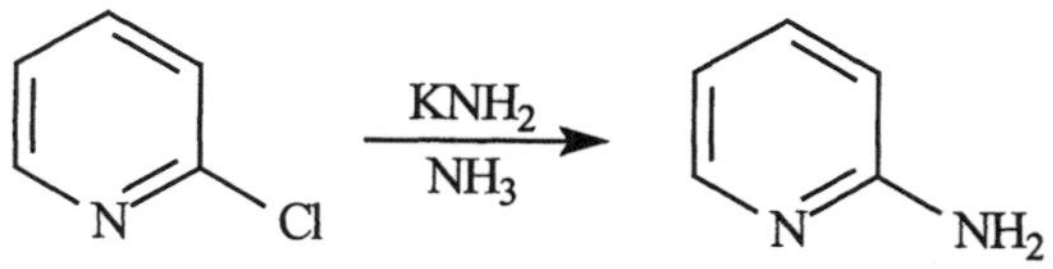

N Cl $\xrightarrow[NH_3]{KNH_2}$ N NH_2

20. 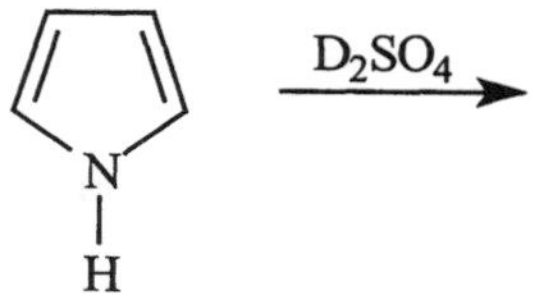 N H $\xrightarrow{D_2SO_4}$

Answer:

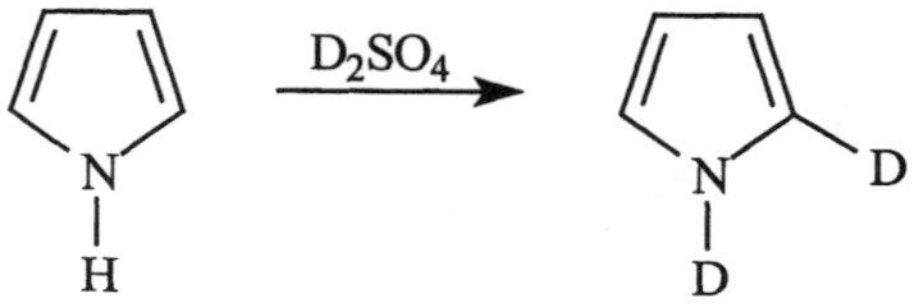

N H $\xrightarrow{D_2SO_4}$ N D D

21. 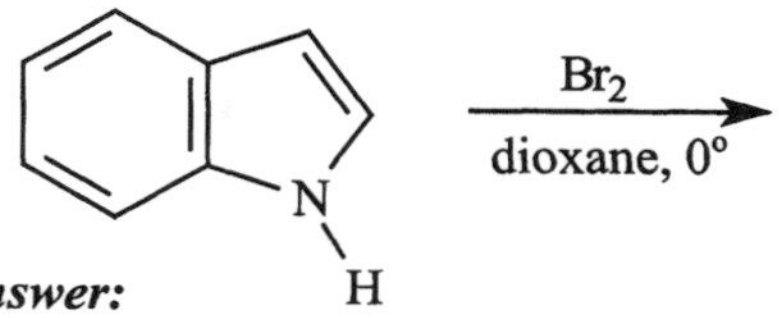 N H $\xrightarrow[\text{dioxane, 0°}]{Br_2}$

Answer:

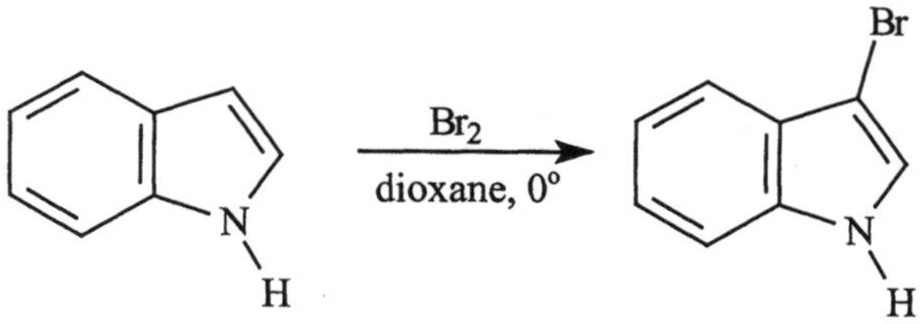

N H $\xrightarrow[\text{dioxane, 0°}]{Br_2}$ Br N H

22. 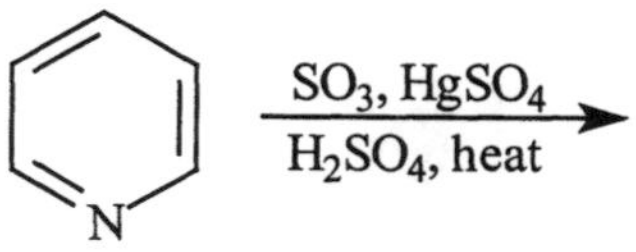 N $\xrightarrow[H_2SO_4\text{, heat}]{SO_3\text{, }HgSO_4}$

Answer:

N $\xrightarrow[H_2SO_4\text{, heat}]{SO_3\text{, }HgSO_4}$ SO_3H N

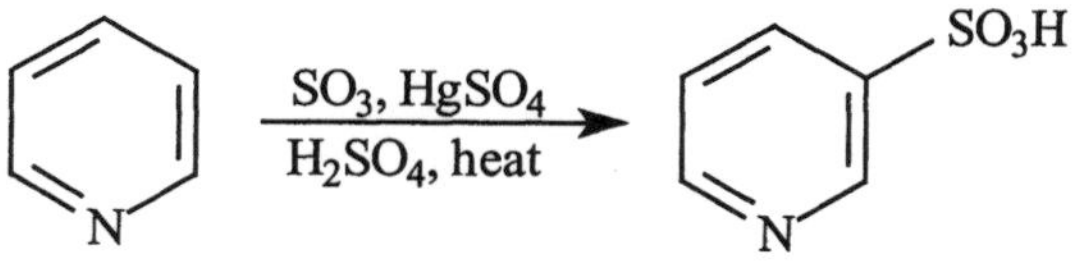

23.

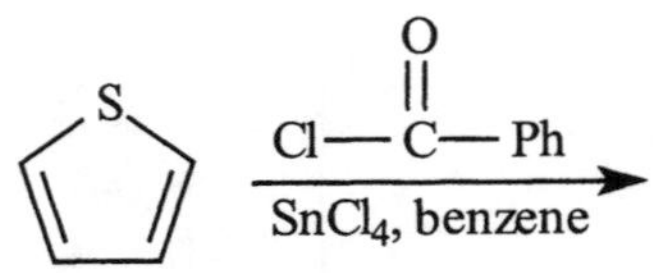

$$\text{thiophene} \xrightarrow[\text{SnCl}_4\text{, benzene}]{\text{Cl—C(=O)—Ph}}$$

Answer:

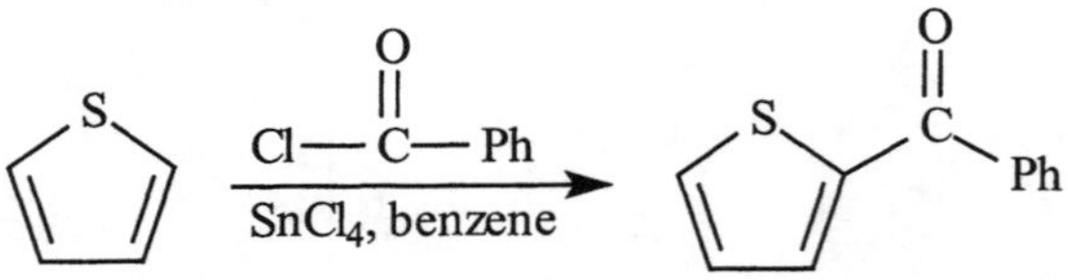

$$\text{thiophene} \xrightarrow[\text{SnCl}_4\text{, benzene}]{\text{Cl—C(=O)—Ph}} \text{2-thienyl—C(=O)—Ph}$$

24.

$$\text{quinoline} \xrightarrow[0^\circ\text{ C}]{\text{HNO}_3\text{, H}_2\text{SO}_4}$$

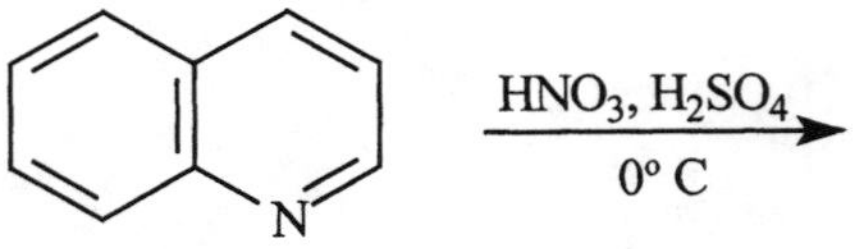

Answer:

$$\text{quinoline} \xrightarrow[0^\circ\text{ C}]{\text{HNO}_3\text{, H}_2\text{SO}_4} \text{5-nitroquinoline } (NO_2) + \text{8-nitroquinoline } (NO_2)$$

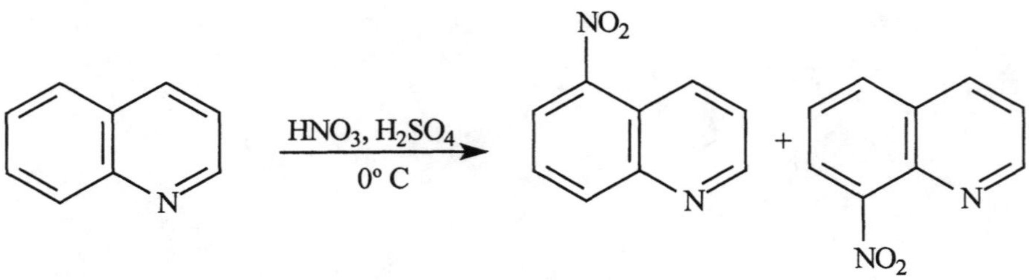

Chapter 29 – The Organic Chemistry of Metabolic Pathways

MATCH a term or structure from the list below to each of the following definitions or names. Place the letter of the term or structure in the blank to the left of the definition or name which it describes.

A. electron-transport chain

B. R, N^+, NH_2, O

C. citric acid cycle

D. Embden-Meyerhoff

E. glycolysis

F. R, H_3C, H_3C, N, N, N, N, O, O, H

G. Hans Krebs

H. catabolism

I. ATP

J. ${}^{2-}O_3POH_2C$, O, H, N^+, H, OH, CH_3

K. fatty acid spiral

L. anabolism

M. acetyl CoA

N. HO, O, O^-, OPO_3^{2-}

O. COO^-–C(=O)–CH_2–COO^- (oxaloacetate)

P. gluconeogenesis

Q. metabolism

1. _____ Pathways that synthesize larger biomolecules from smaller ones.

Answer: L

2. _____ Acetyl groups are oxidized to yield carbon dioxide and water.

Answer: C

3. _____ The "energy currency" of the cell.

Answer: I

4. _____ Coenzyme NAD^+ required in the β-oxidation of fatty acids, glycolysis, and the citric acid cycle.

Answer: B

5. _____ Discoverers of the glycolysis pathway.

Answer: D

6. _____ Pyridoxal phosphate, the cofactor in transaminations.

Answer: J

7. _____ Uses the energy produced in the citric acid cycle to make ATP.

Answer: A

8. _____ The product of the citric acid cycle, which is a reactant in the first step.

Answer: O

9. _____ The pathway by which organisms make glucose from simple precursors.

Answer: P

10. _____ Common fatty acids have an even number of carbons because they are biosynthesized from _____ .

Answer: M

11. Olive oil is comprised of 80% oleic acid, $CH_3(CH_2)_7CH{=}CH(CH_2)_7COOH$. How many molecules of acetyl CoA are produced by catabolism of oleic acid and how many passages of the β-oxidation pathway are needed?

Answer: Since oleic acid is a C_{18} fatty acid, nine molecules of acetyl CoA will be produced by catabolism of one molecule of oleic acid. This will require eight passages of the β-oxidation pathway.

Use the data below to answer the following questions:

Under certain metabolic conditions associated with a high rate of fatty acid oxidation, the liver produces considerable quantities of acetoacetate and *β*-hydroxybutyrate. Acetoacetate continually undergoes spontaneous decarboxylation to yield acetone. The interrelationship of these compounds is shown below.

$CH_3COCH_2CO_2^-$ —(- CO_2)→ CH_3COCH_3 **acetone**

$CH_3COCH_2CO_2^-$ —(dehydrogenase; NADH/H^+ → NAD^+)→ $CH_3CH(OH)CH_2CO_2^-$ **β-hydroxybutyrate**

12. Write a mechanism for the decarboxylation of acetoacetate to yield acetone.

Answer:

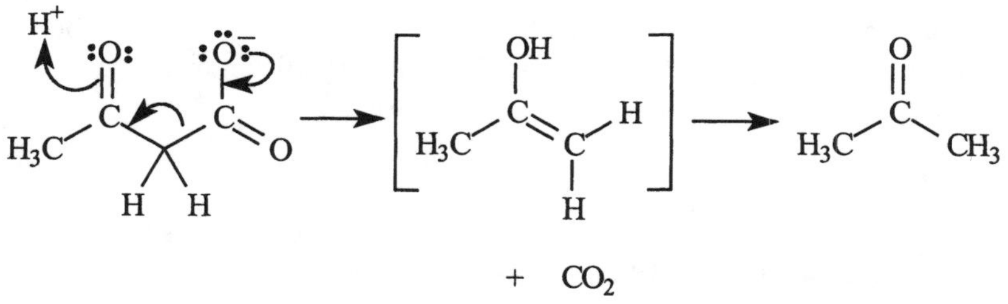

H^+ :O: :Ö:⁻ H_3C C C O H H → [OH H_3C C C H H] → O H_3C C CH_3

+ CO_2

13. The reduction of acetoacetate to β-hydroxybutyrate is analogous to the hydride reductions of ketones studied in Chapter 9. Write the mechanism of this reduction.

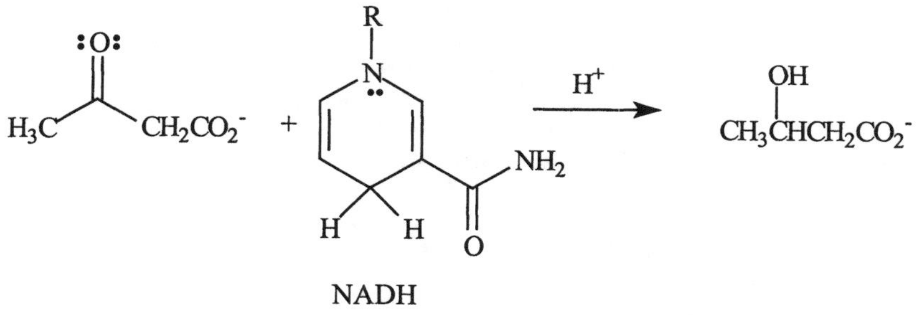

:O: H_3C $CH_2CO_2^-$ + R N H H NH_2 O NADH $\xrightarrow{H^+}$ OH $CH_3CHCH_2CO_2^-$

Answer:

:O: H_3C $CH_2CO_2^-$ R N H H NH_2 O → :Ö:⁻ H_3C $CH_2CO_2^-$ H $\downarrow H^+$ OH $CH_3CHCH_2CO_2^-$

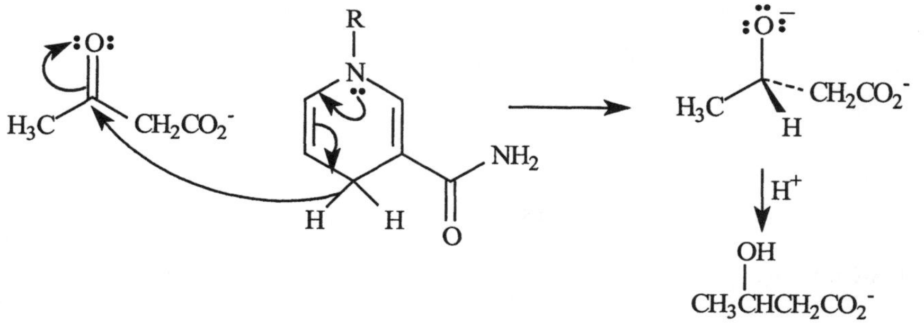

14. The reduction of acetoacetate to β-hydroxybutyrate is an example of a:

a. nucleophilic substitution reaction
b. nucleophilic acyl substitution reaction
c. nucleophilic addition reaction
d. nucleophilic exchange reaction

Answer: c

Use the data below to answer the following questions.

Mevalonate is an important intermediate in the biosynthesis of cholesterol. This six-carbon compound can be formed from acetyl CoA utilizing two separate pathways. The most significant one involves the intermediate β-hydroxy-β-methylglutaryl-CoA.

$CH_3\overset{O}{\overset{\|}{C}}SCoA$ (acetyl CoA) —thiolase→ (?) $CH_3\overset{O}{\overset{\|}{C}}CH_2\overset{O}{\overset{\|}{C}}SCoA$ (acetoacetyl CoA) —($CH_3\overset{O}{\overset{\|}{C}}SCoA$, H_2O; HMG-CoA synthetase)→ ?

$^{-}O\overset{O}{\overset{\|}{C}}CH_2\underset{CH_3}{\overset{OH}{C}}CH_2\overset{O}{\overset{\|}{C}}SCoA$

β-hydroxy-β-methylglutaryl CoA

HMG-CoA reductase ($2\ NADPH + 2H^+$ → $2\ NADP^+ + ?$)

$^{-}O\overset{O}{\overset{\|}{C}}CH_2\underset{CH_3}{\overset{OH}{C}}CH_2CH_2OH$

mevalonate

15. What is the by-product represented as a question mark (?) in each step of this reaction sequence?

Answer: HS-CoA

16. In step 1 of the mevalonate biosynthesis, acetyl CoA is converted into acetoacetyl CoA. This reaction is analogous to:

a. a Claisen condensation
b. an aldol reaction
c. the malonic ester synthesis
d. a carbonyl reduction reaction

Answer: a

17. In step 2 of the mevalonate biosynthesis, acetoacetyl CoA is converted into β-hydroxy-β-methylglutaryl-CoA. This reaction is analogous to:

a. a Claisen condensation
b. an aldol reaction
c. the malonic ester synthesis
d. a carbonyl reduction reaction

Answer: b

18. Propose a mechanism for step 2 of the mevalonate biosynthesis.

Answer:

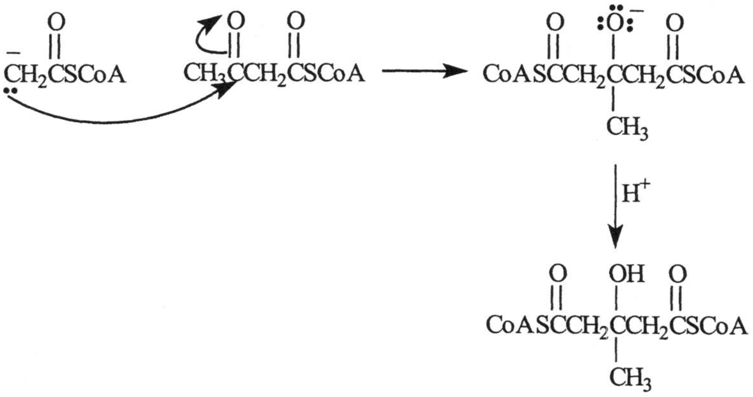

$$^{-}:CH_2C(=O)SCoA + CH_3C(=O)CH_2C(=O)SCoA \longrightarrow CoASC(=O)CH_2C(O^-)(CH_3)CH_2C(=O)SCoA$$

$$\xrightarrow{H^+} CoASC(=O)CH_2C(OH)(CH_3)CH_2C(=O)SCoA$$

19. What is the structure of the α-keto acid formed by transamination of the amino acid isoleucine?

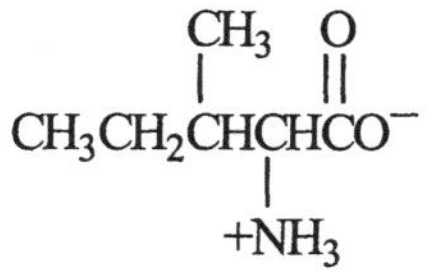

$$CH_3CH_2CH(CH_3)CH(^{+}NH_3)CO_2^- \quad \textbf{isoleucine}$$

Answer:

$$CH_3CH_2CH(CH_3)C(=O)CO_2^-$$

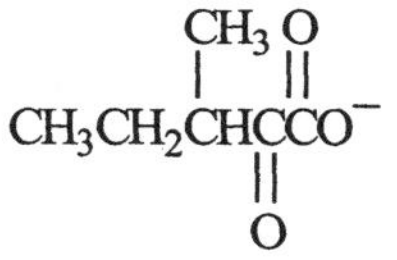

20. Which of the following statements about catabolism is false? Circle the letter of your response.

a. The ultimate products of food catabolism are CO_2, H_2O, and ATP
b. The citric acid cycle is a stage of catabolism
c. Gluconeogenesis is the catabolism of glucose
d. Transamination is the catabolism of proteins

Answer: c

21. Which of the following statements about anabolism is false. Circle the letter of your response.

a. Anabolic reactions "spend" ATP by transferring a phosphate group to another molecule.
b. As a rule, the anabolic pathway by which an organism makes a substance is the exact reverse of the catabolic pathway.
c. Pathways that synthesize larger biomolecules from smaller ones are known as anabolism.
d. Gluconeogenesis is the anabolic pathway by which organisms make glucose from pyruvate.

Answer: b

22. Which of the following statements about ATP is false? Circle the letter of your response.

a. ADP is synthesized from ATP
b. ATP is produced in the fourth stage of catabolism, the electron-transport chain
c. Catabolic reactions "pay off" in ATP
d. ATP is a phosphoric acid anhydride

Answer: a

Consider the reaction below to answer the following questions:

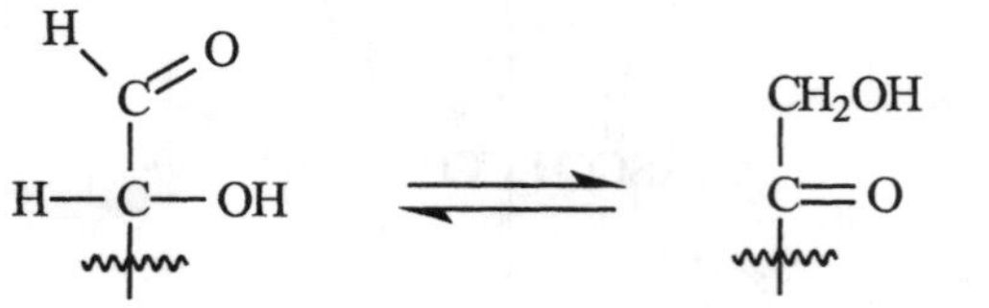

glucose 6-phosphate ⇌ fructose 6-phosphate

23. This reaction proceeds through a common enol structure. Draw the structure of the glucose/ fructose enol.

Answer:

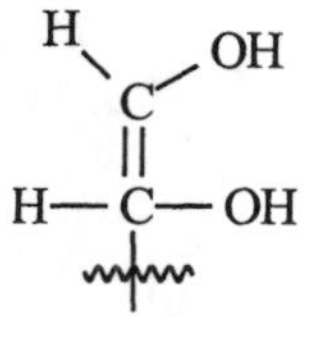

24. Write the mechanism for this isomerization.

Answer:

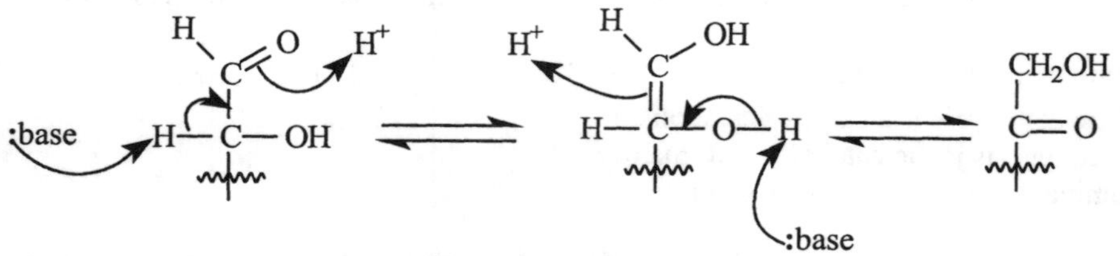

25. The isomerization of glucose 6-phosphate to fructose 6-phosphate is an example of:

a. an elimination reaction
b. an oxidation reaction
c. keto-enol tautomerism
d. a conjugate addition reaction

Answer: c

Consider the reaction below to answer the following questions:

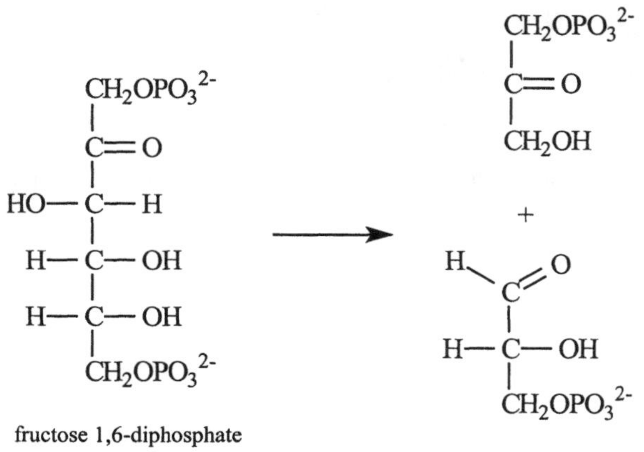

$$CH_2OPO_3^{2-}$$
C=O
HO—C—H
H—C—OH
H—C—OH
$$CH_2OPO_3^{2-}$$

fructose 1,6-diphosphate

⟶

$$CH_2OPO_3^{2-}$$
C=O
CH_2OH

+

H—C=O
H—C—OH
$$CH_2OPO_3^{2-}$$

26. This reaction is an example of:

a. an aldol reaction
b. a Claisen reaction
c. a reverse Claisen reaction
d. a reto aldol reaction

Answer: d

27. Draw arrows on the structure below showing electron flow in this reaction.

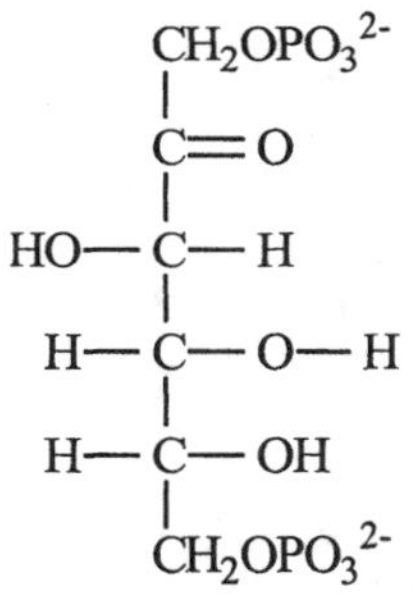

$$CH_2OPO_3^{2-}$$
C=O
HO—C—H
H—C—O—H
H—C—OH
$$CH_2OPO_3^{2-}$$

Answer:

$$CH_2OPO_3^{2-}$$
C=O
HO—C—H
H—C—O—H
H—C—OH
$$CH_2OPO_3^{2-}$$

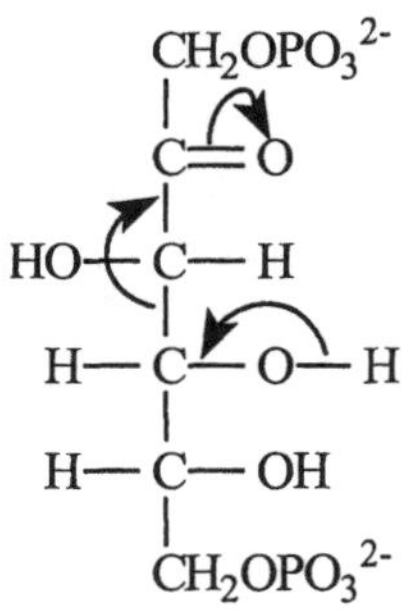

Chapter 30 – Orbitals and Organic Chemistry: Pericyclic Reactions

1. There are three major classes of pericyclic reactions. Which of the following types of reactions is *not* an example of a pericyclic process?

a. sigmatropic rearrangements
b. cycloaddition reactions
c. annulation reactions
d. electrocyclic reactions

Answer: c

2. The mneumonic phrase "The Electrons Circle Around", TECA, assists in predicting stereochemistry of pericyclic reactions. Describe application of this mneumonic.

Answer: The mneumonic TECA assists us in remembering that "*Thermal* pericyclic reactions with *Even* numbers of electrons will occur with *Conrotatory* or *Antarafacial* stereochemistry". As a result, the following statements also apply: Photochemical pericyclic reactions with even numbers of electrons will occur with disrotatory or suprafacial stereochemistry. Thermal pericyclic reactions with odd numbers of electrons will occur with disrotatory or suprafacial stereochemistry. Photochemical pericyclic reactions with odd numbers of electrons will occur with conrotatory or antarafacial stereochemistry.

To answer the following questions, consider the π molecular orbitals of a conjugated diene shown below:

3. Which molecular orbital of a conjugated diene contains two nodes between nuclei?

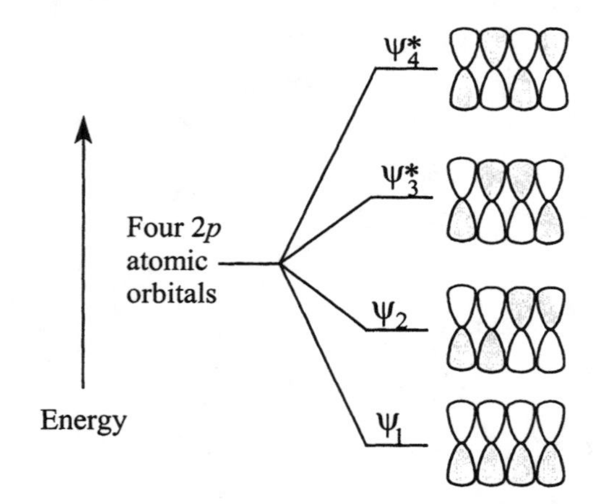

a. ψ_1
b. ψ_2
c. ψ_3*
d. ψ_4*

Answer: c

4. Which molecular orbital of a ground-state conjugated diene is the highest occupied molecular orbital (HOMO)?

a. ψ_1
b. ψ_2
c. ψ_3*
d. ψ_4*

Answer: b

5. Which molecular orbital of an excited-state conjugated diene is the lowest unoccupied molecular orbital (LUMO)?

a. ψ_1
b. ψ_2
c. ψ_3*
d. ψ_4*

Answer: d

6. Draw the product(s) you would expect to obtain from photochemical cyclization of (2*Z*, 4*E*)-hexadiene.

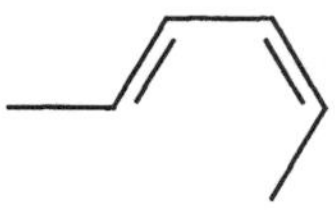

Answer:

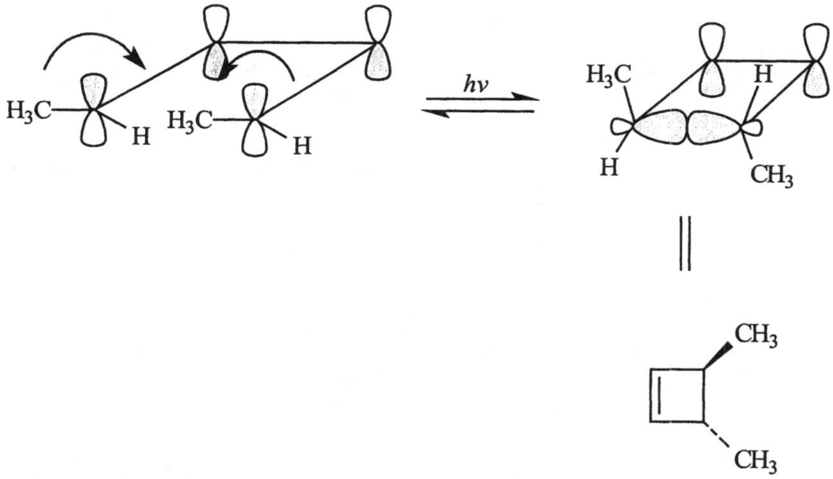

H_3C H H_3C H $h\nu$ H_3C H H CH_3

CH_3 CH_3

Consider the reaction below to answer the following questions:

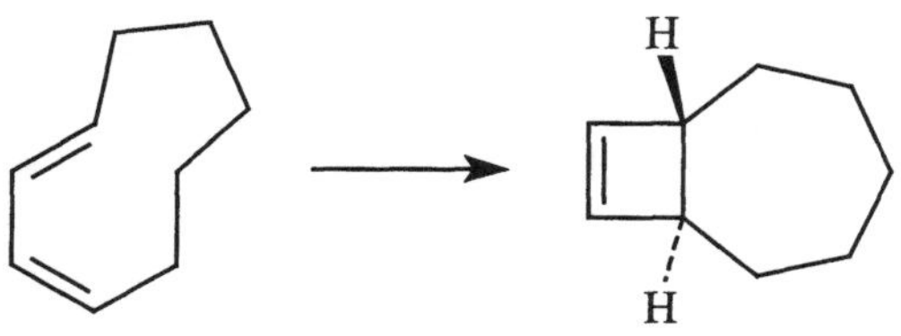

H H

7. Has this reaction taken place in a conrotatory manner or in a disrotatory manner?

Answer: In order for the hydrogens to be *trans* in the product, rotation must occur in a disrotatory manner.

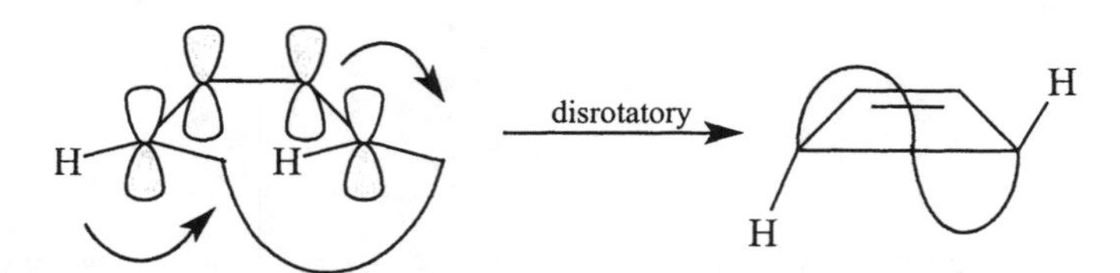

8. Under what conditions, thermal or photochemical, would you carry out this reaction? Explain.

Answer: For a disrotatory cyclization to occur the HOMO must have the symmetry pictured. For a 4 π electron system this HOMO must arise from photochemical excitation of a pi electron (see questions 3-5, above). To obtain a product with the correct stereochemistry, the reaction must be carried out under photochemical conditions.

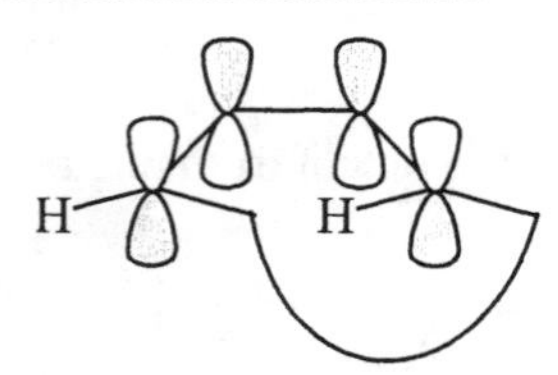

To answer the following questions, consider the reaction below:

9. Two pericyclic reactions are involved in this synthesis of *trans*-9,10-dihydronaphthalene. Draw the structure of intermediate X and name it using IUPAC nomenclature.

Answer:

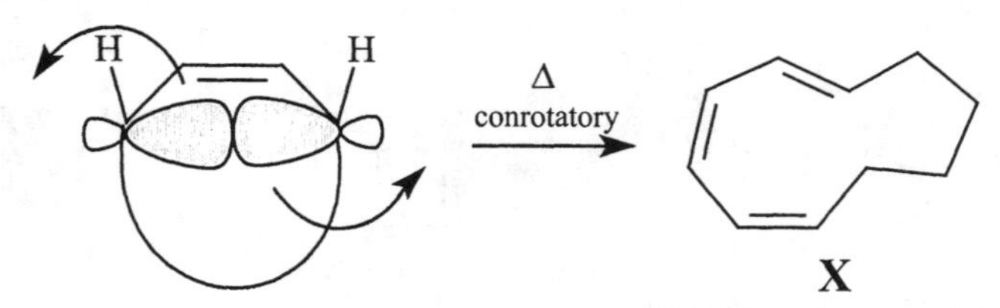

X

(1*E*,3*Z*, 5*Z*)-cyclodecatriene

10. The thermal reaction which generates **X** is an example of:

a. an electrocyclic reaction
b. a sigmatropic rearrangement
c. a reverse cycloaddition reaction
d. a cycloaddition reaction

Answer: a

11. Explain the stereochemistry of the 9,10-dihydronaphthalene product.

Answer: Thermal electrocyclic opening of the *cis*-substituted cyclobutene yields (1*E*, 3*Z*, 5*Z*)-cyclodecatriene (**X**). Symmetry-allowed thermal cyclization of the cyclodecatriene occurs in a disrotatory fashion to yield the observed *trans*-9,10-dihydronaphthalene.

Δ disrotatory

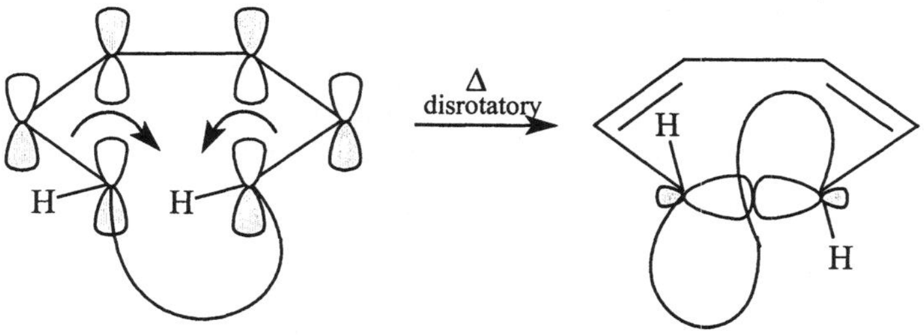

Consider the reaction below to answer the following questions:

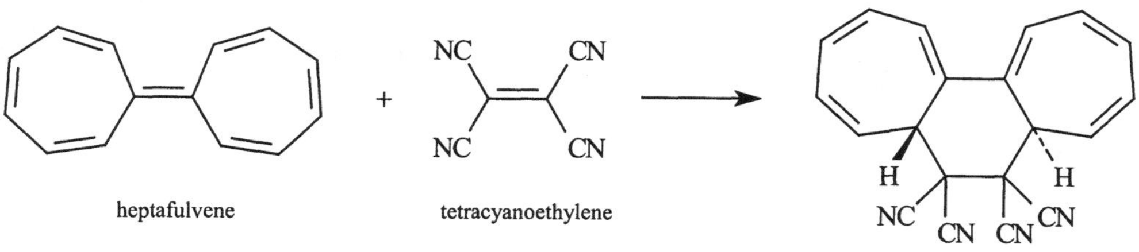

heptafulvene + tetracyanoethylene →

12. What type of pericyclic reaction is involved in this transformation?

a. sigmatropic rearrangement
b. reverse cycloaddition reaction
c. electrocyclic reaction
d. cycloaddition reaction

Answer: d

13. How many pairs of electrons are involved in this pericyclic reaction?

a. two
b. four
c. eight
d. sixteen

Answer: c

14. Explain the stereochemistry of this reaction.

Answer: The reaction of heptafulvene with tetracyanoethylene is a [14 + 2] cycloaddition that has occurred with antarafacial stereochemistry.

15. Would you expect this reaction to occur under photochemical or thermal conditions?

Answer: Since this reaction is a [14 + 2] cycloaddition with eight electron pairs, we would expect the thermal reaction to occur with antarafacial stereochemistry and the photochemical reaction to occur with suprafacial stereochemistry. The product has antarafacial stereochemistry resulting from a thermal reaction.

To answer the following questions, consider the reaction below:

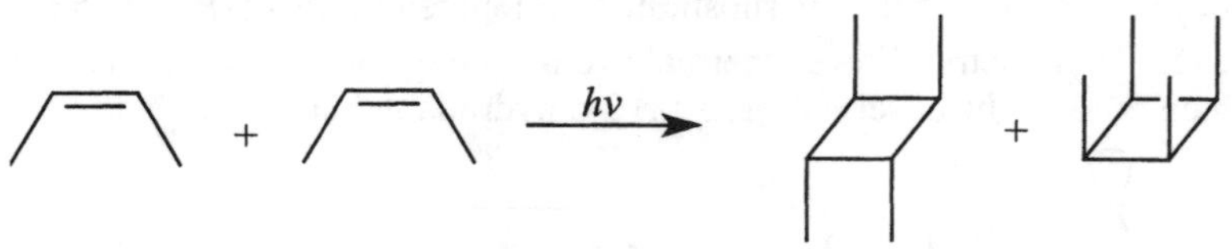

16. What type of percyclic reaction is involved in this transformation?

a. sigmatropic rearrangement
b. reverse cycloaddition reaction
c. electrocyclic reaction
d. cycloaddition reaction

Answer: d

17. How many pairs of electrons are involved in this pericyclic reaction?

a. two
b. four
c. eight
d. sixteen

Answer: a

18. Propose a mechanism for the reaction that fully accounts for the formation of both products.

Answer:

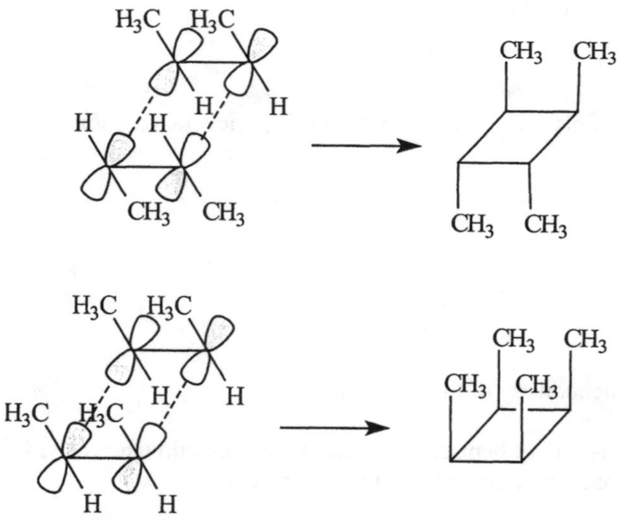

This reaction occurs with suprafacial stereochemistry which would be expected for a photochemical [2 + 2] cycloaddition. However, suprafacial cycloaddition can occur in two different ways— with the methyl groups of both alkenes on the same side or on opposite sides.

Consider the reaction sequence below to answer the following questions:

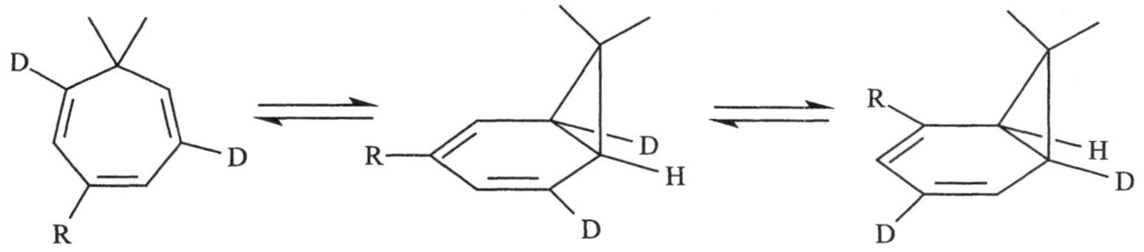

A B C

19. Step 1 is an example of:

a. an electrocyclic reaction
b. a cycloaddition reaction
c. a sigmatropic rearrangement
d. a reverse cycloaddition reaction

Answer: a

20. Explain the stereochemistry of product **B**.

Answer: Step 1 is the thermal electrocyclic reaction of a conjugated triene (three electron pairs) which occurs with disrotatory stereochemistry to yield a *cis*-fused cyclopropane.

21. Step 2 is an example of:

a. an electrocyclic reaction
b. a cycloaddition reaction
c. a sigmatropic rearrangement
d. a reverse cycloaddition reaction

Answer: c

22. Explain the stereochemistry of product **C**.

Answer: Step 2 is a thermal [1, 5] sigmatropic rearrangement (three electron pairs) which occurs with suprafacial stereochemistry.

23. Explain how **C** is formed from **B**.

Answer:

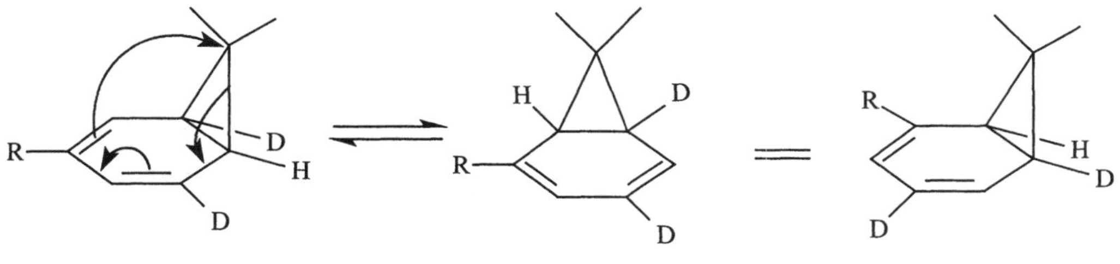

B C

Consider the Sommelet-Hauser rearrangement below to answer the following questions:

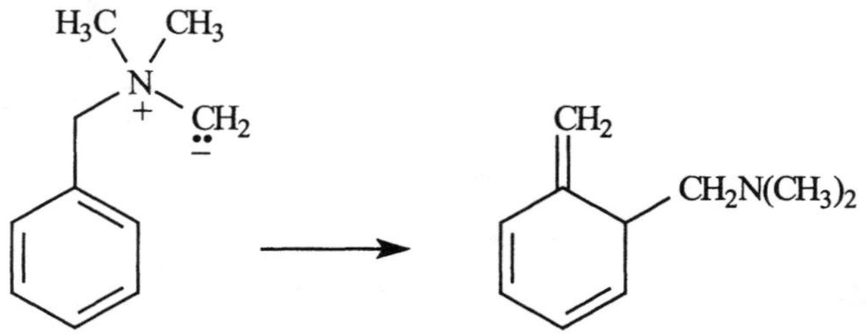

24. The Sommelet-Hauser rearrangement is an example of a [2, 3] sigmatropic rearrangement. How many pairs of electrons are involved in this reaction?

a. two
b. three
c. four
d. five

Answer: b

25. Would you expect the Sommelet-Hauser rearrangement to be antarafacial or suprafacial? Explain.

Answer: Since three pairs of electrons are involved in the rearrangement, the Sommelet-Hauser rearrangement should occur with suprafacial geometry.

Classify each of the following sigmatropic reactions by order $[x, y]$.

26.

Answer: [3, 3]

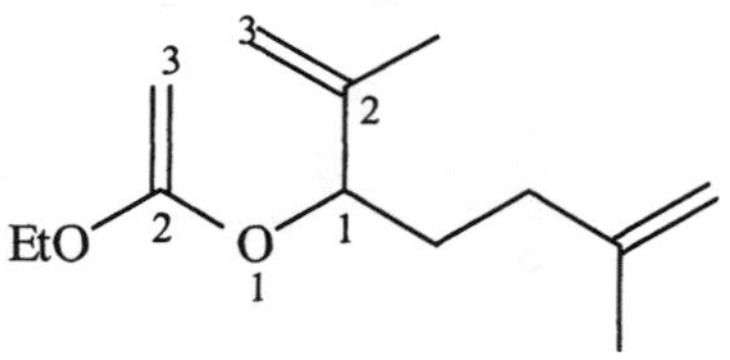

27.

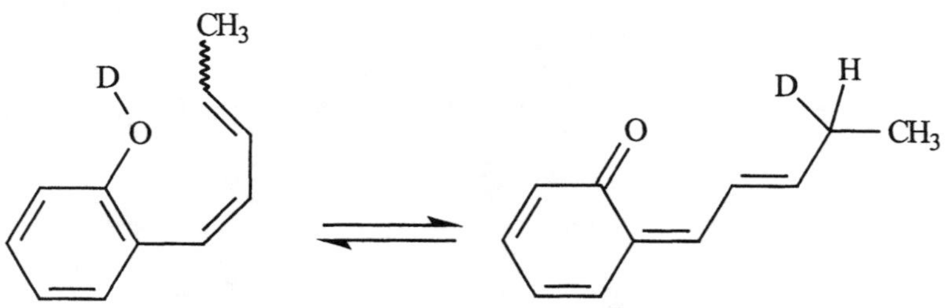

Answer: [1, 7]

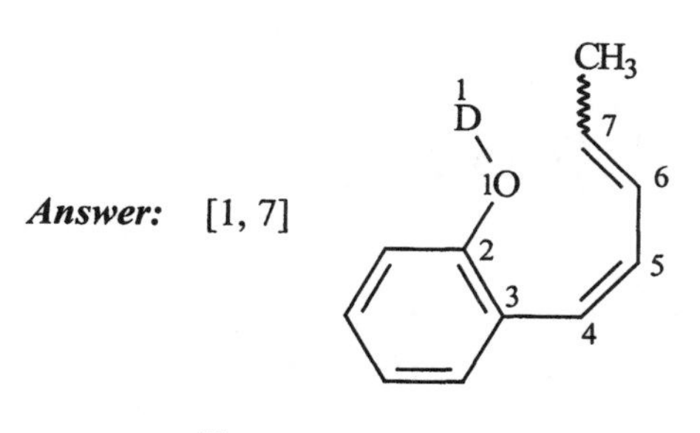

28.

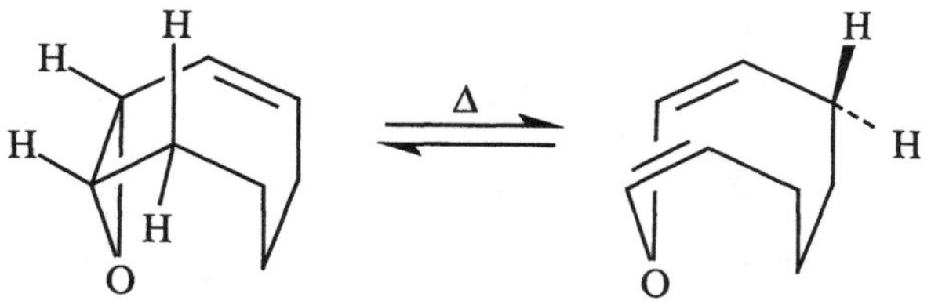

Answer: [1, 5]

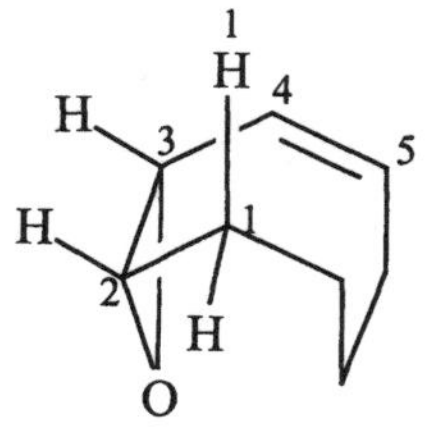

Vitamin D_3, cholecalciferol, is synthesized under the skin by the photochemical pericyclic process shown below. Answer the following questions about these reactions.

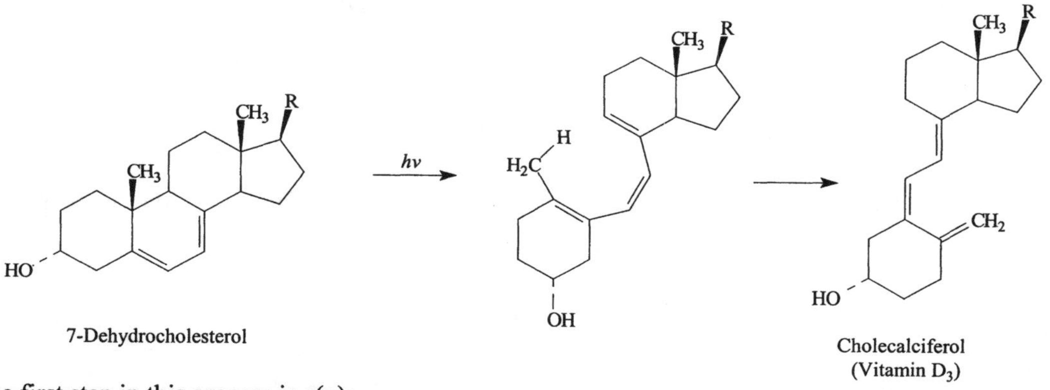

7-Dehydrocholesterol

Cholecalciferol (Vitamin D_3)

29. The first step in this process is a(n):

a. sigmatropic rearrangement
b. cycloaddition reaction
c. annulation reaction
d. electrocyclic reaction

Answer: d

30. The second step in this process is a(n):

a. sigmatropic rearrangement
b. cycloaddition reaction
c. annulation reaction
d. electrocyclic reaction

Answer: a

Chapter 31 – Synthetic Polymers

MATCH a term or structure from the list below to each of the following definitions or names. Place the letter of the term or structure in the blank to the left of the definition or name which it describes.

A. $BF_3 + H_2O$

B. elastomer

C. chain-growth polymer

D. $Al(CH_2CH_3)_3 + TiCl_4$

E. 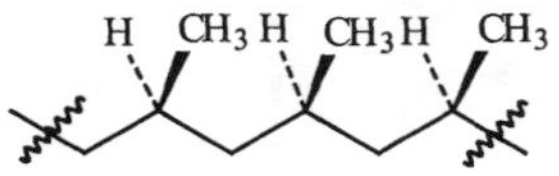 H CH_3 H CH_3 H CH_3

F. 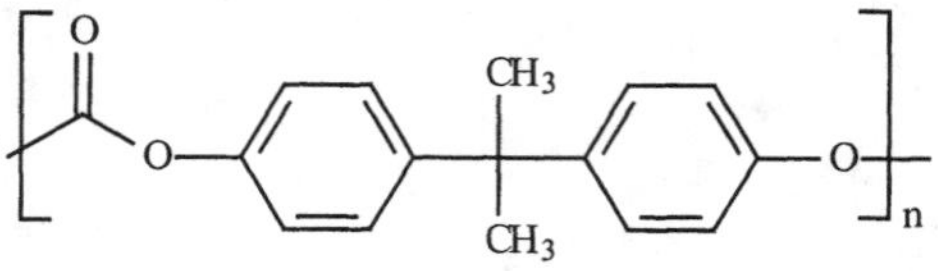 O O O CH_3 CH_3 n

G. thermoplastic

H. homopolymer

I. plasticizers

J. thermosetting resins

K. copolymers

L. step-growth polymer

M. 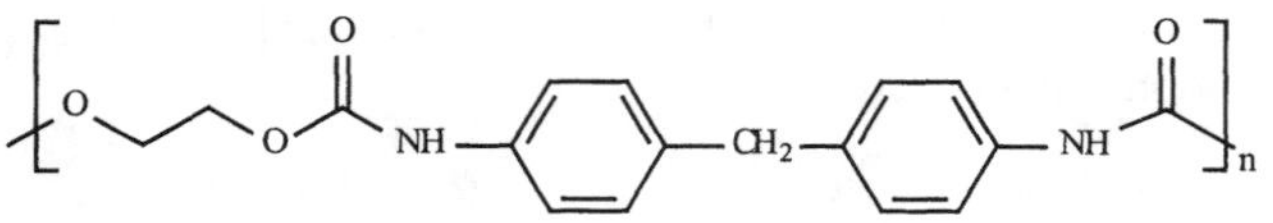 O O O NH CH_2 NH O n

N. H_3C H H CH_3 H CH_3

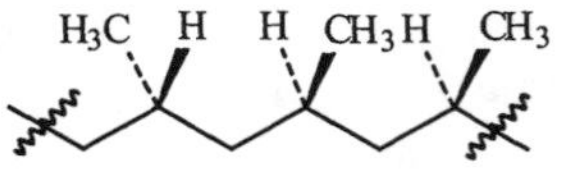

1. ____ Produced by reactions in which each bond in the polymer is formed independently of the others.

   Answer: L

2. ____ Isotactic propylene

   Answer: E

3. ____ Polymers obtained when two or more different monomers are allowed to polymerize together.

   Answer: K

4. ____ a polyurethane

   Answer: M

5. ____ Small organic molecules that act as lubricants between polymer chains.

   Answer: I

6. ____ Amorphous polymers that have the ability to stretch out and spring back to their original shape.

   Answer: B

7. ____ Bakelite is this type of polymer.

Answer: J

8. ____ a Ziegler-Natta catalyst

Answer: D

9. Rank the following monomers in order of *increasing* reactivity toward cationic polymerization (least reactive to most reactive).

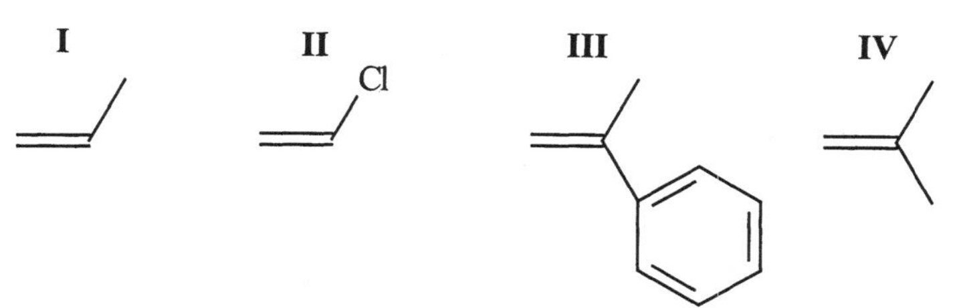

a. III, IV, I, II
b. II, I, IV, III
c. I, II, IV, III
d. IV, III, I, II

Answer: b

10. Rank the following monomers in order of *increasing* reactivity toward anionic polymerization (least reactive to most reactive).

I II CN, CO_2CH_3 III CO_2CH_3 IV Cl

a. III, II, IV, I
b. II, III, I, II
c. I, IV, III, II
d. IV, III, II, I

Answer: c

11. Do you expect nitroethylene to be more or less reactive than ethylene toward cationic polymerization? Explain.

NO_2 **nitroethylene**

Answer: Cationic polymerization is favored when the vinyl monomer contains an electron-donating group (EDG) capable of stabilizing the chain-carrying carbocation intermediate.

$$H^+ \quad H_2C{=}CH(EDG) \longrightarrow \left[H{-}CH_2{-}\overset{+}{C}H(EDG)\right] \xrightarrow{H_2C{=}CH(EDG)} H{-}CH_2{-}CH(EDG){-}CH_2{-}\overset{+}{C}H(EDG) \xrightarrow{etc.}$$

Since the nitro group is an electron-withdrawing group (EWG) it should *destabilize* the chain-carrying carbocation intermediate and, thus, be *less* reactive than ethylene toward cationic polymerization.

12. Do you expect nitroethylene to be more or less reactive than ethylene toward anionic polymerization? Explain.

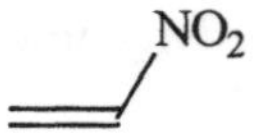

NO_2 **nitroethylene**

Answer: Vinyl monomers with electron-withdrawing groups (EWG) can be polymerized by anionic catalysts in Michael-type reactions. The EWG stabilizes the negative charge of the chain-carrying anionic intermediate.

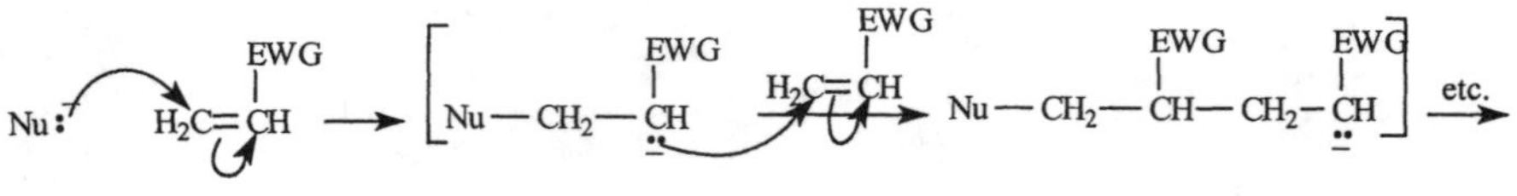

$$Nu:^- + H_2C{=}CH(EWG) \rightarrow [Nu{-}CH_2{-}\ddot{C}H(EWG)] \xrightarrow{H_2C=CH(EWG)} Nu{-}CH_2{-}CH(EWG){-}CH_2{-}\ddot{C}H(EWG) \xrightarrow{etc.}$$

Since the nitro group is a strong EWG it should stabilize the chain-carrying carbanion intermediate in anionic polymerizations, and , thus, be *more* reactive than ethylene.

13. Monomer A is copolymerized with Monomer B and is found to have the following structure:

—(A-A-A-A-A-A-A-A-B-B-B-B-B-B-B-B)—

The type of copolymer formed is:

a. a random copolymer
b. an alternating copolymer
c. a block copolymer
d. a graft copolymer

Answer: c

Draw the structure(s) of the monomer(s) used to make each of the following polymers.

14. $-(CH_2{-}CH(CH_2CH_3))_n-$

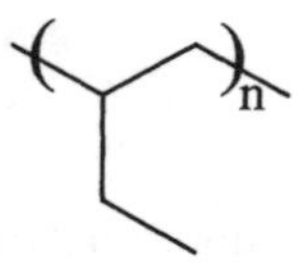

Answer:

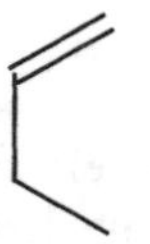

$H_2C{=}CH{-}CH_2CH_3$

15. $-(CH_2{-}CH(N\text{-pyrrolidinone}))_n-$

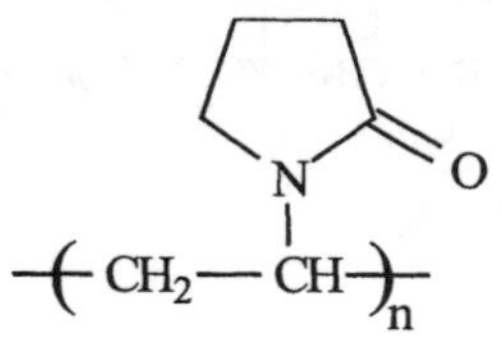

Answer:

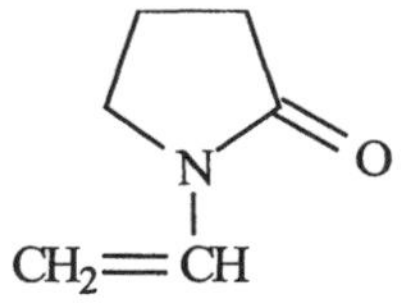

O

N

$CH_2{=}CH$

16. 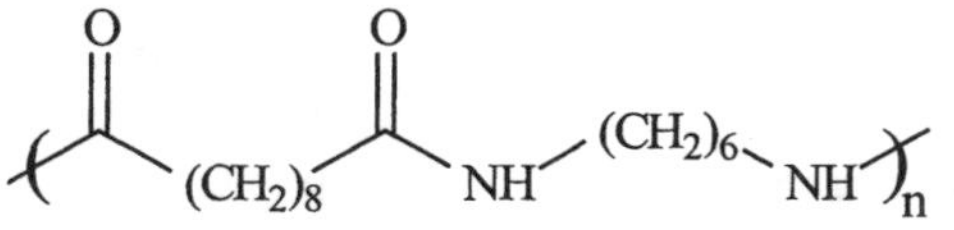 O O

$(CH_2)_8$ NH $(CH_2)_6$ NH n

Answer:

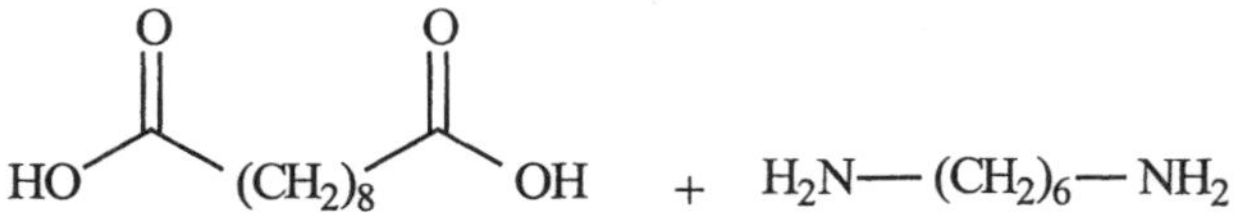

O O

HO $(CH_2)_8$ OH + $H_2N{-}(CH_2)_6{-}NH_2$

17. 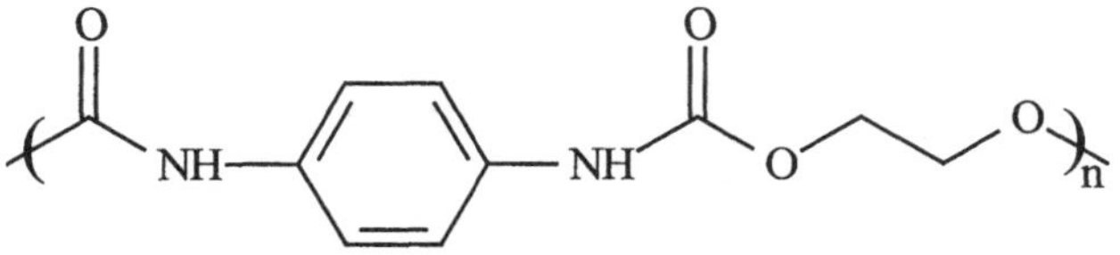 O O

NH— —NH O O n

Answer:

$O{=}C{=}N{-}$ $-N{=}C{=}O$ + HO OH

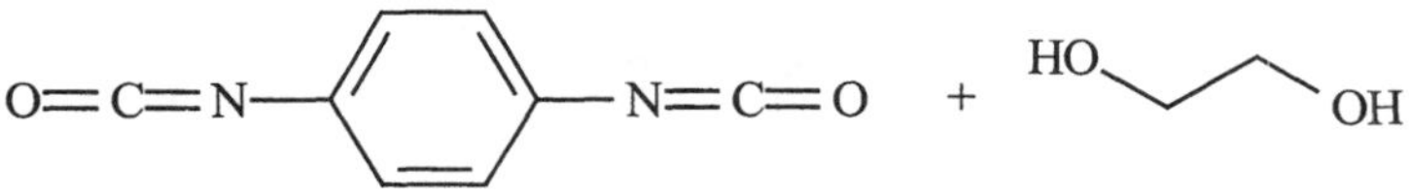

Classify each polymer below as step-growth or chain-growth.

18. 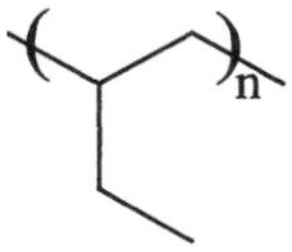 n

Answer: chain-growth

19. 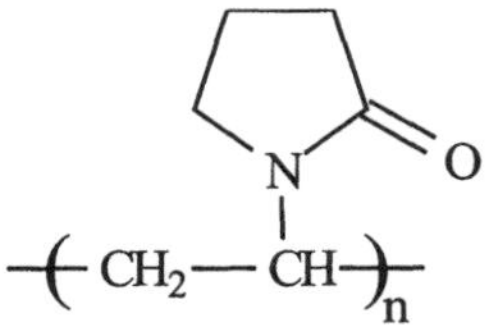 N O

$-(CH_2{-}CH)_n-$

Answer: chain-growth

20. 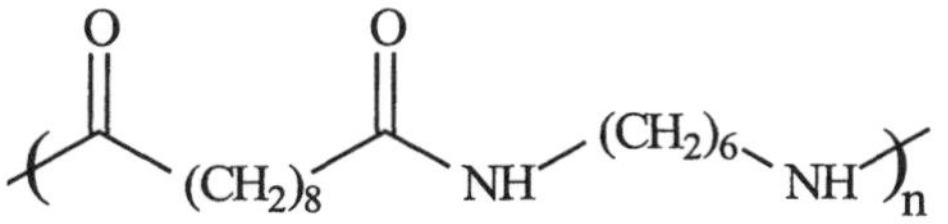 O O

$(CH_2)_8$ NH $(CH_2)_6$ NH n

Answer: step-growth

21.

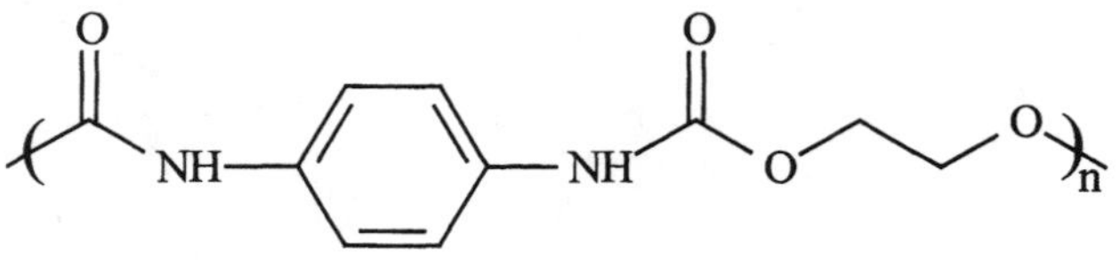

Answer: step-growth

Draw the structure of the polymers obtained from the following reactions.

22.

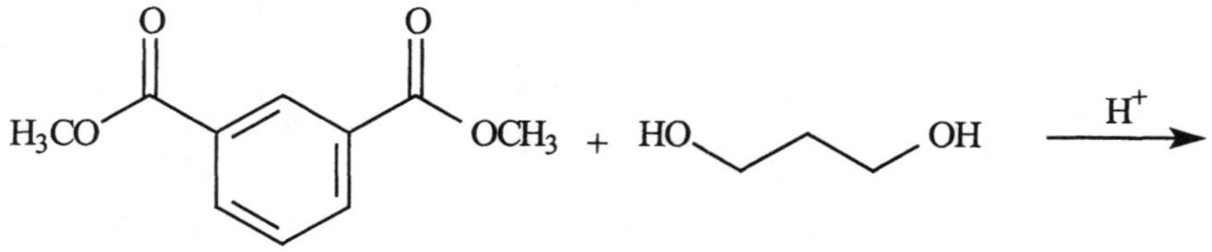

Answer:

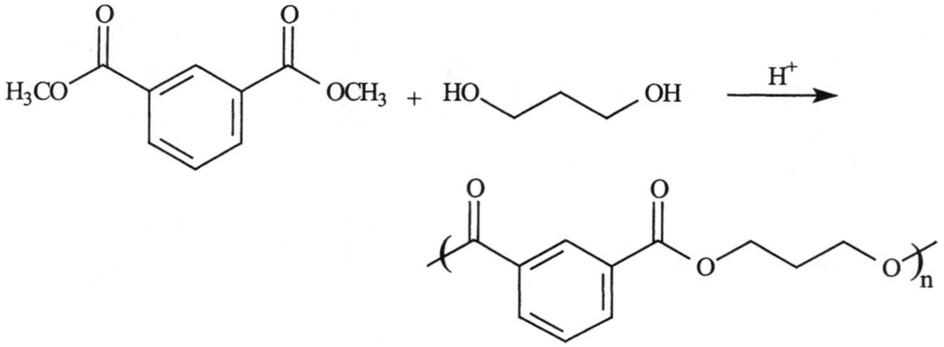

23.

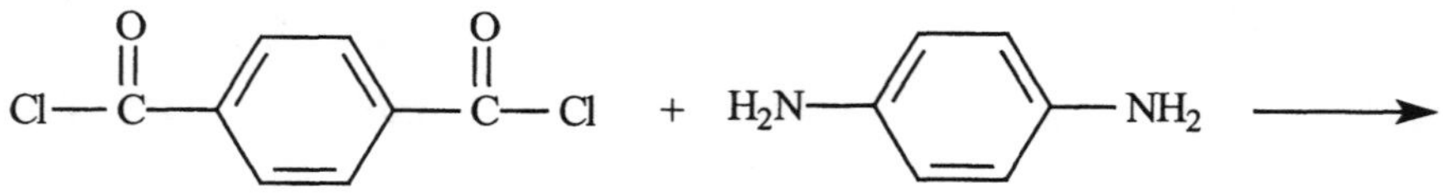

Answer:

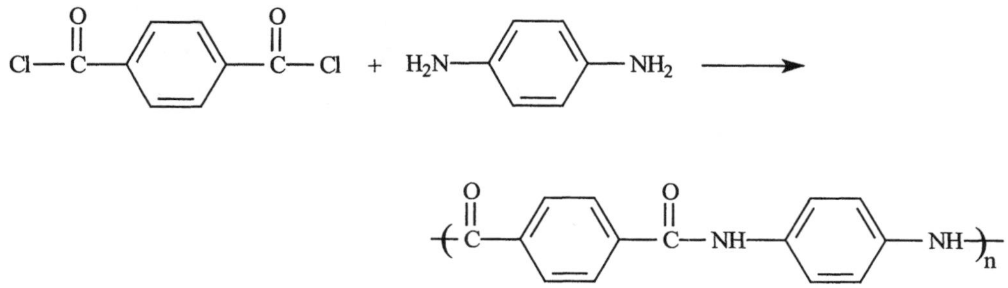

$Cl-C(=O)-C_6H_4-C(=O)-Cl + H_2N-C_6H_4-NH_2 \longrightarrow -\!(C(=O)-C_6H_4-C(=O)-NH-C_6H_4-NH)_n\!-$

24. 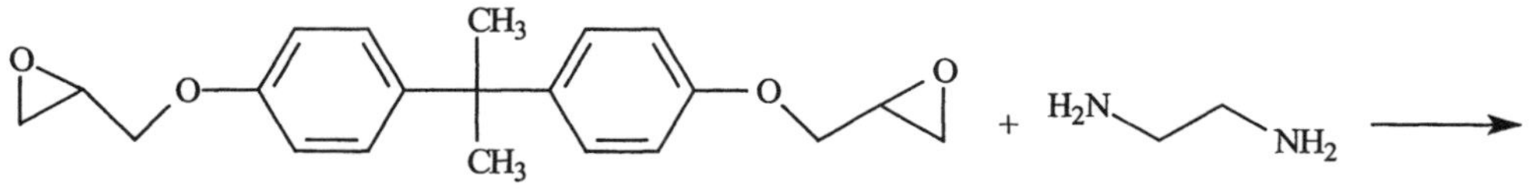 Bis-epoxide $(CH_3)_2C(C_6H_4-O-CH_2-\text{epoxide})_2 + H_2N-CH_2CH_2-NH_2 \longrightarrow$

Answer:

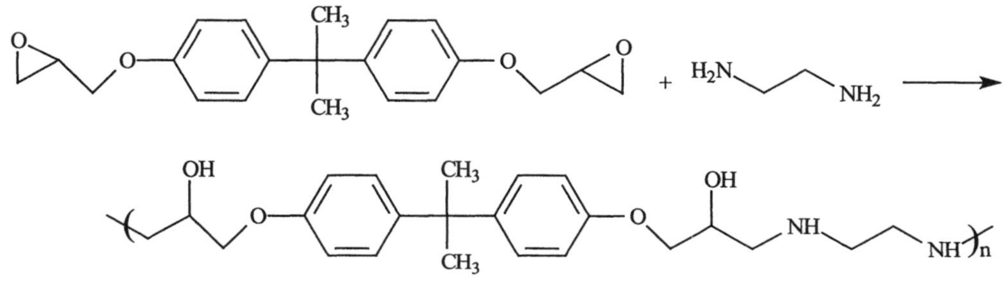

$-\!(CH_2CH(OH)CH_2-O-C_6H_4-C(CH_3)_2-C_6H_4-O-CH_2CH(OH)CH_2-NH-CH_2CH_2-NH)_n\!-$

25. 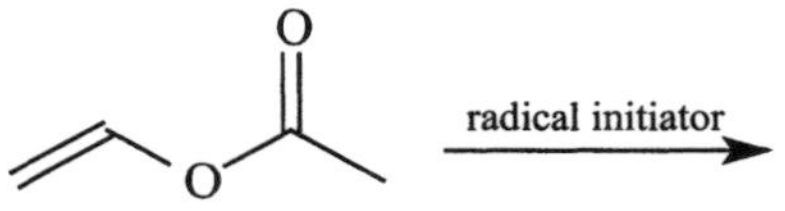 $CH_2=CH-O-C(=O)CH_3$ $\xrightarrow{\text{radical initiator}}$

Answer:

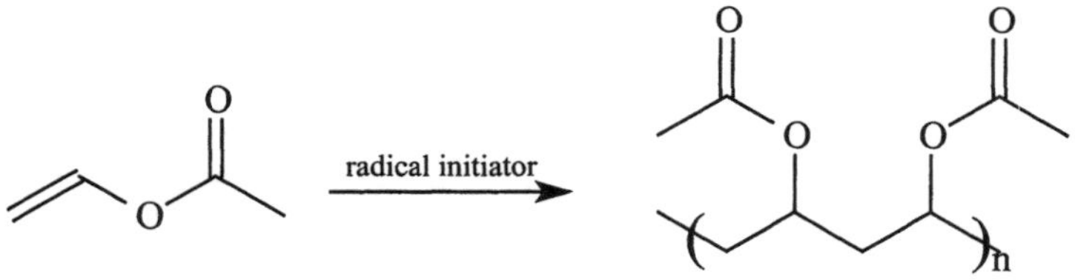

$CH_2=CH-O-C(=O)CH_3 \xrightarrow{\text{radical initiator}} -\!(CH_2-CH(OC(=O)CH_3)-CH_2-CH(OC(=O)CH_3))_n\!-$

26. 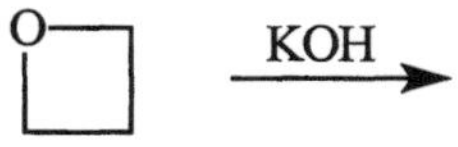 Oxetane $\xrightarrow{\text{KOH}}$

Answer:

Oxetane $\xrightarrow{\text{KOH}} -\!(CH_2CH_2CH_2-O)_n\!-$